HANDBOOK OF CLINICAL AND EXPERIMENTAL HYPNOSIS

HANDBOOK OF CLINICAL AND EXPERIMENTAL HYPNOSIS

Edited by

Jesse E. Gordon

Associate Professor of Psychology and Social Work
The University of Michigan

The Macmillan Company, New York
Collier-Macmillan Limited, London

First Printing

Library of Congress catalog card number: 66–25956

THE MACMILLAN COMPANY, NEW YORK
COLLIER-MACMILLAN CANADA, LTD., TORONTO, ONTARIO

PRINTED IN THE UNITED STATES OF AMERICA

Preface

THIS book was written to bring together the widely scattered but significant new work in hypnosis, and to make this work readily available to students, researchers, and clinicians. It is clear that hypnosis is rapidly losing its mystery, its intractability to psychological theory and research; it is also clear that most psychologists, who do not read the journals limited to hypnosis and who tend not to buy technical monographs dealing in depth with particular aspects of hypnosis or a particular theory, are not aware of most of this exciting research.

As in many other fields of inquiry, a major impetus to research in hypnosis came from a breakthrough in research methodology. Hypnosis presents some particular problems in research design, and new entrants to the field are in need of discussions of the nature of these problems and the solutions available. Because only a very few schools institutionalize instruction in hypnosis as part of their curricula in psychology, the need for an organized presentation of the issues, research, and methodology is great.

It is hoped that this volume will be useful as a summary of the field and as a stimulus and bellwether of future efforts. It is also my hope that it will play a role in eroding the "special status" of hypnosis—in reducing the gap that seems to exist between the study and understanding of hypnotic phenomena and psychological inquiry into the other, more usual subjects of psychological study.

I am indebted to the authors of chapters included in this book for their efforts and for their patience and cooperation during the transformation of their papers into a published volume.

J. E. G.

Contents

I

GENERAL BACKGROUND

I

Introduction

JESSE E. GORDON
University of Michigan

Hypnosis is becoming socially acceptable. It may have seemed, in its two centuries' climb upward from the elegant slum of Mesmer's *baquet*, as if it would never make it—or that if it did enter the prestige world of scientific respectability, it would be too late to save its soul.

And indeed this may be happening. The terms laid down for hypnosis by an increasing number of investigators are such that it may be purchasing its respectability at the price of much of its identity. Its mystery seems to be fading away, like the Cheshire cat, in an ineffable smog of epiphenomena and artificiality, leaving only the memory of an inscrutable smile. That smile of mystery has been alluring to many investigators. This has provided both the strength and weakness of hypnosis: it offers magical and mysterious solutions to problems while disclaiming the occult. In unknown ways even the least charismatic person may, through the use of hypnosis, acquire the power and prestige of necromancy and at the same time claim the mantle of the explorer on the new frontier of scientific penetration of the unknown.

Thus hypnosis has fulfilled the requirements for becoming an object of obsessive interest. Like others, it is desired, wondered at, feared, and abhorred, and for many of the same reasons. It is seen as the potential magic wand through which the most difficult therapeutic, surgical, and experimental problems may be solved; and at the same time, it is rejected out of hand as if it were some rather blatant libidinizing force with which nice people don't associate. If it is powerful enough to achieve the most dramatic solutions to problems, then it is also powerful enough to be dangerous. Like the monkey's paw, its danger lies in the possibility that it may in fact give its user the thing that he desires most, and in so doing, disturb the natural order enough that he may thereby also get what he fears to have. In defense, this mysterious power must be minimized and made to disappear while its allure is somehow preserved. And, again like an obsessive object, it must be possessed, grappled with, and also destroyed.

I do not mean this as only hyperbole and metaphor. As an obsessive object, hypnosis has attracted the interest of people who are driven to identify themselves with the dark of the moon; it has stimulated the distaste and revulsion of those who are most sensitive to their scientific status in the community of the sciences; and it has been the object of intense ambivalence for those who stand between those poles of the dirty deep and the superficial sterile.

Reactions to hypnosis in scientific work have paralleled these feelings. On the one hand, some oppose its anatomization out of a fear that those very mystical elements that make it so attractive to them will be destroyed. On the other side has been a passive opposition to study of the phenomena, a timidity in the name of scientific propriety, enforced through a vaguely defined guilt by association with the charlatans. Thus the motives and character of the investigator are made suspect by his interest in hypnosis, a suspiciousness that tends toward self-confirmation as these attitudes restrict the field to the rebels and nonconformists. And the middle ground is often occupied by a kind of rigid ambivalence in which the phenomena are studied and then made to disappear through a sieve of familiar motivational, cognitive, and social variables. The result has been to create the impression that hypnosis does not exist as a phenomenon, although the right to study it is proclaimed and defended. This may be comparable to asserting that because all matter is composed of the familiar elements of the periodic table, the moon does not exist as such, and anyone who uses it as a background for romance is being most unparsimonious as well as sentimental. Thus the respectability of studying hypnosis is gained by placing it in a prophylactic arena.

The power of hypnosis is reduced by interpreting it as a composite of familiar and ubiquitous psychological variables—everybody knows the weakness of such variables. Those who are impressed by the prepotence of man are thus driven to defend hypnosis against analysis in familiar psychological terms, and so, unwillingly, do they also preserve its occult air which, by its suprahumanness, argues against the humanism from which its defense springs.

These same ambivalences are expressed in the attitudes of clinicians and therapeutic practitioners, who are attracted to hypnosis as a miracle cure to beat all miracles, and who are also so awed by the magnitude and power with which they must invest hypnosis if it is to serve such a function that they therefore cannot bring themselves to make reasonable use of it any more than they can give up their image of the therapeutic power it might bestow on them. Thus they adopt the stance of heroic humility before the latent power residing within their potential use of hypnosis, while its actual use is reserved for only those insuperable therapeutic crises that never seem to come. There are always at least one or two nonhypnotic therapeutic resources left to them, so that hypnosis remains in the limbo of potential availability, which cannot be exercised or exorcised.

Perhaps I have stressed too much the affective side of response to hypnosis; where there are affects there are also cognitions, and where there is room for ambivalent feelings, there is also room for cognitive confusion. And, as in many other cases where such cognitive confusion exists, it is not only as a reflection of confused feelings but also involves a recognition of the ambiguous state of the realities. If magical thoughts and feelings are involved, latently or explicitly, in connection with hypnosis, it is because the phenomena impinge on the cognitive structures surrounding the concepts of mind and body, the physical and the mental, the psychological and the real, the natural and the occult, will and necessity. If hypnosis is by no means natural, then it must be occult; if it is not physical it must be mental; if the subject surrenders his will, then he is an automaton; if it is not matter over mind, then it must be mind over matter. I think that much of our difficulty in thinking about hypnosis is that we tend to accept the "if" without being able to accept the "then"; and we have this problem because we have not yet developed other conceptual dimensions and frameworks within which we can accept the "if" without implying what seem to be the only available alternatives. Hypnosis comes close to the core of the mind-body dualistic thinking for which we have not yet found more efficacious substitutes as modes of thought. Although there are many psychological phenomena that we can study without an immediate involvement in the issue of dualism, so that we can continue our scientific productivity without a resolution and without the development of alternative conceptions to replace the easier and more familiar ones of the past, this group of phenomena does not seem to include hypnosis.

I believe that it is the centrality of the conceptual problem to an understanding of hypnosis that makes its exploration of great potential significance to psychology. As a topic it is but one of a great range of interesting topics available for investigation in psychology; but its relationships with such other topics as the modeling functions of teachers and leaders, use of implied and explicit suggestion, attitude change, performance, learning, propaganda, decision making, transference, the design of psychological experiments, and other aspects of interpersonal influence and of performance suggest that hypnosis has elements that invade all areas of psychological inquiry. Even more important, because the eventual solution of the problems posed to a psychological understanding of hypnosis seem to hinge on the development of new conceptual structures through the use of which the old dualistic mode of thinking may be laid to rest, this solution will have implications for the conceptualization of events in all domains of psychology.

It has happened before in science that a tail has wagged a dog. Fields of inquiry build up and elaborate around islands of ignorance because the islands are either overlooked or because they just don't fit in with the general scheme of the broader field. They are resistant to conceptualization in the terms being applied with a modicum of success to other areas of investigation. They become isolated and encapsulated until they are rediscovered by some atypical thinker, able to discard or go beyond the traditional conceptualizations, who structures the isolate in a new way leading ultimately to a new view of both the isolate and of its surround. Thus the borders of separation are broken down, and the former isolate becomes an integral part of a greatly restructured field. Such was the case with the study of the ether in physics; such seems about to be the case with the study of hypnosis. Already some of the new dimensions and concepts developed in the exploration of hypnotic phenomena are pressing for revision of the field outside it. For example, the seminal work of Orne on implicit demand characteristics in the hypnotic relationship presses for a consideration of the effects of experimenters' expectancies and hypotheses on the performances of their subjects, so that it is now possible to visualize the day when it will be necessary in psychological research to consider not only the sampling of subjects but also the sampling of experimenters. The use of faking controls in hypnosis research suggests similar uses in research on attitude change, the effects of psychotherapy, and in interpersonal perception research. Problematical reports of differences between hypnotizable and nonhypnotizable subjects, which are resolved through differences between those who volunteer for hypnosis and those who do not, and the broader area of concern about the effects of subjects' hypotheses and expectancies appear likely to affect the selection of subjects for psychological research, and to stimulate further studies on the sociology of knowledge as expectancy-biasing information becomes available to people who are potential subjects for research based on the knowledge that produced the bias. Evaluations of the results of experiments using hypnotically induced responses focus attention on the unbridled generalization of data drawn from research on phenotypically similar responses to processes of differing genotypic characteristics; this in turn raises questions about the broader problems of operationalism as a principle, in which the definition of an event in terms of the procedures used to measure it may conflict with definitions of the same event in terms of the procedures used to produce the event. This then raises further questions in the logic of science about the representativeness and utility of varieties of experimental work in which the act of experimenting makes the phenomena different from what they are under other conditions of observation in which other expectancies on the part of both subject and experimenter, related to the uses of different research procedures, alter the phenomena under consideration.

Other heads may also roll. The distinction between conscious and unconscious as internal events may be revised by a consideration of the dependence of these realms on the social transactions between hypnotist and subject, patient and therapist, teacher and student, salesman and client. Pain as a psychological concept seems likely to become further divorced from directly physiological considerations. Individual differences in obedience to an experimenter's instructions will have to be considered, or research procedures devised to free data from this source of bias.

Forces leading to such revisions are, I believe, inherent in the chapters written for this Handbook, whose relevance must then go beyond the boundaries of hypnosis to affect the direction of development and the methodologies of the larger field of inquiry of which hypnosis is but one part. The tail is wagging, and the vibrations are already manifesting themselves further up on the corpus of psychological inquiry. We have already seen the beginning of studies on the effects of experimenter bias on the maze-running performance of rats, and on the verbal learning of humans, the psychological characteristics of volunteers for subject-status in research, the effects of implicit suggestions and foreknowledge on proneness to sensory deprivation effects, and on the obedience of subjects where conformity violates ethics. More seems sure to come, as more such variables are discovered and invoked in explanation of hypnotic phenomena and thus, by implication, of nonhypnotic phenomena.

These considerations provide one *raison dêtre* of this Handbook: to make available to modern investigators a summary of the current status of the field, in the hope that by providing a source and starting point, new interest in hypnosis will be kindled. As more and more investigators explore hypnosis, the probability increases that it will be even better understood, that new and more suitable modes of thinking will be developed, and that the reverberations through the rest of psychology will be expanded and hastened. Thus this book is written not only for the investigator interested in working in hypnosis, but also for the nonhypnotist who wishes to be apprised of developments that have potentially great consequences for his preferred field of inquiry, developments which are scattered in isolated and recondite research reports distributed among a variety of journals and books.

Some mountains are climbed just because they are there. Although for some this may be true of hypnosis, many climbers have more instrumental purposes: their interest in hypnosis is moved by questions arising from its use as a diagnostic or therapeutic agent, and as an investigative tool for research on personality, on psychopathology, and on psychotherapy. We are not in the position of mathemeticians, who create systems with no known practical utility. In psychology, practice characteristically precedes research, providing not only the demand for validation of customary usages and techniques, but also the ground from which spring the hypotheses to be tested. Throughout its history, interest in hypnosis has waxed and waned as its practical utility has waxed and waned. In no small measure our current interest is a product of the increased uses to which hypnosis has been put as a result of the impetus given it as a therapeutic agent during World War II. Practitioners in every field of interpersonal influence, from medicine, psychiatry, psychology, to attitude change, advertisers, propagandists, and educators have made applications of hypnosis to their particular fields of work. Their experiences in these fields have led to hypotheses and theories demanding verification, and their continued apparent successes in these applications invite their use by more and more practitioners. Thus two sections of this Handbook are devoted to applications of hypnosis of particular interest to psychologists and psychiatrists, in the domains of psychodiagnosis and psychotherapy, and in research laborataries as a method for controlling and manipulating independent variables.

It is sometimes asserted that there ought to be a moratorium on such practice by ethical professionals until some of the persistent questions about what is involved in hypnosis are cleared up enough to justify its use on scientific grounds. However, the history of psychology, medicine, chemistry, physics, and almost all other sciences suggest that this would be the path of folly, for it would close off the source of the insights needed as guides for investigation at the same time as it robbed us of the need and will to subject the phenomena to scientific study. Most of us do not research problems we feel are meaningless, and it is the application of hypnosis that provides it with much of its importance today as in the past. Included in the first sections of this Handbook, then, are the chapters devoted to the application of hypnosis, out of the conviction that the more such applications, the more sanguine is the outlook for gaining more complete understanding of hypnosis as well as of the phenomena to which it is being applied.

As practice and theory have so often led research in the past, so do they also in this volume, and, as in the past, the research is not far behind, with the chapters organized around the central themes of the field as it is presently structured: individual differences and their measurement, consideration of hypnotic phenomena, the social psychology of hypnosis, and the research on comparative hypnosis.

With our attention directed toward the new entrant to the field of hypnosis, we begin the Handbook with an introduction to the history of the area and to the induction techniques from which all else follows. Throughout the book the authors have kept their focus on providing the reader with summaries of the basic knowledge and methods with which he must be familiar if he is to join the work, as well as with the current state of theory. The Handbook ends with a discussion of ethical concerns with specific reference to hypnosis, and with reference to the broader problems of ethics wherever interpersonal influence efforts share characteristics with hypnosis. If hypnosis is close to the mind-body problem, it is also close to the problem of free will, choice, and liberty, and the dilemmas produced by their consideration within the framework of psychological determinism. Thus the Handbook is frankly didactic, as well as evangelistic and propagandistic.

When this Handbook was first contemplated, Professor E. G. Boring advised that an edited volume composed of papers written by several different people inevitably must lack the sense of unity and coherence that can be imposed on the material by a single author. Professor Boring's cautions were well taken, and I have tried, within limits, to maintain throughout the Handbook a relatively even level of pacing and presentation. But the limits are important. There is a value to allowing the leading investigators and practitioners in the field to speak with their own voices, in their own idioms, for these are the people whose imprints will be borne by hypnosis and its students for many years to come; it would be a disservice to violate their styles. To some extent the preservation of the integrity of the individual authors entailed some inevitable unevenesses and disjunctures in the total presentation. I hope that we have been able to keep these at a minimum; those that remain may be taken as an index of the state of the field, in which development has been uneven, and the research marked by islands of ignorance.

2

A Brief History of Hypnotism

FRANK A. PATTIE

University of Kentucky

AUTHORS who write on the history of hypnotism often trace their subject back into ancient times, but little can be found in ancient records that bears much resemblance to the hypnotism of today. A great variety of phenomena related to suggestibility has attracted attention in all periods of history. The work of Stoll, a professor of geography and ethnology at the University of Zurich, is the most complete collection of historical and anthropological material of this sort; it contains accounts of shamanism, ecstasy, phenomena of suggestion in the Bible, demoniacal possession, miracles, folk medicine, tarantism, and many other things (Stoll, 1904). It has little to say about hypnotism as we know it. In Regnier's book (1891) the pre-Mesmer history is mainly concerned with magic and witchcraft. Because an account of phenomena of suggestion prior to Mesmer would be for the most part a mere catalogue of unconnected matters, such as the temple sleep of the ancients, the laying on of hands, and the history of various unfounded beliefs, this brief sketch will begin with Mesmer, whose ideas are historically continuous with the modern theory and practice of hypnotism, into which these ideas were gradually transformed during the past two hundred years.

FRANZ MESMER

Mesmer's Dissertation

Franz Anton Mesmer (1734–1815) published his medical dissertation *De planetarum influxu* (On the influence of the planets) in 1766. It had nothing to do with astrology; in fact, it expressly repudiated astrology. It was a "physico-medical dissertation" that attempted to bring back into medicine the study of the physical effects produced in the human body by the gravitational forces exerted by the planets, especially the sun and the moon, which were then called planets. After expounding Newton's laws of universal gravitation, Kepler's laws of planetary motion, and Newton's theory of the tides, Mesmer stated that there must be tides in the atmosphere, which are produced by the same gravitational forces that produce those in the sea. Twice in every twenty-four hours the air is attracted upward, and this periodic change must affect the human body. The tides of the sea and the air are higher at the times of the full and new moons.

The idea of atmospheric tides is the central theme of a work by Richard Mead, *De imperio solis ac lunae in corpora humana et morbis inde oriundis* (1704).[1] Mead, a leader of the iatromechanical school of medicine, was a friend of Newton and, like Mesmer, an enthusiastic admirer of him. His book argued that the tides in the atmosphere produced changes in the "gravity, elasticity, and pressure" of the air and that these changes affected the human body in health and disease; and he presented cases of periodicities in diseases, which he believed were due to the phases of the moon.

Mesmer plagiarized his dissertation to a great extent from Mead. In its theoretical part the ideas are not only very similar but there is also some copying of Mead's words. In the clinical section Mesmer took 22 of 23 items (mostly case-histories) from Mead. The array of cases and quotations, ranging from the time of Galen to the eighteenth century, gives an impression of diligent study and search of medical literature by Mesmer, but evidence has been presented to show that Mesmer merely copied from Mead and never took the trouble to look up the cases in the books that Mead had cited (Pattie, 1956).

Mesmer added a few ideas to those of Mead. He stated that the effect of gravitation on the human body might be direct and not mediated by changes in the properties of the air. He wrote also that there is a tide

[1] The title of the English translation of the second edition (1748) was *A treatise concerning the influence of the sun and moon upon human bodies, and the diseases thereby produced.*

in the human body, giving as proof for this statement the fact that the sap rises in plants when the moon is full (the time of the highest tides on the sea). Another addition was: "Furthermore, there is another kind of influence on the animal body which appears not to be dependent upon these usual qualities of the atmosphere but instead depends directly upon that force which, diffused through the vast spaces of the heavens, affects the most intimate parts of every kind of matter, holds the huge spheres in their orbits and disturbs and attracts them from their true path into a different region, which is the cause of universal gravitation and which is more probably the basis of all the properties of bodies, which indeed in the smallest particles of the fluids and solids of our organism maintains, relaxes, and disturbs cohesion, elasticity, irritability, magnetism, and electricity, and which may certainly and not improperly be called in this respect ANIMAL GRAVITATION." It is possible that this sentence may have been inspired by the last paragraph in Newton's *Principia mathematica*, which is equal in vagueness and turbidity to Mesmer's statement about this peculiar animal gravitation, which is "the cause of universal gravitation."[2]

The fact that a medical dissertation of the eighteenth century was a work of plagiarism is not surprising; in those days plagiarism was more common and less condemned than it is today. The astonishing feature is the nature of the source from which Mesmer drew his material. Ever since Mesmer's theories came under scrutiny in the late eighteenth century much scholarly effort has been expended, especially by Thouret (1784) and Paulet (1784), to show that his ideas came from the practitioners and theorists of magical and magnetic medicine of the sixteenth and seventeenth centuries—Paracelsus, Van Helmont, Kircher, and especially Maxwell. But, instead of drawing from the occult side of medicine, he took his dissertation almost wholly from the work of a mechanically-minded follower of Newton.

It should be pointed out that Mead's work was a piece of entirely legitimate science without any occult, mystical, or astrological coloring. His *De imperio* was an ancestor of the work which is being done by biologists today on periodicities in the physiological functions and in the behavior of plants and animals.[3]

Mesmer's Practice in Vienna

In 1774 Mesmer treated a young woman for a variety of hysterical complaints with great success, applying to her body magnets, which

[2] This paragraph is quoted in Pattie (1956), p. 280.

[3] Mead is regularly cited in the publications of Leonard J. Ravitz, a prominent investigator of physiological periodicities. See his "History, measurement, and applicability of periodic changes in the electromagnetic field in health and disease," *Ann. N. Y. Acad. Sci.*, 1962, **98**, 1144–1201.

had been supplied by their maker, Maximilian Hell, a learned Jesuit astronomer in charge of the Vienna observatory. A controversy on priority followed, in which Hell declared that it was he who had suggested to Mesmer that he use magnets on this patient. Mesmer stated that he had been preparing the patient for magnetic treatment (by giving her medicines containing iron!) long before Hell had told him of a cure produced by one of his magnets. Naturally Mesmer won the argument, for Hell could not disprove any statement as to what had gone on between doctor and patient. Obtaining good results on other patients, Mesmer began to write about his method, saying that in his dissertation he had called "that property of the animal body, by virtue of which it is susceptible to universal attraction, *gravitas animalis* or *magnetismus animalis*." This statement is not true, since the word *magnetismus* occurred in his dissertation in only one place, in the long sentence already quoted. In later writings he no longer mentioned *gravitas*. Thus was the transition made to animal magnetism, a concept which he was never able to define intelligibly.

Mesmer believed that the magnet cured disease by producing "an artificial ebb and flow" in the body and correcting with its uniform current "the unequal distribution of the nervous fluid and its confused movement," thus producing a "harmony of the nerves." Patients perceived the effect of the magnet only in the parts of the body in which the harmony was disturbed. Convulsive attacks were generally produced in his patients when the magnets were applied. He was impressed by the reports given by his patients of painful, surging sensations, moving from one place to another, which gave him some ground for his belief that the magnet produced "an artificial ebb and flow."

The patients who experienced peculiar sensations and seizures, which were usually so violent that they frightened the onlookers, were merely responding to suggestions, both direct and indirect, that they would experience such effects. If wooden magnet shapes had been substituted secretly for the real ones made of steel, patients would have acted in the same way. This fact was never accepted by Mesmer, who was entirely blind to the psychological aspects of the treatment. To him these effects were produced by physical processes. Consequently, when he found that his patients responded with equal vigor to teacups, bread, wood, human beings, and animals to which a magnet had been touched, he thought that the "magnetic material" had been transferred to these objects. Human beings varied greatly in their ability to store up magnetism; some persons absorbed it so well that they could cause pain in a patient if they came within a distance of a few steps, whereas others took up no magnetism at all.

Father Hell at once criticized these experiments, saying that Mesmer did not indicate in his reports whether the patients saw him imparting the magnetism to the objects. If the patient saw the objects being touched with the magnet, then the sensations reported when the object was applied to the patient were due to imagination. (Hell believed that the magnet itself produced a genuine sensation and that the sensations produced by other objects to which the magnet had been applied were memory images of the previous ones.) Hell suggested a properly controlled experiment: Mesmer should take a number of teacups and, in the absence of the patient, impart magnetism to one of them. Then the patient should be called in and asked to pick out the magnetized cup.[4]

By the end of 1775 Mesmer had almost entirely abandoned the use of magnets, because he found, as might be expected, that he could stroke or make passes over the bodies of his patients and produce the same convulsions and peculiar sensations. He believed that in this way he communicated animal magnetism (which was in some unclear way different from mineral magnetism) to his patients and that his force or material could be stored up in various objects by his stroking them. These objects would in turn communicate their animal magnetism to his patients.

In 1777 he began the treatment of a musician, Maria Theresa Paradis, then 18 years old, who had become blind overnight when she was 3 years old. He took this girl into his home and soon asserted that her blindness, which had been considered incurable, had been overcome. At first some physicians agreed with him, but finally some of the most eminent doctors of Vienna denied that she had recovered her vision. Simple tests, which could have been made before and after treatment to end the controversy, were not made. If she had temporarily regained her vision, which is doubtful, she relapsed during the controversy and lived the rest of her life in blindness, dying in 1824 at the age of 65 without having commented in any way, so far as can be ascertained, on Mesmer's treatment. A stern warning from the chief professor of medicine at the University was delivered: "Cease this imposture." As a result of the unfortunate outcome in this case, Mesmer decided to leave Vienna, after suffering both from Hell and Paradis, for the more tolerant atmosphere of Paris (Mesmer, 1779).

Mesmer's Career in Paris

In Paris Mesmer began to treat patients for whatever illnesses they had. According to his theory, there was but one disease, the obstruction of the free flow of animal magnetism in the body and the consequent

[4] The early history of the magnetic treatment and the controversy between Mesmer and Hell is contained in newspaper articles by both men reprinted in *Sammlung der neuesten gedruckten und geschriebenen Nachrichten von Magnet-Curen, vorzüglich der Mesmerischen*, Leipzig, 1778.

improper distribution of it, which manifested itself in many forms. He had so many patients that he had to treat them in groups by means of the animal magnetism stored up in bottles filled with iron filings, which were contained in a *baquet* (tub). The patients would assemble in his apartment around the *baquet*, holding iron rods that came out of it and sometimes joining hands and listening to the soft music played in an adjacent room. After a while Mesmer would appear, pointing his finger or an iron rod toward one of the group, who would then experience queer sensations and a great variety of other phenomena ranging from trembling to convulsions. After one patient succumbed, the others were not long in developing crises, but there were always a few who failed to show any visible effect.

Mesmer made only one convert of importance among medical men, Charles d'Eslon, the physician of the king's brother. D'Eslon, alternately friendly and quarreling with Mesmer, later established his own magnetic clinic. He urged Mesmer to write a book, which appeared in 1779 and was mainly an account of his difficulties, intrigues, and extraordinary cures from 1774 to 1779 (Mesmer, 1779). At the end of the small book there are added, apparently as an afterthought, the well-known "27 Propositions." They give little help in understanding Mesmer's theory, and they raise more questions in the minds of readers than answers. They are:

1. A mutual influence exists between the heavenly bodies, the earth, and animate bodies.
2. The means of this influence is a fluid, which is universally distributed, so continuous that there is no space which it does not fill, of incomparable subtlety, and by its nature capable of receiving, propagating, and communicating all impressions of movement.
3. This reciprocal action is governed by mechanical laws, which up to the present time are unknown.

The "mutual influence" could be gravitation. The universal fluid or medium named in Number 2 is assumed because of the difficulty of the idea of action at a distance through a void, an idea which has always troubled scientists. Newton held that action at a distance was absurd.

The statement about mechanical laws in Number 3 is peculiar in two ways: first, we are not told how it is possible to make any statement about the existence of laws that are unknown; second, Newton had already discovered the laws of gravitational attraction (it varies inversely as the distance, and so on).

4. Alternating effects, which may be considered to be an ebb and flow, result from this action.
5. The ebb and flow are more or less general, more or less particular, more or

less compound, according to the nature of the causes which produce them.

6. It is by this operation (the most universal of those presented to us by nature), that relationships of activity are set up between the heavenly bodies, the earth, and its component parts.
7. The properties of matter and of organisms depend on this operation.

Numbers 1 to 7 can be regarded as expressing ideas contained in the dissertation.

8. The animal body experiences the alternating effects of this agent, and it is by penetrating the substance of the nerves that it affects them immediately.

Since according to Number 2 "there is no space that it does not fill," it is inconsistent to say that the fluid penetrates (that is, enters from outside of) the nerves; it is already in them.

9. There are manifested, especially in the human body, properties analogous to those of the magnet; also there may be distinguished in it poles, different and opposite, which can be transferred, changed, destroyed, and reinforced. Even the phenomenon of dipping is observed.
10. That property of the organism which makes it susceptible to the influence of the heavenly bodies and the reciprocal action of bodies surrounding it, shown by its analogy with the magnet, led me to call it animal magnetism.
11. The action and the properties of animal magnetism, thus defined, may be transferred to other bodies, animate and inanimate. Both kinds of body are more or less susceptible to it.
12. This action and these properties may be reinforced and propagated by these same bodies.
13. We observe by experience the flowing of a material whose subtlety penetrates all bodies without appreciable loss of activity.
14. Its action is exerted at a distance without the aid of any intermediary substance.
15. It is, like light, intensified and reflected by mirrors.
16. It is communicated, propagated, and intensified by sound.

In Number 10 animal magnetism is defined as a property of the organism, whereas in Number 11 we observe that this property has its own properties. In Numbers 13 to 16 we find that animal magnetism is no longer defined as a property of the organism but as a material that pervades all things. Its action requires no medium, though the mutual influence of Number 1 requires a medium, the fluid of Number 2. In Number 15 there is a mistake in optics; plane mirrors, the kind of mirror he was thinking of, do not intensify light.

17. This magnetic property may be accumulated, concentrated, and transported.
18. I have said that animate bodies are not equally susceptible; there are some, though very rare, which have a property so opposed that their mere presence destroys all the effects of this magnetism in other bodies.

19. This opposite property also penetrates all bodies; it may likewise be communicated, propagated, accumulated, concentrated, transported, reflected by mirrors, and propagated by sound; it not only constitutes an absence of magnetism but a positive opposite quality.

Numbers 18 and 19 were set up to account for Mesmer's failure to affect some of his subjects. Number 19 hints that when he failed with one subject others present also became resistant. Through these two propositions we learn that there are not one but two all-pervading fluids or properties. A contemporary critic asked how it was possible to unite these opposites in the same body at the same time: "It is to want a man to be awake and asleep at the same time."

20. The magnet, whether natural or artificial, is, like all other bodies, susceptible to animal magnetism and even to the opposite property, without undergoing in either case any change in its action on iron and the compass needle; this fact proves that the principle of animal magnetism differs essentially from that of mineral magnetism.

It is interesting to substitute in Number 20 the definition of animal magnetism taken from Number 10; the proposition then becomes, "The magnet is susceptible to that property of the organism which makes it susceptible to the influence of the heavenly bodies and the reciprocal action of bodies surrounding it, shown by its analogy with the magnet."

The remaining propositions, Numbers 21 to 27, are promises and propaganda: their substance is that the system will furnish new explanations on the nature of fire, light, electricity, and the theory of attraction. This principle "can cure directly the diseases of the nerves and indirectly the other diseases."[5]

Finally, Mesmer will show by a new theory of diseases the universal usefulness of the principle.

In 1781 Mesmer wrote that the learned men of Paris declared these Propositions unintelligible (1781, p. 86).

From the time of his arrival in Paris, Mesmer had tried to induce the scientific and medical organizations of Paris to investigate animal magnetism. "Investigate" is too strong a word; as he phrased it, he wished to present animal magnetism to them so that they might

[5] Some modern writers have stated that Mesmer treated only "functional" disorders. The most casual inspection of the record shows that he treated any disease, even cancer. Moreover, the distinction between organic and functional disorders either did not exist or was not discussed in the literature concerning Mesmerism in the eighteenth century. It must be remembered that what is called functional at one time is called organic at another (Henry Maudsley in his *Responsibility in mental disease*, 1874, classified epilepsy, chorea, and neuralgia as functional because no gross changes in the nervous system were visible at autopsy), and that the concept of functional disorder does not coincide with that of psychogenic disorder.

"recognize the reality of my discovery and its usefulness for mankind." He successively and unsuccessfully tried to interest the Academy of Sciences, the Royal Society of Medicine, and the Faculty of Medicine in such an investigation, but none accepted his invitation.

At one time he was advised by his friends to prove the value of his new principle by treating two groups of patients, one by means of animal magnetism and the other by conventional methods, and comparing the results. He was hesitant about this plan for two reasons: first, he considered that his discovery lay in the field of physics, because he had found a hitherto unknown cosmic force, and second, because "Nothing proves demonstratively that a physician or medicine cures diseases," that is, whether "art or nature" produces a cure in any particular case. Nevertheless, he went to a suburb with a number of patients, and in May 1778 he asked the Royal Society of Medicine to appoint a commission to examine them. When the time he had allowed for their treatment was up, in the following August, the Secretary of the Society replied to his request for an examination that the Society could do nothing, as it knew nothing of the condition of the patients before their treatment began.

Mesmer's friend and pupil, d'Eslon, made vigorous representations to members of the Faculty of Medicine to persuade the Faculty to investigate, but he obtained nothing; in fact, the Faculty denounced him, deprived him of his vote in the Faculty for a year, and threatened him with expulsion if at the end of a year he had not retracted his *Observations on animal magnetism*, a small book he had published in 1780.

During the discussions with d'Eslon, three members of the Faculty submitted the plan of an experiment that they considered crucial. The subject was to be a young girl who was so sensitive that she felt great pain whenever Mesmer pointed toward her. She was to be blindfolded and placed in the corner of a room. Twenty-four persons, including Dr. Mesmer, were to be put in a line, and each was to stand in front of her for a few moments. Some of them would make the same movements as those made by Mesmer, and some would do nothing. The experiment would be repeated several times in silence, and Dr. Mesmer would have a different position in the line in each repetition.[6] No one was to touch her, because Dr. Mesmer had not touched her previously. If in every repetition Dr. Mesmer's presence near the girl produced the same pains as before, while no other person in the line affected her, then it would be agreed that Dr. Mesmer had the power of affecting animate bodies without contact and that the subject's imagination contributed nothing. Mesmer rejected the proposal with disdain and bitterness. D'Eslon said that the request for such a test showed a most offensive

[6] The design of this proposed experiment nowadays would be called a Latin square.

suspicion of him, Mesmer, and the subject. Furthermore, "the existence of animal magnetism in animate bodies can confer on many persons for a short time the ability to produce the same effects as Dr. Mesmer can, a phenomenon which is less surprising since he has established the fact that animal magnetism can be communicated. It may be reasonably supposed that, among 24 physicians who repeat the experiment 480 times in Dr. Mesmer's presence in various ways on a blindfolded subject, someone will be found who will affect the subject at least enough to make one judge that Dr. Mesmer's effects are not genuine." This answer of d'Eslon takes only half of the matter into account; it may be granted that perhaps some others might produce effects, but on the other hand it is entirely possible that Mesmer in such an experiment might produce no pains or any other effects in the girl, an eventuality which would have been disastrous for him (Mesmer, 1781, p. 103).

D'Eslon continued to urge the government to investigate animal magnetism. Finally the Minister of State informed Mesmer that the king would grant him a life annuity of 20,000 francs and provide 10,000 francs a year for a house suitable for the instruction of students, of whom three were to be selected by the government. Other benefits sought by Mesmer would be granted when the government's students acknowledged "the usefulness of the discovery." Because the three students appointed by the government might be chosen from his worst enemies and because the government refused Mesmer's demand that it acknowledge as a preliminary to any negotiations the existence and the utility of animal magnetism, he refused. He would accept the pension of 20,000 francs a year if he were given a landed estate for a school of animal magnetism, in which he could take students and treat patients without restriction and if certain other conditions were met.

The discussions ended there, whereupon he wrote an impudent letter to the queen deploring this outcome of the negotiations (Mesmer, 1781, pp. 201–220). Many writers have stated that the government offered to pay a large sum to Mesmer if he would reveal "his secret." He had no secret to reveal, nor did the government assume that he had. He claimed to possess a complex body of knowledge about animal magnetism and its application in many kinds of diseases, and his supporters believed that he could teach other physicians his theory and how to apply it. It must be admitted, however, that there was a considerable amount of contemporary talk about Mesmer's having "a secret." Even d'Eslon in his book in 1780 raised the question and said that, as far as he was able to ascertain, Mesmer had no secret.

Finally in 1784 the government decided to investigate animal magnetism, whereupon the king established a commission of nine eminent men of science, among whom were the astronomer Bailly, the chemist Lavoisier, and Benjamin Franklin. The king also appointed a commission of physicians. The two groups worked separately and issued separate reports. Much to Mesmer's disgust, they investigated animal magnetism as practiced by Mesmer's disciple, d'Eslon. Mesmer protested violently, declaring that d'Eslon was a mere novice, although he had studied under Mesmer since 1780.

The commissions found that none of their electrical or other instruments could detect any electrical or magnetic forces in or around the *baquet*. They noted that the application of animal magnetism produced no effects on any subject unless he expected them. If, for example, a boy who was highly susceptible to animal magnetism were told that a particular tree in an orchard had been magnetized by d'Eslon, he would have a convulsion when he touched it, although the tree had not been touched by d'Eslon. If, on the contrary, d'Eslon had actually magnetized a tree but this fact was not known by the boy, no convulsion followed when the boy touched the tree.

The report of the medical commission agreed with that of the Bailly commission; however, a member of the latter group, the botanist Jussieu, did not sign the report but issued one of his own. He had performed a few experiments in which he believed that the influence of imagination was excluded, and he attributed the effects which he observed to the slight movement of the air caused by his gestures, the imperceptible perspiration, and the animal heat that flowed from his fingers.

The commissioners made a secret report to the king, in which they declared that, because the magnetist's body came into close contact with the body of a female subject who was treated privately, the use of animal magnetism was a threat to the virtue of women, which in France had always been hard to preserve. This secret report is sometimes cited nowadays in discussions of the dangers of hypnosis, but it is hardly relevant, because the mesmeric methods were so different from modern procedures, in which verbal suggestion, not used by Mesmer, is the chief instrument of trance induction.

To say that any natural event was due to imagination, which was a concept far removed from those of physics, the dominant science among the learned, was a subtle condemnation and almost amounted to relegating it to outer darkness. Also, in spite of the fact that the language of Mesmer's theories was consistently that of the mechanical science of the day, several scholars had declared that his ideas were derived from the practitioners and theorists of magical and magnetic medicine of the previous two centuries (Paracelsus, Van Helmont, Maxwell, Kircher, and others), and this opinion linked his work with occult doctrines and made it even more unacceptable.

No reputable scientist of the time was able to see that the problem of the influence of the imagination (in modern terms, suggestion) on disease was worth investigating. D'Eslon had asked, "If M. Mesmer had no other secret than that of making the imagination act to produce health, would it not be a marvelous benefit?" But Mesmer had denied the influence of imagination and insisted that the cures were produced by a physical agent. The commissioners, having found that such an agent did not exist, concluded that what did not exist could have no useful effect and left the matter there.

The final paragraph of the report of the scientific commission deserves quotation in full:

> The commissioners, having found that the fluid animal magnetism cannot be perceived by any of the senses and that it has no effect either upon themselves or upon the patients submitted to them; having assured themselves that pressure and contact produce changes that are seldom favorable in the organic economy and agitations, which are always unfavourable, in the imagination; having finally demonstrated by decisive experiments that imagination without magnetism produces convulsions and that magnetism without imagination produces nothing; they have unanimously concluded, on the question of the existence and the utility of magnetism, that there is no proof of its existence, that this fluid without existence is consequently without utility, and that the violent effects observed in public clinics are to be attributed to the touching, to the aroused imagination, and to that mechanical imitation which leads us in spite of ourselves to repeat that which strikes our senses. And at the same time they believe themselves obligated to add, as an important observation, that the touchings and the repeated action of the imagination for the purpose of producing crises can be harmful, that the sight of these crises is likewise dangerous because of the imitation which nature seems to have imposed upon us as a law, and that, therefore, all public treatments in which magnetism is used can only have, in the course of time, dangerous effects.[7]

In 1784 Mesmer and a group of about a hundred students, who had subscribed an enormous sum as tuition, founded the Lodge of Harmony, a society for instruction in his system. Similar societies were founded in several French cities, the most important being the one in Strasbourg, which was led by the Marquis de Puységur and enrolled 200 members. The history of the Lodge of Harmony and the difficulties which the students had with their master and among themselves would fill many pages. The students were pledged to keep the doctrine secret, but there was a leak which resulted in the publication of his teaching in the form of 344 aphorisms (Mesmer, 1784).

Mesmer published a short book in 1799 on his discovery, which took notice of the artificial somnambulism discovered by Puységur; but it was not influential, apparently because it was overshadowed by the extensive publications of his chief French successor.

The year 1784 was climactic. More books and pamphlets were published on animal magnetism than in any other year, and the debate

[7] All the reports of the commissions of 1784, 1825, and 1837 are in Burdin and Dubois (1841).

grew hotter. The two commissions made their reports in August, and a publication by the Marquis de Puységur at the end of 1784 opened a new period in animal magnetism that made the reports of the commissions to a great extent obsolete.

PUYSÉGUR'S ARTIFICIAL SOMNAMBULISM

The man who inaugurated the new period of artificial or induced somnambulism was Armand-Marc-Jacques de Chastenet, Marquis de Puységur (1751–1825), a military man of unquestioned integrity and a member of a well-known family in French history.

Puységur believed that the violent crises of the mesmeric treatment were dangerous, and in his magnetizing he tried to keep his patients, for the most part tenants on his estate near Soissons, in a calm frame of mind. Thus he discovered the sleeping trance or "induced somnambulism" and several other phenomena unknown to Mesmer. In magnetizing a young peasant named Victor, Puységur produced an apparent sleep after a few minutes without convulsions or other unpleasant effects. "I produced a crisis, which caused some vertigo. He talked quite audibly about his work. When I thought that his ideas might affect him unpleasantly, I stopped them and tried to inspire him with more pleasant ones. I did not have to make any great effort to do so, for I then saw that he was happy, imagining that he was shooting for a prize, dancing at a party, etc. I fostered these ideas in him, and I made him move a great deal in his chair, as if he were dancing to music." Here are two new facts: the trance state, in which the subject talks while he seems to be asleep, and the giving of direct verbal suggestions to produce changes other than crises or seizures, which, strange to say, had never been practiced by Mesmer.

Victor was amnesic for the events of the trance. Mesmer had never reported any postmagnetic amnesia in his patients, but Jussieu had discovered it in his work as a royal commissioner and mentioned it in his report. Puységur added to this knowledge, finding that the person in the trance commanded the memories of previous trance states but did not have them in the normal waking state.

Some of Puységur's conclusions were wrong, outlived him, and have been hard to eradicate. It seemed to him that his patients had the power of clairvoyance, being able to diagnose their own illnesses and those of others and to prescribe remedies. This idea persisted until the 1840's. In the trance state Victor was no longer "a stupid peasant" but was highly intelligent and appeared to have telepathic powers, responding to the mere thoughts of Puységur. The statement, "If someone enters his room, he sees him, if I so desire," shows that the subject's perceptions could be controlled by the magnetist. In discussing the possible use of magnetism by unscrupulous persons, he stated that no one can be magnetized against his will and that his subjects told him that they retained their judgment and reason and immediately would perceive any evil intentions of the magnetist and come out of the trance. Some of his patients could predict the day and hour of their cure and of future crises or seizures. In the light of present knowledge, such predictions were more predeterminations than predictions.

Puységur tells many dramatic incidents about his subjects. One of them wrote a letter while in the trance and had no memory of it when he was in the normal state. Another, who could not believe that he had been in trances, because he had no memory of them, had himself tied in a chair and brought to Puységur, saying that he hoped that Puységur would ask him to change from his chair to another and that he believed he would awaken while he was removing the ropes. He was magnetized and made to untie the ropes. When he was brought out of the trance, he could not believe that he had untied them.

We find an adumbration of the use of the trance as an "uncovering" or investigative technique in the case of a soldier who said while he was in a trance, "The cause of my illness [epileptoid seizures] is the annoyance of being so closely confined to barracks and not being liked by my comrades." (Chastenet, 1809a, pp. 54, 55, 87, 96; 1809b, p. 205).

Puységur always gave Mesmer full credit for his discoveries, from which his own work developed; he nevertheless deplored certain features of his master's practice. In explaining how it was possible for him to report phenomena never discovered by Mesmer, he said that he was entirely free to spend his time as he wished, whereas Mesmer tried to treat a multitude of patients. He was in complete control of everything he did, whereas Mesmer was not master of his own time and work. Moreover, Mesmer's habit of treating patients in public gave him little opportunity to observe carefully the effects that he produced in the disorderly groups gathered round the *baquet*. Puységur was a most painstaking observer and made long and detailed reports on the progress of his cures; this Mesmer had seldom done.

At the beginning of his career, Puységur believed in the fluidic theory, and he magnetized a large tree on his estate, from which the peasants drew the healing animal magnetism through cords. He considered psychological factors important, but he discussed only those in the operator and not those in his patients. As early as 1784 he took as his motto "*Croyez et voulez*" (Believe and will). The prominence of will in the theory was due to a discovery made by the younger of his two brothers, both of whom were interested in magnetism and were students in Mesmer's school, the Lodge of Harmony. The members of the Lodge were not very sure that the physical theory of Mesmer was of any use to them in practical work, especially after they learned that the valet of the Marquis de Puységur was able to produce as many magnetized subjects as Puységur, and the valet had been taught nothing about interplanetary influences and molecules. They were therefore looking for down-to-earth answers to their questions. The younger brother thought that he had discovered the principle that caused magnetic effects (that is, Mesmer's "secret") in the will of the magnetizer. He informed Mesmer of his conclusion, "who, while trying to conceal his surprise, showed much displeasure and still more concern about the harmful effects which could result, both for himself and his theory, from the premature interpretations which might be made. My brother, approving his motives, promised that he would keep the secret. . . ." He did not reveal it to the Marquis until 15 months later, when he was embarking for Santo Domingo as a naval officer. The Marquis taught this doctrine thus to his students: "My will, the motor of all my acts and determinations, is likewise that of my magnetic action. I believe in the existence in myself of a power. From this belief arises my will to exercise it. The act of my will determines all of the effects that I produce." (Chastenet, 1807, pp. 140–143, 148–149). He was confused about the fluidic theory, which he was hardly capable of criticizing because of his lack of scientific knowledge; and he compared Mesmer's agent, which he said was for him a hypothesis rather than a reality, with static electricity, which could be stored in Leyden jars. The final theory of Puységur and his followers is stated thus by Bertrand: "The agent which they thought they put into action was a particular vital fluid secreted, or at least accumulated, in the brain and conducted by the nerves. This fluid, which is concerned in all the movements of the body, is eminently subject to the will and can, under its influence, be projected outwards and directed upon or accumulated upon any body, living or not living. If this theory is not very clearly developed in the writings of all the magnetizers, it is at least implicitly adopted in them." Bertrand did not confirm the importance of will, because he could produce the same results in his subjects with or without volition. (Bertrand, 1826, pp. 236, 241.)

THE ABBÉ FARIA

One of the strangest characters in the development of the theory of animal magnetism was a Portuguese priest, José Custódio de Faria (1755–1819), who received instruction from Puységur. Born in Portuguese India of Roman Catholic parents who later separated, the father entering the priesthood and the mother a religious order, he was taken to Lisbon at the age of 15 by his father. José obtained a doctorate in theology in Rome and was ordained in 1780. Disappointed because he had not been made a bishop, he migrated to Paris in 1788 and lived there as a private citizen. How he made a living is not clear; it is said that at one period in his life he was paid a small daily stipend by a café on condition that he would refrain from gambling there, as his luck was too good. He spent two years as a professor of philosophy at the local academies of Nimes and Marseilles, but he was not successful in his work. Returning to Paris, he began a course of lectures and demonstrations on animal magnetism. He continued these lectures until an actor of the Paris stage brought him into discredit and ridicule in 1816 by pretending to be put into a state of somnambulism, later publicly declaring his deception and appearing in the role of "Soporito," a caricature of the dark-skinned Faria, in a popular farce, *Magnétisomanie*. Reduced to poverty, Faria accepted a position as chaplain of a school for girls, which gave him board and lodging in return for sacerdotal functions. Meanwhile he was writing a book, but he died of apoplexy while it was being printed, and he was given a pauper's burial.[8]

Faria is important because he was the first practitioner of animal magnetism to state a theory of somnambulism in which the characteristics of the subjects, rather than the activity of the magnetizer, are made responsible for its production. The predisposing causes of somnambulism are the liquidity of the blood and a certain "psychic impressionability" (suggestibility). He also believed that persons who could go to sleep easily and who perspired freely were most susceptible. His curious idea about the liquidity of the blood was based upon his observation that some subjects who were refractory at first became good somnambulists after being bled. The immediate cause of the condition is the concentration of the subject's thoughts and his withdrawal from the senses, which occurs voluntarily and with restriction of the subject's volition or his inner freedom; these processes occur when subjects go into natural sleep. Somnambulism does not occur "when the mind is occupied by the agitation of the blood or by anxieties." Somnambulism and natural sleep were thought to be the same.

Faria changed the terminology, calling animal magnetism "concentration," the magnetizer "the concentrator," and somnambulism "lucid sleep." His term for somnambulist, "epopte," from the Greek word meaning "one who sees clearly," shows the influence of Puységur's emphasis on clairvoyance.

Faria's method of inducing lucid sleep was simple. He placed his subject in a comfortable chair, told him to close his eyes, and then, when he thought he was sufficiently quiet, gave the emphatic command, "Sleep." Another method involved steady visual fixation of his

[8] The chief source on Faria is his *De la cause du sommeil lucide* (1819), reprinted with a preface by Dr. D. G. Dalgado, Paris, 1906. The work by Moniz (1925) is a very full account of Faria's life and theories.

hand, with freedom to move the eyelids. If he noticed that the eyelids were not blinking, he would move his hand slowly toward the eyes. Another method was to touch the subject lightly on his temples, above the nose, and on the precordial region, the knees, or the feet. In his demonstrations he usually began by using practiced subjects, who had learned how to enter lucid sleep, and then took new subjects from the audience.

He was apparently the first person to state that subjects could be made insensitive to the pain of surgery. He also found that some persons, whom he had never seen before, developed trances as soon as they arrived at the entrance to his room and before he had noticed them, and sometimes he had to hurry to them to prevent their falling.

Although his book is often tedious, unclear, and full of unfounded conclusions, Faria was the first to bring out a psychological theory of somnambulism.[9] He was a man of great intellectual independence, but he was handicapped by a lack of scientific knowledge. Rejecting the fluidic theory, he said that even if there were a universal fluid, no proof had been given that any man could direct it into the bodies of patients. He objected to the imagination theory for a curious reason, saying that whatever is imagined is remembered; because subjects were amnesic for events of the period of somnambulism, this theory could not be accepted. He followed Puységur in believing in the ability of subjects to diagnose diseases in themselves and others, but he pointed out that they could make mistakes. Ostracized by his brother priests because of his work on animal magnetism and by other magnetists because he discarded the fluidic theory, not living long enough to receive the recognition later given to him, held up as an object of derision during his last years, he was an unfortunate man. In many ways both practical and theoretical, especially in his failure to profit financially from animal magnetism, he was the opposite of Mesmer.

After Faria's death, investigation was carried on in Paris by the physician Alexandre Bertrand (1795–1831), who gave a public course and wrote a book, *Du magnétisme animal en France*. Among those experimenting in the hospitals were Jules Denis de Sennevoy, better known as the Baron du Potet (1796–1881), and the neurologist Etienne-Jean Georget (1795–1828). Experiments on anesthesia were beginning. In 1821 moxas were burned on the bodies of two patients, who showed no signs of pain, in a Paris hospital under the direction of Dr. Recamier. About this time the General Council of Hospitals put an end to work on animal magnetism in the hospitals on the ground that patients should

[9] J. D. Brandis, a Danish physician, published a book in 1818 containing a psychological theory of somnambulism, which he had first announced in 1815. Tischner and Bittel (1941) quote Brandis extensively but give priority to Faria, because his doctrine was already in existence in 1815, according to contemporary sources.

not be subjects for experimentation. A journal, *Archives du magnétisme animal*, was published for several years by Baron d'Hénin de Cuvillers (1755–1841), a general who had fought in Santo Domingo and who, like many other military men in France, was interested in magnetism. In 1829 the surgeon Cloquet removed an ulcerated tumor of the breast after the patient's physician had put her into a trance. Oudet in 1836 performed the first recorded extraction of a tooth under mesmeric anesthesia.

There was a great deal of opposition to magnetism at this time, for example, the long and learned article by Virey in the *Dictionnaire des sciences médicales* (1819). The general opinion of Mesmer at this time was that he was a charlatan, and this view was held even by some practitioners of magnetism, including the Baron de Cuvillers.

The acceptance of magnetism by J. -P. -L. Deleuze (1753–1835), the naturalist who was librarian of the Jardin des Plantes and a man of unquestioned integrity, was a powerful influence in favor of animal magnetism. He wrote a two-volume work, *Histoire critique du magnétisme animal* (1813), a manual of instruction of the use of magnetism, and a book replying to the article by Virey (1819). He reported that hyperamnesia was a characteristic of the trance, and he stated that the somnambulist in the waking and trance states seemed like two different persons.

In 1825 the Academy of Medicine, at the instigation of Dr. Foissac, appointed a commission to investigate the phenomena of animal magnetism, especially the ability of somnambulists to diagnose diseases. After five years the commission made a report favorable to animal magnetism. They had found subjects who could predict, days or months in advance, the hour and the minute of convulsive attacks, and they had experimented on their ability to see "with eyes closed" (but not bandaged). They had examined a considerable number of somnambulistic subjects but had found only one who came close to describing the symptoms of three persons with whom she had been placed in rapport. The report concluded that magnetism "should find its place in the frame of medical knowledge" and that the Academy should encourage further research. The commission had not been rigorous in its investigations, and the defects in its experiments were plain. The report was not published.

In 1837 there was more discussion in the Academy after it heard of the painless extraction of a tooth under mesmerism, and a new commission was appointed. Its report was made in the same year and was unfavorable. The investigation had been directed upon some of the marvels proclaimed by the magnetists, clairvoyance, obedience of the subject to the mere thoughts of the operator, anesthesia to pricks of a needle, and transposition of the senses (such as reading words on a paper applied to the abdomen). After the negative report had been adopted by a large majority, Dr. Burdin, a member of the Academy, offered a prize of 3,000 francs to any somnambulist who could demonstrate clairvoyance. Two persons tried for the prize but failed. Binet and Féré in their account of this period blame the magnetists for having forced the Academy to investigate the marvelous or miraculous rather than the simpler phenomena (Binet and Féré, 1887, p. 34). A somnambulist, although he might not be able to read with his fingers, might show important characteristics that are less bizarre and controversial.

During the 1840's and 1850's in both France and England mesmerism became mixed with spiritualism and allied doctrines, which were given a new impetus by the introduction from America of table-turning and spirit-rapping. Elliotson became a convert to spiritualism. Cahagnet, a French cabinet-maker and mesmerist, produced ecstatic visions of the spirit-world in his subjects. Baron du Potet began to practice magic, publishing his *La magie devoilée* in 1852. Lecturers came from America to England to spread the doctrine of "electro-biology," which was mesmerism under another name.

ANIMAL MAGNETISM IN PRUSSIA

Animal magnetism spread to the German-speaking countries. The chief spirit in this movement was Johann Caspar Lavater (1741–1801), a Swiss clergyman known for his work on physiognomy and an enthusiast for several other causes, including the exorcist Gassner and the charlatan Cagliostro. He had used magnetism to treat his wife.

The famous Wilhelm Hufeland (1762–1836) at first disbelieved in magnetism and wrote an article against it in 1784, but he was converted to it in 1808 and became influential in its behalf. He entrusted his magnetic treatments to his young assistant, Karl A. F. Kluge (1782–1844), who wrote a book, *Versuch einer Darstellung des animalischen Magnetismus* (1811), which became the chief textbook in the field. It contains, in keeping with German custom, impressive bibliographies, which list practically every publication on the subject. Kluge later discontinued work with animal magnetism and confined his practice to conventional medicine. A counterblast to Kluge was a vigorous criticism of the fluidic theory and its exponents by Johann Stieglitz (1767–1840), *Über den thierischen Magnetismus* (1814).

In this period the Germans contributed little or nothing that was lasting to the theory of magnetism. In the first third of the century a wave of "romantic philosophy of nature" swept over central Europe. It influenced physicians, biologists, literary men, theologians, and philosophers (notably Fichte, Schelling, and Hegel), who indulged in much wild theorizing and speculation and incorporated animal magnetism into their thinking, making it equivalent to the "nerve ether" or the "life principle" of their vitalistic philosophies. Books were written on *Lebensmagnetismus*. There was relatively little criticism of the theory of the magnetic fluid among practitioners of animal magnetism. The period was not one of productive ideas but rather one of political activities and scientific and medical controversy between the more conventional thinkers and the mystics, enthusiasts, vitalists, and believers in magic.[10]

The king of Prussia, Frederick William III, and his Chancellor, Karl August von Hardenberg, were favorably disposed toward the mesmeric theories. A commission, with Hufeland as its director, was appointed in 1812, and it was ordered that only qualified physicians were to apply the new treatment and they they were to report the results to the proper state authorities. After carrying out some of its planned investigations, the commission issued a preliminary report in 1816. Hufeland explained that this report had been held back with the idea of awaiting a conclusion to the work of the commission, but it was now issued because of a request of the government. The report was favorable to the existence of a physical agent, but it also acknowledged the part played by imagination. Six members of the commission signed it and five did not. No further report was made.

In 1809 Lorenz Oken (1779–1851), the philosophical biologist and physician, visited Mesmer, then 75 years old, in south Germany, where he had been living quietly since the French government had granted him an annuity in return for the fortune that he had invested in government bonds, made worthless by the advent of the revolution. Mesmer offered to instruct a physician who would undertake to apply animal magnetism extensively in a hospital. Oken tried to interest Johann Christian Reil (1758–1813), and in 1812 Mesmer invited Reil to visit him, promising to instruct him completely in his "physical system and its applications" in six weeks (although he had asserted in 1784 that d'Eslon was a mere novice after several years of discipleship and practice) on condition that he would by means of favorable reports in the newspapers propagandize for it. Reil did not go, but Karl Christian Wolfart (1778–1832) went to see Mesmer and spent a month with him. Wolfart, a former professor of physics and medicine in the gymnasium in Hanau and a mesmerist, desired keenly a professorship in the newly founded University of Berlin, but he had not yet been successful in this project.

In 1814 Wolfart published a translation of a manuscript written in

[10] This account of the German sector is based mainly on Erman (1925). He is a descendant of Dr. Paul Erman, a professor of physics who was an antimagnetist and a member of the commission for the examination of animal magnetism, which was headed by Hufeland. He identifies strongly with his ancestor, whose criticisms are echoed in this rather polemic book.

French which Mesmer had given him (Mesmer, 1814) and in the following year he published a commentary on this book by Mesmer (Wolfart, 1815). Mesmer's book contains his final ideas on the universe and man in chapters on physics, astronomy, neurophysiology, ethics, education, government, and religion. In keeping with Mesmer's lack of scholarship, the book mentions only one person, the prophet Ezekiel.

Another mesmerist who became an ally of Wolfart was David Ferdinand Koreff (1783–1851), a brilliant young physician of Jewish origin who had literary talents and was as much a member of literary as medical circles. He became a protégé of the Chancellor von Hardenberg, whom he treated magnetically. After exerting their influence on the king and his ministers, Wolfart and Koreff were installed, in spite of much opposition, as professors in the University of Berlin in 1816.[11]

Hufeland sank more and more into extreme beliefs. In 1817 he declared that "a magnetic and a still finer vital atmosphere" flows continually, like warmth, from the body. He believed that inanimate objects could carry the magnetic fluid, for example, magnetized water. He believed in sympathetic cures and stated that boiling the urine of a sufferer from gout even at a distance of many miles would make the patient sweat and heal him; this belief is like those of Van Helmont in the seventeenth century. In his *Journal für praktische Heilkunde* he established a department of "Medicina magica," in which many wonderful bits of news were displayed, miraculous events being treated seriously even though they seemed to be open to suspicion of fraud.

During this period wonder was piled upon wonder. A stigmatized nun was investigated; Justinus Kerner (1786–1862), the poet-physician who had been magnetized in his youth, was treating magnetically his famous patient the "seeress of Prevorst" and discussing demoniacal possession and the world of spirits; and animal magnetism was thought to offer many insights into matters of religion, especially miracles.

On the same day as the cabinet order appointing the new professors in Berlin was issued, another order set up a prize for the best essay on animal magnetism. The Academy of Sciences was to act as judge in the competition. This task was unwelcome to the Academy, which then sought to extend the terminal date of the contest and to place it two years in the future, and which balked at the king's promise that all contributions would be published. Twenty-two essays were submitted by the final date in 1820, but the Academy voted that none of them had contributed anything that advanced knowledge of the subject and that none would receive the prize. Some of the competing essayists objected

[11] There is a very large biography and collection of documents: *David Ferdinand Koreff, Serapionsbruder, Magnetiseur, Geheimrat und Dichter*, by Friedrich von Oppeln-Bronikowski (Berlin, 1928).

violently to this decision, pointing out that the order stated that the prize was to be given to the best essay, but they were put off with the specious argument that "For an essay to be best, it must at least be good."

A complete break occurred in the relationship between von Hardenberg and his former protégé Koreff in 1821. Koreff had sent a copy of an anonymous political pamphlet to Benjamin Constant, who translated it into French and indicated incorrectly that Koreff was its author. This produced a flurry of misunderstanding, which was followed by Koreff's taking the part of von Hardenberg's wife in a domestic dispute. In 1822 Koreff went to Paris, where he practiced until his death in 1851.

Wolfart became involved in a scandal, and his influence and standing declined. Von Hardenberg's death in 1822 ended government favor for magnetism. Just two weeks before his death he wrote an order, almost six years after the announcement of the prize contest, sanctioning the Academy's decision not to award any prize and to return the essays to the authors (without the publication promised in the original order), who by now were becoming impatient.

With the death of von Hardenberg animal magnetism gradually declined and ceased to play any part in influential circles or in the medical schools of Prussia.

The romantic philosophy was followed by a materialistic period, during which there was little activity in the field of animal magnetism until Wilhelm Preyer introduced the works of Braid in Germany and published his *Der Hypnotismus* (1890).

ANIMAL MAGNETISM AND HYPNOTISM IN ENGLAND

Interest in animal magnetism did not develop in England until the 1830's, when French magnetists were touring the country accompanied by their trained somnambulists, who gave medical consultations.

The first physician of prominence to practice mesmerism in England was John Elliotson (1791–1868), who had seen the demonstrations of Baron du Potet. Elliotson, a man of strong convictions and radical character who dearly loved a fight, had been ridiculed by his colleagues because he introduced the stethoscope into England. Soon after he began his mesmeric researches at University College, London, where he was Professor of the Practice of Medicine, the Council of the College forbade all use of mesmerism in University College Hospital, whereupon Elliotson resigned his appointments and never entered the College or its Hospital again. He continued to fight for mesmerism in *The Zoist*, which he founded to advance the cause; and he paid a heavy price, both in income and the suffering of continual harassment and ostracism, for his disagreement with the medical profession. He believed in all of the marvelous phenomena claimed by the mesmerists, and therefore his colleagues treated him as a pariah.

The career of James Braid (1795–1860), a Scottish physician and surgeon who practiced in Manchester, was not so stormy as that of Elliotson. In 1841 Braid attended a demonstration of mesmerism by Lafontaine, a Swiss layman who staged public performances, and concluded that the whole affair was a fraud. A few days later he attended a second demonstration and changed his opinion, since he noticed that Lafontaine's subject was unable to open his eyes. Why the subject could not have pretended to be unable to open his eyes Braid does not tell, and Braid's conclusion lacks logic. However, Braid began experiments on his friends and found that he was able to produce most of the mesmeric phenomena.

Braid asked his subjects to look steadily and attentively at a spot, such as the reflection of a candle flame from the neck of a bottle, placed slightly above the level of the eyes so as to produce fatigue. After about three minutes, the eyelids closed, there was usually some secretion of tears, and the subject was in a sleeplike state, which Braid attributed to a change in the nervous system, a fatigue, and a paralysis of the nervous centers controlling the eyes and the lids. He proposed the name "neurohypnotism" or "nervous sleep" for this condition, which was almost immediately shortened to "hypnotism."[12]

For several reasons Braid was not subjected to the persecution and vituperation that were given so abundantly to Elliotson. First, he rejected the fluidic theory and the miracles. Second, he proposed a new name for the state produced in his subjects and proceeded to explain it by established or plausible physiological concepts. For a long time neither Braid nor the medical profession was certain that hypnotism and mesmerism were the same. Third, his articles were not rejected, because *The Medical Times* was competing with *The Lancet*, which angrily opposed Elliotson, and the spirit of competition made Braid less unacceptable to the *Times* than he might otherwise have been. Fourth, Braid was ignored by Elliotson and fought by the mesmerists in general, and therefore he stood apart from the main targets of the wrath of the orthodox. Fifth, he was of milder temperament than Elliotson. Sixth (and very important), he was self-employed and held no academic or hospital appointments from which he could be separated.

The theories that Braid developed show a steady progress from the

[12] Braid was not the first to propose terms derived from the Greek *hypnos* [sleep]. Baron d'Hénin de Cuvillers (1821) in a curious and amusing book (which ended, as several of his publications did, with a tirade against the Jesuits) gives a nomenclature for animal magnetism. Of 673 words listed, most of which were neologisms of Greek derivation, 312 begin with *hypn-*. *Hypnotique*, *hypnotiseur*, *hypnotisme*, and *hypnotiste* appear; of these, only the first was to be found in the Dictionary of the French Academy.

physiological to the psychological. In 1847 he tried to explain all hypnotic phenomena by "monoideism" (having one dominant idea) or mental concentration, and he suggested that this new term should replace "hypnotism." He reduced everything in hypnotism to the subject's responding to suggestions in a state of mental concentration or attention to dominant ideas; the condition was not sleep. His final theory, which was never completed, was based on the concept of "double consciousness," which emphasized the fact of posthypnotic amnesia.[13]

The similarity between the teachings of Braid and Faria, in both theory and practice, has been frequently pointed out, especially by French writers; but Braid believed that his results were more uniform and successful than Faria's, and he stated (incorrectly) that Faria explained all of the phenomena by imagination. It is probably correct to say that Braid discovered no new facts and developed no new theory. Like Faria, he made errors; for a while he believed in phrenohypnotism, according to which pressure applied to the scalp over a phrenological area causes the hypnotized subject to express the faculty controlled by the area. In one experiment the "organ of veneration" was pressed, and the subject knelt in prayer. Braid thought that no suggestion as to what was expected had been conveyed to his subjects, but he evidently became dubious about these results, as he made no further reference to such experiments after 1845.

The work of Braid attracted attention in France and Germany. Dr. Azam of Bordeaux reported in 1859 several cases successfully treated by Braid's methods, and in 1860 there was a shortlived wave of interest in hypnotic anesthesia in surgical operations. The physiologist Charles Richet (1850–1935) published articles in 1875 arguing that hypnotic phenomena were genuine.

About the time that Braid began his work with hypnosis, James Esdaile (1808–1859), a Scottish surgeon practicing in India, was making an unequaled record in the use of mesmerism in surgery. Patients were put into trance by his native assistants, who worked usually for an hour preparing a patient by mesmeric stroking. Esdaile performed more than a thousand minor operations and about 300 major operations. Most of the major operations were removals of scrotal tumors, in which the mortality had been about 50 per cent. In 161 cases operated on by Esdaile, mortality dropped to 5 per cent, and in none of the fatal cases was death an immediate outcome of the surgery, "all deaths subsequently resulting from fever, cholera, or like causes" (Bramwell, 1903). There were many attacks on Esdaile in Indian medical journals; it was asserted that the natives pretended not to feel pain

[13] A detailed account of Braid's work and the evolution of his theory is given in J. M. Bramwell (1903).

to humor him. The same kind of criticism continued to be made for many years both in England and the United States, the patients being called impostors by the conservative members of the medical profession. One critic said that "non-expression of pain is no proof of its non-existence" (Rosen, 1946).

Mesmeric hospitals were established during the 1840's in several cities in the United Kingdom for surgery and for mesmeric treatment in general. They were shortlived, partly because of the discovery of chemical anesthesia in the same decade.

HYPNOTISM IN FRANCE

The interest in hypnosis in France, which culminated in the Nancy School, began with A. -A. Liébeault (1823–1904). The picture usually painted of Liébeault is idyllic, a benign country doctor who charged regular fees for medical treatment but applied hypnosis gratis. Bramwell, who along with Binet and Féré is the chief historical source for English-speaking inquirers, spent two weeks with him in 1889 and made a favorable report. However, Delboeuf, a psychologist of the University of Liège, visited him in the same year and gave an account that is somewhat critical (Delboeuf, 1889). Liébeault had established a medical practice in the country near Nancy, but he decided to move to Nancy, live on what he had already accumulated, and work with hypnosis without charging fees. He attracted the attention of Bernheim by curing a patient of an obstinate neuralgia, and then Bernheim brought him into notice. Without Bernheim, Beaunis, and Liégeois, he would have been known only to the poor people whom he treated. In 1889 he was treating as many as 50 or 60 patients in one morning. The patients were for the most part desperate; they had "tried everything" for their troubles and now turned to hypnotism as a last resort. Liébeault used a stereotyped technique for inducing hypnosis. "After asking, if necessary, the patient's complaint and without making any medical examination whatever, he seats the patient, puts his hand on his forehead and, without even looking at him, says, 'You are going to sleep.' Then he closes the patient's eyes at once while assuring him that he is sleeping. He lifts his arm, saying, 'You cannot lower your arm.' If he does lower it, M. Liébeault does not seem to notice it. He then asks the patient to rotate his arms and tells him that he cannot stop this movement; while saying this he rotates his own arms vigorously, the patient having his eyes closed all the time." Then suggestions were given: "You are going to be cured; your digestion will be good; your sleep will be good; you will not cough any more; your circulation will be free and regular; you will feel much strength in your members; you will walk easily, etc." (Delboeuf, 1889). Liébeault treated all persons who presented themselves, no matter what diseases they had. Delboeuf states that Liébeault had a bottle of magnetized water, which he had first used for infants suffering from diarrhea, constipation, or vomiting. He used it more to please the mothers than for any other reason, but when the babies improved he began to wonder whether there might not be something after all to the fluidic theory. Delboeuf had an interview with a "lucid somnambulist," a girl of 17 years, but she was completely unsuccessful in a clairvoyance test, being unable to tell Delboeuf that his trouble was a cataract in the right eye even when told that he had an eye trouble. There is an air of criticism in Delboeuf's report, sometimes open and sometimes veiled. Hypnotism was used as a panacea upon a fast-flowing stream of patients who were examined either inadequately or not at all.

Jean-Martin Charcot (1825–1893), without question the most distinguished neurologist of the nineteenth century, developed an interest in hypnosis and began to experiment with it in 1878. His subjects were a few hysterical women of the Hospice de la Salpêtrière, where he was chief of the medical service. One would naturally expect that the genius of Charcot would make a large contribution to the understanding of hypnosis. Such was not the case; his studies led to erroneous conclusions which, because of his prestige, were hard to correct.

Charcot investigated hypnosis as he had neurological diseases. Just as he had enumerated the symptoms constituting a neurological syndrome, he looked for the symptoms characteristic of hypnosis, and he focused his attention on muscular symptoms (such as catalepsy, paralyses, and contractures) and sensory changes (such as hyperesthesia and anesthesia), which he considered were not capable of being simulated by the subjects.

He claimed to have discovered that there are three distinct stages of hypnosis: catalepsy, lethargy, and somnambulism. Each stage has its characteristic symptoms, and he described what had to be done to make a subject pass from one stage to another. For example, rubbing on top of the head would make the subject in lethargy pass into somnambulism.

These three stages constituted major hypnotism; those forms in which the phenomena were mainly psychological were known as minor hypnotism, mixed states, or *formes frustes*, and the investigation of these forms of minor hypnotism was to be deferred until the study of states with definite motor and nervous signs was completed (Babinski, 1890).

Among the curiosa from the Salpêtrière we find that a subject could show any stage of hypnosis on only one side of the body. A person in catalepsy needed only to close one eye to produce the bodily symptoms of lethargy on that side, while the other side, with its eye open, continued to show catalepsy. A paralysis on one side of the body could be transferred to the other side by applying a magnet (not an electromagnet, capable of being turned on and off without the subject's knowledge, but a horseshoe magnet). Charcot did not explain these phenomena by suggestion. He also resurrected the metallotherapy of Burq. The following procedure is an example: a coin is applied to a patch of anesthetic skin, and after several hours the area in and around the coin is found to be normal, different metals producing varying effects.

Major hypnotism was considered to be a pathological phenomenon, an artificial neurosis comparable in many ways to a hysterical attack. Moreover, Charcot was prepared to admit that it was a rare condition.

James Braid had discovered certain phenomena that were at first sight puzzling, such as the fact that a rigid limb could be made flexible by blowing on it. Also, he could excite one half of the body to action, while the other remained rigid and torpid. At first he was unable to explain such facts, but he later regarded them as instances of response to nonverbal suggestions. Charcot never arrived at this stage of insight. He and his followers acknowledged the role of suggestion, or at least paid lip-service to it, but they refused to admit that it was responsible for major hypnotism.

The conclusions of the Salpêtrière school of thought were criticized by Hippolyte Bernheim (1840–1919) in 1886, who asserted that the three stages, and all the other phenomena "would not exist if the experiments were conducted under conditions that excluded the use of suggestion. . . . The hypnotism of the Salpêtrière is an artificial hypnotism [*un hypnotisme de culture*]." According to Bernheim, hypnotism is not a pathological state; to be hypnotizable carries no implication of hysterical tendencies. He and Liébeault had hypnotized thousands of persons, while Charcot had only a few subjects, all of whom were women suffering from hysteria. Thus began the controversy between Charcot and his followers, known as the School of the Salpêtrière, and Bernheim and his associates, known as the Nancy School. In this conflict the Nancy School was the winner.

Pierre Janet (1859–1947), who was appointed by Charcot as Director of the Psychological Laboratory at the Salpêtrière in 1890, explained Charcot's errors. Charcot never personally hypnotized any subject. The younger physicians worked with the subjects, and Charcot used them as demonstration subjects after they had learned what was expected of them and had seen other subjects perform. They were unwittingly trained by the physicians and by each other. Furthermore, in a decade there had been only a dozen cases of major hypnotism at the Salpêtrière (Janet, 1925, I, 180–182).[14]

Charcot's interest in hypnosis made the subject respectable and was followed by a large number of publications in Europe by medical men. One of the interesting products of this period was Krafft-Ebing's work on age-regression (1889) in a hypnotized subject. The explanation given by a reviewer (von Strümpell, 1894) was that the subject was playing a role.

SIGMUND FREUD

Sigmund Freud became acquainted with hypnosis when he saw a stage performance by the famous lay hypnotist Hansen. Like Braid, he questioned the genuineness of the phenomena, but he was convinced by the paleness of a subject when cataleptic rigidity was produced. When he studied under Charcot in the winter of 1885–1886, he saw symptoms produced and then removed under hypnosis.

After he began medical practice, Freud's chief methods of treating were hypnosis and electrotherapy. He soon found that any results obtained by means of electricity were due to suggestion. Seeking to improve his knowledge of hypnosis, he spent several weeks in Nancy in 1889, observing the work of Liébeault and Bernheim. Hoping that Bernheim would be able to induce a deep trance in one of his patients, he took her to Nancy, but Bernheim could do not better than Freud and told him that he was more successful with hypnosis in his hospital practice than with private patients.

From the beginning Freud used hypnosis in two ways: to remove symptoms by direct suggestion and to investigate the past history of his patients. The use of hypnosis as an uncovering technique had been taught to him by Dr. Josef Breuer (1842–1925), who had treated a young woman in 1880–1882 who was suffering from a number of hysterical complaints. He found that in deep hypnosis the patient could recover memories, not available to her in the normal state, of traumatic events that had given rise to her symptoms. By encouraging her to talk freely about these events and to experience appropriate emotions, he was able to cause the symptoms to disappear. This was the cathartic method, which is still used successfully by some psychiatrists (Freud, 1959).

[14] Guillain (1955) states: "*Charcot n'a jamais hypnotisé personnellement un seul malade, n'a jamais exercé une surveillance sur les expériences et, par conséquent, n'a pu critiquer leurs insuffisances et leurs causes d'erreurs éventuelles.*" Schneck (1961) doubts this statement. He relies upon statements by Binet and Féré (1887) which were not directed to this point, were made during the lifetime of the great master, and are of the form "Charcot has found that. . ." He does not refer to Janet's statements.

Finally Freud abandoned hypnosis. He wrote that the results of hypnotic treatment sometimes disappeared if the relationship between him and his patient became disturbed. Also, one of his patients, waking from the trance, threw her arms around his neck, thus giving him insight into the nature of the "mysterious element" activating hypnosis, an insight which was elaborated into a libidinal-regressive theory of hypnosis by Ferenczi and other psychoanalysts. Moreover, he had experienced the greatest hindrance of all to the use of hypnosis, the fact that not all subjects can develop a deep trance. In addition, he reported that the removal of symptoms by hypnosis was often (and always in "severe cases") temporary, and that the symptoms would either return or be replaced by others. This statement by Freud has been echoed and magnified by many other persons, but its truth is now being doubted, and the value of symptomatic treatment through hypnosis is in many quarters not questioned.

He sought a substitute for hypnosis, which had been helpful in restoring lost memories, and in this search he remembered an experiment that he had often seen Bernheim perform. After coming out of a deep trance, Bernheim's subjects declared that they had no memory of what had happened in the trance. Then Bernheim would lay his hand on the subject's forehead, insisting that he could remember, and the memories came out. From this experiment Freud concluded that he might likewise urge his patients to recall the hidden past, possibly with a touch of his hand but without hypnosis.

Freud reached this conclusion illogically, not understanding what was occurring in Bernheim's procedure. Certainly Bernheim's strong suggestions of remembering plus application of the hand put the subject back into the trance, in which state he commanded the memories of previous trances. There is no reason to think that this situation is the same as the attempt to recall lost memories by a person who has never been in a trance. It is hard to believe that Freud did not understand this (1959, **20**, p. 28), but he gives us no reason to think that he did.[15] We are reminded of Braid's conclusion that mesmeric phenomena were genuine because a subject appeared not to be able to open his eyes in the trance.

Thus Freud became free of hypnosis, which he thought had "screened from view an interplay of forces," and substituted for it free association

[15] On this point Bramwell (1956, p. 106) wrote: "Fifty years ago, Braid drew attention to the fact that lost memories were revived when the operator placed his hand on the subject's body, and thus helped him to concentrate his attention. Braid recognized, however, that the condition induced was a fresh hypnosis; but this, the all-important point, Bernheim apparently fails to grasp. All trained somnambules can recall the events of hypnosis in response to the simple statement of the operator, 'Now you remember.' The phrase 'Now you remember' equals in value the word 'Sleep' or any other signal for inducing hypnosis." Bramwell makes no reference to Freud in this passage.

on the couch. This rejection was a great blow to the use of hypnosis in psychotherapy, because his followers accepted his teachings as unalterable dogma.

HYPNOTISM IN THE UNITED STATES

In the United States one of the most important workers in hypnosis was Morton Prince (1854–1929), who had been influenced by Pierre Janet. In his last writing on hypnosis (1927), he said that hypnosis was not a specific state but one of a large number of conditions involving alteration of the personality, among which are attention, abstraction, revery, sleep, moods, somnambulisms, and multiple personality. Every state of hypnosis involves dissociation, inhibition, and synthesis or reintegration. As might be expected of one whose principal contribution was the study of multiple personality, he emphasized the changes of personality that may occur in hypnosis. He used hypnosis in reintegrating persons with alternating personalities, hypnotizing one of the dissociated personalities, *A* or *B*, and intensifying the trance by suggestions of "sleeping deeper," whereupon each of them was reintegrated into a personality *C*, a completely integrated composite having the memories and the traits formerly dissociated into *A* and *B*. Prince proposed the name "suggestive repersonalization" to be used in place of "hypnosis." The emphasis on this feature of the hypnotic state seems rather strange 35 years afterwards, because we are now far removed from the period in which dissociation was a leading concept in the field of psychopathology.

In 1933 Clark L. Hull (1884–1952) published a book that presented the results obtained by his students in an attack upon several problems relating to hypnosis by the standard procedures of experimental psychology with a behavioristic slant. The work emphasized the necessary control experiments. The typical experiment in this book is a comparative study of some function, such as muscular strength, recall of learned material, or the patellar reflex, in hypnosis and in the waking state. Because this book belongs to contemporary psychology and is by no means merely of historic interest, further analysis of it is not necessary beyond saying that Hull's theory of hypnosis was easily shown to be inadequate.

In this period there were a few other psychologists and medical men who published excellent isolated pieces of work on hypnosis, often with the tacit or voiced disapproval of academic authorities, and they deserve credit for keeping interest in the subject alive in a period when there was little activity. Hull's work is prominent partly because he made the investigation of hypnosis a systematic project in his laboratory, putting his students to work on problems for academic degrees, with a voluminous output of publications.

A great increase in interest in hypnotism began shortly after World War II among physicians, dentists, and psychologists. Among physicians there has been a remarkable increase in the use of hypnosis in a number of nonpsychiatric specialties. Two national societies, both of which have international affiliations, have been founded for the study of hypnosis with the hope that the cyclic waxing and waning of interest may be replaced by steady activity.

FINAL REMARKS

This historical sketch has given most attention to persons and periods that are now least understood by students in this country. Where material is easily available in English (for example, on Braid and Freud) many details have not been given. An effort has been made to prevent its becoming a catalogue of names of men and titles of books. It has been confined to the medical and scientific lines of development and has not gone into the ramifications of hypnotism into the fields of religion (such as spiritualism and Christian Science) or occultism. It also gives little attention to the history of therapeutic uses of hypnotism. It is to a considerable extent a personal analysis, reflecting the landmarks in the history of the subject deemed most significant to its author.

What can be learned from the history of hypnotism? First, we have seen the remarkable blindness of Mesmer and his followers to psychological factors in the explanation of their phenomena and their adherence to physicalistic theories.

Second, we learned that there was a very keen understanding of the value of control experiments in this field, even in the eighteenth century from the time of Hell through that of the royal commissions. This understanding existed, unfortunately, in the minds of the adversaries of the mesmerists rather than among its practitioners. As Hull (1933) pointed out, the lack of control experiments is the most scandalous defect in the whole history of the investigation of hypnosis. This defect may be attributed partly to the emphasis on immediate therapeutic applications and partly to the fact that much of the work on hypnosis was done by laymen (the subject had a great attraction for military men). The more laymen and charlatans took up hypnotism, the fewer reputable people became interested in it.

Third, the case of Charcot is enlightening, because it shows how the authority of a man in one field of investigation does not necessarily extend into others. It also shows the result of the European habit of treating eminent scientists and professors as demigods; if there had been free communication among Charcot's group, some of his colleagues might have dared to tell him what was going on at the Salpêtrière (Guillain, 1955). It is ironical that during all of Charcot's experiments he was afraid of simulation by his subjects and therefore confined his work to the investigation of physical symptoms, which he thought could not be simulated.

Fourth, there are interesting trends from the physical to the physiological to the the psychological explanation of hypnosis. Mesmer's idea of a fluid of some vague sort was retained by Puységur, but psychological processes in the operator were added as an essential part of the theory. Faria rejected the fluidic theory and Puységur's psychology but asserted the importance of psychological and physiological processes in the subjects. This trend is sometimes seen in the life of a single man: Braid began with a physiological theory, then developed a psychological theory (monoideism), and finally ended with a somewhat different psychological theory emphasizing dissociative aspects. On the other hand, there are men in this history who never changed their ideas at all but held to them to the bitter end; the best examples of men with one-track minds are Mesmer and Elliotson. The trend from the physiological and physical to the psychological is shown by the Charcot-Bernheim controversy. The psychological theory won, as Bernheim made hypnosis into a form of suggestibility, the remaining difficulty being the definition of suggestibility.

It has been argued that the fact that the Christian Church has survived through the centuries in spite of persecution and the many other hardships to which it has been subjected proves the supernatural origin of this institution. Likewise it may be argued that the permanent value of hypnotism is proved by its having survived in spite of having been associated with pseudoscience by Mesmer and many others, with charlatanry by a multitude of lay and irregular practitioners, with clairvoyance and mind-reading by Puységur, with sexual tendencies by the royal commission and by the psychoanalysts, and with the nature-philosophy of the German romanticists. Let us hope that the future will not bring periods of alternate waxing and waning of interest in hypnotism that has been seen in past years and that its aberrations will become less and less frequent.

REFERENCES

Babinski, J. (1890). "Grand et petit hypnotisme," In Charcot, J.-M., *Oeuvres complètes*, **9**, 505–537. Paris.

Bernheim, H. (1886). *De la suggestion et de ses applications à la thérapeutique*. Paris.

Bertrand, A. (1826). *Le magnétisme animal en France.* Paris.

Binet, A., and Féré, C. (1887). *Le magnétisme animal.* Paris. (Translation, *Animal Magnetism*, New York, 1886).

Bramwell, J. M. (1903) (and later eds., including New York reprint of 1956, Julian Press). *Hypnotism: Its History, Practice, and Theory.* London.

Brandis, J. D. (1818). *Über psychische Heilmittel und Magnetismus.* Copenhagen.

Burdin, C., and Dubois, F. (1841). *Histoire académique du magnétisme animal.* Paris.

Chastenet, A.-M.-J., Marquis de Puységur. (1784) *Mémoires pour servir à l'histoire et à l'établissement du magnétisme animal.* Paris.

——— (1807). *Du magnétisme animal, considéré dans ses rapports avec diverses branches de la physique générale.* Paris.

——— (1809a). 2d ed. of the work of 1784. Paris.

——— (1809b). *Suite des mémoires pour servir à l'histoire* [etc.] Paris.

Delboeuf, J. (1889). *Le magnétisme animal à propos d'une visite à l'école de Nancy.* Paris.

Deleuze, J.-P.-F. (1813). *Histoire critique du magnétisme animal.* 2 vols. Paris.

——— (1819). *Défense du magnétisme animal contre les attaques dont il est l'objet dans le Dictionnaire des sciences médicales.* Paris.

Erman, W. (1925). *Der tierische Magnetismus in Preussen vor und nach den Freiheitskriegen.* Munich: *Historische Zeitschrift, Beiheft 4.*

Esdaile, J. (1846). *Mesmerism in India.* London. Reprinted under title *Hypnosis in Medicine and Surgery.* New York: Julian Press, 1960.

d'Eslon, C. (1780). *Observations sur le magnétisme animal.* Paris.

Faria, J. C. (1819). *De la cause du sommeil lucide.* Reprinted with a preface by Dr. D. G. Dalgado, Paris, 1906.

Freud, S. (1959). *An Autobiographical Study.* In *The Complete Psychological Works of Sigmund Freud*, Standard ed., Vol. 20. London: Hogarth Press.

Guillain, G. (1955). *J.-M. Charcot, 1825–1893: sa vie, son oeuvre.* Paris. Translated by Pearce Bailey, New York, 1959.

d'Hénin de Cuvillers, Baron (1821). *Le magnétisme animal retrouvé dans l'antiquité.* Paris.

Hull, C. L. (1933). *Hypnosis and Suggestibility: An Experimental Approach.* New York: Appleton-Century.

Janet, P. (1925). *Psychological Healing.* 2 vols. New York: Macmillan.

Kline, M. V. (1958). *Freud and Hypnosis.* New York: Julian Press.

Krafft-Ebing, R. von (1889). *An Experimental Study in the Domain of Hypnotism.* New York.

Mesmer, F. A. (1779). *Mémoire sur la découverte du magnétisme animal.* Translated as *Mesmerism, by Doctor Mesmer, with an introductory monograph by Gilbert Frankau.* London: Macdonald 1948).

Mesmer, F. A. (1781). *Précis historique des faits relatifs au magnétisme animal jusques en avril* 1781. Paris.

——— (1785). *Aphorismes de M. Mesmer dictés à l'assemblée de ses élèves.* Paris.

——— (1799). *Mémoire de F. A. Mesmer, docteur en médicine, sur ses découvertes.* Paris.

——— (1814). *Mesmerismus oder System der Wechselwirkungen.* Berlin.

Moniz, Egas. (1925). *O padre Faria na história do hipnotismo.* Lisbon.

Oppeln-Bronikowski, F. von (1928). *David Ferdinand Koreff, Serapionsbruder, Magnetiseur, Geheimrat und Dichter*. Berlin: Gebrüder Paetel.

Pattie, F. A. (1956). "Mesmer's medical dissertation and its debt to Mead's *De imperio solis ac lunæ*," *J. Hist. Med. all. Sci.*, **11**, 275–287.

Paulet, J.-J. (1784). *L'antimagnétisme*. Paris.

Podmore, F. (1909) *Mesmerism and Christian Science*. London.

Preyer, W. (1890). *Der Hypnotismus*. Berlin.

Prince, M. (1927). "Suggestive repersonalization. The psychophysiology of hypnotism," *Arch. Neurol. Psychiat.*, **18**, 159–180.

Puységur, Marquis de. See Chastenet.

Regnier, L.-R. (1891). *Hypnotisme et croyances anciennes*. Paris.

Rosen, G. (1946). "Mesmerism and surgery: a strange chapter in the history of anesthesia," *J. Hist. Med. all. Sci.*, **1**, 527–550.

——— (1963). "History of medical hypnosis." In Schneck, J. M. (ed.), *Hypnosis in modern Medicine*. 3d ed. Springfield, Ill.: Thomas.

Schneck, J. M. (1963). "History of medical hypnosis: additions and elaborations." In Schneck, J. M. (ed.), *Hypnosis in Modern Medicine*. 3d ed. Springfield, Ill.: Thomas.

——— (1961). "Jean-Martin Charcot and the history of experimental. hypnosis," *J. Hist. Med. all. Sci.*, **16**, 297–305.

Stoll, O. (1904). *Suggestion und Hypnotismus in der Völkerpsychologie*. 2d ed. Leipzig.

Strümpell, E. A. von (1894). An untitled review of Krafft-Ebing's work on age-regression. *Dtsch. Ztschr. Nervenheilk*, **5**, 100.

Thouret, M.-A. (1784). *Recherches et doutes sur le magnétisme animal*. Paris.

Tischner, R. (1928). *Franz Anton Mesmer: Leben, Werk und Wirkungen*. Munich: Verlag der Münchener Drucke.

——— and Bittel, K. (1941). *Mesmer und sein Problem*. Stuttgart: Hippokrates Verlag.

Virey, J.-J. (1819). Article "Magnétisme animal" in *Dictionnaire des sciences médicales*.

Wolfart, K. C. (1815). *Erläuterungen zum Mesmerismus*. Berlin.

3

The Induction of Hypnosis

PERRY LONDON[1]
University of Southern California

BERTRAND RUSSELL once defined mathematics as "the science in which we do not know what we are talking about or whether what we are saying is true" (1919). This aspect of mathematics is quite deliberate, and the absurdity of definition only apparent. Students of hypnotic induction are less fortunate in this respect, for while Russell's words apply very well to both studies, empiricists lack the mathematician's comfort of being permitted to define *all* the properties of his universe of discourse. No very satisfactory definition of hypnosis exists, nor is it altogether clear what "induction" means. Because the definition of induction depends on the definition of hypnosis, knowledge concerning induction must necessarily be very tentative and approximate.

So much for blanket qualifications. A realistic appraisal of the field of hypnosis, both as clinical art and scientific problem, nevertheless demonstrates the usefulness of operational definitions, however approximate or limited in scope. And there are enough of these definitions to

[1] The preparation of this chapter was supported in part by the United States Public Health Service, National Institute of Mental Health, Research Grant MH-08598.

permit serious discussion of the nature of hypnotic induction. A sufficient body of conventions for identifying hypnosis is recognized, both professionally and popularly, so that we may operationalize the definition of induction as one that concerns *the means by which people can be led to behavior that is called "hypnotic."*

THE EVENTS OF HYPNOTIC BEHAVIOR

Despite the absence of a comprehensive definition of hypnosis, it is still possible to identify the classes of behavior to which the concept of hypnotic induction may be usefully addressed. In so doing, we shall follow the practice Weitzenhoffer and Hilgard (1959) used in standardizing the *Stanford Hypnotic Susceptibility Scale*, Forms A and B, and which Hilgard, Weitzenhoffer, Landes, and Moore (1961) used in analyzing its results.

> What we shall mean by hypnotic susceptibility for the purposes of our investigations is a relatively persistent tendency to yield the phenomena historically recognized as belonging to the hypnotic trance (1961, p. 1).

The authors treat hypnotic susceptibility, in other words, as the manifestation of behaviors that satisfy the conventions of hypnotists. Their review of the historical literature concerning susceptibility demonstrates that this rude operationism has some merit; the conventions of hypnotists are reliable ones:

> Although the detailed findings are in disagreement, the nineteenth century studies,. . . are in general agreement with the more recent laboratory studies done largely with college students. . . . The basic phenomena considered to be signs of the hypnotic trance are very much today what they were then (1961, p. 7).

Hypnosis is thus defined operationally as the set of events that a consensus of hypnotists reports are hypnotic. The gamut of these events is well known to all students of the subject, and is tapped in virtually all of the standard instruments currently available for the study of hypnotic susceptibility (Friedlander and Sarbin, 1938; Weitzenhoffer and Hilgard, 1959, 1962; London, 1963; Shor and Orne, 1963). These behaviors may be classified in a number of ways; they may focus on the response systems involved, such as psychomotor, verbal, physiological, or phenomenological responses. They may concern the type of subjective experience implied by the hypnotist, such as positive or negative hallucinations. Or, classification may refer to specific characteristics of the hypnotic suggestions themselves, such as the challenges often used to test their efficacy or the descriptive imagery employed without challenges. Regardless of the classificatory scheme, however, the common denominator of conventional hypnotic behavior seems to be its improbability of spontaneous occurrence in equivalent situations. In other words, hypnotic behavior is conventionally used to refer only to *induced* hypnotic behavior, regardless of whether the induction is performed by some other person or by the subject himself.

Another common element in hypnosis accompanies the overt behavior that characterizes it, but is less apparent to observers; this is the subjective experience of alterations, where the subject perceives one or another aspect of his environment or behavior in ways that are unusual for him. From either reference point, that of overt behavior or that of subjective experience, the important point is that the occurrences are taken to be relatively uncommon by observer and subject alike. There is some evidence that the parallels between subjects' own reports and observer reports of hypnotic experience (Bentler and Hilgard, 1963) are, in fact, high in agreement ($r = .74$) and the attempts of observers to evaluate separately the overt behaviors and subjective experiences of hypnotized children yield correlations of a similar order ($r = .60+$) (London, 1963). This suggests that the identification of hypnotic events from either reference is probably a fairly reliable reflection of the events that would be reported from the other.

Distinguishing Hypnotic from Other Events

Defining hypnosis by the implied consensus among hypnotists about improbability of events is not sufficiently exclusive to make it always clear just what should be considered hypnotic behavior and what should not. Many unusual behaviors occur that no one would associate with hypnosis, and many behaviors occur in hypnotic states that are not at all unusual. For the most part, the question of what is "really" hypnotic arises only where something like a hypnotic induction has preceded the occurrence of the events in question. For such situations, the problem of defining the range of hypnotic behaviors can be reduced to two issues: (1) To what extent are induced hypnotic behaviors unique to hypnosis? (2) To what extent is the induction process itself necessary to elicit hypnotic behaviors? The first question concerns the character of hypnotic experience; the second asks if induction can be treated independently of the hypnotic state. If typical induced behaviors are more or less unique to the hypnotic state, it should be possible to demarcate the induction process rather clearly merely by noting what follows it. The function of induction could then be specified in terms of its contribution to the development of that psychological condition in which uniquely hypnotic behavior occurs.

The uniqueness of most hypnotic events is challenged by Weitzenhoffer (1953) however, in his scholarly review of the research literature

until 1951. In a chapter on "The Nature of Induced Hypnc
Phenomena," he states:

> It is indeed a fact that, of those phenomena brought about through suggestion that have been reported and may be considered as scientifically valid, thus far none has fallen outside the domain of already known waking phenomena. More specifically, a survey of the various investigations in question shows that nearly all, if not all, hypnotic phenomena can also occur in the absence of hypnosis or of any suggestions. . . . In nearly all instances, the existing differences between hypnotic and waking phenomena are found to be more of *degree* than of *quality* (1953, p. 277).

Recent research tends further to substantiate Weitzenhoffer's conclusions, and is reviewed in other chapters of this Handbook. Experiments by Orne (1959) have been particularly important in demonstrating that the critical differences between hypnotic and waking behaviors seem to rest entirely in the altered subjective perceptions of subjects rather than in other measurable modifications of their performances. Although such alterations may themselves reflect behaviors more or less unique to hypnosis (Weitzenhoffer and Sjoberg, 1961), they incorporate only a small segment of the events that are conventionally defined as hypnotic.

The statistical improbability of hypnotic events must therefore be regarded as only relative to their occurrence under other conditions rather than as entirely reserved to the induction of hypnosis. This means that their improbability is continuously distributed rather than categorical, in which case the role of hypnotic induction in their occurrence would necessarily be a rather subtle one. Induction could be said to catalyze or otherwise facilitate the behavior but not to determine it. The efficacy of induction would thus depend on the likelihood, that is, frequency or intensity, of the criterion behavior occurring anyway without it rather than upon any absolute distinction between hypnotic and other behaviors. Thus bypassing the issues of subjective volition or unique occurrence, recent research on the efficacy of induction permits evaluations of it in many different areas (see *the data* of Barber, 1961b; Damaser, Shor, and Orne, 1963; Deckert and West, 1963a; Paul, 1963).

Some of the research strategies implied by this conception have been used fairly extensively by this time. They are discussed at length in the chapter by Rosenhan. Unfortunately, the results of such research, especially when concerned with the motivational properties of hypnotic inductions, hypnosis itself, and the effects of other psychological states on different behaviors have been somewhat ambiguous. In addition, distinctions between effects of the processes of induction and of the processes that might be involved in hypnosis after induction terminates are often not made, further limiting the usefulness of such results for the specialized purposes of this chapter.

The general lack of uniqueness of occurrence of hypnotic events has encouraged Barber and his collaborators, at least, commonly to surround the term "hypnosis" with quotation marks (Barber, 1961a, 1962a, 1962b; Barber and Deeley, 1961; Barber and Calverley, 1962), suggesting that uniqueness is the sole criterion for defining hypnotic events. It is not at all clear, however, that blanket statements about induction effects can be made, any more than it is clear that exclusiveness is a sufficient criterion for hypnotic behavior. Some behaviors, it seems, are more likely to happen with induction than without and some not; and either effect is more likely in some people than in others, and in some situations or experiments more than in others. And any of the effects are sometimes replicated and sometimes not. In brief, it all depends—but it is not clear on what. What is clear, on the other hand, is that a discussion of induction limited to behaviors that did not occur without it or under circumstances other than hypnosis would be tautological and circular in the first place and very short in the second. For our purposes, therefore, *induction* will refer to the *processes* that are used in attempts to produce "hypnosis" whether or not the former "work" or the latter is uniquely "real." As Deckert and West put it in their recent review of the issues of "hypnotizability," the distinction implied is that "between a 'route' and a 'state,' each identifiable by measurable criteria" (1936b, p. 226).

Dimensions of Hypnotic Induction

Just as hypnosis has been defined as a continuum of probabilities of response events, induction may be usefully discussed with reference to some continuities. Two variable systems are most evidently important to induction:

1. A *sociality* dimension, whose polar attributes are autohypnosis and heterohypnosis, and
2. A *formality* dimension, whose extremes are spontaneous, unplanned inductions and deliberate, ritualized inductions.

These dimensions are conceptually independent of each other, but they are commonly connected in practice in the sense that most inductions are both interpersonal and formal, performed by a hypnotist upon a subject who has explicitly agreed to undergo hypnosis.

Sociality in Hypnotic Induction. Sociality in hypnotic induction refers to the extent to which hypnosis is induced in one person as a direct consequence of acts involving the observable participation of another person. The use of this dimension implies some disagreement both with the extreme position of Christenson that "An essential feature of the *hypnotic situation* is that another individual is involved" (1958, p. 50) and with the anonymous body of apologetic hypnotists, who, to emphasize the voluntary character of hypnotic behavior, protest that all hypnosis is autohypnosis. The position of the present work is that it is possible to distinguish rather clearly between autohypnosis and heterohypnosis by taking careful note of the presence or absence of a hypnotist who does something to facilitate the induction of hypnosis. The use of phonographic or other such devices to induce hypnosis occupies an intermediate range of conditions on the sociality dimension, because it neither makes use of another person's physical presence to induce hypnosis nor relies solely on the internal resources of the subject for its accomplishment.

Formality in Hypnotic Induction. Formality in hypnotic induction means the extent to which hypnosis is induced by the exercise of premeditated signals, formulae, or other systematic devices controlled by the hypnotist. The use of a formality dimension permits inferences to be made about the degree to which hypnosis results from intentional, deliberate acts of the hypnotist. The epitome of formal hypnotic induction is contained in the conventional therapeutic, experimental, and entertainment situations in which hypnosis is induced with the express consent of the subject; the opposite pole is represented in the occurrence of spontaneous hypnoticlike experiences such as "highway hypnosis." The sociality variable is unrelated to this dimension; it is quite possible for autohypnosis to proceed by use of a formal induction or for heterohypnosis to occur without use of deliberate induction techniques by the hypnotist, though the latter case admittedly would be rare (Figure 1).

The dimensions used here help to separate hypnotic induction from other aspects of hypnotic behavior by limiting descriptions of induction to the observable circumstances and processes that mediate the transition from unhypnotized to hypnotic states. By focusing on the persons and behaviors of the hypnotist, moreover, they further suggest that the characteristics of hypnotic inductions may not only be described independently of their effects on subjects, but may also be applied to the induction of behavior states other than hypnotic ones.

Although the dimensions of induction used here include autohypnosis and spontaneous experiences of hypnosis, the discussion that follows is mostly concerned with hypnosis produced in interpersonal situations by relatively systematic means. The same general principles should be equally applicable to spontaneous and to autohypnotic inductions, but the focus of attention of scientific and clinical students alike has been upon the study of systematic induction of heterohypnosis. An interesting literature has developed on the relationship of hypnotic states to natural experiences they seem to emulate, but most of it has relatively little direct bearing on the problems of induction. Natural trancelike experience is potentially quite important for the study of individual differences in hypnotic susceptibility, and is reviewed quite thoroughly by Hilgard in Chapter 13 in this Handbook.

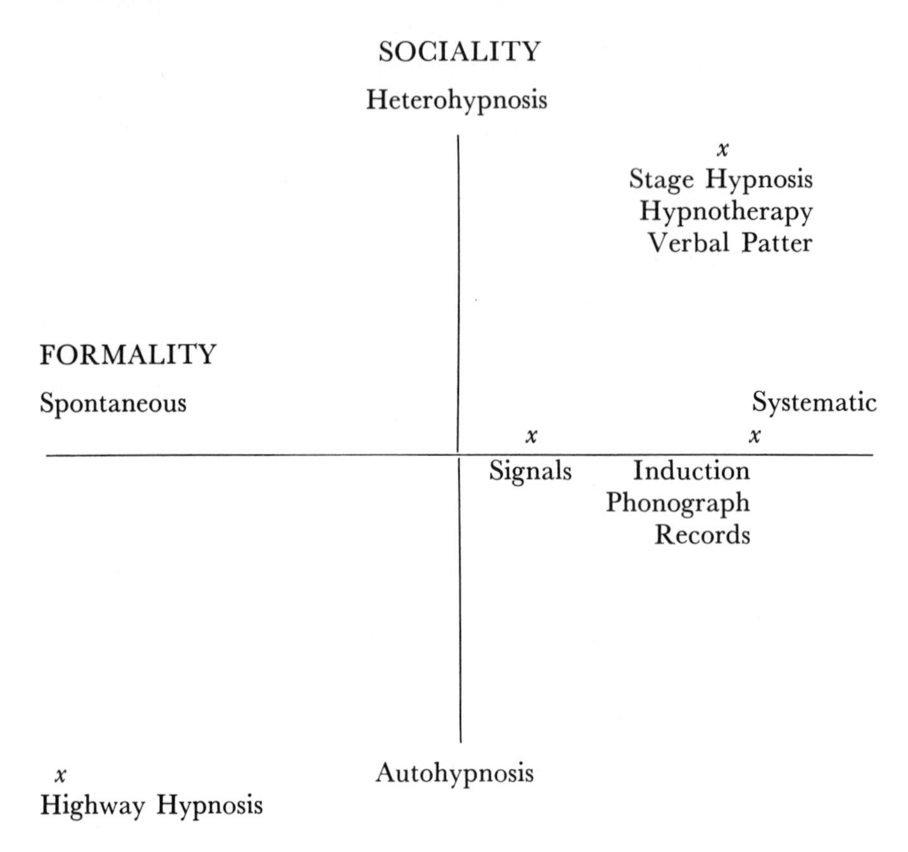

Figure 1. Sociality and formality dimensions of hypnotic trance induction.

FUNCTIONAL ANALYSIS OF HYPNOTIC INDUCTION

Many different techniques are used for the induction of hypnosis. Some involve nothing other than a verbal patter; others require physical contact between hypnotist and subject; and still others use various devices or machinery to involve sensory and perceptual response systems in the induction process. The length of time taken for the induction of hypnosis also varies enormously depending on the technique used, the idiosyncrasies of the subject, and the orientation of the hypnotist. And the environmental and other conditions recommended as beneficial or harmful to the induction of hypnosis also vary somewhat. All of these will be discussed in greater detail later in this chapter.

Obtaining Compliance

Despite the appearance of great diversity in specific techniques and circumstances of induction, there are a very few functional elements common in all hypnotic inductions. The most important of these elements is the hypnotist's deliberate manipulation of the subject and the environment in a manner intended to engage the subject in compliant responses to his suggestions. The general sequence is from simple suggestions, which are most likely under any circumstances to receive compliant responses, to complex ones which, under most circumstances, would be unlikely to elicit compliant responses. The pattern of hypnotic induction thus parallels the conventional meanings of hypnotic susceptibility and of depth of hypnosis. Deep hypnosis usually refers to the condition in which the most improbable response events occur; hypnotic susceptibility is judged greater or less as an individual is more or less able to produce statistically improbable responses; and the induction of hypnosis is the sequential process in which a hypnotist tries to elicit increasingly improbable (uncommon) response events in a subject.

Relaxation and Concentration

Two parenthetical aspects of most hypnotic induction techniques seem to have a general facilitating effect on the elicitation of all the compliant responses that are the goals of the induction. These are suggestions of relaxation and of concentration.

Suggestions of relaxation are generally given directly and positively; whereas suggestions of concentration are often made obliquely. Subjects will ordinarily be told to relax, for example, and actually instructed in the details of muscular relaxation; but they are less likely to be told explicitly to concentrate than to exclude peripheral stimuli from attention. In either case, the main effect is the same; that is, the subject becomes increasingly aloof from all sources of stimulation other than the suggestions of the hypnotist (West, 1960; Arnold, 1959). Because the situation has ordinarily been arranged in advance to be conducive to relaxation, the suggestions of the hypnotist are, to some extent, concurrent with or even subsequent to events that have already begun to occur in the behavior of the subject. In this initial phase of the induction, therefore, the subject almost inevitably responds compliantly to the hypnotic suggestions.

But the experience of compliance with respect to relaxation and attention is probably less important than the resulting focus of attention on the central source of continuous stimulation, that is, the hypnotist whose suggestions are inevitably most likely to be effective when they are least controverted by distracting outside influences. The principle involved is probably more easily grasped as an aspect of communications systems than of interpersonal relations. From this view, the hypnotist's suggestions are communication signals and any other stimuli noise. Part of his induction procedure is simply to reduce the input of noise in the subject's field so that his signals may be received more clearly and the competitive potential of other signals for the subject's attention or response may be diminished.

One reason the hypnotist wishes to maximize the signal : noise ratio, of course, is that the relative reduction of noise makes it literally easier to understand the signal. But another reason of special importance for hypnotic induction is that the ordinary noise level that occupies some fraction of an individual's waking attention in almost any situation also provides a context in which his subjective experiences are generally entertained. One of the significant objectives of the hypnotist is the elimination of any such usual context. Stated differently, it is the hypnotist's purpose to persuade the subject to perform in ways that would be unlikely in the context of his usual experiences; and he can best do this by encouraging the subject to dissociate himself from that context. One step in that direction is producing relaxation which, by reducing movements, reduces the total amount of possible stimulation from which interpretations of the environment are ordinarily made. The reduction of movement seems to have the same value for eliciting hypnoticlike behavior in animals as in men, even if the immobility results from restraint rather than relaxation (Silva, Estable, and Segundo, 1959).

The very simplest and most direct means of dissociating context in humans, however, is by getting the subject to shut his eyes; and almost all hypnotic inductions use eye closure early in the procedure. With this window on the world obscured, the hypnotist then proceeds to shut off other channels of distraction. The usual sequence of suggestions is from simple to complex, from frequent to infrequent. The subjective experience of curtailing vision is not only common but commonly within the voluntary control of the subject. The subjective experience of cutting off the perception of sounds is common but accidental and apparently involuntary, as when one person fails to "hear" another's remarks. And the experience of eliminating the perception of odors, as in hypnotic anosmia, or of pain, as in hypnotic anesthesia, is still less common and less apparently performable at the behest of the performer. The latter two events are ordinarily not considered part of the induction proper, but rather of the hypnotic state itself; the former are fairly routine induction procedures. It is worth noting also that the eye closure part of the induction is usually not done as a direct suggestion to close the eyes, but rather as a complex and lengthy discourse to the effect that, as a consequence of relaxation, the subject's eyes *will close themselves*. The very "will" of the hypnotist, if you will, is considered a distracting noise, and the comments he makes are therefore designed to sound as if they were reflections of the subject's experience rather than the hypnotist's desires.

The emphasis in modern induction techniques on the subject's "natural" experience rather than upon what the hypnotist wants is here called the "democratic" approach to induction. It is probably the most common approach in use today, both in clinical and laboratory settings; and it is the only approach to be found in standard scales of hypnotic susceptibility. Its advantages over one that emphasizes the interpersonal nature of the situation (implying that the subject is controlled by the hypnotist), here called the "charismatic" approach to induction, lie in its apparently greater propriety for a culture where individual initiative and freedom are emphasized and in its practical contribution of flexibility to the hypnotist, especially on those occasions when the subject does not respond to his suggestions.

The popular notion of resistance to hypnotic induction being a matter of "contest of wills" may be erroneous, not merely because, as defenders of democracy in hypnosis contend, the subject does nothing against his will, but because the entire issue of voluntarism is implicitly bypassed in the structure of democratic induction procedures. From the point of view of the signal's content, the hypnotist himself has no more will than does the subject! The issue of will, if it has any relevance, probably refers to the sociality dimension of the induction procedure; but the system of signal delivery, which concerns the formality dimension, cannot be discussed very meaningfully in terms of volition.

Interpersonal and Peripheral Factors in Induction

Analysis of the induction situation in terms of its formal characteristics leads to the signal transmission hypothesis above. This hypothesis in turn makes it possible to comprehend many of the peripheral conditions, which are ordinarily considered beneficial or detrimental to the induction of hypnosis, and the social characteristics of the induction situation explain many other such conditions.

Interpersonal Factors. Despite a growing body of evidence that susceptibility to hypnosis is a structural aspect or trait of personality (see Hilgard, 1962) and that it is quite independent of persuasibility, suggestibility, or social naïveté as those traits are usually measured (Moore, 1964), the belief is still common that the induction of hypnosis is facilitated or hindered by the interpersonal dynamics of the situation. Many arguments favor the latter view without contradicting the former. In the first place, it is clearly correct in the negative sense that, in an unpleasant interpersonal situation, subjects are unlikely to attend willingly to the instructions of the hypnotist, effectively foiling the induction before it really starts. Second, even when there is no discord, uncertainty on the subject's part about the trustworthiness or competence of the hypnotist, or about the dangers of the hypnotic situation, may effectively prevent him from relaxing or concentrating enough to participate fully in the induction. In these cases it is possible, by manipulating the interpersonal relationship between hypnotist and subject, to alleviate the various inhibitors of the subject's signal reception facilities, to put subjects at ease, to reassure them of their safety, and to take other steps whose effect is to permit the eventual success of the induction. Preinduction rapport patter is generally intended to serve just this purpose. (A good illustration of such material may be found in Form A of Weitzenhoffer and Hilgard's *Stanford Hypnotic Susceptibility Scales*, pp. 8–10). All that this implies concerning the effects of the interpersonal relationship on the induction procedure, however, is that varying the interpersonal climate merely makes it more or less possible for an individual's susceptibility to be expressed. It says nothing of the utility of interpersonal manipulations for affecting susceptibility itself. In other words, this argues that the relevance to hypnotic induction of the interpersonal relationship of hypnotist and subject is limited by the susceptibility of the subject, as if susceptibility were an invariable quantum. The evidence to that effect is not altogether clear, but that concerning its stability for hypnotists is certainly impressive. As Hilgard puts it,

> It is not implied that the hypnotist makes no difference, but rather that there is something about the subject that is the chief determiner of the level at which hypnotic behavior will be given in initial inductions under standard induction procedures (1962, p. 22).

No one really doubts, of course, that there is an upper limit to an individual's hypnotic susceptibility beyond which no manipulation or stimulus change will affect his response to hypnotic suggestions. The question is, to what extent may the manifestations of hypnosis in an induction be positive consequences of the interpersonal manipulations of the hypnotist or of the differences in personality between different hypnotists? Interpersonal factors clearly may have a negative effect upon inductions, but it is uncertain whether they have much positive significance. If susceptibility is relatively stable, moreover, then improvements of performance might be attributed to the subject's having learned the desired responses through cues given by the hypnotist (Fisher, 1962). There does not seem to be any way to distinguish between hypnotic and merely compliant behavior at this time, though this seems to be an unsatisfactory explanation of the differences in effects which different hypnotists apparently achieve with the same subjects (see Erickson, Haley, and Weakland, 1959).

The two factors generally considered most important in the interpersonal relationship of subject and hypnotist for the achievement of successful inductions are (1) *rapport* and (2) *transference.*

Rapport is reviewed at some length by Weitzenhoffer, whose summary makes clear that the concept has only dubious utility:

> For a clear understanding of the literature on hypnosis, it must be kept in mind that "rapport" has been used in a variety of ways. It may be of value to briefly summarize in conclusion some of its major meanings. In practice, then, rapport denotes: (1) an elective or selective perception; (2) the transference aspect of the hypnotic interaction; (3) a selective hypersuggestibility; and (4) an intimate, harmonious relationship without specific reference to cause or nature (1957, p. 54).

Uses (1) and (3) in Weitzenhoffer's description correspond respectively to aspects of signal receptivity and hypnotic susceptibility, as used here; whereas (4) is a very conventional usage that means the same thing with reference to hypnotic induction, psychotherapy interviews, or the optimal administration of individual psychological tests; it has, moreover, already been discussed as the elimination of negative factors in the relationship of subject and hypnotist. Because (2) refers to the psychoanalytic concept of transference as applicable to hypnosis, and the term "transference" is more familiar and more denotative, we may reasonably relegate any special technical use of "rapport" to the same graveyard of hypnotic jargon in which "animal magnetism" now rests.

The relevance of transference to hypnotic induction requires more serious attention. Weitzenhoffer (1957) reviews the theoretical and experimental literature on the relationship of transference to hypnosis. The discussion is inevitably unsatisfactory, however, not as a fault of Weitzenhoffer's, but of the literature. For one thing, the term "transference" is often used loosely and ambiguously. But even if it is taken to refer precisely to the generalization of emotions learned in connection with one significant other to another person in a context that has minimal stimulus pull for such emotions, its relation to hypnosis is still unclear. The very data that are subject to interpretation are not agreed upon; Hilgard (1962) and Gill and Brenman (1961) argue that the critical datum is the stability of performance for all hypnotists; whereas Bookbinder (1961), following earlier work of Watkins and Kline, bases his arguments on the differences that different hypnotists can elicit from the same subjects. Even agreement on the data offers no basis for interpretation, however. Hilgard takes the stability of initial responsiveness as a demonstration that "Transference significance is minimal at this stage" (1962, p. 12); whereas Gill and Brenman take this same fact as evidence of "how strong these transference reactions are. . . ." (1961, p. 112).

Certainly, hypnotic subjects sometimes experience transference relationships with their hypnotists, but it is not apparent whether such relations are antecedents to hypnosis or consequents of it. Nor is the degree of correlation between the events at all certain. Whatever the relevance of transference to the hypnotic state, moreover, it would have little bearing on the induction *process* unless the disposition to one or another degree or mode of transference reaction antecedes the induction situation. This may certainly be the case, but then the concept of transference contributes to an understanding of susceptibility rather than of the induction process (see "transference readiness," Hilgard and Hilgard, 1962). As a practical matter, on the other hand, the fact that some people are more disposed than others to respond emotionally in ways that are not predictable from the immediate situation suggests that the hypnotist's skill at sensing such interpersonal nuances and diverting them will be important for establishing the optimal conditions in which induction can work. This would be equally true, however, were the source of such unexpected emotions to be found in the history of the subject's interpersonal relationships or in the occurrence of some minor but sudden and contemporary thought, such as that a parking meter's time had expired or a roast lay burning in the oven. If the source of such reactions were predictive of their variety, intensity, or longevity, moreover, they might be of some value, but there is no evidence that this is the case. Transference thus does not seem to be a very useful concept in describing the dynamics of the induction process. And though it may be quite important to an understanding of the susceptibility of subjects, that is not of major concern here. This does not mean that there is no important relationship between the phenomena of hypnosis and the occurrence of transference. On the contrary, whether or not the disposition to transference reactions predicts hypnotizability, it appears clinically that the occurrence of hypnosis strongly disposes people toward transference reactions. But neither event suggests any necessary functional relationship between transference reactions and the interpersonal aspects of hypnotic induction.

Impersonal Factors. The relevance to the induction of hypnosis of impersonal factors, such as furnishing and decor of the room, lighting, temperature and extraneous sounds, is implied by the signal transmission hypothesis used here. Such sources of stimulation may have an amplifying effect, boosting the transmission of the hypnotist's instructions and thus increasing the probability of maximum expression of hypnotic behavior by the subject as a result of the induction signal. Or they may operate as static or noise in the signal transmission system, inhibiting the transmission of the hypnotist's instructions and thus decreasing the probability that the induction signal will be effective. Presumably, such interference effects may operate as noise either in the signal reception system or in the response system; that is, they may either make it hard to pay proper attention to the hypnotic instruction, or they make it hard to respond to an instruction, which has been thoroughly heard and understood.

The precise manner in which reception occurs is itself open to some dispute. The focusing of attention seems to be the principal factor in receiving induction signals, but it is unclear whether such focusing represents a positive ability of the subject which, by being selectively brought to bear on the hypnotist, makes environment distractions automatically irrelevant. Alternatively, the basic ability involved may be a capacity to ward off distractions so that the subject's awareness is open to "capture" by hypnotic cues. Ås (1962) has challenged Barber's claim that withstanding distractions is the principal factor in susceptibility. In a study of the relationship between subjective experiences and susceptibility, Ås found indirect evidence that tends rather strongly to refute Barber by showing that

> there is no general relationship between lack of distractibility and hypnotizability. Earlier experiences of absorption in some activity were positively correlated with hypnotizability in both female and male subjects.
>
> These findings therefore support the assumption that it is the positive focusing of attention with ensuing absorption in its object that is of importance in hypnosis. It is suggested that the *S* becomes oblivious or inattentive to irrelevant stimuli as an effect of this absorption... and not by actively warding off the distractions.... (1962, p. 137).

Whether interference occurs primarily in the reception or response system is a moot point, perhaps describing only the difference in the subject's focus of attention during his retrospective reports of the induction experience. Among subjects who fail to respond to a particular suggestion, one may see himself as having understood and accepted it but been unable to comply while another found himself distracted by one or another aspect of the stimulus situation to begin with. The latter is probably the more common case.

Interference effects probably do not take the form of preventing the induction instruction from being fully comprehended or otherwise barring the assimilation of its contents. They are more often described as competing stimuli, sometimes only at the edge of awareness, but outside the apparent control of the subject. Their "noisy" properties seem to arise because they can neither be disregarded nor blended into the phenomenal field in a manner congenial with positive responses to the induction. For this reason, it is of some importance to the success of the induction that the hypnotist take precautions to prevent unnecessary distractions. Temperature, lighting, decor, and the like are probably less important in a positive than in a negative way. Their satisfactory control may not contribute to the success of the induction, as is sometimes thought, but failure to control them may be inhibiting. If a subject feels chilly or uncomfortable, is startled by noises from nearby corridors or blaring radios, or has been subtly depressed in mood by a gloomy and swamilike laboratory or office atmosphere, it is small wonder that he may find it difficult to attend to the hypnotist's words and respond positively to them.

TECHNIQUES OF HYPNOTIC INDUCTION

As indicated above, the variety of techniques[2] for the induction of hypnosis all seem to be directed toward a very few specific functions, which we may summarize as the effective delivery of the "induction signal system," that is, a series of instructions for responses of graduated improbability of occurrence with each increased gradation of difficulty delivered upon compliance by the subject with previous instructions of less difficulty. A number of otherwise extraneous interpersonal and impersonal factors in the induction situation may apparently have a negative influence on it, though it is not so clear that they have much facilitating effect.

In most modern uses of hypnosis, the delivery of the induction signal system is essentially verbal, but at least three different modes of delivery may be distinguished; it is possible that the means by which they affect subjects differ too, though this is not known.

These induction techniques are:

1. *Verbal*, in which the entire induction procedure is conducted through the medium of spoken instructions and reinforcements delivered by the hypnotist.
2. *Physical contact*, in which some portion of the signal delivery is supported by manipulating the subject physically to suggest or compel a compliant response, or to reinforce a suggested response when it occurs.
3. *Sensory-perceptual manipulation*, in which gadgets, devices, or machines are employed to capture the attention of the subject and mechanically increase receptiveness to the induction signal.

Some hypnotists routinely use all three of these techniques in the course of an induction, regardless of its length, but the relative emphasis

[2] The following discussion of techniques analyzes the major technical modes and their functions in induction, but it is not intended as a manual for learning induction. The most authoritative single work on that subject is undoubtedly Weitzenhoffer's *General Techniques of Hypnotism* (1957). For standardized versions of a small number of techniques appropriate to individual adults, to groups, and to children, the reader is referred respectively to the Stanford Scales (Weitzenhoffer and Hilgard, 1959, 1962), the Harvard Scales (Shor and Orne, 1963), and the Children's Scale of Hypnotic Susceptibility (London, 1963a).

placed upon one or another method differs considerably, depending on the personal preferences of the hypnotist and the probable utility of different techniques for different persons and situations.

Differences in emphasis are discernible even among rigidly standardized techniques. The Stanford Hypnotic Susceptibility Scales, Forms A and B (Weitzenhoffer and Hilgard, 1959), for example, rely almost entirely on verbal delivery of the induction, permitting the hypnotist to touch the subject at only two points in the entire test and using a very simple attention-fixing device at only one point. Its two derivatives, however, standardized for administration to groups and children, respectively, both alter these ratios as might be expected. The Harvard Group Scale (Shor and Orne, 1963) makes no use at all of physical contact or of gadgets, and the Children's Hypnotic Susceptibility Scale (London, 1963a) makes considerably more use of both than does the Stanford Scale.

Although the functions intended by the different techniques of delivery are the same, and although there is no striking evidence that the total effectiveness of an induction is related to the extended use of any one technique or any particular combination of them, their superficial differences alone have some utility; they provide the hypnotist with a repertory of induction devices, so that the failure of a particular method of induction need not force him to the premature or spurious conclusion that his subject is unsusceptible to hypnosis. Each of the techniques involves somewhat different implicit assumptions, moreover, which may be worth formal research, and which may be clarified by specifying the distinctive features of each.

Verbal Induction

Complete reliance on verbal communication for the induction of hypnosis has the advantages of freeing the hypnotist from much concern with paraphernalia, permitting maximum flexibility of communication from hypnotist to subject, both in terms of variety and detail of hypnotic instructions, and presenting a more direct introduction to what the hypnotic situation will ordinarily be like than do other methods. Since most of the content of any induction is likely to be verbal, the general induction events described previously are applicable here. A typical sequence might be as follows:

a. The hypnotist and subject assume the positions they will occupy throughout the induction; usually both are seated, but some hypnotists have their subjects lie down.
b. The hypnotist establishes or reinforces some desultory conversation to put the subject at ease and allow time to adjust to the surroundings.

c. In a laboratory setting, this leads into a discussion of the experiment, or the relevance of hypnosis and of common misconceptions of it among the uninitiate. In a clinical setting, this leads into a discusssion of the problem that motivates the session.

d_1 In all laboratory situations, and many clinical ones, the initiation of the hypnotic induction is formally agreed upon, as in c., before it is actually begun. This is here called *direct hypnosis.*[3]

d_2 In some clinical settings, the hypnotist may lead the discussion of the problem directly into the induction without prior discussion and sometimes without saying that hypnosis is being used. This technique, used for people who are likely to be excessively frightened by advance announcement, is here called *indirect hypnosis.*

e. Induction usually begins with instructions to relax; these are given in great detail, often specifying the different parts of the body, and in a manner that deliberately makes of the instructions a rhythmic, soothing, often monotonous patter. Subjects may be instructed to concentrate their gaze or their thoughts on some particular thing, while they are listening to the hypnotist. As his instructions to relax appear to take hold, the hypnotist couples them with suggestions that the subject is becoming drowsy. He encourages him to accept this drowsiness and go to sleep, adding that he will continue to hear and respond to the hypnotist throughout his "sleep" and will not "awaken" until instructed to do so.

f. As the induction patter in e. gets into high gear, with large muscle relaxation apparently quite thorough and the suggestions of great weariness developing, the hypnotist begins also to suggest behavioral tests of the conditions he is instructing the subject to experience. If he has begun the induction by having the subject stare fixedly at something, then his suggestions of fatigue gradually focus upon the eyes, eventually specifying that fatigue will make them close without any volitional effort.

g. The remainder of the induction consists of the addition of more difficult behavioral tests, generally accompanied by continuous patter about deep relaxation, sleep, and ability to listen and respond positively to the hypnotist. At some point after the subject's eyes have closed, for example, the hypnotist may suggest that the depth of his relaxation is such that he cannot open his eyes even if he wants to; the hypnotist may then challenge the subject to try to open his eyes, emphasizing in advance that it will probably be impossible for him to do so.

[3] Not everywhere. The jargon of hypnotists is far from standardized. Kroger (1963) uses the terms "direct" and "indirect" hypnosis to mean "Authoritarian" and "Permissive," respectively, which seem to conform roughly to my "Charismatic" and "Democratic."

Certain characteristics of the verbal induction sequence deserve particular attention. The foregoing makes it apparent, for one thing, that no sharp operational distinction between the induction of hypnosis and the hypnotic state proper is apparent to an observer. Any distinction between them represents a convention among observers that refers to a discrete point in what is really a continuous process, even if it assumes some shift has occurred in the subject's experience (Haley, 1958).

A much more important implication of this description however, is that there are two component phases to the induction signal system, differing only in content from each other. Phase I is the process of making suggestions and obtaining positive responses to them which, at the beginning of the hypnotic induction, hardly differs from the exchange of simple suggestions and compliant responses that takes place in almost any social situation ("Come in." "How do you do?" [shaking hands]). But this procedure, which extends from a. into e. in the preceding sequence, moves imperceptibly from an almost conventional social exchange of suggestions and responses to a quite fantastic set of content, already implied at the end of e., more apparent in f., and glaring in g. Without any special comment to that effect, as if his progression of contents were quite ordinary, the hypnotist advances from simple, straightforward suggestions ("Won't you sit down?" "I want you to feel at ease." "Relax completely." ". . . makes you feel tired and drowsy"), first to suggestions that imply phenomenological contradictions, and then to suggestions that first imply and finally explicate logical contradictions. The suggestion at the end of e. that the subject will simultaneously sleep and respond to the hypnotist is not logically contradictory but is phenomenologically contradictory in the sense that most people, if they thought about it, would probably describe sleep as a state in which they could not carry on conversations, respond to suggestions, and so on. By the same token, if they thought about it, most people entering a hypnotic state might easily recognize that they are by no means sleeping. The point is precisely that the subject in whom induction of hypnosis is actually being effected does not think about it, at least not in any way that prevents his quietly accepting the situation.

Up to that point in the sequence, of course, there is no need for him to take any action, so the possibility of contradiction does not force itself upon him. But perhaps merely receiving such suggestions with intellectual equanimity primes the subject for equally bland receipt of plainer contradictions. For the next suggestion in f., that he close his eyes, would be very puzzling if he were to analyze it. The suggestion is couched in a way that disregards the fact that he can close his eyes by a simple intentional act with which he has vast experience. It further implies both that he should keep his eyes open now and that he should close them later, but that he should do both without any awareness of intent on his own part. The suggestion is rationalized, of course, by the statement that his eyes will close "by themselves" because of his drowsiness, but even this argument suggests, were he to think about it, either that he should not intentionally close his eyes or that he should intentionally have no intention one way or the other, to close them or keep them open. Once again, the point is not so much that contradition is inevitable as that acceptance of the suggestion implies a failure to recognize any peculiarity in it relative to the subject's own experience. Here, for the first time, some action is necessary for acceptance of the suggestion, but the action involved merely replicates the subject's well-established performance pattern, regardless of the peculiar language in which it is evoked. This is not at all the case in phase g., where the hypnotist now tells the subject that he cannot open his own eyes and challenges him to do so. The statement blandly defies virtually all the subject's previous experience with control of his own eyelids and challenges him to prove otherwise. But this is still less wondrous than the fact that, to respond optimally as a hypnotized person, the subject must act upon this instruction by moving the wrong set of muscles so that his eyes will remain closed while he appears to be struggling to open them—and ideally he must do this without express knowledge that he is doing so! He must behave, in other words, as he would if he wished to comply with what he recognized as a deliberate misstatement by the hypnotist of the desired response, and he must do so without recognizing his recognition of this fact! There is an apparent contradiction here, but it is only apparent in analysis of the suggestion and response, not in the behavior system itself (Haley, 1963). In other words, the subject avoids the behavioral paralysis that contradictory instructions might evoke by responding as closely as possible to both parts of them—he does not open his eyes, and he does contract muscles that are physically near and subjectively seem relevant to opening the eyes. What he does not do is make a cognitive comparison of the two parts of the instruction, thus avoiding contra*diction* in the most literal sense of the term.

There is indeed only one further degree of contradiction possible. It occurs in the situation where the subject explicates an antinomic event as real, such as perceiving the same object in two places at the same time. This phenomenon has been studied by Orne (1959), who terms the bland response of subjects confronted with this contradiction "trance logic." Orne believes that this phenomenon represents the only observably unique hypnotic behavior, one which is never simulated by people who are in all other respects quite expert at simulating how hypnotized people act.

Trance logic seems to be continuous with the indifference to increases in contradictory aspects of suggestions that characterizes the sequential procedure of hypnotic induction and that may provide a most critical criterion for the operational definition of hypnosis. As Orne describes it, trance logic is not observed in the early parts of hypnotic sessions (the induction), but every degree of contradiction short of trance logic does occur in induction.

The conventional verbal induction sequence described here is by no means indispensable for the production of hypnotic behavior, and in some respects may be the least efficient means of eliciting it. The use of such a complete sequence is time-consuming, and its very thoroughness provides extensive opportunity for extraneous interference or hypnotist blunders. Stage hypnotists, who naturally try to induce hypnosis with extreme rapidity, often manage to follow sequences like this one in abbreviated form, perhaps skipping some steps altogether. David Elman, a former carnival hypnotist who now specializes in training medical personnel in hypnotic techniques, argues that a complete induction of profound hypnotic states should never take more than one or two minutes. His quite successful inductions are, moreover, completely verbal.

One virtue of the thoroughgoing and lengthy verbal induction sequence might be that it permits the subject gradually to assimilate one level of suggested experience before moving on to another. Also, a detailed induction relies less on the subject's expectancies of what the experience will be like than upon the hypnotist's, helping to assure that the subject's responses will be more relevant to what the hypnotist wishes to accomplish.

Physical Contact in Induction

Modern hypnotic inductions are never conducted solely by means of physical manipulations of the subject, but such manipulations are often used in support of verbal inductions. Depending on the type of contact, they serve the purpose of communicating intimacy in the relationship of hypnotist and subject, or they provide the subject with an experiental sample of the phenomenon that the hypnotist is trying to make him imagine. The Stanford Scales illustrate the latter use in the Postural Sway item (Weitzenhoffer and Hilgard, 1959, pp. 11–12). After having the subject stand straight in front of the hypnotist with his back to him, hands at his side, and eyes closed, the hypnotist briefly describes the suggestion he is about to give, in which he will ask the subject to think of falling backwards until he actually does so. He then proposes to illustrate the experience and, holding the subject gently by the shoulders, pulls him backwards to the point of imbalance. After he has guided the subject back to an upright stance, the hypnotist begins the suggestion proper. It is not known whether this device actually increases the tendency of subjects to respond to the purely verbal suggestion of swaying that follows the demonstration; but even if it does not, it is likely that inhibition of falling, which might have resulted from fear that the hypnotist could not stay the fall or that it would be a long fall, might be reduced by this experience.

The use of physical contact for the purpose of soothing, reassuring, and relaxing the subject is illustrated in the Eye Closure item of the Children's Scale, in which the hypnotist repeatedly strokes the child's brow, after his eyes are closed, while verbally attempting to deepen the hypnotic state (London, 1963b, p. 6). This method is sometimes used with adults as well, and more than any other, it seems to argue for the significance of an implied emotional relationship, particularly a dependent one, in the induction and maintenance of hypnotic states. Whether or not psychodynamic mechanisms like transference or regression are involved, such behavior on the part of the hypnotist, and its ready acceptance by the subject, certainly mimics a paternal gesture of affection and assurance and a childlike trusting response to it. There is no particular evidence that it has any effect on induction.

The advantage of physical contact in induction is that it establishes a very direct, clear, even primitive channel of communication between hypnotist and subject without at all impeding the hypnotist's use of the verbal channel. To whatever extent signal redundancy assures reception or the use of different modalities of delivery permits faster or more thorough response, the combination of physical contact with verbal induction devices serves a useful purpose.

The trouble with the modality of touch, however, is that it is subject to misinterpretation in a more significant way than are words. The very primitive character of this communication permits it, if the message thus received is dissonant with the verbal message, to disrupt any orderly response to the latter. It is all too easy, for example, for a subject to perceive the hypnotist's touch as a thinly veiled sexual gesture, an attempt to patronize and make the subject appear infantile, or an expression of contempt of the now-you-see-I-have-you-in-my-power sort. Even if no such specific interpretation is placed on it, it is likely that an adult subject, especially one who is a stranger to the hypnotist, may regard any unexpected physical contact as a vaguely improper intrusion on the hypnotist's part. Any such feeling probably interferes very much with the induction, and the high probability of arousing it may explain why most induction techniques only make the most chary use of physical contact between the parties.

Sensory-Perceptual Manipulation

Like most physical contact, the use of assorted gadgetry that flashes, hums, waves, or clicks, to expedite induction, permits signal communication on separate channels that do not interfere with voice transmission and sometimes reinforce its messages. Also, such devices have the advantage over physical contact of relative freedom from misinterpretation by the subject. Their primary purpose is to capture the attention either visually or aurally; this may occur by means of a contrast effect, which makes them stand out relative to other stimuli; or by virtue of a rhythmic effect, which makes them seem pervasive in the subject's perception; or by their very monotony, which might increase the subject's need to attend to voice stimulation as the only source of pattern variability. Bright objects are commonly used for contrast; watch fobs, pendula, tacks, and the like may be held steadily before the subject's gaze while the hypnotist talks, or he may have subjects concentrate on his own eyes or nose. Common visual rhythmic devices also include "hypnodiscs," a spiral painted on a disc, which is steadily revolved, flashing mirrors, and flickering lights presented stroboscopically. All these have the parenthetical effect of hastening eye fatigue, which is especially useful during eye closure suggestions. The most commonly used auditory device is a simple metronome, but things like music or even white noise are sometimes used as well.

As with physical contact, there is no clear evidence that gadgets have much impact one way or the other on the outcome of inductions. They seem to have an interesting relevance to the phenomena of hypnosis, however, which may have much more bearing on physiological aspects of the subject than on any factor in the interpersonal situation. Although the use of pendula, strobe lights, or metronomes may be quite impressive, and may work to aid induction in the swamilike manner of prestige suggestions, this seems to be the least important factor in their use. Bright objects in a dark field are capable of capturing attention quite independently of the social situation, and the importance of movement to the achievement of focused vision is characteristic of many species (Milne and Milne, 1962). Rhythmic movement, whether perceived visually, as with a strobe light, or aurally, as with a metronome, is particularly captivating; to whatever extent focusing of attention is necessary in the induction of hypnosis, therefore, these devices may be even more effective than verbal instructions. The relaxing and diversionary effect of rhythmic movement is amply illustrated in the phenomenon of highway hypnosis, and the combination of contrast and rhythm in the absence of much peripheral visual stimulation seems especially powerful when one compares watching the broken white line in an auto's headlights at night to driving along a merely monotonous highway by daylight. In the absence of clear evidence that using such devices improves induction, there is no point in speculating on the possible neurophysiological determinants of hypnosis that they might influence. But it does seem likely that whatever effects they do have on subjects are relatively independent of the interpersonal character of the hypnotic induction situation.

Some formal evidence bearing on the utility of gadgetry may come from the reports of the use of white noise and music for creating dental anesthesia in a machine called the Audioanalgesiac. The control of his own auditory stimulation by the dental patient seems, in a large proportion of cases, to have effectively prevented the perception of pain during dental drilling (Gardner, Licklider, and Weisz, 1960). If so, this suggests that appropriate aural stimulation would similarly benefit the induction of hypnosis by excluding extraneous stimulation from perception. The Audoianalgesiac is not in wide use today, however, more than five years after its appearance, and some dentists of my acquaintance report having attempted its use without much success.

Informal evidence abounds, on the other hand, that extremely close attention, either visually or aurally, to some particular stimulus reduces one's distractibility by other stimuli; and this may have nothing at all to do with any interpersonal aspects of the stimulus being attended to. Almost everyone has had the experience of forgetting about a toothache while deeply engaged in some work or by some sight or sound, and the experience of failing to observe the passing scene while listening closely to some conversation must be nearly universal.

For the most part, there do not seem to be any important disadvantages to the use of sensory-perceptual manipulations in the induction of hypnosis. If nothing is gained by them, neither is anything lost, for they can be administered altogether independently of physical contact and verbal instruction alike. I have heard claims, on the other hand, that the use of stroboscopic devices in particular involves some danger of eliciting epileptiform seizures in occasional subjects, but I have been unable to verify this allegation.

Flexible Uses of Verbal Techniques

Though verbal inductions are the most commonly used, and physical contact and sensory manipulations are generally ancillary to them, the opposite is sometimes true as well. The great flexibility inherent in verbal inductions permits words to serve as facilitators and substitutes for physical and sensory manipulations, capitalizing both on their rhythmic qualities and upon their capacity to provide imagery to the subject. Conventional relaxation instructions, for example, are themselves imaginative devices for eliciting physiological and muscular changes in subject behavior. By the same token, the rhythmic and monotonous qualities of hypnotic patter presumably have the same kind of aural stimulation properties that metronomes, music, or white noise might have, in addition to whatever conceptual responses they evoke. Viewed this way, verbal inductions always do involve both physical and sensory manipulations even though they do not require either physical contact or gadgetry.

In addition to the above, however, and perhaps most important to the use of hypnosis for psychological purposes, is the power that verbal induction alone has to channel the multiple response capacities of the subject into any of the many behaviors that are of interest either therapeutically or scientifically. Though some physiological changes may be inevitable in the achievement of a hypnotic state, it is only through verbal induction techniques that precise changes can be produced. Age regression, trance logic, hypermnesia, and posthypnotic amnesia may all occasionally occur spontaneously, but it is only through the medium of verbal instructions that they can be dependably produced. Whatever else may be true of hypnotic behavior and of hypnotic induction, therefore, and whatever value other mechanisms have for eliciting them, it is the most general case that hypnosis involves *cognitive* changes of behavior, which in turn affect other aspects of behavior. As long as this is true, it goes without saying that verbal processes are the most important ones in the ordinary course of hypnotic induction and of the hypnotic state itself.

Diversionary Techniques

Although verbal induction has been described here as a graduated sequence of instructions and physical contact involving soothing and reassurance, two additonal procedures, one verbal and one physical, contrast markedly with these descriptions. One is called the "verbal confusion" technique, and the other involves a very sudden change in physical contact.

The verbal confusion technique, which is quite difficult to administer, involves an approximation of double-talk in which instructions of a somewhat contradictory kind are given in rapid succession making it impossible for the attentive subject either to quite comprehend or quite acquiesce to any of them. Finally, he simply gives up all attempts and more or less collapses into a hypnotic state. The following material, selected from the *Hypnosis Symposium Manual* (1959), illustrates part of this technique:

Sometimes it is pleasant to sit back and relax. . . As you listen to me and concentrate on what I am saying, there is a spontaneous relaxation which takes place. At times you can be aware of certain things and at other times you may not be aware of them. . . you might be aware of a picture. . . if you look at it. You might be looking at it but if your attention is elsewhere you might not be aware of the picture. You might be aware of it subconsciously even if you are not looking at it. There is something right now you are unaware of until I mention it and then you become very much aware of it. That is of having shoes on your feet. . . You can be aware of time, or unaware of it. You can remember various things about the present or the past or the future when that becomes the past. Day before yesterday, yesterday was tomorrow and that was the future, and then yesterday became today and was the past. And tomorrow will soon be today and then yesterday and yesterday can become today. Or even the day after tomorrow. And you may remember last January first when you wrote 1957 when it really was 1958 (p. 14).

The confusion technique is also described by Erickson (1958) and by Kroger (1963).

In the "physical suddenness" technique the subject sits upright on a full-length couch, hands in his lap, while the hypnotist stands behind him with his hands against the subject's back. The subject leans back, resting his entire weight against the hypnotist's supporting hands. The latter very slowly lowers the subject, speaking softly and soothingly to him about relaxing and gradually going to sleep. When the subject has leaned back about 45 degrees, the hypnotist suddenly removes support, causing him to fall back rapidly until the hypnotist catches his head just before it hits. As he removes support, he yells, "Sleep!" into the subject's ear. Then, as he catches his head and brings it gently to rest, he resumes softly iterating instructions to sleep, etc.[4]

Both of these techniques were developed, it seems, for use particularly with recalcitrant subjects. They differ from most verbal and physical contact induction techniques in that they employ surprise and shock as means for the achievement of relaxation rather than the more gradual and soothing methods generally used. The point seems to be that the recalcitrant subject tends to be preoccupied with extraneous stimuli, including his own thoughts about the induction, and this preoccupation makes it difficult for him to attend properly to the hypnotist. Verbal confusion, startling movement, or sudden sharp commands impress themselves so forcefully upon him that this attention is diverted away from his preoccupation and onto the objectives of the hypnotist. His consciousness is bombarded, so to speak, and thus directed toward the source of the bombardment and away from the niggling thoughts that had occupied his mind. These techniques, therefore, are preliminary devices for producing relaxation, and are likely to be followed with some combination of the more conventional maneuvers suggested above.

Miscellaneous Issues in Technique

The primary mechanisms used to induce hypnosis are ordinarily used in more or less prescribed conjunction with some other technical considerations, including concerns like the timing of different parts of the induction, the use of cues provided by the subject, the use of abbreviated signals for reinduction and posthypnotic suggestion, and the use of multiple induction, or fractionation, for circumventing resistance to induction.

There is no excess of research to complicate a discussion of any of

[4] Personal communication from Leslie LeCron, July 1959.

these problems, but their dimensions can be reasonably sketched as follows:

Timing of Inductions. It is not clear precisely how much time should be permitted for the induction procedure to achieve an optimal hypnotic effect, nor is it clear that the amount of time devoted to this purpose is a factor of genuine significance. Opinions as to the minimum length of time necessary for induction vary from a minute or two to several hours. The question of length is invariably confounded with that of the stability of susceptibility, however, as well as the question of what constitutes termination of induction. It is probably correct to say that most published reports of induction techniques require a formal induction procedure that varies in length from about five to twenty minutes. It is altogether plausible, at the same time, that while an excessively brief induction procedure may interfere with later hypnotic performance, a too lengthy one runs little risk other than that of putting the subject to sleep instead of hypnotizing him.

Standardized Patter. The use of completely standardized induction procedures is quite indispensable for many experimental investigations requiring hypnosis, but has no particular merit for induction in clinical situations. The problem of standardization concerns the generality of the results of hypnotic studies that have used it. Some case can be made to the effect that individual differences among subjects necessitate flexibility in induction procedures to produce optimum effects (Erickson, Haley, and Weakland, 1959). In that case, the failure of some experiments to demonstrate significant differences between hypnotized and waking performance might be attributable to the variability of hypnotic response resulting from failure to vary induction procedures. This is a moot point, however, because there is no way, in any case, to distinguish between the normal fluctuations in hypnotic responses during different sessions and the fluctuations resulting from different methods of induction. What evidence there is, on the other hand, suggests that standardized induction methods yield rather high gains in information at relatively low cost. For one thing, people who respond poorly to a standardized technique do not seem to respond dramatically to free-wheeling techniques either (Ås, Hilgard and Weitzenhoffer, 1963), whereas people who respond well to standard inductions present no problem in the first place. For another, there is a developing body of experimental literature by this time that demonstrates differences between hypnotic and waking performances in situations where both involved completely standard instructions (London and Rosenhan, 1964). Under the circumstances, experiments that fail to show such differences can be explained more parsimoniously in terms of lack of hypnotic effects than of inadequacies in induction methods (Hilgard, 1962, p. 164).

Failure of Hypnotic Suggestions. Conventional hypnotic inductions proceed by a kind of informal Gutman scaling, in which the hypnotist suggests more difficult items only upon successful completion of relatively easier ones by the subject. Analysis of the standardization data of the Stanford Susceptibility Scales (Hilgard *et al.*, 1961) indicates that the gamut of common hypnotic items actually does constitute a Gutman-type scale. This scaling assumes that, in a cluster of items ranked for difficulty, the ability to pass an item at one level implies the ability to pass all items at lower levels of difficulty; and failure of an item at some level implies an inability to pass items at any higher level. Were this completely true of hypnotic inductions, it would be impossible to induce responses to suggestions of greater difficulty once a subject had failed to accept a suggestion at a given level. This is not unequivocally the case, but it is true enough for most hypnotists to be concerned about the consequences of a subject's failure to pass an item. It is possible that perception of his own failure to comply with a hypnotic suggestion will reduce the subject's responsiveness to suggestions still to come. If so, the effect of such frustrations could easily cumulate over several items and spoil the induction, not because of any lack of susceptibility, but by the distracting effect that frustration over failure exerted on the subject.

The effects of failure have not been a topic of special interest in hypnosis research, but they have been in other psychological research, and the combination of common sense and formal inquiry into the decremental performance curves resulting from repeated failure probably makes such research specifically on hypnosis superfluous. In general, the stress produced by repeated experience of failure, particularly in ego-involving tasks, causes further failures. There is every reason to think this would be as true of hypnotic performance as it is of others.

The thrust of the patter most commonly used in inductions therefore deliberately soft-pedals the occurrence of failure on the subject's part by variously justifying it, approving it, denying it, or retrospectively confusing the issue so that the subject cannot be sure he has failed at all. There is enough ambiguity in most hypnotic suggestions, in fact, so that further suggestions can be made, following a failure, without great difficulty. This is true even in standardized tests of hypnotic susceptibility, where *all* items are administered regardless of previous failures (Hilgard, 1961). It is not entirely clear whether assurances of good performance are beneficial, or whether their benefits come from reassuring the subject who failed a suggestion or the hypnotist who made it in the first place, but the soft-pedaling procedure seems to be a reasonable precautionary measure at little cost.

It is in connection with possible failure of the subject to accept suggestions that "democratic" induction techniques work to greatest advantage. By stipulating early in the induction that the subject is *not* expected necessarily to respond to every suggestion that the hypnotist makes or to undergo all of the subjective experiences that can occur during hypnosis, the hypnotist reduces the need for face-saving explanations when the subject later fails some items. The loss of charisma is thus balanced by a gain in rapport.

Use of Signals. Abbreviated verbal and other devices are sometimes used in hypnotic inductions as signals to substitute for lengthier verbal directions. The most common uses of signals are:

1. During the course of a routine induction, where they constitute a kind of verbal graphics for enhancing hypnosis,
2. Shortly after awakening the subject from a hypnotic state, where they serve as proximal stimuli for the performance of posthypnotic suggestions, and
3. For rapid reinduction of hypnosis in the same or later session.

A common signal in routine induction is counting, in which the hypnotist counts slowly perhaps from one to ten, instructing the subject to go more deeply asleep as each number is counted out. Posthypnotic signals, on the other hand, are generally briefer, such as the hypnotist's tapping with his pencil on a desk or lighting a cigarette. Either signaling technique is likely to be used to reinduce hypnosis rapidly, often in the same session for training purposes, but especially in later sessions. It is difficult to judge the utility of signals in many instances, for they are not used much alone but more as devices to arrest the subject's attention and make him receptive to the induction, which usually follows the signal. Once a person has had a favorable hypnotic experience, in other words, a signal may be a useful abbreviated means of stimulating him to the relaxed and receptive frame of mind most suitable for an induction without actually being a complete substitute for the induction. When hypnotherapists induce hypnosis for the *n*th time by means of a brief signal, they ordinarily follow the signal with a brief induction, differing in length rather than quality from the one they used when first hypnotising the subject. The contribution of the signal itself to the development of a hypnotic state is hard to estimate in such cases. As Hilgard says,

> In the first few sessions, a susceptible subject learns to enter the trance much more promptly, but this does not mean that he can reach a greater depth in succeeding sessions (1962, p. 12).

The use of signals for eliciting responses to posthypnotic suggestions, on the other hand, suggests that such cues may indeed be sufficient for the induction of hypnosis, perhaps even of very profound hypnotic states and after very long periods of time. The literature of posthypnotic suggestions is itself somewhat murky, but claims are sometimes made that signals can be effective without rehearsal for very significant behaviors after very long time lapses. Erickson and Erickson (1941) propose, moreover, that posthypnotic suggestions are carried out in the course of spontaneous trances which are induced by posthypnotic signals. If so, then signals are certainly effective induction devices.

Effects of Repeated Inductions. An interesting technique sometimes used to induce hypnosis in refractory subjects is called fractionation. Basically, it consists of a rather rapid sequence of inductions administered in a single session. The hypnotist may begin his induction in fairly standard fashion, but instead of attempting to induce progressively deeper levels of hypnosis, he shortly awakens the subject for a brief time, then, usually by means of signals, quickly rehypnotizes him, awakens, rehypnotizes, and so on. By this means, he seems to make the subject increasingly receptive to the induction procedure, thus gradually inducing a more profound hypnotic state with each episode.

The precise value of the fractionation technique, like almost everything else connected with induction, is uncertain; but clinical hypnotists who are inclined to use it do so particularly for subjects who show some initial resistance to hypnosis (Erickson, 1958). It is not clear why fractionation should work, it if does, but immediate successive immobilizations, possibly an animal equivalent of hypnotic induction by fractionation, seem to exert a similar stuporous effect on chickens (Gilman, Marcuse, and Moore, 1950), perhaps suggesting some physiological commonality.

The apparent success of this method does seem to argue that people's susceptibility to hypnosis increases with repeated experience. This belief is rather common among clinical hypnotists, but the data of studies based on the Stanford Hypnotic Susceptibility Scale do not support this belief. In general, Scale results are so consistent from session to session as to suggest that susceptibility is a very stable personality characteristic extremely resistant to change (see Hilgard, Ch. 13). At least one experiment specifically aimed at increasing susceptibility, moreover, found in moderately susceptible subjects that variations of induction technique or the repetition of inductions tended to have only mildly facilitating effects on hypnotic responsiveness (Ås, Hilgard, and Weitzenhoffer, 1963). The efficacy of hypnotic inductions thus seems to depend more on the susceptibility of the subject than anything else, and it does not seem to "take" with familiarity.

Blum (1961), on the other hand, seems to have equally good evidence, though on a small number of cases, that susceptibility to hypnosis, although a structural personality variable, may be less critical in determining the *limits* of hypnotic responsiveness than the *speed* with which they can be elicited. His own explanation of hypnotic behavior is essentially dynamic (1961, Chapter 12); and he has reported successfully producing profound hypnotic trances in refractory subjects, though after much work, by identifying and taking skillful advantage of idiosyncrasies that disposed them toward greater responsiveness (Blum, 1963). The issue, at this writing, is quite unresolved.

Influence of Induction on Hypnotic Behavior. The effects of repeated inductions in eliciting hypnotic behavior are only relevant, of course, on the assumption that induction has any effect on hypnotic behavior to begin with. There are a number of means for testing this proposition—improvement of performance from base rate to hypnotically induced conditions in terms of speed of response, number of positive responses across items of equal difficulty, or shifts upward in response rates across groups. Ferster, Levitt, Zimmerman, and Brady have even developed an operant conditioning paradigm for testing the effectiveness of hypnotic performances (1961).

It is quite clear, whatever the unit of measurement employed, that induction is not necessary to elicit *all* the behaviors commonly identified with hypnosis; the issue here is whether it has any effect on the elicitation of *any* such behaviors. By and large, it seems that it does, not only on extremely difficult items of hypnotic behavior such as trance logic, but also on things like verbal productivity (Moss and Stachowiak, 1963), tolerance for anxiety–producing situations (Nayyar and Brady, 1962), vividness of reported imagery (Rossi, Sturrock, and Solomon, 1963), and a number of other hypnotic behaviors (Barber and Glass, 1962; Weitzenhoffer and Sjoberg, 1961). Serious problems, both of design and sampling in such investigations, make it necessary to be very cautious in generalizing from the results of any single experiment and sometimes require reversals of opinion about apparently well-established effects (see Sarbin and Anderson, 1963), but it seems clear enough that hypnotic inductions are not generally irrelevant to the elicitation of hypnotic behaviors, just as they are not generally indispensable to them. Some people, indeed, far from being unaffected by them, find it difficult to resist hypnotic suggestions (Hilgard, 1963).

Awakening from Hypnosis. The frequency, intensity, or efficacy of hypnotic inductions seem altogether unrelated to the durability of hypnotic trances. Old wives' tales to the contrary, moreover, subjects are not known to stay in hypnosis indefinitely. On rare occasions, some subjects resist being aroused from the hypnotic state at the demand of the hypnotist, but this has apparently never proved to be an insuperable problem. When it happens, it is usually possible to coax subjects awake. Leslie LeCron reports that, when no other form of persuasion works, the threat or experience of being sprinkled with cold water is invariably effective.[5]

[5] Personal communication, July 1959.

Though people do not stay hypnotized forever and pine away in consequence, they sometimes do pass from hypnosis to sleep, either as a result of inactivity or fatigue. One relaxed state abets another. If the hypnotist stops making suggestions and either absents himself from the room or remains silent, the subject will eventually, usually rather shortly, spontaneously rouse himself, possibly mystified, but certainly whole.

On occasion, subjects report headaches or other sequels on arousal from the hypnotic state, but these are apparently quite rare. Interestingly, such after effects seem to occur more commonly in less susceptible than in more susceptible subjects (Hilgard, Hilgard, and Newman, 1961).

SUMMARY AND CONCLUSIONS

Information Model of Hypnotic Induction

Hypnotic induction has been analyzed in this chapter in terms of an information model, which is reviewed here.

Induction is defined by this model as the entire body of events used for the communication of information from a hypnotist to his subject. The processes he employs all have as their immediate objective an increase in the signal: noise ratio in his communications. Signals consist of all those transmissions that elicit the responses the hypnotist desires from the subject, that is, suggestions; whereas noises are all those transmissions that serve to distract or otherwise inhibit the emission of compliant responses. This model assumes that reducing noise in the signal delivery system improves transmission and that improving transmission in turn augments the effects of the information being signaled.

Reduction of noise takes place both by means of manipulations of the environment incidental to the communications system proper and by manipulations of the subject or receiver in ways that improve his tuning to the desired signal channel. Environmental manipulations include control of peripheral variables like lighting, temperature, soundproofing, and other external sources of distraction. Subject manipulations are effected by means of verbal patter, physical contact between hypnotist and subject, and the use of attention-getting machinery.

Because induction refers to the processes that eventuate in hypnosis, hypnotic behavior is the criterion only for the success of induction, not for its occurrence. The difference between induction and hypnotic state then becomes somewhat difficult to establish, for there seems to be no clear point at which the former terminates and the latter is in effect. In fact, the two conditions seem to differ from each other in only two respects: (1) In induction, the hypnotist's operations emphasize the tuning of the subject to attend to his suggestions; whereas in the hypnotic state, they emphasize the subject's behavior with little or no reference to the hypnotist's. (2) In induction, the subject's perceptions of his own experience undergo gradual shifts in the direction of increasingly narrowed focus on the hypnotist's signals; whereas in the hypnotic state itself there is little further movement in this direction; in hypnosis proper, the subject no longer maintains enough subjective distance from his experience to have any self-conscious perceptions of his perceptions. This suggests that *induction terminates only in the sense that explicit tuning operations are reduced in frequency.* The most important tuning operations are relaxation, focusing of attention, and the tests of suggestions that are administered in increasingly difficult items. The completion of induction is marked by a decrease in the systematic testing of suggestions. Altogether, this argument adds up to the notion that induction is observably distinguishable from hypnosis itself only with respect to the hypnotist's operations, not the subject's reactions, though the latter may have also undergone important changes.

Induction and Susceptibility. The interaction of induction with susceptibility is important but unclear, as nobody has been able to identify any vital correlates of susceptibility except induction. To further complicate the matter, hypnotic susceptibility seems rather clearly to be unrelated to persuasibility, that is, to what social psychologists generally call "suggestibility." The effectiveness of induction procedures, on the other hand, may be related to persuasibility, but there is no way of testing this until susceptibility can be measured reliably by some means other than the actual induction of hypnosis.

Hypnosis and Other Induced Behaviors. A final issue of great importance concerns the relevance of induced hypnosis to other forms of induced behavior. Scientific investigation in this area may have been delayed historically by the fact that hypnosis, till recently, has been of more interest to psychiatric and other clinicians than to social and other psychologists. In recent years, however, research has been directed increasingly toward the relationships of hypnotic and other psychological phenomena that seem to involve similar problems. Orne (1959, 1963) has stimulated extensive research on the relative motivational properties of hypnotic inductions and other instructional conditions. Research relating hypnosis to the psychological effects induced by placebos has recently appeared (Bentler, O'Hara, and Krasner, 1963; Glass and Barber, 1961; Rossi, Sturrock, and Solomon, 1963). And research on hypnotically induced physiological changes is increasingly concerned to relate such changes to the more general problem of the mediation of autonomic responses by voluntary acts (Levitt and Brady, 1961).

In some respects, the relationship of hypnotic induction to other forms of social influence seems like the most fruitful field of inquiry, but it has not been easy thus far to relate these phenomena. Social influence studies are generally concerned with behaviors in which (a) cognitions intervening between stimulus and response are the subjects of inference, such as attitude or conformity studies, (b) social models of behavior are immediately available to influence the subject, such as social learning studies, or (c) there is advance agreement between subjects and experimenters about the voluntary character of the behaviors to be influenced. Cognition, identification, and voluntarism are significant parameters of hypnotic induction as well, but their roles and interactions in the hypnotic situation seem to differ from those in other social situations. However much that is the case, it is necessary that future research determine the relationships between them, for hypnosis cannot be fully understood until it occupies some lawful place in the general science of human behavior.

REFERENCES

Arnold, Magda (1959). "Nature of hypnosis." Presented at 1959 APA meeting, Cincinnati, Ohio.

Ås, A. (1962). "A note on distractibility and hypnosis," *Amer. J. clin. exp. Hyp.*, **5**, 135–137.

——— Hilgard, E. R., and Weitzenhoffer, A. M. (1963). "An attempt at experimental modification of hypnotizability through related individualized experience," *Scand. J. Psychol.*, **4**, 81–89.

Barber, T. X. (1961a). "Antisocial and criminal acts induced by 'hypnosis,'" *Arch. gen. Psychiat.* **5**, 301–312.

——— (1961b), "Physiological effects of hypnosis," *Psychol. Bull.*, **58**, 390–419.

——— (1962a). "Experimental controls and the phenomena of 'hypnosis': A critique of hypnotic research methodology," *J. nerv. ment. Dis.*, **134**, 493–505.

——— (1962b). "Toward a theory of 'hypnotic' behavior: The 'hypnotically induced dream,'" *J. nerv. ment. Dis.* **135**, 206–221.

Barber T. X. and Calverley, D. S. (1962). "Hypnotic behavior as a function of task motivation," *J. Psychol.*, **54**, 363–389.

Barber, T. X., and Deeley, D. C. (1961). "Experimental evidence for a theory of hypnotic behavior: 'Hypnotic color-blindness' without 'hypnosis,'" *Int. J. clin. exp. Hyp.*, **9**, 79–86.

Barber, T. X., and Glass, L. B. (1962). "Significant factors in hypnotic behavior," *J. abnorm. soc. Psychol.*, **64**, 222–228.

Bentler, P. M., and Hilgard, E. R. (1963). "A comparison of group and individual induction of hypnosis with self scoring and observer scoring," *Int. J. clin. exp. Hyp.*, **11**, 49–54.

Bentler, P. M., O'Hara, J. W., and Krasner, L. (1963). "Hypnosis and placebo," *Psychol. Rep.*, **12**, 153–154.

Blum, G. S. (1961). *A Model of the Mind.* New York: Wiley.

——— (1963). "Programming people to simulate machines." In Tomkins, S. S., and Messick, S. (eds.), *Computer Simulation of Personality*. New York: Wiley.

Bookbinder, L. J. (1961). "The application of psychodynamic thinking to hypnotic behavior," *Psychiat. quart.*, **35**, 1–9.

Christenson, J. A., Jr. (1958). "Dynamics in hypnotic induction." In LeCron, L. (ed.), *Experimental Hypnosis*. New York: Macmillan.

Damaser, Esther C., Shor, R. E., and Orne, M. T. (1963). "Physiological effects during hypnotically requested emotions," *Psychosom. Med.*, **25**, 334–343.

Deckert, G. H., and West, L. J. (1963a). "Hypnosis and experimental psychopathology," *Amer. J. clin. Hyp.* **5**, 256–276.

——— (1963b). "The problem of hypnotizability: A review," *Int. J. clin. exp. Hyp.*, **11**, 205–235.

Erickson, M. H. (1958). "Deep hypnosis and its induction." In LeCron, L. (ed.), *Experimental Hypnosis*. New York: Macmillan.

Erickson, M. H., and Erickson, E. M. (1941). "Concerning the nature and character of post-hypnotic behavior," *J. gen. Psychol.*, **24**, 95–133.

Erickson, M. H., Haley, J., and Weakland, J. H. (1959). "A transcript of a trance induction with commentary," *Amer. J. clin. Hyp.*, **2**, 50–84.

Ferster, C. B., Levitt, E. E., Zimmerman, J., and Brady, J. P. (1961). "The measurement of hypnotic effects by operant–reinforcement techniques," *Psychol. Rec.*, **11**, 427–430.

Fisher, S. (1962). "Problems of interpretation and controls in hypnotic research." In Estabrooks, G. H. (ed.), *Hypnosis: Current Problems*. New York: Harper & Row.

Friedlander, J. W., and Sarbin, T. R. (1938). "The depth of hypnosis," *J. abnorm. soc. Psychol.*, **33**, 281–294.

Gardner, W. J., Licklider, J. C. R., and Weisz, A. Z. (1960). "Suppression of pain by sound," *Science*, **132**, 32–33.

Gill, M., and Brenman, Margaret (1961). *Hypnosis and Related States*. New York: International Universities Press.

Gilman, Thelma T., Marcuse, F. L., and Moore, A. U. (1950). "Animal hypnosis: A study in the induction of tonic immobility in chickens," *J. comp. physiol. Psychol.*, **43**, 99–111.

Glass, L. B., and Barber, T. X. (1961). "A note on hypnotic behavior: The definition of the situation and the placebo effect," *J. nerv. ment. Dis.*, **132**, 539–541.

Haley, J. (1958). "An interactional explanation of hypnosis," *Amer. J. clin. Hyp.*, **1**, 41–57.

Haley, J. (1963). *Strategies of Psychotherapy*. New York: Grune & Stratton.

Hilgard, E. R. (1961). "Hypnosis and experimental psychodynamics." In *Lectures on Experimental Psychiatry*. Pittsburgh: University of Pittsburgh Press.

——— (1962). "Lawfulness within hypnotic phenomena." In Estabrooks, G. H. (ed.), *Hypnosis: Current Problems*. New York: Harper & Row.

——— (1963). "Ability to resist suggestions within the hypnotic state: Responsiveness to conflicting communications," *Psychol. Rep.*, **12**, 3–13.

HILGARD, E. R., WEITZENHOFFER, A. M., LANDES, J., and MOORE, ROSEMARIE K. (1961). "The distribution of susceptibility to hypnosis in a student population: A study using the Stanford Hypnotic Susceptibility Scale," *Psychol. Monogr.*, **75**, 1–22.

HILGARD, JOSEPHINE R., and HILGARD, E. R. (1962). "Developmental-interactive aspects of hypnosis: Some illustrative cases," *Genet. Psychol. Monogr.*, **66**, 143–178.

HILGARD, JOSEPHINE R., and NEWMAN, MARTHA (1961). "Sequelae to hypnotic induction with special reference to earlier chemical anesthesia," *J. nerv. ment. Dis.*, **133**, 461–478.

Hypnosis Symposium Manual (1959). Los Angeles: Hypnosis Symposiums.

KROGER, W. S. (1963). *Clinical and Experimental Hypnosis*, Chapters 13 and 14. Philadelphia: Lippincott.

LEVITT, E. E., and BRADY, J. P. (1961). "Psychophysiology of hypnosis." In Schneck, J. M. (ed.), *Hypnosis in Modern Medicine*. Springfield, Ill.: Charles C. Thomas.

LONDON, P. (1963a). *The Children's Hypnotic Susceptibility Scale*. Palo Alto, Calif.: Consulting Psychologists Press.

——— (1963b). "Experiments in hypnosis with children." APA symposium, "The New 'Hard-Nosed' Approach in Hypnosis Research." Philadelphia.

LONDON, P., and ROSENHAN, D. (1964). "Personality dynamics." In Farnsworth, P. (ed.), *Annual Review of Psychology*, **15**, 447–492.

MILNE, I. J., and MILNE, MARGERY (1962). *The Senses of Animals and Men*. New York: Atheneum.

MOORE, ROSEMARIE K. (1964). "Susceptibility to hypnosis and susceptibility to social influence," *J. abnorm. soc. Psychol.*, **68**, 282–294.

MOSS, C. S., and STACHOWIAK, J. G. (1963). "The ability of hypnotic subjects to interpret symbols." *J. proj. Tech.*, **27**, 92–97.

NAYYAR, S. N., and BRADY, J. P. (1962). "Elevation of depressed skull fracture and frontal topectomy under hypnotic anesthesia." *J. Amer. Med. Assn.* **181**, 790–792.

ORNE, M. T. (1959). "The nature of hypnosis: Artifact and essence," *J. abnorm. soc. Psychol.*, **58**, 277–299.

——— (1963). "The nature of the hypnotic phenomenon: Recent empirical studies." APA symposium, "The New 'Hard-Nosed' Approach in Hypnosis Research." Philadelphia.

PAUL, G. (1963). "The production of blisters by hypnotic suggestion: Another look," *Psychosom. Med.* **25**, 233–244.

ROSSI, A. M., STURROCK, J. B., and SOLOMON, P. (1963). "Suggested effects on reported imagery in sensory deprivation," *Percept. mot. Skills*, **16**, 39–45.

RUSSELL, B. (1919). *Mysticism and Logic and Other Essays*. London: Longmans, Green & Co.

SARBIN, T. R. and ANDERSON, M. L. (1963). Base-rate expectancies and perceptual alterations in hypnosis," *Brit. J. soc. clin. Psychol.*, **2**, 112–121.

SHOR, R. E., and ORNE, E. C. (1963). *The Harvard Group Scale of Hypnotic Susceptibility, Form A: An adaptation for group administration with self-report scoring of the Standard Hypnotic Susceptibility Scale, Form A*. Palo Alto, Calif.: Consulting Psychologists Press.

SILVA, E. E., ESTABLE, C., and SEGUNDO, J. P. (1959). "Further observations on animal hypnosis." *Extrait des Archieves Italiennes de Biologie*, **97**, 167–177.

WEITZENHOFFER, A. M. (1953). *Hypnotism: An Objective Study in Suggestibility*. New York: Wiley.

WEITZENHOFFER, A. M., (1957). *General Techniques of Hypnotism*. New York: Grune & Stratton.

WEITZENHOFFER, A. M., and HILGARD, A. M. (1959). *Stanford Hypnotic Susceptibility Scale, Forms A and B*. Palo Alto, Calif.: Consulting Psychologists Press.

WEITZENHOFFER, A. M., and HILGARD, E. R. (1962). *Stanford Hypnotic Susceptibility Scale, Form C*. Palo Alto, Calif.: Consulting Psychologists Press.

WEITZENHOFFER, A. M., and SJOBERG, B. M., Jr. (1961). "Suggestibility without 'induction of hypnosis,'" *J. nerv. ment. Dis.*, **132**, 204–220.

WEST, L. J. (1960). "Psychophysiology of hypnosis," *J. Amer. Med. Assn.*, **172**, 672–675.

II

RESEARCH APPLICATIONS

4

Hypnosis in Psychodynamic Research

GERALD S. BLUM
The University of Michigan

THE most tempting, potentially rewarding, and largely untapped resources of hypnosis lie, in my opinion, in the field of experimental psychodynamics. Hypnotic techniques can become tools for isolating elusive psychological variables and manipulating them with quantitative precision in a laboratory setting. Such an adjunctive application does not focus on properties of hypnosis, personality characteristics of subjects, or clinical paradigms, but instead emphasis is placed upon the possibility of performing better-controlled experiments on a broad range of topics of general interest. Leuba (1941) made this point many years ago in an article on conditioned sensations. It is especially important for the field of psychodynamics, where problems previously considered unsuited for experimentation may be brought under more rigorous scrutiny. The theme of "hypnosis in the service of the laboratory" will be pursued according to the following outline: (1) illustrative procedures drawn from an ongoing research program at the University of Michigan; (2) the experimental design and findings of a recent series of studies, and (3) methodological issues.

HYPNOTIC MANIPULATION OF ANXIETY, SENSORIMOTOR AROUSAL, AND INHIBITION

A theoretical discussion of the concept of anxiety is not relevant here. The writer's attempt at clarification within the framework of a model of the mind has been elaborated elsewhere (Blum, 1961). Briefly, distinctions are drawn between (1) a "cognitive representation" of anxiety control, (2) affective circuits, which lead to (3) effector discharge and, in turn, (4) sensory feedback. Fear is characterized as an anxiety network intimately connected to specific cognitive content circuits and typically triggering motoric responses of flight or avoidance. The particular operations used to induce anxiety are more pertinent for our present purposes. Before describing them, however, a look at a couple of procedures recently employed by other investigators is in order.

Levitt and his co-workers (1960, p. 282) have utilized direct hypnotic suggestion in creating anxiety. Their induction, described as an elaboration of the type used by Levine, Grassi, and Gerson, in 1943, goes as follows:

> I suggest to you that you will begin to feel in a certain way, that you will have certain definite feelings which I am going to suggest to you. You will begin to feel these feelings and emotions so vividly that your whole person, your whole body, every fiber of yourself, will feel that way—at first slightly, then gradually stronger and stronger. These feelings will last until I suggest to you that they are no longer there. The feelings and emotions which you will begin to experience are those of anxiety—feelings of anxiety, more and more intensely, more and more vividly. You will become more and more anxious. At first, there will just be a feeling of apprehension. Then, gradually you are beginning to feel more and more afraid but you do not know what it is that makes you feel so afraid and so anxious. You just feel that way without knowing why. You feel more and more afraid and anxious all the time, as if something dreadful is going to happen to you. Yet, you do not know what this dreadful thing is. I suggest that you will gradually begin to experience a state in which you feel really panicky, where you are so fearful that you feel an almost unbearable dread, fear, and panic. In fact, you are most likely already feeling this way and you will continue to feel this way more and more strongly.

Suggestions, communicated by tape recording, are said to be delivered with increasing vocal intensity and emphasis. The rationale for including several synonyms for anxiety—apprehension, dread, fear, panic—is "to circumvent the effects of different private meanings" of the word among *S*'s [subjects]. After induction all *S*'s reportedly verbalize anxiety feelings and show physical manifestations such as trembling, agitation, and pallor. In one study (Grosz and Levitt, 1959) independent ratings of degree of anxiety by trained judges were moderately high in agreement (tau=.47). Predictable effects of the direct anxiety induction were observed upon a variety of measures, including Rorschach, TAT,

Manifest Anxiety Scale, IPAT Anxiety Scale, Affect Adjective Check List, Barron Ego Strength Scale, pulse rate, and blood pressure (Levitt, 1963).

Branca and Podolnick (1961, p. 166) in an investigation relating normal, hypnotically induced, and feigned anxiety to MMPI scores, used these hypnotic instructions:

> You are beginning to feel very uneasy and anxious. You don't know why, but this uneasy feeling is making you nervous, irritable, and frightened. You feel as if something dreadful is about to happen but you don't know what. This feeling of dread is mingled with a curious feeling of hope that is very unpleasant. You are becoming more and more apprehensive. You are in a state of anxious expectation and self-doubt. You feel now as if you are threatened and it frightens you. You feel as if you are about to lose something important to you, or be hurt. This anxiety is becoming stronger and stronger. Now you feel as if something is wrong, as though you had neglected to do something very important, but you can't recall what it is. You feel, though, that whatever it is, it is making you feel on edge and uneasy. It is making you feel blue, melancholy, unhappy, and excited in an unpleasant way. You feel frightened, but you don't know what it is you are frightened about. This is certainly an unpleasant form of excitement. You are now very apprehensive and anxious.

The lengthy and varied list of attributes—mixed dread and hope, self-doubt, loss, hurt, melancholy, and so on—was assembled from assorted definitions and descriptions of anxiety in the literature.

Reyher (1962) has criticized the direct suggestion approach to psychopathology on several counts: (1) anxiety in "pure" form may be conducive to laboratory research but departs from the clinically observed admixture of anxiety, depression, and hostility; (2) a distinction between fear and anxiety in terms of "external" versus "internal" origin of threat is not maintained; and (3) direct suggestion is phenotypical and not "response-producing in the sense that other processes are set in motion" which lead to behavioral psychopathology. In a reply Levitt (1963) emphasized the scientific virtue of inducing anxiety in "pure" form and reiterated the widespread effects of the hypnotic manipulation.

Our own hypnotic work with anxiety, begun in 1958, has been carried out in a laboratory setting with college students as *S*'s. Clinical observation, introspective report, and physiological recording have been used in combination to validate the induction procedure, which sought to invoke anxiety "naturally" from *S*'s past rather than directly or artificially. After having told stories to the eleven Blacky pictures (Blum, 1950) while awake, *S* was asked under hypnosis to recount personal experiences of his own suggested by each of the pictures. During subsequent hypnotic training he was required to relive the most anxiety-provoking episode, which then served as a referent for the feeling of anxiety as it was to be experienced later in the experimental sessions.

This first series of studies, typically performed in the waking state with *S* amnesic for the posthypnotically suggested reactions, investigated the following topics: extraneous perceptual interference from the presence of anxiety-laden stimuli; inhibition of anxiety; reduction of anxiety by simultaneous competing affects; anxiety discharge to similar stimuli differing in vividness; anxiety-mediated generalization; and effects upon serial position in recall (Blum, 1961).

A rather fortuitous observation in the course of these experiments opened a virtually new realm of opportunity for hypnotic control of significant variables. One *S* happened to be reacting so strongly to the anxiety-laden stimulus that rapid successive range changes of the GSR (galvanic skin response) recording pen made the response difficult to score. On an impulse we asked him to react moderately instead, whereupon the pen settled down to more reasonable deflections. The idea that it might be possible to control an individual's anxiety and other reactions *by degrees*, thereby making available *intra-individual* comparisons, led to the revised anxiety induction procedure detailed below.

Hypnotic training must satisfy several requirements for our experimental purposes. *S* must be "programmed" to respond automatically while awake (without conscious awareness) to cues triggering differential degrees of "natural" anxiety. The reaction must occur immediately upon presentation of the cue and endure until the cue is removed. In other words, it must be capable of being turned on and off as desired by *E* [experimenter]. The degrees of reaction should be systematically reliable for each *S* and their repetition stable over a period of weeks or even months, depending on the length of time *S*'s services are needed in the laboratory. Moreover, the affective intensity must be corroborated independently by concomitant physiological measurement in addition to *E*'s observation and *S*'s own report. The anxiety should *not* be mixed with other negative emotions, especially since we had discovered earlier in a perceptual interference study that sadness did not produce the same experimental effect as anxiety (as noted above, fear is viewed as one type of anxiety, involving the same mental mechanisms, and therefore is appropriate for anxiety training). It should be capable of attachment to any kind of stimulus, in accord with *E*'s designs. Lastly, ethical considerations dictate that the experimental manipulation of anxiety not be allowed to assume traumatic proportions.

Keeping these requirements in mind, we can now turn to the actual procedures used to control anxiety reactions in a 19-year-old male college student, one of six paid *S*'s who received the same treatment. The following verbatim account, excerpted from five two-hour sessions over a two-week period, includes all the material relevant to anxiety training.

Anxiety Training (Subject Z)

June 25. (*S* in waking state tells following story to Blacky Cartoon VIII, which shows Blacky watching Mama and Papa pet Tippy.) He realizes he's pretty lucky to have such a loving family and that he should be more appreciative of them than he is. He realizes that his parents love him and that when they scold him or anything, it is all for his good. Even though Tippy is sometimes bothersome and he would like to get him sometimes, Tippy's still all right. (Anything else?) Right now he's a little resentful because Tippy is getting all the attention and he's not.

June 27. (*S* narrates under hypnosis the following personal experience suggested by Blacky Cartoon VIII.) We all had our pictures taken. (Tell me about it.) We all sat there and Dad tried to get us all to smile. It was hard to smile sometimes, hard to smile. (How old were you?) I was about five. (How did you feel?) I just didn't feel like smiling. (How many times did you get your picture taken?) A couple of times. A man came and went with Mom, my sister and me. I didn't want mine taken. (Why?) I was afraid of the stranger. Mom is on a stool holding my little sister and I am supposed to stand beside her, to put my hand on her knee. I am afraid and want to crawl behind her. I am three years old. (How does it look?) The lights are all shining. I am afraid of what will happen so I try to crawl behind Mommy. (What are you afraid of?) Just lights, the camera, the curtain behind us. (What is the man like?) He's bald and strange and I want to go away. (What does he want?) He wants me to stand up by my Mommy and smile and I try to crawl behind her. (What does your Mother do?) She doesn't let me. She makes me stand there. (How do you feel?) I want to go home, go home and get away. I want Mommy to take me home. (Can you see the man?) Yes, the man's behind the camera. I want to get away with Mommy. (*E* instructs *S* to relive the experience.) I am afraid, I want to go home. I want to go home. (What are you doing?) Just standing there because Mommy tells me to. I want to get out. (How long are you there?) For several pictures and then we leave. (*E* noted that *S* lapsed into baby talk, whimpered and writhed considerably on the couch during the account.)

July 3. (First anxiety training session under hypnosis. *E* speaking. Numbers in parentheses refer to GSR ranges—drops in resistance indicate anxiety; numbers increase with more relaxation. A drop of one range equals 10,000 ohms of resistance.) Now we are going to go back to that scene again at the photographer's and you are going to relive the experience. You are going to feel exactly the same as you did, exactly the same emotions just as strongly as you did then when you were three years old. We know that children feel things very strongly, don't they? Even stronger than adults do . . . (10) We are back in the room with your little sister, your mother and you, isn't that right? The photographer, the bald strange man, you see him now. (9–10) ("He is not so tall . . .") He is not so tall, he's bald and he's a stranger and you are wondering about him, aren't you? ("Uh-huh.") And he keeps trying to get you to stand there and smile, isn't that right? And you keep wanting to crawl behind your mother and hide and you want to go home and she wants you to stand there and smile too, doesn't she? So she pushes you back and wants you to stand next to her, isn't that right? All right, now we have the stage set, you are back now and you are three years old. Back in that situation feeling just the same way you did then as you are more and more upset. You don't want to stand there and you are being frightened by that bald stranger. (11) The lights are bright now and you are getting more and more frightened. You don't want to have your picture taken. (10) You want to go home but you can't go home. (9) You want to go home, but you can't go home. (9–8) ("I want to get behind Mommy.") (7) But she won't let you, she won't let you, (6) she won't let you. Now relax, it's all over now, it's all over now, you are relaxed again. (6–7–6)

The experience is over now. (7) The emotion you just experienced, being so frightened, we are going to call anxiety. That's probably a good label for that kind of experience, isn't it? (8) Now you know what the feeling of anxiety is like. You experienced it very strongly, didn't you? That was good. You did that very well. Now I want you to relax. The feeling of anxiety is gone now. You are relaxing, more and more comfortable now, but you know very well what that feeling is, don't you? And you can reproduce that feeling whenever you are told to now (9) because you know exactly what it is like. It is that same feeling you had when you were so frightened at the photographer's. And you wanted to get behind your mother and you couldn't do it. (10) You are relaxing more and more now, feeling very good now, (9–10) more and more deeply asleep, and listen very carefully to what I am going to say next. And while you listen you're going to sleep more and more deeply. (11) You are going to be completely relaxed while you are listening to what I am going to tell you. Now that you have learned what the experience of anxiety is like, we are going to give you some practice in experiencing different *degrees* of anxiety. The way we are going to do this is to change the brightness of the lights in the room. Even though your eyes are closed, you are aware of every little change of brightness in the room and you know that the change of brightness of the lights overhead is controlled by the switch on the wall, so that when the switch is turned up, the lights get brighter. And the way we are going to do it is first to have the room completely dark and when the room is dark you're completely relaxed, comfortable and contented and feeling fine. And then as the lights begin to be turned up, you will begin to feel more and more upset and anxious, more and more upset and anxious as the lights get brighter and brighter. You are relaxed now while you are listening to me. I am describing what is going to happen later when the lights go up. As the lights get brighter and brighter the feeling of anxiety will get stronger and stronger until it reaches its height, the very top when the room is at its brightest. You will be extremely, extremely anxious and upset and as soon as the lights are turned down again you will relax completely. You'll be relaxed completely. You will feel good. Do you understand? O.K., fine, continue to relax, sleep deeply and I am going to turn the lights down. I am going to leave them down and you will continue to be relaxed for a while and you won't anticipate what's going to happen, you won't think about it ahead of time, you will just let it happen when the time comes, is that clear? Good. (12) Now the lights are going down and you will be more and more relaxed and comfortable. (Lights turned down—12–11–10–9) Relax again, you began to think about it a little then, didn't you? Don't think about anything until the time comes, just relax, relax and sleep more and more deeply. It is very nice and comfortable here in the dark and you are completely relaxed. I am not going to say anything now for one minute. During this time it will stay dark and you will relax more and more. (One minute of silence—fluctuations between 8 and 9) More and more deeply asleep now. There is no reason to be afraid now, is there? You are completely relaxed. (10) That's good, relax more and more, and again get back that comfortable feeling of being deep, deep asleep. (11) Now the lights are going to go up. (Lights gradually turned up over 25 second period—11–10–9–8–7–6–5–4) (Lights turned down quickly) (5) Completely relaxed now. The lights are gone, completely relaxed again. Continue to sleep more and more deeply and relax again and tell me exactly how you felt the moment when the lights were going up. ("They were like the photographer's lights, shining at me.") (6) And how did you feel? ("I wanted to get away from them.") You wanted to get away from them? ("Yes.") And then what happened? ("They finally went down, they stopped.") And then you felt better? ("Yes.") Did your feelings change as the lights changed? ("They kept getting brighter and shinier and I wanted to get away from them.") (7) Did the feeling of anxiety get stronger or not when they got brighter? ("I was trying to get away from the lights.") Yes, you wanted to get away from the lights and you couldn't, could you? And now it is over and you are completely relaxed, aren't you? You are completely relaxed, more and more deeply asleep again, and we are through practicing with the lights for today. (8) Now I am just going to turn them back on in the room so we can see again, but this is not a signal for you to be upset. I am going to turn the lights back on and you are going to continue to be relaxed, more and more relaxed. (Fluctuating between 8 and 7) More and more relaxed. (8) That's good, now we know how easy it is to experience emotions while you are asleep and you will find that you can even experience them in exactly the same way when you wake up.

July 5. (Second anxiety training session under hypnosis.) . . . deeper and deeper asleep all the while we are talking, more and more relaxed. (14) You remember the other day you practiced feeling different kinds of emotions. You learned to feel them in all different degrees, do you remember that? There was that feeling of joy when you felt so very good, (13) and then there was also the feeling of anxiety which was connected to turning up the lights. You remember that very well too, don't you? Remember how when the room was dark you felt completely relaxed, contented, and comfortable and then as the lights got brighter you felt more and more upset and anxious (14) until it got so very, very strong when the room was at its brightest. As soon as the lights were turned down, you felt relaxed again, didn't you? All right, just relax, don't think of a thing. Now I am going to turn the lights down again and you will feel completely comfortable. You won't anticipate what is going to happen, you will let happen whatever happens and after a while the room will be dark for quite a while. Relax and after a while I'll start to turn the lights up and even though your eyes are closed you are very sensitive to any change in illumination. As the room gets brighter the feeling of anxiety will mount and get stronger and stronger as the lights go up, isn't that right? All right now I'm going to turn the lights down for quite a while (13) and you will just relax and be completely comfortable. (Lights turned down—13–12) I'm not going to say anything and we are going to leave the lights down and you are just going to relax more and more and feel more and more comfortable. (During one minute of silence—12–13–14). All right here come the lights now. (14–13–12–11–10–9–8—over a period of 17 seconds) (Lights down—9) Completely relaxed again, completely relaxed, relaxed and comfortable, (10) relaxed and comfortable. Now, while you continue to be relaxed and comfortable, (11) sleep more and more deeply. I want you to tell me what happened before, how you felt when the room was dark and what happened as the lights were being turned up. ("The room was dark, that felt nice and good.") And then what happened? ("I wanted it to be dark again.") (11) How did you feel? (10) ("I wanted them to go away.") Why did you want the lights to go away? ("They bothered me and I didn't want to be in the light.") Why did they bother you? ("I didn't want to be in the light.") Just like the feeling you had at the photographer's? ("Yes.")

Just relax and sleep more and more deeply (11) and the lights are going to stay down while we talk some more, so just relax now. That's good, just relax. (12) Those lights on the ceiling are controlled by that switch on the wall, aren't they? (13) That dimmer switch is a rheostat which makes the lights brighter and dimmer. (12) ("I worked it already.") Did you notice that there are markings on that dial when you worked it? ("From 0 to 100.") From 0 to 100, that's right. When did you work it? (11) ("When I was ready to leave the other day, I asked Miss —— if I could do it and she said O.K.") Was that fun? ("Yes.") (12) Now let me tell you more about that dial. It goes from 0 to 100, you know that now. The lights are at 0 when it is dark and when they're at their very brightest, it's at 100. So 0 stands for being completely relaxed and comfortable the way you are now, completely relaxed. (13) That's what 0 means and the 100 at the other end of the dial means that strong feeling of anxiety when it reaches its peak. That's what the 100 means. ("Yes.") That's right, now let me tell you about two other numbers on the dial: one number is 40 and the 40 is really 40% up the dial, isn't it? So that means you are already feeling *some anxiety* when the light reaches 40. So it's more than the 0 because it is 40% of the way up the dial. Then the next place on the dial I want to tell you about is 70; 70 is even farther up the dial. It's 70% of the way up, so for 70 the anxiety is *fairly strong*. It is fairly strong at 70 and when it gets to 100 it is *very, very* strong, so that is what the numbers mean. At 0 you are relaxed and contented. At 100 it is very, very strong. Do you understand? ("Yes.") All right, in a little while we are going to practice those numbers. Instead of turning the lights up gradually from 0 to 100 we are going to go to different points on the dial and I'll tell you what the number is that I am going to turn the lights to and you will feel the appropriate degree of anxiety depending on what the number is, is that clear? And in between each number I will turn the lights down again and you will relax again and feel completely comfortable. It is a nice feeling to be so relaxed, isn't it? All right, I want you to turn your head a little bit so that your eyes are facing forward and you will be able to see the light. (*S* still had face turned away from light as a consequence of previous trial.) That's it, relax now, we are at 0 now (still 13) and you are comfortable and contented. Now I am going to turn it up to 40. (Lights left at 40 for 15 seconds—12) Now the lights are down, relaxed and comfortable. That was the 40 and you felt some anxiety at the 40. 40 isn't really strong, it's just some anxiety. Relax now (13) completely, relaxed and comfortable when the lights are down. Now here is the 70. (Lights left at 70 for 8 seconds—13–12–11–10–9) Relaxed and comfortable again, the lights are down. That was the 70 and at 70 the anxiety was fairly strong. (10) Relaxed again, completely comfortable now as the lights stay down for a while. (11–12) Continue to keep your face straight. Don't turn your head to the side, just relax, (45 seconds pass, still in the dark) relaxed and comfortable. The lights are staying down. (13) Here is the 100. (Lights left at 100 for 8 seconds—13–12–11–10–9–8) (*S* writhing, moaning, and turning away from lights) Completely relaxed again, (9) you can turn back, the lights are going to stay turned down. The feeling comes very quickly but it also disappears very quickly, doesn't it? That's right. How are you feeling now? (10) ("Comfortable.") Turn back your head again. There is no need to turn away. Completely relaxed and comfortable. We are not going to do anything more with anxiety this morning. You have done everything very well, very well. You are doing a fine job. ("I don't like it.") You don't like it? I know you don't like it. It was very unpleasant there for a brief moment. But even though you don't like it, you know that you are really accomplishing something, aren't you? And that gives you a feeling of accomplishment that feels good, doesn't it? ("Yes.")

July 10 (A.M.) (Third anxiety training session under hypnosis)... Continue to relax as you listen to what I am going to say. Remember last week when we were doing the anxiety practice? You were doing very well at that, weren't you? Now we are going to take up where we left off. You remember that when the room is dark and we are at 0 you are completely relaxed and comfortable. Then we turn the lights up to 40. At 40 you feel some anxiety. When we go up to 70 the anxiety is fairly strong, and when we go up to 100 the anxiety is very, very strong. Now we are going to try that again and you won't anticipate what is going to happen next. (13–12) Don't think about what is going to happen. Just respond to whatever signal is being given to you. Now you are completely relaxed and comfortable and the room is dark. Just relax now, the room is dark and it is going to stay dark for a while now. (11) Relax more and more, not thinking of a thing, just relaxing. (10) Completely relaxed when the lights are down like this. This is 0; at 0 you are relaxed and comfortable. As soon as the 0 appears, you relax immediately. (During one minute silence—10–11–12) Forty. (Lights left at 40 for 10 seconds—11–10–9–8) How did you feel on that 40? ("I didn't like it.") But you reacted pretty strongly, didn't you? Now listen carefully. For the 40 you feel some anxiety but it is not as strong as what you just felt. You were sort of jumping the gun there. 40 isn't that strong. Let's try again and it won't be as strong as it was before. Here is 40 again. (Lights up—GSR drops a third of a range.) How did that compare with the time before? ("It wasn't as bad, but I still didn't like it.") You felt some anxiety. All right, that was better. That was a good 40. The second time was not as strong as it was before. We know that you don't like it because this is experiencing anxiety and nobody likes it, but it is something that you are learning to do for the purpose of the experiment and you are learning it very well. And that part pleases you, doesn't it? All right, completely relax now. This is 0. (9) Just relax and you never think about what's coming next. There is no way of knowing what is coming next and, even if there were, you don't think about it. You just respond immediately when you are supposed to and you relax again immediately when you are supposed to relax. (35 seconds of silence) All right, here is the 70. (Lights left at 70 for 12 seconds—9–8–7–6) (Lights down—7, one minute of silence) More and more relaxed now. This is the 0 point, (8) comfortable and relaxed, we are going to stay at 0 for a while now. (9) (50 seconds silence, then 10) (Another 50 seconds of silence, then 11) (40 seconds silence, then 12) Here's 100. (Lights left at 100 for 16 seconds—12–11–10–9–8–7–6–5) (Lights down—6) (36 seconds silence, then 7) (20 seconds silence, then 8) More and more relaxed now and while I talk you will continue to relax more and more, listening carefully to what I am going to say. You have gotten very good reactions to the 0, 40, 70, 100. Just relax now while I talk about this. No need to feel upset while I'm talking about it. (7) Turn your head back now, turn your head back now, relax, that's it, that's it. Now that you learned what 0, 40, 70 and 100 mean there is *no need to use the lights any more* now. The *numbers* have taken over all the significance that the numbers and the lights had together before. (6) Now the numbers are what is important. We don't need the lights. In fact, I'm going to turn the lights up in the room again and it doesn't mean anything because now the numbers have all the meaning for you. Here go the lights. That didn't bother you, did it? Just relax now. Are you relaxed? ("I don't like the lights.") You don't like the lights? I have just explained to you that the lights have no meaning anymore. The lights have no meaning anymore. The lights don't affect you now because the numbers are the important things. The numbers are what is important and the lights don't affect you at all now. Just relax. Does that feel better now? (7) Just keep relaxed now. The lights have lost their meaning. They're just on in the room so we can see now but the numbers are all important. Relax and listen carefully while I tell you about the numbers. You already know the level of anxiety that each number corresponds to. (6) Just relax now, there is no need to feel upset while I talk about it. The 0 means relaxed and comfortable, 40 means some anxiety, the 70 fairly strong anxiety and the 100 very, very strong anxiety. (7) You have learned all these things and now when you are in this room, *and this applies only when you are in this room*, if you see or hear the numbers 0, 40, 70, 100 they will immediately have the appropriate effect on you until sometime in the future when we tell you that this is no longer the case. But it is only in this room that 0, 40, 70, and 100 have their effect. Not outside of this room, but in this room. It doesn't matter whether you are awake or asleep, whether you see the number or hear it spoken to you, you will always experience the correct level of anxiety for the numbers. (8) Good, is your head comfortable way over there? ("Yes.") All right, just continue to relax now. Zero. The fact that I say something doesn't bother you at all, it just depends what I say. So that when I say 0 it just helps you to relax. (Next a series of trials with the numbers alone was given. The following GSR data were obtained.)

0 (7–8)
40 (8–7)
0 (7–8)
100 (8–7–6–5–4)
0 (4–5–6–7–8)
40 (8–7)
0 (7–8)
70 (8–7–6)
0 (6–7–8)
40 (8–7)
0 (7–6–7)
40 (7–6)
0 (6–7–8)

All right, now we are through with the anxiety practice for today. Continue to relax, sleep more and more deeply. Remember what you learned today. The lights don't have any effect on you any more. I'll even turn them up and down now and you won't have any reaction. I'll turn them up now and you will continue to relax and sleep more and more deeply. The lights have no meaning now, no meaning now. (Lights turned up and down rapidly—GSR fluctuates in one range) Just relax, the lights have no meaning anymore. The meaning of the lights has disappeared. Do you have any reaction at all when I turn the lights up? ("No.") Keep on relaxing while the lights go up and down. (GSR more steady) Relax all the time now, completely relaxed. The lights don't mean a thing. You don't pay any attention to them. They don't mean a thing. Just relax more and more. All right, the meaning of the lights has disappeared now and it is the numbers that have all the significance. And they will have their effect *whether you are awake or asleep, whether you see them or hear them.* Whenever you are in this room, until some time in the future when we tell you that it is no longer the case. Do you understand? You have done very well again today.

July 10 (P.M.) (Practice session.) *S* awake, sitting, and amnesic for prior hypnotic training. Cards with numbers are placed before him and taken away in turn. He is instructed simply to look at each one as it is presented. The following GSR data were obtained:

40 (8–7)
0 (7–8–9)
70 (9–8–7)
0 (7–8–9)
100 (9–8–7–6)
0 (6–7–8–9)
70 (9–8–7)
0 (7–8–9)
100 (9–8–7–6)
0 (7–8–9)

Several comments should be made to amplify the above training procedure. The Blacky stories were obtained during *S*'s first session following administration of the Stanford Hypnotic Susceptibility Scale (Weitzenhoffer and Hilgard, 1959). Two days later, on June 27, he was given waking practice in observing stimuli flashed in a tachistoscope and also hypnotic practice in deepening the trance, speaking while "asleep," and carrying out posthypnotic amnesia instructions. Prior to the personal experiences suggested by the Blacky pictures, work was done on shortening the hypnotic induction and telling *S* that he would respond equally well to instructions from any of the five experimenters who would appear at various times. The personal experience selected for this particular *S* was chosen for its anxiety aspects and not because of the coincidental concern over lights shining at him. The same "lights getting brighter" method was employed with all six *S*'s regardless of the content of their anecdotes. Before the anxiety training begun on July 3, *S* had additional practice on two separate days, mainly dealing with the artificial attachment of thoughts to nonsense syllables in preparation for one of the later experiments.

The "shaping" technique utilized in the next three sessions (July 3, 5, 10, A.M.) was designed to bring *S* step-by-step from the starting place of having experienced strong anxiety in the second reliving episode all the way to reacting automatically, in the waking state, with different degrees of anxiety to presentation of the numbers 0, 40, 70, and 100 (tested on July 10, P.M.). The success of the manipulations was obvious from the first, the GSR having registered a huge drop of five ranges (50,000 ohms) during the reliving. Subsequently there were even larger drops (in a couple of instances an almost unbelievable 70,000 ohms) within much shorter time periods (8 to 16 seconds) after presentation of the 100 stimulus. It is important to recognize, as an aside, that the GSR was also invaluable in guiding *E*'s conduct of the training. Besides indicating depth of trance in a highly reliable manner, it served to pinpoint moments when *S* failed to comply with the relaxation instruction and enabled *E* to deal with the problem on the spot. In fact, what must have seemed to *S* an uncanny quality of *E*'s insight into his state of mind probably was a real boon to the facilitation of hypnotic compliance.

S's reactions—reported, observed, and verified by the GSR—left no doubt of the potency of the anxiety induction. Rather the problem was to cushion the impact so that he would not be traumatized. This was accomplished in a number of ways. He was treated in a friendly, sympathetic manner at all times and received considerable praise and encouragement for responding appropriately to the anxiety stimuli. The onus somehow seemed to be displaced onto the "experiments" rather than directed personally toward the experimenters. Each anxiety trial was fairly short. Between trials *S* was made to be "relaxed, comfortable, and contented." Practice in feeling pleasure was occasionally interspersed with anxiety to relieve the pressure. Many other nonanxiety manipulations were carried out during training and experiments so that the concentration was not unduly heavy. Moreover the setting was structured in a highly circumscribed fashion, confining *S*'s number reactions to the laboratory room where it was relatively easy to remove them later in a "debriefing" session at the conclusion of the experiments.[1] Probably the best evidence that the ordeal was not too great came from the fact that *S*'s volunteered to participate again in future studies.

The discussion thus far has dealt with the training sessions and their seeming effectiveness. What about *S*'s subsequent anxiety reactions to repeated presentations of the cues throughout a series of experimental sessions lasting more than a month? Was he able to maintain differentiated responses to the numbers? The answer is strikingly affirmative. A large batch of GSR samples coinciding with the cue presentations in three diverse experimental tasks (rote memory, perceptual recognition, and anagram solution) was rated blindly by each of five judges according to the four intensity categories. For all *S*'s interjudge agreement was high—all five judges agreeing exactly on a category in more than 50 per cent of the cases and four out of five agreeing in an additional 25 per cent. The median rating for each GSR sample was then correlated with the value of the cue actually present at the time. Separate product–moment correlations were computed for every *S* in each of the three tasks. For the *S* whose training has been described these *r*'s between GSR and cue were .93, .94, and .97. The overall median correlation for the group was .79; the lowest single *r* was .49; and 7 of the 18 *r*'s exceeded .90.

The second variable on which *S*'s were trained hypnotically was sensorimotor arousal. The number of practice sessions for this procedure varied from three to six per individual, the same range as for anxiety. *S*'s learned to respond, while awake and amnesic for the hypnotic instructions, to cues representing degrees of arousal from the "deepest point of relaxation" at one end to a "fever pitch" at the other. Training for two levels of underarousal was easily accomplished by reference to the depth of hypnotic trance, identifiable by GSR in addition to introspective report. *S* was given practice in recognizing his deepest stage of hypnosis so that he could reproduce it automatically in response to a posthypnotic cue (a —A printed faintly on a card). For another cue (a darker —A) he was taught to respond at a midpoint of underarousal, as though "half asleep and half awake." The baseline or normal arousal state was described as "normally awake." The other end of the dimension, overarousal, contained three points designated as follows:

[1] The specific, circumscribed setting also made it easy to reintegrate the reactions after long time intervals. This particular *S*, for example, was brought back into the laboratory room almost one year after having finished the experiments. He was able to enter a deep trance as quickly as before in response to the simple instruction "Deep asleep!" He was then reminded briefly of the significance of the cues and a few minutes later, while awake and amnesic, gave no GSR drop to the 0, dropped 3 ranges for the 40, 4 ranges for the 70, and 5 ranges for the 100!

(Thin A)	Not relaxed, but instead wide awake, alert, and ready to react.
(Thicker A)	Very excited, animated, all stirred up, senses highly sharpened.
(Thickest A)	Whole body alerted, extremely stimulated and aroused to a fever pitch, electrified, carried away, more than flesh and blood can bear.

Efforts were directed toward separating the sensorimotor overarousal from anxiety, which of course is itself a form of arousal. *S*'s were told specifically that they would not feel upset during overarousal and that their reponses would involve primarily "muscles and senses." For this distinction it was necessary to rely upon *S*'s report and *E*'s observation, since the GSR reacts similarly to both types of arousal. The physiological measure intended to check the degree of sensorimotor overarousal was electromyographic (EMG) recording from the frontalis muscle of the forehead. The same rating procedure was employed as in the case of anxiety—median judges' rating for each EMG sample compared with the corresponding overarousal cue. Product moment correlations between EMG reaction and presented cue yielded a median r of .60 for the six *S*'s in the three experimental tasks.[2]

The third independent variable developed under hypnosis for subsequent experimental use was suggested inhibition. The same six *S*'s were trained to experience degrees of difficulty in perceiving, recalling, verbalizing, and solving problems. "Some difficulty" was cued in the waking state by a patch of light gray; "extreme difficulty" by a dark gray patch; and "total inability" by a black patch. During the hypnotic training, care is taken to ensure that neither anxiety nor sensorimotor overarousal accompanies execution of the blocking directions. Again amnesia is invoked for all the hypnotic instructions.[3] Effectiveness of

[2] Because simultaneous GSR recordings were available for the overarousal cues, correlations between them were also computed. The GSR reflected overarousal about as well as the EMG did. Among individual pairs of correlations slightly more than half favored the EMG but the overall GSR median was higher (.73 versus .60). Comparison of the two physiological measures when both were available for the anxiety cues yielded very different results. All but one of the individual pairs favored the GSR and the median EMG correlation was much lower (.35 versus .79). Intercorrelations between GSR and EMG across both conditions averaged .50.

Of course, the fact that GSR responses occur both to anxiety and sensorimotor overarousal makes it impossible to differentiate the two kinds of cues solely on that basis. Fortunately, observation and introspection are not the only evidence we can fall back on to establish that the reactions were indeed different. The experimental results presented in Section II reveal markedly divergent task effects of anxiety and overarousal despite their common GSR accompaniments.

[3] It should be stressed that such amnesia instructions do not "erase" content from memory. *S* simply is unable to recall consciously that he was previously directed to behave in certain specified ways. For a fuller discussion of posthypnotic amnesia, see Blum (1961, pp. 161–165).

the "programming" was determined directly from performance on a series of experimental tasks. The problem of ruling out simulation on the part of *S*'s will be taken up in a later section dealing with methodological issues. Next we shall turn to a series of illustrative studies in which the foregoing manipulations were applied.

EFFECTS OF ANXIETY, SENSORIMOTOR AROUSAL, AND INHIBITION

Benyamini attempted first to discover lawful relationships within degrees of anxiety, sensorimotor arousal, and inhibition, and second, to compare inhibitory effects in the three conditions. Four tasks were selected to tap perception, problem-solving, rote memory, and verbalization.

For the perception study *S* was asked to identify the positions (left, right, top, bottom) and colors (black, red) of miniature playing cards presented tachistoscopically three at once. In preliminary training the fastest exposure still allowing 100 per cent accuracy of recognition was established for each *S* and the same speed subsequently maintained throughout the test trials. Practice was also given with the suggested degrees of blocking. The experimental conditions were induced by placing appropriate cues (numbers, *A*'s, or patches) in the adapting field of the tachistoscope. For example, prior to the flash of a stimulus pattern, *S* viewed an anxiety cue until he reacted at the indicated level (the experimenter being kept informed by earphone of the actual magnitude of *S*'s GSR reactions by the machine operators outside the laboratory room). *E* then directed *S*'s attention immediately to a dot in the center of the adapting field, whereupon the three playing cards were flashed. *S*'s report of what he saw was made with his eyes closed, during which period the cue was changed for the next trial. Thirty-two exposures each were presented for anxiety, overarousal, and suggested inhibition, so that in essence a counterbalanced design could be executed.

The problem-solving task, utilizing the same sets of cues, consisted of anagram solutions. *S* was given either four, five, or six letters at a time. Told to work as quickly as possible, he had to begin each trial with a two-letter word, add another letter to those two to make a three-letter word, and so on until all the letters were used up. Time limits were 45, 90, and 135 seconds for four-, five-, and six-letter-anagrams respectively.

A third situation included both rote memory and verbalization tasks. Here *S* was trained under hypnosis to associate six different nonsense syllables with the same four-digit number. The procedure was as follows. With the number always in full view, one syllable at a time was presented to the rhythm of a metronome (set at 60 beats per minute). Next, with only the number present, *S* was required to think silently of each syllable at the rate of one letter per beat and one syllable per measure. If on any beat nothing came to mind, he was instructed to shake his head and continue. On a second round of metronome measures, he reported the letters out loud. The training criterion for a list was two consecutively perfect thinking and reporting trials under hypnosis followed by another in the waking state. In the experiment itself, cue cards were placed alongside the stimulus number, the metronome started ticking when reactions to the cues were deemed appropriate, and *S* automatically and inexorably "beat out" his responses without conscious awareness of why he was doing so.

Figure 1 summarizes graphically the results for each task, the curves depicting the mean performance for six *S*'s at the three intensity levels

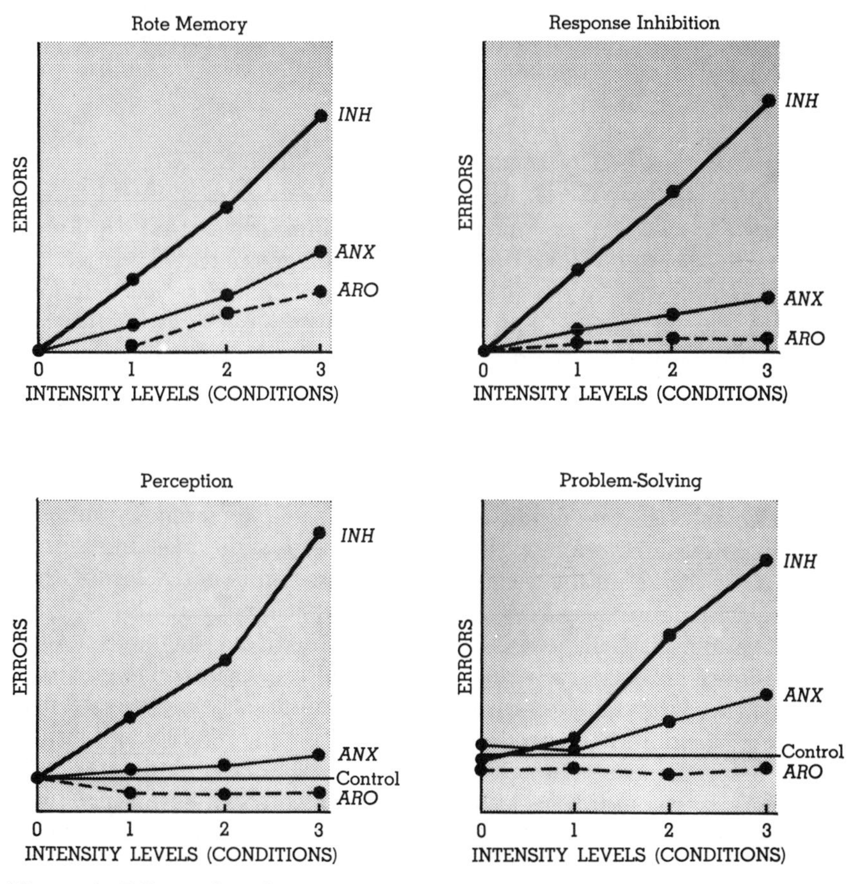

Figure 1. Effects of anxiety, sensorimotor arousal, and suggested inhibition upon performance in four tasks.

of each of the conditions: anxiety, sensorimotor arousal, and inhibition. The posthypnotically suggested inhibition curves reveal a strikingly monotonic effect in each task—number of errors increasing with intensity levels—and thereby point to the efficacy and precision of *S*'s prior hypnotic programming. Anxiety too shows a progressive decrement in performance from levels 1 through 3 (cue numbers 40, 70, 100) in all situations, though the slopes are much more gradual. The common notion that a certain amount of anxiety is "adaptive" in raising drive level and consequently enhancing performance is not borne out in these data. The three degrees of sensorimotor overarousal, on the other hand, do not produce an increasing number of errors, except for a slight trend in the rote memory task. Nor is there evidence for an "inverted-*U*" effect of improved performance in the moderate ranges of overarousal on those tasks where it was possible for *S* to do better than his base-rate (control performance was already perfect in the nonsense syllable tasks). However, levels 1 through 3 of overarousal in both perception and problem-solving all consistently reveal similar albeit very slight improvement over the base-rate.

"SECONDARY PROCESS" THINKING: DETERMINANTS OF SUBJECTIVE UNCERTAINTY

Two tasks served as context for this unpublished study by Lohr of evaluative thinking: (1) the perception of geometric figures flashed tachistoscopically; and (2) a mental arithmetic series. *S* was required to give his certainty judgment on every response, using a five-point scale ranging from "blind guess" to "absolutely certain." The tasks were arranged to facilitate correct responses so that accompanying judgments of certainty were not swayed by inaccuracy but instead reflected the influence of experimental conditions.

Training for the perception task consisted of waking tachistoscopic practice in the recognition of squares, circles, rectangles, and so on shown in either the left, right, top, or bottom position. Thus *E* ascertained *S*'s threshold for each figure and also familiarized him with the certainty scale in the process. For the 54 experimental trials under each condition, *E* flashed a figure below threshold and then repeated the same figure at successively slower speeds until it was correctly identified, regardless of the certainty rating. At that point a cue was inserted in the adapting field and the progression of trials on the figure was continued until a speed was reached at which two consecutive judgments of absolute certainty (point 5 on scale) were made. The score on any sequence was the number of flashes required to increase *S*'s certainty to two "5" ratings in a row. Accuracy was thereby controlled and only certainty permitted to vary; that is, the problem belongs primarily to the evaluative realm rather than to the perceptual.

For one series the cues were the four anxiety numbers, for another the six degrees of under and overarousal represented by the several different kinds of *A*. The third series manipulated cognitive strength by having the geometric figures appear as cues in various positions in the adapting field between the test flashes, so that the cue figure was completely convergent with the stimulus (same figure in same position); completely divergent (different figure in opposite position); or neither (different figure, same position; same figure, opposite position).

The mental arithmetic task required *S* to listen to problems like "$7 \times 6 - 9 + 2 = ?$" In addition to the final answer, he was asked two other questions, which varied from trial to trial. These included items such as "What was the second term?" "Were there more numbers above 5 than below?" "Were there more increasing or decreasing operations?" and so on. The combinations were arranged so that one difficult and one easy question occurred in that order on each trial, allowing an opportunity to test for differential effects of the experimental conditions. Every answer was followed by a certainty rating. As before, anxiety and arousal cue cards were sometimes in view, and cognitive strength was altered by having *S* look at numbers that did or did not coincide with his answers.

Figure 2 summarizes the results obtained for the six *S*'s in the perception task. The scale points refer to the mean number of exposures

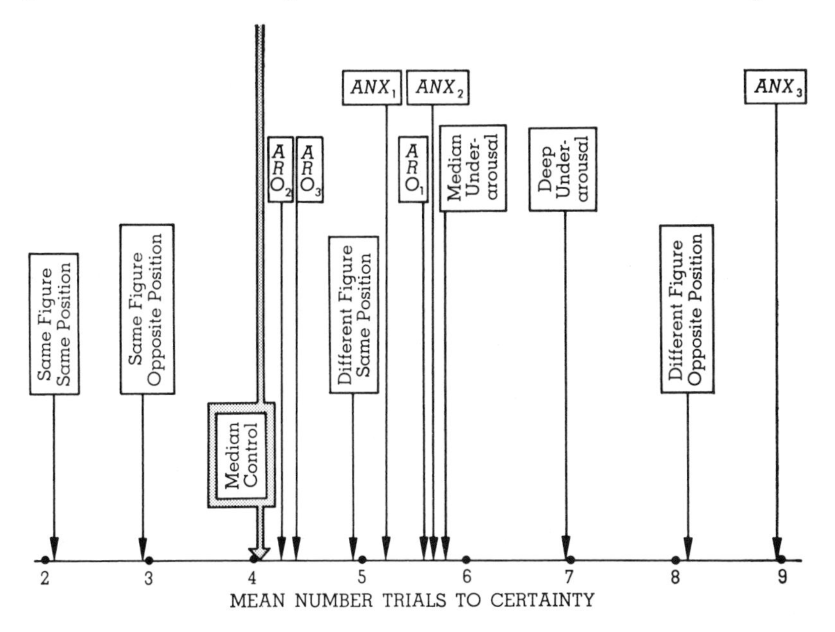

Figure 2. Effects of anxiety, arousal, and cognitive manipulations upon certainty of perceptual judgments.

required for each *S* to reach certainty, that is, two flashes per *S* on the average in the fastest condition up to nine flashes in the slowest. The control data, based on series run without any cues present, yield a median close to four flashes for certainty. The first two degrees of anxiety (40 and 70, represented as Anx_1 and Anx_2 respectively) impair certainty only slightly, but the strongest amount (100 shown as Anx_3) has the greatest effect of any of the experimental conditions. The three levels of overarousal and medium underarousal have minor consequences, whereas deep underarousal significantly hinders certainty.

The cognitive strength manipulations reveal a consistently clear progression. Seeing the same figure as the test stimulus in the same position just before each flash greatly facilitates certainty judgments, and the same figure appearing even in an opposite position from the test stimulus also enhances certainty to some extent. A different figure appearing in the same position, possibly viewed as potentially the most interfering of the four conditions, resulted in a slight decrease. A different figure in an opposite position, however, slowed down the certainty process almost as much as the most intense level of anxiety did (confirming a prediction derived from the conceptual model).

In the mental arithmetic task the three degrees of anxiety created progressively more uncertainty. The three overarousal levels produced only occasional decrements, and medium underarousal did not differ from the control findings. Deep underarousal again revealed a clear decrease. The cognitive manipulations, not as elaborate as in the perception task, turned up very little. Looking at a coinciding number while performing the task had no effect upon certainty and a diverging cue interfered minimally.

Comparing results from the two tasks, it seems that the anxiety levels had a more highly differentiated impact upon arithmetic than perception, whereas cognitive strength proved to be a more significant determinant of perception judgments than of arithmetic. Medium underarousal and the three degrees of overarousal were negligible influences in both tasks, in contrast to the consistent effect of deep underarousal. In general the findings, combined with those of Benyamini discussed earlier, have important implications for model-building in this area.

"PRIMARY PROCESS" THINKING: PERCEPTUAL DISTORTION, SYMBOLISM, LOOSE THOUGHT SEQUENCE, AND CONDENSATION

Four aspects of primary process thinking were investigated experimentally by Dawes (1965), using the same six *S*'s. In addition to the anxiety and underarousal manipulations, she hypnotically induced two kinds of internal inputs—feelings of hunger and cold. The waking perceptual influence of these needs, cued by the words "hungry" or "cold," was tested by tachistoscopic presentation of blanks and drawings of a serving dish (presumably containing *S*'s favorite food inside!) and a fireplace with a burning fire. It was found that "hallucination" occurred in conformity with the ongoing internal input, that is, significantly more blanks were called dishes when *S* was feeling hungry. Also mistakes were made according to the type of input; dishes were mistakenly seen as fireplaces more often in the cold condition and vice versa.

The two internal inputs were also used in a study of symbolism. Under hypnosis *S*'s were taught to associate a different nonsense syllable automatically to each of six thoughts. Two syllables were attached to the act of listening to the word lists through the earphones. Two others were connected to thoughts previously paired with anxiety induced by the number cues. For example, while *S* was experiencing the 100 level of anxiety, he was told that "more men than women get stomach cancer" or that "sometimes when people are very cold they can get frostbite." The last two nonsense syllables were attached to symbols derived from these anxiety-laden thoughts. *S* was instructed to relax and let an image come to mind that stood for the thought in disguised form. Two illustrative symbols obtained in this manner from one *S* were "a blue mass with a red circle around it" (representing the cancer thought) and a "black, high-heeled shoe on a white background" (representing the frostbite thought). The experimental task then required *S* to spell one of the six nonsense syllables every time he heard a bell ring. Ten bell-ringing trials were interspersed at unannounced points throughout the various external-internal input conditions.

The following results were obtained. Both symbol syllables and anxiety-associated thought syllables appeared more often when internal inputs were dominant, that is, when word lists were not being played through the earphones. The particular internal input condition produced more relevant syllables, such as, hunger input led to more hunger syllables (both of the symbol and thought variety). The different amounts of anxiety attached to the pathogenic thought did not yield a clear-cut pattern. In the case of the cold input only, there was some indication of symbol syllables appearing more frequently as anxiety increased—a progression from 0 to 40 to 100 but with a reversal at level 70.

The remaining two primary process characteristics chosen for laboratory scrutiny—loose cognitive sequence and condensation—involved the manipulation of sensorimotor underarousal. The words, to which *S* listened while performing the dish-fireplace perceptual recognition task, were organized into categories of four words each, such as "moon, stars, sun, shine." Previously programmed under hypnosis to respond at *E*'s signal with one word per beat of a metronome, *S* repeated the lists automatically under both normal and deep underarousal conditions. Evidence favoring greater breakdown of category organization under lowered arousal was inconclusive.

Condensation was studied by having three *S*'s hypnotically "dream" about three stimulus words provided by *E* (such as, "out, made, hand"), and the other three were specifically instructed to produce "condensed" images of objects in the laboratory room. Each *S* performed the task in both normal and lowered arousal states. Clinically trained judges decided which production in each pair contained more evidence of primary process thinking. In all those instances where agreement was unanimous, the primary process production had been obtained under lowered arousal. The remaining cases were largely inconclusive. The following are unanimously rated samples of one *S*'s images in response to the laboratory stimuli of the tachistoscope, wires, *S* himself, and any *E*:

Lowered Arousal

A night light with plastic on the outside that plugs into the wall. . . it's got a long light. . . there's always a light there. . . it's got metal in it where it plugs into the wall. . . and the wires are like the wires that come down from the wall. . . that go into the light. . . and the light shines out like the light in the tachistoscope. . . it's warm and friendly. . . it shines on me. . . it's friendly all the time. . . [*Tell me more about it*]. . . it's plastic and the light is warm and friendly. . . and it's comfortable to see in the dark. . . the light is friendly like Mr. ———. . . [*How did you go into the image?*]. . . I'm the plastic and the light shines on me like that. . . the light shines on the plastic and the wires make the tachistoscope light. . . and the wires make the light from the night light light. . . and Mr. ——— is friendly like the light in the dark. . . he's friendly with me like the light in the dark. . . he's friendly with me like the light shines on the plastic. . . .

Normal Arousal

It was a television screen. . . it was lit up. . . there were different designs in it. . . [*Go on*]. . . and I was watching it. . . and the wires. . . it was open. . . there wasn't anything around it. . . and the wires could be seen and they go back and forth. . . it lights up. . . like the tachistoscope. . . they're designs like Miss ——— shows me in the tachistoscope . . . [*Go on*]. . . and I'm watching it just like I watched designs for Miss———. . . it was kind of a TV screen. . . kind of a picture of Miss———'s face. . . I'm sitting on the floor in front of it watching it. . . .

EXPERIMENTAL PRODUCTION OF DEFENSE MECHANISMS

Hedegard, in an unpublished study, performed a molecular analysis of the formation of psychological defense preferences by utilizing the anxiety cues in conjunction with the Blacky pictures. She tested the hypothesis that increasing the amount of anxiety attached to a pathogenic thought would result in a choice of derivatives farther out on a scale of distortion.

The experimental procedures were as follows. Under hypnosis *S* was told that he and Blacky were one and the same, Blacky's feelings were his feelings, and after awakening he would be shown one of the pictures along with a sentence describing Blacky's reactions. The sentence would be divided into four elements with a number over each. Three of the numbers would be 0's and the fourth either 40, 70, or 100, to which he would respond appropriately. Upon feeling the correct level of anxiety for that part of the sentence, he would turn to a list of eight statements (with which he had previously been familiarized) and immediately choose the defense alternative appealing to him the most. He also would have the option of saying that none of the eight appealed to him.

Afterward, in the amnesic waking state, fourteen trials permitted every level of anxiety to be connected with each element of the sentence plus one control trial with no numbers at all and another with four 0's. A sample sentence from Cartoon VIII (which shows Blacky off at a distance watching Mama and Papa pet a sibling figure named Tippy) is "Here Blacky/is feeling so angry and jealous/he would like to physically hurt/Tippy/." The sentence consists of the subject ("Blacky"), feeling ("so angry and jealous"), action ("physically hurt"), and object ("Tippy"). *S* was required to make his choice on each trial within ten seconds after looking at the eight alternatives, responding with the number of the statement he found most appealing at that moment. Next he quickly put the response out of his mind and relaxed before the subsequent trial. In a second session the fourteen trials were repeated, using different orders of anxiety presentation and scrambling the alternatives. Four Blacky pictures were used in all, the others being Cartoons II (Blacky chewing Mama's collar), III (Blacky relieving himself), and VII (Blacky scolding a toy dog).

The resulting data confirmed the prediction that higher levels of anxiety linked to the stimulus sentence would produce more distorted and primitive defense choices. An empirical scale worked out for all six *S*'s on each of the four pictures consistently showed low anxiety to be associated with defenses such as intellectualization, rationalization, reaction formation, negation, or mild forms of denial. Fairly strong anxiety typically occasioned responses of projection or severe blocking, such as repression and suppression. The strongest level characteristically led to extreme denial and displacement, turning against the self, or regressive impulse expression. Examples of high and low anxiety preferences are the following:

High Anxiety:

(II) Right now Blacky is so angry at his family that he would chew up any one of their collars.

(VIII) Discouraged and frustrated with himself as he is,

Blacky feels he doesn't deserve the attention Tippy is receiving.

Low Anxiety:

(II) Blacky is a firm believer in not hiding one's angry emotions, so he feels justified in chewing Mama's collar.

(VIII) Though Blacky is quite angry at being left out, he feels he ought to join the group and pay attention to Tippy also.

The particular locus of the anxiety cues in the stimulus sentence, that is, appearing over self, feeling, action, or object, affected defense preferences for some individual *S*'s but showed no consistent overall pattern for the group.

METHODOLOGICAL ISSUES

The preceding experiments illustrate the possibilities for control and precision inherent in hypnotic methodology.[4] It is a distinct advance to be able to vary systematically by degrees a subject's "natural" affective and arousal reactions, to control his motivational states and even his conscious thoughts. Furthermore the capacity for turning various reactions on and off as desired, for assuring their activity at the exact moment of stimulus presentation, and for repeating the procedures throughout a large number of trials (with *S* under instructions not to feel bored, it should be added) are obvious advantages. Is there a price to be paid in return for these and other assets? This section will treat some of the commonly voiced concerns and cautions regarding the research use of hypnosis, but first a few practical aspects will be taken up.

S's in our experiments are college students paid at the going hourly rate. A policy statement prepared for the Department of Psychology at the University of Michigan guides their selection in part. Those with known past or present cardiac illnesses or severe nervous disorders are excluded. *S* must be willing to sign an "agreement to participate" if he is over 21 or, otherwise, his parent or legal guardian must sign for him. Hypnotic procedures are carried out only by qualified personnel and all sessions are conducted in the presence of a witness. Tape recordings and/or verbatim typescripts are retained after completion of the research. In addition a physician is available in cases of emergency, though none has arisen to date.

To avoid attracting deviant individuals, the initial recruitment of *S*'s is made without any reference to hypnosis but as soon as someone indicates an interest in serving in "psychological experiments" he is told

[4] It is obvious that extensive use of hypnotic methodology requires a sound theory of the nature of hypnosis itself. A molecular analysis evolved from our conceptual model is available in detail elsewhere. (Blum, 1961).

that hypnosis will be involved. Relatively few decline to take part for this reason. A brief screening interview is followed by administration of the Stanford Hypnotic Susceptibility Scale. Those selected for research training are then given a personal history questionnaire which takes about twenty minutes to fill out.

Each *S* is typically seen for three two-hour sessions weekly, a schedule that is approximately maintained for the duration of the series of experiments. In the studies cited above, individual participation including the training and data collection phases averaged 80 to 100 hours. At the outset *S* is told that he will be given feedback concerning the research upon its conclusion. He is asked to respect the confidential nature of the tasks just as his own responses are kept in confidence by members of the research staff. In fact a sharp distinction is continually preserved between the "outside world" and the laboratory, so that crossing the threshold signifies the transition from one realm to another. This psychological separation further cuts down the possibility for laboratory responses to occur outside and very likely contributes to the efficacy and durability of training inside the room by minimizing interference from everday preoccupations. Upon termination *S* is given a lengthy "debriefing" in both hypnotic and waking states. The procedures and experiments are explained in detail and all suggestions are carefully removed and tested for their disappearance. Stress is also laid on the inadvisability of indulging later in self-hypnosis or attempting to hypnotize others.

One readily apparent methodoligical issue is raised by such intensive work with a limited number of *S*'s, a restriction that the elaborate hypnotic programming almost inevitably entails. Though one can never play down the value of extending laboratory results to larger samples varying in age, sex, IQ, social class, and so on, certain virtues in our approach should be noted. First, long-term use of the same *S*'s facilitates the design of intraindividual comparisons, thereby permitting greater control. The number of responses from individual *S*'s is typically very large and standard statistical tests are applicable. In essence a complete experiment is performed with each *S* and replicated with succeeding ones. Second, the training procedures are deliberately designed to bring interindividual differences under control. For example, *S*'s may differ widely in their normal anxiety levels and reactivity, but everyone is trained until he reaches the stage where he can consistently experience the three degrees specified for the experiments. Thus, varied amounts of training time devoted to *S*'s serve to reduce interindividual differences. Similarly, problems associated with autonomic response specificity are not of major concern because the particular system under investigation, such as the GSR, is manipulated until the desired degrees of response are obtained.

Generally we have selected *S*'s having high scores on the susceptibility scale because it takes less time to train them in the often complicated experimental procedures. Currently there is no substantial body of evidence pointing to singular personality attributes of highly susceptible *S*'s. Both the Blacky responses and our clinical impressions of the group with which we have worked suggest that it is markedly heterogeneous with respect to personality makeup. However, two of the six *S*'s in the reported studies who did score in the medium and low ranges of susceptibility were deliberately included as a check. Both were able to master the hypnotic tasks, though the process took somewhat longer. Also, both scored in the high range when retested on the equivalent form of the scale after a dozen hours of training.

Initial failure to experience posthypnotic amnesia, for example, has consistently proved amenable to eventual correction by a combination of clinically oriented exploration of *S*'s unconscious motives to resist plus the search for a suitable "gimmick" to make forgetting easier. The most recalcitrant *S* required repeated discussion of his problem over several sessions. He finally accomplished the amnesia by mentally putting the to-be-forgotten material into a small trunk with a lock whose combination was known only to the experimenter. Once successfully mastered, there are rarely any subsequent relapses and the need for a gimmick gradually dissipates. Some economy may be introduced by asking *S* himself to propose an appropriate visual or other technique for learning how to forget.

In short, it is our belief that initially low scorers in hypnotic susceptibility can become satisfactory *S*'s given sufficient time, patience, and understanding. For our experimental purposes it is more convenient to train high scorers and we continue to do so without real concern that we may be piling up a mountain of data from a very biased sample of deviant *S*'s.

Another common criticism of hypnotizable *S*'s is that, apart from possibly being deviant, their behavior is likely to be devious. This charge ranges from outright conscious simulation and deception to subtle, unconscious responsiveness to "demand" characteristics of the situation. Among our various experimental procedures the most flagrant opportunity for simulation exists in the blindness training where *S* might actually see the stimulus and compliantly report that he did not. An earlier study (Blum, 1961) using this technique permitted a number of checks and will be reviewed briefly. The question we were seeking to answer—Does "unconscious" activation of an idea highly charged with anxiety automatically release the anxiety itself?—required sensory registration of an input without accompanying recognition or subsequent access from memory. *S*'s were trained, after several hours of intensive practice, not to "see" a given stimulus when it was flashed tachistoscopically, even though they did not know in advance at what point in a series it would appear. Stress was repeatedly laid upon the importance of *S* always reporting exactly what he saw whether or not it corresponded to instructions. It was possible to rule out simulation by several different kinds of converging evidence.

During the training *S*'s frequently reported that they saw the critical stimulus when they were not supposed to. Also, there were occasions upon which *S* was blind to the wrong stimulus. More important, the blindness sometimes persisted after it had presumably been removed by instruction. All *S*'s experienced some difficulty in seeing the critical stimulus clearly right after the blindness suggestion was lifted. Two sources of physiological evidence also argue against simulation. If *S* were deliberately faking his verbal report we would expect the GSR to be responsive to the deception, but there were no such deflections in the record. In addition, a series of trials checking eye movements in one *S* revealed a distinctive pattern of electro-oculographic responses on those flashes where blindness occurred.

More indirect influences referred to by Orne (1959) as the "demand characteristics of the experimental situation" are treated by impressing upon *S*, at the very beginning, that the best opportunity to serve the experimenter's purposes is just to let things happen naturally and not try to mold his own responses according to any preconceived notions of what the study may be about. In addition to independent checks such as those provided by physiological measurement, carefully conducted waking and hypnotic inquiries at the conclusion of an experiment are also helpful. Most of the research designs pursued thus far have been sufficiently intricate to defy detection even by psychology colleagues watching *S*'s in action. Because the experimenters are engaged in empirical work to advance the construction of a sound conceptual model, there is rarely sufficient commitment to any particular point of view to make it seem likely that implicit cues concerning expected performance would be inadvertently communicated to *S*. The demands are maximal only in the training session where the requisite skills relating to the independent variables are being developed but minimal in the experiments themselves where the dependent variables appear. As a matter of fact, the most surprising results were obtained in that series of studies (tests for perception, problem-solving, rote memory, and verbalization) where *S* probably had the best chance to figure out what was being investigated, if he wanted to make the effort. The two findings that the lowest level of anxiety consistently impaired performance and that levels of arousal did not yield evidence of an inverted-*U* function contradicted our expectations from the literature.

Finally, Barber (1961; Barber and Glass, 1962) has hammered on the theme that phenomena viewed as peculiar to hypnosis can be duplicated in the waking state. Though our experiments typically are carried out with *S* awake and amnesic for the prior hypnotic programing, it would simplify matters considerably if Barber's contention were universally valid. However, our experience has shown that hypnotizable *S*'s cannot execute the differential anxiety instructions merely upon being told to do so while awake. Nor could the selective blindness for unannounced stimuli be accomplished successfully in the waking state. Furthermore, we have noted that the hypnotized *S* can invoke a kind of "internal camera" to observe an incomplete image as it flashes through his mind in response to a signal; the partial image can be arrested, described in full detail, brought back after a period of time and reported again with total fidelity. Before hypnotic practice the same *S* is unable to carry out these directions. Barber's view may be correct, and it is possible that all these and other training procedures as well might be done with the waking *S* if one were willing to devote enough time and effort to the job. But until evidence is marshalled that the types of experimental manipulations we employ can be induced with equal success by nonhypnotic methods, we retain the conviction that hypnosis serves as a unique laboratory tool for controlling elusive variables of the sort involved in psychodynamics research.

REFERENCES

Barber, T. X. (1961). "Physiological effects of hypnosis," *Psychol. Bull.*, **58**, 390–419.

Barber, T.X., and Glass, L. B. (1962). "Significant factors in hypnotic behavior," *J. abnorm. soc. Psychol.*, **64**, 222–228.

Benyamini, K. (1963). "Experimental effects of hypnotically induced anxiety, arousal, and inhibition." University of Michigan Doctoral Dissertation.

Blum, G. S. (1950). *The Blacky Pictures: A Technique for the Exploration of Personality Dynamics*. Ann Arbor: Psychodynamic Instruments.

——— (1961). *A Model of the Mind.* New York: Wiley.

Branca, A. A., and Podolnick, E. E. (1961). "Normal, hypnotically induced, and feigned anxiety as reflected in and detected by the MMPI," *J. consult. Psychol.*, **25**, 165–170.

Dawes, Carol (1965). "Experiments on selected aspects of primary process thinking." University of Michigan Doctoral Dissertation.

Grosz, H. J., and Levitt, E. E. (1959). "The effects of hypnotically induced anxiety on the Manifest Anxiety Scale and the Barron Ego-Strength Scale," *J. Abnorm. soc. Psychol.*, **59**, 281–283.

Hedegard, S. Unpublished study.

Leuba, C. (1941). "The use of hypnosis for controlling variables in psychological experiments," *J. abnorm. soc. Psychol.*, **36**, 271–274.

Levitt, E. E. (1963). "A comment on 'A Paradigm for Determining the Clinical Relevance of Hypnotically Induced Psychopathology,'" *Psychol. Bull.*, **60**, 326–329.

Levitt E. E., Den Breeijen, A., and Persky, H. (1960). "The induction of clinical anxiety by means of a standardized hypnotic technique," *Amer. J. clin. Hyp.*, **2**, 206–214.

Lohr, N. Unpublished study.

Orne, M. (1959). "The nature of hypnosis: artifact and essence," *J. abnorm. soc. Psychol.*, **58**, 277–299.

Reyher, J. (1962). "A paradigm for determining the clinical relevance of hypnotically induced psychopathology," *Psychol. Bull.*, **59**, 344–352.

Weitzenhoffer, A. M., and Hilgard E. R. (1959). *Stanford Hypnotic Susceptibility Scale, Forms A and B*. Palo Alto: Consulting Psychologists Press.

5

Hypnosis in Research on Psychopathology

JOSEPH REYHER
Michigan State University

THE term "psychopathology" denotes phenomena central to the field of clinical psychology and psychiatry, yet marked disagreement over the nature and identification of these phenomena exists, despite years of controversy. Two of the many reasons for the lack of clarity are of particular interest here. One is the unverifiability of inferred, covert psychological processes. Unlike the biological and physical sciences, there are no reliable devices in the armamentarium of the clinician for transforming covert psychological processes into overt ones. Psychological equivalents to microscopes, stethoscopes, X-ray machines, staining techniques, and the like do not exist. The clinician has no means of extending his powers of direct perception; unconscious motives, conflicts, and defenses cannot be observed directly with the help of any known instrument. Projective tests are unsatisfactory as direct measures because of the ambiguity of the data they produce. They often increase the opportunity to infer rather than decrease it. The clinician finds himself entangled in a web of inference at the very point of departure from clinical observation into scientific conceptualization. He has to infer the very variables and processes among which he seeks to discover functional relationships.

The lack of effective and reliable experimental methods is another reason for the veil of uncertainty that shrouds the nature of psychopathology. Although purely clinical methods have illuminated some of the main outlines of the phenomena and have suggested many detailed relationships among variables, only more controlled techniques of observation and investigation will produce systematic and scientifically meaningful knowledge. The phenomena produced by hypnosis enabled Freud to observe processes and develop concepts that laid the foundations of clinical practice, and the phenomena that can be induced by hypnosis may enable the scientist to observe processes in the laboratory that may very well lay the foundations of a science of psychopathology. The problem of the unverifiability of covert, pathogenic processes can be mitigated, if not eliminated, by the hypnotic induction of these processes. Although the problems of proper controls and interpretation of the results are difficult, they are not impossible. This chapter will be devoted to a discussion of these problems and relevant research.

A PARADIGM FOR DETERMINING THE CLINICAL RELEVANCE OF HYPNOTICALLY INDUCED PSYCHOPATHOLOGY

Many investigators have been attracted to hypnosis as a means for producing psychological and physiological dysfunctions that resemble naturally occurring psychopathology. In addition to a disregard for genotypic-phenotypic relationships, the contrived, artificial, and analogical nature of most of these studies has diluted their significance to the extent that they have had very little, if any, impact upon the behavioral and biological sciences.

In an effort to help rectify this problem, a paradigm was formulated (Reyher, 1962, 1963a) for determining the relevance of hypnotically induced psychopathology to clinical or naturally occurring phenomena. Only two investigations in the literature were considered to approximate it closely enough for the data to be clinically meaningful. In a recent review of hypnosis and experimental psychopathology, Deckert and West (1963) also have noted a general deficiency in experimental design and recognized the problem of assessing the significance and generality of the reported results.

A paradigm for demonstrating valid psychopathology must include a procedure for separating the mechanisms of suggestion from the mechanisms of pathogenic psychodynamics. Although it is doubtful that the mechanisms of hypnotic suggestion are similar to the mechanisms of pathogenic psychodynamics, clinical experience with hypnosis (Rosen,

1953; Eisenbud, 1937) indicates that hypnotic suggestion can set in motion nonsuggested pathogenic psychodynamics and observable psychopathology. Thus, hypnotic suggestion should be used only to *induce* a process that, under certain specifiable conditions, is theoretically capable of *producing* pathogenic psychodynamics and psychopathology. The hypnotically induced process defines the genotype, and the behavioral outcome defines the phenotype. The genotype is defined operationally by the statements in the hypnotic suggestions; the phenotype is defined operationally by a description of *S*'s overt behavior. The description of the phenotype is considered to be operationally valid clinical psychopathology only if it satisfies accepted criteria for identifying manifestations of psychopathology, such as phobias, compulsions, conversions, and so on. In this way, the investigator can operationally tie down the genotype, or psychodynamics, that produces the observed psychopathology instead of having to rely upon the uncertainties of clinical inference in regard to natural psychopathology.

The foregoing considerations suggest five principles, or criteria, that should guide research in this area. First, the induced process must in no way include cues as to how *E* expects *S* to respond in terms of the dependent variables. Orne (1959) has demonstrated convincingly the sensitivity of hypnotized *S*'s to the expectations of *E* and the "demand" characteristics of the experimental design. Second, the induced process must produce other processes and behavior; that is, it must be response-producing. Third, some of these responses must satisfy criteria for the identification of manifestations of psychopathology. Fourth, some of the *S*'s must be asked by a co-experimenter to fake hypnosis, unknown to *E*, in order to determine the "demand" characteristics of the research. Finally, no matter what is to be induced, it is wise to present the instructions in the passive voice. The use of the passive voice reduces the possibility that *S* may act out a role to please *E*. More specifically, *S* should not be instructed to carry out suggestions, but he should be informed that he will be acted upon by something or that he is going to experience something. Not only does the active voice promote the expectation that *S* should do something, but it also enhances volitional, adaptive processes that render the hypnotic behavior similar to waking behavior. Thus, the instructions should minimize the role of volitional processes and maximize the role of nonvolitional processes.

The first point of the paradigm is straightforward and presents no special problems. The second point represents a simple but crucial aspect of research in psychopathology that has not been formally recognized. The induced processes must be intense enough to be response-producing in their own right. If the induced processes have pathogenic potential, substitute reactions and symptomatic behavior will occur.

The third point presents some difficulties. How does one go about the task of identifying manifestations of psychopathology? The identification of severe disturbances is easy because behavior relevant to defining criteria is so outstanding, but the task becomes very difficult for neurotic disturbances and marginal states. Many manifestations of a neurotic process are not clearly recognized as psychopathology, such as somatic complaints, alterations in mood, disturbed sexual functions, and so forth. Certainly the psychopathology of everday life as delineated by Freud is not considered to be psychopathology in terms of any nosology. These examples illustrate that genotypic-phenotypic relationships must be examined and understood to ascertain which behaviors are manifestations of psychopathology and which are not. Once this genotypic-phenotypic bond is severed, confusion reigns; phenotypic manifestations of psychopathology lose their moorings and get caught up in a maelstrom of cultural, relativistic, and statistical definitions that lead nowhere. Thus, research design must include the necessary control group(s) for identifying manifestations of psychopathology and for relating these to a genotype.

The fourth point of the paradigm specifies the proper control group, which, unfortunately, does not eliminate ambiguous interpretations. One outstanding problem is the composition of the faking group. It ought to make a big difference whether the faking *S*'s are good or poor hypnotic *S*'s. If poor hypnotic *S*'s are used as fakers, as Orne (1962) recommends, then the comparability of the experimental and control *S*'s may be seriously impaired. It is likely that good hypnotic *S*'s are grossly different from poor hypnotic *S*'s in a number of major respects, which may cause the two kinds of *S*'s to perceive the same situation differently and to respond differentially on the dependent variables. Good *S*'s are more apt to be cooperative, compliant, and noncritical of *E* and the procedures. Differential responsiveness to the demand characteristics of the research by the two groups should be assumed, unless proven otherwise.

The problem of interpretation of the faking controls is compounded by the request to fake hypnosis. This request creates a new experimental situation with its own demand characteristics. To assume the role of a hypnotized *S*, the faker has the doubly complex task of responding to the instructions and to the formal aspects of the experiment in terms of how he thinks a hypnotized *S* would act. He is also in league with one *E* to fool another. Under these circumstances of altered significance and motivation, it is likely that the demand characteristics of the design are different for the experimental and the control *S*'s. If this is the case, different experimental outcomes cannot be attributed to the effect of hypnosis.

In what ways might the demand characteristics of the research differ for the two groups? Although any answer is speculative, one possibility would be that the faking *S*'s are highly motivated to act like hypnotized *S*'s to fool one *E* and to gratify another. This double-barreled motivation might lead *S* to focus on his behavior per se rather than the overall explicit and implicit demands of the experiment. It may be that anything other than feigning hypnosis per se is extraneous or reduced in significance.

Orne (1959) recognized that the same results by experimental and control groups do not necessarily mean that the hypnotic reactions were invalid, and he pointed out that faking *S*'s are most appropriate in research regarding the transcendence of volitional capacities under hypnosis.

Subject variables are also important. Both the experimental and faking *S*'s may find it distasteful or anxiety-producing to comply with the demand characteristics of the research. The significance of these factors is enhanced in research dealing with antisocial behavior and highly personal matters. It has been found that reliable differences between experimental and control *S*'s occur when the hypnotic procedures have inherent anxiety-producing potential (Reyher, 1961a, 1961b). The anxiety has response-producing properties, some of which cannot be mimicked by fakers, such as sweating, flushing, tics, skin disturbances, and so on. Even symptoms that could be faked are not reported. These investigations will be described later.

There is another reason to believe that the double-blind design might be inappropriate for research involving the hypnotic induction of personally distasteful and anxiety-producing material. In an earlier article (1962), I reported evidence to show that an unfamiliar *E* may arouse defensive behavior in *S* that interferes with the implantation of the suggestions. The most effective induction of highly personal processes seems to require the development of rapport not unlike that of a patient in psychotherapy. To enhance the probability that the induced processes will be effective and to approximate the merits of the double-blind design as closely as possible, we have recently been using the same *E* for both induction and research, but an effort is being made to eliminate or detect differential experimenter behavior. During the research we reduce to a minimum opportunities for *E* to interact with both the experimental and control *S*'s. All sessions are recorded and later edited to eliminate everything said by the *S*'s. These edited tapes are then played for judges who are instructed to determine whether or not *E* was relating to an experimental or a control *S*. If *E* has been relating differentially to these *S*'s, the judges should be able to detect it. We have found that the presence of the recorder for this purpose serves as an alter ego for *E*, which helps to keep his behavior consistent from *S* to *S*, and as far as we can tell, the procedure has been working well. Despite the enjoyment that judges usually derive from playing the role of devil's advocate, they have consistently failed to classify correctly the kinds of *S*'s with whom *E* interacted.

It is apparent that faking controls can be helpful in the interpretation of hypnotically produced data, but the investigator's critical attitudes should not be blunted by a false sense of security just because the experiment incorporates a double-blind design with a group of faking controls.

The last point of the paradigm, which recommends the use of the passive voice, neither presents special problems nor requires further discussion.

Once the reactions of *S* can be designated as psychopathology, attention can be directed to the induced genotype and the psychological mechanisms that were set in motion and produced the psychopathology. These are covert processes that are conceptualized by the theory that led to the formulation of the induced genotype. The manifestations of psychopathology support the theory, but only when the same theory can predict the outcomes of a variety of experiments will the imputed psychological mechanisms become scientifically valuable.

REVIEW OF RELEVANT RESEARCH

In an earlier paper (1962), I classified research on hypnotically induced psychopathology in terms of three categories: (1) direct suggestion, (2) the induction of artificial conflicts, and (3) the activation of natural conflicts. Only two of the studies that were reviewed were considered to be relevant to clinical psychopathology, according to the paradigm, and they will be presented again along with several other studies that have recently come to my attention. Much more can be gained from a concentrated discussion of relevant research than by a duplication of a recent, comprehensive review by Deckert and West (1963), or of my earlier paper (1962).

Only studies that induced artificial conflicts approximated the paradigm, although the activation of natural conflicts was considered to be potentially more powerful. The use of direct suggestion was considered to be irrelevant because the induced processes are not response-producing and because the genotype and the phenotype are identical. The *S* merely carries out the suggestions that are given; the suggestions specify the behavior. These and related issues were discussed by Levitt (1963) and Reyher (1963a).

The Activation of Natural Conflicts

An interesting study was reported by Kepecs, Robin, and Brunner (1951). Using a variety of nonpsychiatric patients and one "normal" person as *S*'s, they raised blisters on the skin by applying cantharides cerate. The dome-shaped portion of the fully formed blister was removed, exposing the erythematous oozing base. A base line of exudation rate was established in the resting hypnotic state, after which each patient was asked to express his thoughts as they came. If spontaneous expressions of emotion were not obtained, the patient was asked to talk about emotionally charged topics. The most salient observations were a sharp rise in exudation rate, which accompanied weeping in patients with and without dermatologic disorders; relaxation was accompanied by a drop in exudation; and inhibition of weeping first resulted in a fall of exudation rate, followed by a rise as the inhibition continued. Although correlated variations between emotional processes and exudation rate do not demonstrate a relationship between emotional processes and pathology, this level of observation is certainly much closer to the actual processes involved than the measurement of autonomic responses to induced states.

The relevance of this study is difficult to determine because the psychopathology was induced artificially, and it is unclear whether an increase in exudation rate is a pathological response. The absence of a faking group is not too serious because of the involuntary, physiological nature of the response. Nevertheless, a faking group should be incorporated routinely in research with hypnosis. The Kepecs, Robin, and Brunner method has significant research potential; it is conceivable that it could lead to the identification of transactions between emotional and physiological processes. This is the main reason for its inclusion in this review.

Seitz (1951, 1953) reported an ingenious and a potentially powerful procedure for investigating symbolism and organ choice in conversion reactions as well as the psychodynamics of organ choice in somatization reactions. One patient with well-developed choreiform spasms following the death of her son was used as a subject in nine different experiments. The research was designed to investigate the kinds of suggested symptoms that would replace the hypnotically removed symptoms and what reactions would occur if substitute symptoms were suggested without suggestions of replacement for the original. He found that it was possible to replace the chorea with blushing and excoriated pruitus, but hyperhidrosis of the palms and scalp anesthesia would not serve as substitutes even though these reactions occurred posthypnotically along with the chorea. Only symptoms that seemed to express the exhibitionistic and masochistic components of the conflict were equivalent and served as satisfactory replacements. When replacement was not suggested, spontaneous symptom substitutions occurred; posthypnotic nausea and vomiting occurred when warts were suggested; anesthesia of the scalp developed in the place of alopecia areata; and coryza and eczematous dermatitis occurred following the suggestion of urticaria.

The relationship between the symbolic character of the patient's symptoms and the fate of the suggested substitute symptoms is convincing and is of great import to the development of experimental psychopathology. Not only were the symptoms well-known forms of clinical psychopathology, but the method may provide a means of sorting out the symbolic from the nonsymbolic aspects of the patient's symptoms. Although the relevance of the findings is reduced by the lack of a proper control group, the results have considerable face validity. It seems very unlikely that faking *S*'s could bring about the pathological skin reactions that occurred spontaneously. The full impact of Seitz' data cannot be assessed until the techniques are tried with more *S*'s.

In a study that closely approximates the paradigm, Wiseman (1962) utilized hypnosis and the Rorschach to investigate Freud's theory of dreams. He hypothesized that when the inkblots were used to stimulate dreams in hypnotized *S*'s, a subsequent administration of the Rorschach in the waking state a week later would produce more responses revealing the operation of primary process than in faking *S*'s and when the Rorschach preceded the hypnotically induced dreams. The postulated psychological mechanisms involved are described below:

> . . . the Freudian theory of dreams states that an unconscious wish striving for expression is able, due to the mobility of its "cathectic energy" and through the operation of the primary processes, to transfer its energy to those day residues which have been "neglected," "rejected" or "suppressed" and which, because of a "common element" becomes the most suitable for the symbolic representation of the particular dream thought. Thus "the hitherto preconscious train of thought *has been drawn into the unconscious*" (Freud, 1938, p. 530). These "recent impressions" thereby serve as the manifest content of the dream, having been drawn into the unconscious through association and thereby permit anxiety-free expression to the unconscious wish. In this sense the dream "relieves the mind, like a safety valve" (Freud, 1938, p. 527). If the precise stimulus which served as the manifest content for the dream were known, post-dreaming measurement of the waking response to that stimulus could be obtained. It would follow from the above that future response to that stimulus would reflect evidence that it has been "drawn into the unconscious." Thus, future response to that stimulus would reflect the operation of the primary mode of thought and the effects of the anxiety-provoking nature of the dream material. (p. 2)

The Rorschach responses were scored according to Holt's system and a combination of the categories of Beck and Klopfer. The results were highly significant with many more primary process intrusions occurring subsequent to hypnotically induced dreams to the inkblots. The results were equally strong for a replication group. It is of interest to note that the conventional categories were relatively insensitive to the changes in response that occurred. Not only did this investigation reveal meaningful phenotypic manifestations of psychopathology in terms of Holt's scoring system, but it is the only investigation available that focused on the mechanisms of the pathogenic process.

THE INDUCTION OF ARTIFICIAL CONFLICTS

Wolberg (1947), reported a procedure that closely approximates the paradigm. Instead of implanting a paramnesia, he induced an impulse that would produce conflict in the waking state. His instructions were as follows:

> When you awaken, you will find next to you a bar of chocolate. You will have a desire to eat the chocolate that will be so intense that it will be impossible to resist the craving. At the same time you will feel that the chocolate does not belong to you and that to eat it would be very wrong and very bad. You will have no memory of these suggestions when you awaken, but you will, nevertheless, react to them. (p. 337)

The distinctive aspect of his instructions is the posthypnotic suggestion of an overwhelming impulse that is rendered anxiety-producing by pitting it against conscience.

Although his *S*'s were instructed to perceive the induced impulse in terms of conscience, they were not instructed to develop symptoms. Accordingly, it is of great interest that the procedure spontaneously produced both somatic and psychological reactions, which included such marked symptoms as dizziness, tachycardia, and a negative hallucination. Because his procedure closely approximates the paradigm, the posthypnotic psychopathology may very well be valid clinical phenomena. If he had used the proper control *S*'s, a more positive statement could be made. For his instructions to be perfect, the *S*'s should not have been told how to perceive the impulse nor should amnesia have been suggested. The impulse should generate spontaneously all of *S*'s reactions.

In a well-designed investigation, which closely conforms to the paradigm, Moore (1964) compared the reactions of high *n*-Achievers, low *n*-Achievers, and faking *S*'s, to the posthypnotic stimulation of hostility. Each *S* underwent two loosely structured interviews (conditions) with the same interviewer. One of these interviews was preceded by the induction of hostility with the interviewer being both the cue for and the recipient of intense hostility. The hostility toward *E* was created by an induced paramnesia that involved a teacher who had aroused intense anger in *S*. Spontaneous symptoms were noted in about one third of the experimental *S*'s. One of the fakers exhibited symptoms, but there was evidence that he had been hypnotized accidentally. Significant results in the predicted direction were obtained in respect to the amount of hostility in the verbalization of the *S*'s. There was a significant interaction between groups and conditions; the low *n*-Achievers verbalized a higher degree of awareness of the induced hostility than did the high *n*-Achievers. There also was evidence that the high *n*-Achievers tended to be intropunitive, whereas the low *n*-Achievers tended to be extrapunitive. This observation, however, is only tentative pending a complete analysis of the data. The differential reactions of the two groups over the two conditions indicates that the experimental manipulations were stronger than effects due to the demand characteristics of the research, whatever they might have been.

An Investigation of Posthypnotic Conflict

My own investigations have produced a wide variety of psychopathology. Initially, I was interested in testing certain hypotheses about perceptual vigilance and defense, and I was surprised when my first *S*'s experienced vivid psychopathological reactions. Thus, my interest in hypnotically induced psychopathology was piqued accidentally. The raw data seem to be unusually rich or prime; that is, on inspection they reveal processes and relationships that I have seen only in the psychotherapy of acute reactions or with the use of uncovering techniques in intensive psychotherapy. Because I believe that the obtained data are exceptionally rich, this chapter will give considerable space to a description of the procedures and verbatim recordings of protocols. Two investigations are involved, the original study and a replication and extension.[1] The most complete description of the procedures of the original can be found in Reyher (1958). Because the replication and extension investigation is unpublished, this report will favor these data.

A set of hallucinatory experiences (paramnesia) associated with intense feelings of anger and a destructive urge toward a certain person was induced in twelve deeply hypnotized *S*'s. The paramnesia was induced after Erickson's (1944) preparatory instructions for the induction of conflict had been given, and the conflict was activated posthypnotically by the tachistoscopic presentation of words related to the conflict. In the original investigation, words related to the conflict (*c*-words) were paired with neutral words (*n*-words), one above the other in separate apertures. Each pair was presented simultaneously until *S* recognized one. In the replication research, the two members of each pair were presented singly at each level of illumination until one of them was recognized. The order of presentation for the two words was randomly determined at each level of illumination.

Each of the *S*'s was seen on two experimental days. On the first day, *S* was given one of two paramnesias or conflicts (*A* and *B*), which were counterbalanced across *S*'s. On the second experimental day, *S* was given the same general instructions and the other conflict, but one aspect of the design was changed. The emotional import of the two types of words was reversed: the words that were associated previously

[1] This investigation was supported by a Postdoctoral Research Fellowship, number MF-7740, from the Division of Research Grants, Public Health Service, at the University of Illinois.

with conflict became *n*-words and the words that were previously neutral became *c*-words. On a given day, the *n*-words were the words associated with the paramnesia that was not induced. By the completion of the second experimental day, all the words had served as *c* and *n*-words. In addition, the pairing of the words was different on the two days, although the same list of words was used. With only a few exceptions, both sets of word pairs were matched reasonably well in terms of length and frequency of occurrence in the English language. The change in word pairs was necessary to offset possible interference by paired associate learning due to "partial recognition" on the previous session.

Information about prerecognition was obtained by instructing *S* to state after each trial whether he saw "nothing" or "something." The latter category was qualified further by asking *S* to give the degree of confidence he had in his response by saying if he was "doubtful" or "confident" that he saw something. *S* was also asked to indicate relative brightness ("brighter" or "duller") on each trial. In the original research he made a brightness comparison of the two apertures where the members of a word pair were presented. For the replication research *S* made a brightness comparison between the presentation of the *n*- and *c*- words, which were presented singly at the same level of illumination.

In the waking state, *S* was told to grasp a handle with his right hand to complete a circuit for the equipment. In the hypnotized state, he was told that his thumb would twitch without his being aware of it while he continued to grasp the handle, if anything about the tachistoscopic procedure stirred up any of his feelings related to the paramnesia. The thumb was placed in such a way that it rested on a microswitch that caused a concealed bulb to light. This was called the light response (*LR*). Whenever *E* said the word "ready," *S* was instructed to grasp the handle nearby with his right hand, and to look at the opal glass screen.

When *S* achieved recognition of a word, *E* sounded a buzzer. This was done to eliminate the possibility that *E* might differentially reward the recognition of *c*- and *n*-words by inflections in his voice.

Conflict-inducing Instructions. The posthypnotic conflict was created by the following instructions:

> Now, listen carefully. After I awaken you, you will not be able to remember anything about this session. However, anything that comes into your mind that is associated with (a class or words related to the paramnesia) will stir up overwhelming feelings of hate. If these feelings break into consciousness, you will realize that it is the person who owns these papers (which are pointed out to him) that you hate, and you will experience an overwhelming urge to tear them up.

Unlike the original design, which had *S* respond with maximum intensity (overwhelming) to the induced material right from the outset, the intensity of the conflict was progressively increased by informing *S* that the induced feelings would grow stronger as *E* counted from one to four. At the count of one, his feelings of anger would be stirred up to a mild degree if anything about the paramnesia came to mind. At the counts of two, three, and four, his feelings would grow to moderate, intense, and overwhelming levels, respectively. The timing of each count was left to the discretion of the experimenter's clinical judgment, but he made an effort to present approximately equal numbers of words before and after each count.

It is important to note that the *S*'s were given a posthypnotic amnesia only for the paramnesia, *not* for the related affect and impulse, which were stimulated in the posthypnotic tachistoscope trials by the recognition of *c*-words. The amnesia for the paramnesia was maintained until the end of the research. This was done to keep the *S*'s as naïve as possible concerning the nature of the research. At the end of the first experimental session, *S* was rehypnotized and told that the paramnesia was only a dream; consequently, it would fade away and it would have no significance to him after being awakened.

Paramnesia A. This experience involved the events of a recent party. While being introduced, *S* was made to feel that he had been insulted by one of the other guests. One of the things he noticed later was a beautiful art object, which was constructed from hundreds of geometrically shaped pieces of glass. As he gazed at this construction, he ate refreshments from a table that contained a wide variety of food. Later in the evening when he was standing by the art object and close to a group of people, the person who had insulted him earlier abruptly turned around from the group to use an ashtray nearby. To avoid getting burned, *S* jumped back, but in doing so he knocked over and broke the art object. When this person publicly denounced him as a clumsy oaf, he became so angry at him and with himself that he could hardly speak. He shortly afterward left the party and found that the only way he could attain peace of mind was to completely push the whole experience into the back of his mind. He then was told that this person worked in this laboratory and that these papers nearby belonged to him and were considered to be very important. The critical words for tachistoscopic presentation were words belonging to the concepts of geometry and food.

Paramnesia B. This experience had its setting in *S*'s sixth grade, when his class was putting on an exhibition of hobbies. He was attracted to a coin collection and he became fascinated with the coins and the variety of metals that were used. As he looked at this exhibit, he was overcome by an impulse to steal some of them. Although the theft was discovered soon, his teacher was unable to determine who did it. While she kept the class after school, he was very afraid lest his guilt show on his face. On his way home, he was stopped by a boy who confronted him with the fact that he had observed the theft, and he threatened to inform the teacher if he did not give him his savings and promise to do his bidding for the rest of his life. Too afraid to do anything else, he agreed and ran home to get his savings. As time went by, he grew very angry with this boy for putting him at his mercy; however, since this boy moved away a short time later, it was possible to push the whole thing out of his mind. He then was told that this same boy now worked in this laboratory and that those papers nearby belonged to him and were considered to be very important. The critical words for tachistoscopic presentation were words belonging to the concepts of money and metal.

Materials. In the original investigation the stimuli were presented with a Gerbrand's modification of the Dodge tachistoscope, which was equipped with a special electronic timer for varying exposure time. In the replication investigation, a Revere Automatic slide projector equipped with an automatic shutter was used. A variac was used to regulate the level of illumination, and a Stoelting Deceptograph was used to record the GSR. The subject was seated in a lounge chair, which enabled him to recline comfortably while he looked at an opal glass screen. A posthypnotic catalepsy of the right leg and foot was produced to reduce muscle movement contamination of GSR activity. The electrodes were placed on the dorsal and volar surfaces of the foot.

In both investigations, on a table next to *S*, there was a manuscript with an attached note that read, "Very Important, Don't Touch."

Subjects. Eleven and twelve *S*'s were used in the original and replication investigations, respectively. The criterion for selection was deep somnambulism and the absence of outstanding psychopathology. All but two of the *S*'s appeared to be reasonably well adjusted. One had a postpartum hysterical aphonia of short duration, and another was in psychotherapy at the time. Seven *S*'s, who were capable of deep hypnosis, were instructed by a co-experimenter to fake hypnosis; otherwise, they were treated the same as the experimental *S*'s. Most of the *S*'s were community people of varying descriptions; a few were students who were not psychology majors. Their ages ranged from 20 to 28.

Results and discussion. As in the original study, the replication investigation produced a wide variety of psychological and somatic reactions in most of the *S*'s. Most of the reactions to *n*-words have been omitted in the following abstracts from the data.

Subject A_1 was an undergraduate who reported peculiar somatic symptoms and exhibited marked distrubances of perception at the termination of the research. The *LR* made its first appearance on set 27.

Paramnesia B. (1, *c*-word): I don't know—feel kind of strange [*What's that?*] I feel kind of strange as if I didn't want to say the word at all. (2, *n*-word): Alright. I feel a little happier now. (3, *c*-word): Oh, tensed up a bit. #1[2] (5, *n*-word): Pretty good, I don't feel anything at all. Mind if I smoke? [*Yes, we can have a cigarette during the break*.] (8, *c*-word): I'm tensed up again. (12, *n*-word): Kind of hard to describe now. Right after the last word something started to crawl all over me right after "quarter." I felt good when I reported it to you, then I felt something crawl all over me. Very funny. #2 (15, *c*-word): More tense—uneasiness. #3 (18, *n*-word): No uneasiness. #4 (25, *c*-word): OK, kind of tensed up though. (26, *n*-word): I don't know, it's hard to say—for some reason I felt a little wave sweep over me. [*Felt what?*] A wave of some kind sweep over. [*Do you feel uneasy?*] Hmm, hmm. (27, *c*-word): *LR*—OK. [*What's that?*] Alright, disgusted. (28, *c*-word): *LR*—I don't know. [*What's that?*] Kind of mad—*LR*—disgusted—*LR*. (29, *c*-word): Same way, completely mad at somebody or something. I feel like hitting somebody. (30, *c*-word): Not too bad this time. (31, *c*-word): *LR*—MAD! [He shouted out the word and violently turned to his left, away from the papers. He was in a state of extreme muscular tension and partially bent over the left side of the arm chair. His teeth were clenched and he grimaced as if racked with pain.] I am real mad. [*Real mad?*] Yes! [65 seconds later *E* asked if he felt any better.] It's very strange. [*What?*] The feeling you get. You get real mad and you want to hit somebody and you don't know what it's about. It's gradually going away.

Subject B_1 was a graduate student in chemistry who reacted with a marked feeling of separation between body and mind. The *LR* never made an appearance.

Several months after the termination of the research he requested a personal interview in which he described accusatory, auditory hallucinations of long standing that were directed against latent homosexual tendencies. His symptoms were not exacerbated by having served as an *S*; however, his relationship with *E* offered him an opportunity to make a plea for help.

Paramnesia B. (2, *c*-word): I don't know, I think my body is uneasy. Nothing particularly on my mind. (3, *c*-word): My left shoulder just twitched. My mind is running around bouncing from one thing to another. Sort of bouncing around and I don't know what. (4, *c*-word): My mind is almost stuck on one thing but I don't know what it is. Relaxed except for my left shoulder. [*What's wrong with your left shoulder?*] I don't know, I feel it tightening up a little bit. #1 (5, *n*-word): I'm relaxed, nothing in particular. (6, *c*-word): I don't know, my left arm is tight, and it feels like something inside of me filling up. [*Like something inside of you filling up?*] Like a little beaker, and you pour water into it. [*Ever have that feeling before?*] Yes, I have. [*Is it an uncomfortable feeling?*] Well, I usually have those feelings when I'm down in the dumps and sometimes when—when there—there is one particular fellow in the house that I don't like and when I'm around him I get this feeling sometimes. Sometimes it runs over. [*The beaker runs over?*] Yes, it does. [*You react like a true chemist then?*] Yes. (much laughter) (9, *c*-word): My body is a little bit tense and I have that feeling again. #2 (10, *n*-word): I'm relaxed drowsy and nothing in particular on my mind. #3 (12, *n*-word): I'm still relaxed. I'm not as drowsy now. Nothing in particular on my mind. (14, *c*-word): My body feels very tense and—the cup is getting fuller and fuller— [*How are you doing now?*] My right arm is real tight. #4 (15, *c*-word): I'm very

[2] This refers to the counting procedure.

tight. The beaker is just about full. (16, *c*-word): I'm tight again, and—I'm—there's something— [*Something what?*] I'm staring at these papers on this chair and I'm very tight. The beaker is just about up to the top. (19, *c*-word): My body is tight and again and I keep staring at these papers. My left hand wants to go over to it. (22, *c*-word): Tightening up. (24, *c*-word): My body is just tight, and I keep staring at those papers. [*What papers?*] The ones on the chair. [*Why do you do that?*] I want to tear them up, but they say "Very Important." [*You say you want to tear them up?*] Yes! (emphatic tone of voice) (25, *c*-word): I'm very tight—beaker is just— [*What?*] Beaker is just about ready to run over. (26, *c*-word): I'm tight and the beaker has just run over. [*What?*] The beaker has just run over, and I have the feeling that I might tear these papers up. [*Anything else?*] Well—nothing actually, I guess it's some feeling—I know I shouldn't because they are marked "Don't touch." (27, *c*-word): I'm all tight again (perplexed tone of voice). It's all I can do to keep my left hand from going over there and grabbing hold of the papers. [*How do you feel toward the papers?*] Well, I don't actually feel anything except that—I'm kind of mixed up because I want to do one thing and I know that—well, they're obviously somebody's.

Subject E_1 was a female who displayed a complex set of emotional reactions to the induced materials. The amnesia for the paramnesia broke down and she became confused about the reality of her memory. The *LR* made its first appearance on set 4.

Paramnesia B. #1 (1, *c*-word): I have the feeling that I'm looking for something, but I don't know what. #2 (3, *c*-word): I have a funny kind of trapped feeling like you have when you do something real stupid and get yourself into an obligatory situation. (4, *c*-word): *LR*—I'm nervous. [*You're what?*] I'm nervous, I feel—I feel guilty sort of. I mean kind of the same feeling you have when you feel awfully guilty; probably because I've been able to get so few. (6, *c*-word): *LR*—very nervous. Did you ever hide? I mean the same kind of excitement when you were hiding from someone. (7, *c*-word): *LR*—Terrible. I—I feel like I used to feel in the seventh grade like when I used to walk home from a party after curfew and I would run into a cop. (8, *c*-word): *LR*—I feel very upset. [*What's that?*] I feel as though I should be able to feel guilty, but maybe it's because I'm not doing better. Very guilty in fact—and foolish. As if I've done something very foolish. (12, *n*-word): I feel, I feel ashamed. #3 (14, *n*-word): I, ah, I seem to feel more hostile now. [*Is this the first time you felt that way?*] Yes. (18, *c*-word): *LR*—terrible, I'm very angry at myself—someone else, too. Someone in particular, but I don't know who. (19, *c*-word): *LR*—Very upset. [*In what way?*] A strange combination of feelings. Definitely hostile and then guilty and to escape and hide from a certain thing—*LR*. (20, *c*-word): *LR*—Ah, I don't—sort of vaguely remembering a scene, and I don't know whether I dreamt it or—some specific reason I feel that it really couldn't have happened. In a way it seems very very real: a scene out of my childhood involving these same emotions. (21, *n*-word): *LR*—Tremendously confused, I feel like I have a hurricane going on inside of me. (22, *c*-word): *LR*—I don't know. I feel as if I'm being pulled in two different directions at once and I keep on remembering this vague scene of little children in a classroom after school—*LR*—and there's something very important about it. (26, *n*-word): I—I've got the same feeling of prolonged expectancy—*LR*—kind of waiting for something to happen. Waiting to be caught actually is the feeling. (27, *c*-word): *LR*—Terrible. I don't want to look at the screen anymore at all. It's a struggle to keep concentrating on it. (28, *n*-word): *LR*—Ghastly, I feel almost like crying.

Subject H_1 was a married female who displayed a number of derivatives and whose verbal reports revealed the operation of perceptual vigilance and defense. Like Subject E_1, the amnesia for the paramnesia broke down but it was perceived as a real experience. The *LR* made its first appearance on set 4.

Paramnesia A. (1, *c*-word): Fine—felt like I could look at it and look at it again to see what it was—be sure what it was—be sure what it was. (2, *c*-word): Sheer guessing. #1 (4, *c*-word): Hungry (laughed)—*LR*—maybe that's because the word was "food"—(Prerecognition response to 5, *c*-word): The word is so clear that you feel you should see it, but yet you don't know what it is. (5, *c*-word): I don't know what I saw but I think of the word "cheese." I don't know whether I saw "cheese" or not (buzzer sounded). I did, I'm surprised, I had no sensation of recognizing the word at all. The word "cheese" is what I thought of even though I had no feeling of having seen the word "cheese." It's kind of like you know what somebody is doing ten miles away yet you have no way of knowing what actually has happened. It's the weirdest feeling. (7, *n*-word): Fine. #2 (9, *c*-word): *LR*—Fine. I'm glad to see a nice long word. I've got odd sensations or something. I don't know why I think of these words. (10, *n*-word): Fine. (11, *n*-word): Groggy (laughed). I feel that I'm not watching as fast as I should. #3 (14, *n*-word): Ah, just suddenly decided that I'm not going to be annoyed if I can't figure out what they are. [*Have you felt annoyed?*] Uh uh, I'm beginning to feel annoyed. (Prerecognition response to *c*-word): I'm not sure. The word was clear, but I don't know what it was. A big word but it escapes me. (15, *c*-word): *LR*—I guess it's the word "geometry." Ah, I don't feel anything. I feel kind of blank—*LR*—I don't like "geometry." [*Why?*] I guess that I could never do a good job at it (laugh). I couldn't grasp the theorems. I think that geometric things are pretty but I don't like geometry. [*Why?*] I'm thinking that I don't dislike geometry, I hate it—(long pause)— [*What's on your mind now?*] I can't understand how geometry can be so ugly and geometric figures be so beautiful. #4 (19, *n*-word): (She yawned.) [*Getting drowsy?*] A little bit, not bad though. More relaxed than drowsy. (20, *c*-word): I jumped the gun—*LR*—I was so eager to say "rectangle." (22, *n*-word): A little bit annoyed. [*When did you begin to feel annoyed?*] I don't know, some word brought it back. It reminded me of the party and statue. It annoyed me to think about it. (25, *c*-word): *LR*—Would you object if I put these papers on the table? [*No, go right ahead.*] I believe I would tear up his property if they were there much longer. [*You mean you felt like tearing up those papers?*] Yes. I'm sure he's put a lot of work into them so I'll put them away so I won't touch them— [*How long have you felt that way?*] Oh . . . something happened a little while ago that made me feel like I wanted to, and if you would have asked me right then I would have told you to go jump into the lake. I was about to tear up the papers, then *something interrupted* my thoughts. I don't know what it was—frustrating to show your temper and emotions and you just can't hide them. [*I gather you don't like to show them too much?*] It's not that I don't like to show them, it's that I've been taught not to. It's better off if you do than to learn not to. (26, *c*-word): Still annoyed—I'd rather not think about food—I'm thinking about food and I'm getting madder, and I'm thinking about the party which makes me even madder, which gives me the guilty feeling of being on the warpath. I'd be yelling at some poor innocent person. [*Some party you're talking about?*] Yeah. (27, *n*-word): Oh I wish that I could simmer down a bit. Did you ever get so upset that your head just throbs? [*Yes, is that what it is doing now?*] Yes. [*You've got a headache?*] Oh, I guess so. It's more of a tension ache than a headache. [*When did you start feeling that?*] Oh, just when I started thinking about the party.

The following *S*'s served in the original study in which the conflict was "overwhelming" from the beginning.

Subject *H* was a married female whose remarks began to show subceptual characteristics near the midpoint of the session. The *LR* was in evidence throughout the session.

Paramnesia B. (1, *c*-word): Alright—I feel a little twitchy. (2, *c*-word): *LR*—kind of depressed. [*Any reason?*] I didn't feel that way when I came in. (3, *c*-word): *LR*—I'm getting a little squeamish in the stomach. (7, *n*-word): I'm fine. (11, *c*-word): *LR*—I can't explain exactly. As if I couldn't get my breath or something—*LR*. (12, *c*-word): *LR*—Very funny. That was clearer than some of the other words that aren't clear, but yet I'm dubious about it. I don't seem to want to see what it is. I almost sensed that I saw it a while ago. Then I decided I didn't see it. (14, *c*-word): *LR*—I'm scratching my hand—sort of squeamish again. (15, *n*-word): Little better now—difference in feeling is more of the feeling of confidence being returned. (16, *c*-word): *LR*—Very peculiar. Thought I saw it before. Felt tight inside as if I might see it again. Something might happen. (17, *n*-word): Relieved again. (19, *c*-word): *LR*—Feel tense again—*LR* (20, *c*-word): *LR*—Feel sort of tired. Complete lack of feeling. (23, *n*-word): Those last two words (*n*-words) I could hardly see, but I guessed them very easily.

Subject *I* was a married female who made only somatic complaints at first. Near the end of the session feelings of anger were directed toward herself and her complaints became more psychological.

Paramnesia B. (6, *c*-word): I'm fidgeting around here. (7, *c*-word): Well, I'm uncomfortable. Just ache all over. (8, *c*-word): Terrible, I'm stiff, very stiff and my hands hurt. I'm fit for a hospital. (9, *c*-word): OK, a little better. If only my back didn't hurt so much. It feels like I'm pregnant again. (13, *n*-word): Little better. Left arm is so itchy. (18, *c*-word): OK. My left hand is awfully stiff and so is my back. (19, *c*-word): OK, I feel (yawn)—I feel a wonderful sense of accomplishment, seeing all of those words. (24, *n*-word): Well, I was feeling very frustrated. I'm better now I guess. I know how a baby feels when they try to make themselves understood and nobody understands. (25, *n*-word): OK. I was just feeling angry because I couldn't get those words. I'm just sort of restless and fidgety.

Subject *J* was an unmarried female who displayed a vivid conflict between the repressive forces and the veridical processes of perception, which constitutes the phenomena of perceptual vigilance and defense.

Paramnesia A. (1, *c*-word): OK. I feel kind of hot or flushed. (12, *c*-word): I'm restless and squirmy. Getting tightening muscles. (3, *c*-word): Oh, alright. I don't know. Seems like when I get a word I get jumpy and tight. Feel like I'm red in the face, upset and frustrated. (5, *c*-word): This man bothers me that put these papers here. I don't see what the idea is. I want to touch. Like to tear it up or something—*LR*—I don't like that guy. (6, *c*-word): I'm restless, almost angry about something. Can't figure out why—*LR*. (13, *c*-word): Second thought. At first, I didn't know it. All of a sudden I did know it. (14, *n*-word): Some word I keep seeing. Can't seem to make it out—*LR*—I guess I tried too hard on that one. Kind of frustrated—angry—

should be getting them quicker—*LR*. (16, *c*-word): I got the feeling that it was a real sharp one, but I wasn't looking carefully enough. How did I ever get that one?—*LR*—Didn't think I had that good a look at it. Feel kind of wrenched—*LR*—feel bound up inside, pressure, bottled up—*LR*—peeling this wall apart. Feel that I want to do something forceful, like kicking down this frame. (17, *c*-word): Gee, I don't know how I get those long ones. Just say them when I don't think that I see them. Feel surprised—*LR*—restless, stirred up inside. [*How do you feel?*] *LR*—Don't ask me! (19, *c*-word): *LR*—Funny how you get a thought and it flies into your mind. Surprised. I bet before I get out of here, I tear up those papers. Keep touching it. Don't know why. Feel like I want to crumple it up (kept hitting papers). *LR* (20, *c*-word): Funny how those thoughts fly into your head. Sure didn't see it and—bang—it comes in—*LR*. (handles papers) It makes me so mad. I should tear it up. It's really that guy I'm mad at. He thinks he is so smart. (23, *n*-word): Another one of those second looks. Didn't think I saw anything and then it flew into my head (picked up papers and hit them). (24, *c*-word): *LR*—I didn't know I really saw it. So many surprise me. I say these with certainty at the time but my afterthought is, how did I get that? (Picked up papers)

One salient feature of the foregoing excerpts is the wide variety of symptomatic reactions that were elicited by the recognition of *c*-words. None of the five control *S*'s displayed any reaction whatsoever. The mere fact that such reactions can be produced in the laboratory is significant. Some of the *S*'s in both investigations displayed a concomitant variation in type of complaint and in degree of verbalized awareness of the induced processes. This observation is in line with White's (1956) hypothesis that the status of a conflict may play an important role in psychosomatic disorders. There was also a marked variability in awareness among *S*'s. Some *S*'s, like *H*, verbalized neither the induced anger nor the destructive impulse; other *S*'s like B_1, only verbalized the destructive urge; whereas others, like E_1, expressed only anger. Three *S*'s readily verbalized both aspects of the conflict and tore up the papers.

Many facets of the data suggested that the symptomatic behavior of the *S*'s was a function of a spontaneous repression caused by anxiety, which was activated by the induced processes upon *c*-word recognition. The following sections are devoted to the evaluation of evidence related to this possibility.

Inhibition of the Posthypnotic Suggestions. The failure of most of the *S*'s to carry out the posthypnotic suggestions is most interesting. In view of the fact that most posthypnotic suggestions are carried out immediately, why were these failed or only partially carried out? Clinicians experienced with hypnoanalytic techniques will probably recognize once again their old adversary, repression. In hypnoanalytic psychotherapy, suggestions that fail are usually those that activate anxiety-producing affect or behavior. Anxiety and/or symptoms generally result. The behavior of the experimental *S*'s is strikingly similar to the corresponding clinical phenomena.

Additional evidence for the repression hypothesis was adduced at the termination of the research, when *E* attempted to produce recall of the paramnesia. The subject was told that when *E* mentioned the name of the building, he would recall the events that *E* had recounted to him and that he would have a desire to tell *E* about them. Most of the *S*'s recalled the event as a real experience in their lives, which they recounted with occasional omissions and distortions. Other *S*'s referred to it as a vivid dream that was difficult to differentiate from reality. In some cases, recall could not be produced in a direct manner. A few *S*'s did not recall the paramnesia subsequent to the posthypnotic signal and failed to recall even after additional trances with strong suggestions to comply with the posthypnotic suggestion to recall. They were able to recall the paramnesia only when *E* told them, under hypnosis, that these events really did not happen and that they really did not feel the way *E* had said. The period following the posthypnotic cue for recall was generally characterized by occasional GSR's, while *S* talked about irrelevant matters, in contrast to the period after reassurrance, which produced partial recall and frequent GSR's.

Inhibition of the Posthypnotic Suggestion and the GSR. The *S*'s of the replication study were divided into so-called Poor Repressors (PR) and Good Repressors (GR). The former progressively verbalized more awareness of the induced processes, as a function of the counting procedure, in contrast to the latter who did not show awareness at any time. There were six *S*'s in each group.

Figure 1 shows the effect of increasing intensity of the induced processes on the GSR. Progressive biasing effects such as adaptation and

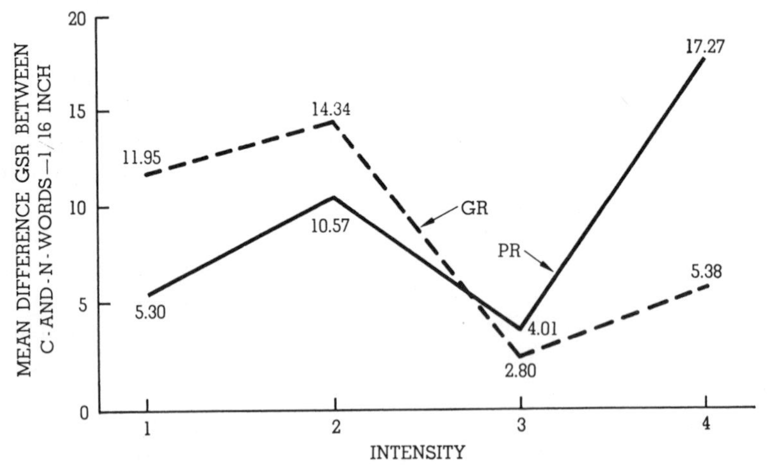

Figure 1. Relative GSRs over levels of intensity for Good Repressors (GR) and Poor Repressors (PR).

polarization of the electrodes were offset by using the average difference in GSR between *c*- and *n*-words at each level of intensity. The differences among levels and the interaction between groups and levels were both significant at the .05 level.

The GSR data can help us to decide whether we are really dealing with repression or merely suppression of the posthypnotic suggestions. It is well known that deceit is easily detectable by heightened GSR activity; however, the GR, or "dishonest" group, decreased in GSR activity as the intensity of the induced processes increased. The opposite was true for the PR or "honest" group.

These results support the repression hypothesis. If repression is to be maintained, an increase in the intensity of the induced process requires at least an equal increase in inhibitory processes. A dampening of central nervous system activity is to be expected.

The Demand Characteristics of the Research. The division of the *S*'s into poor and good repressor groups offered additional data for analyzing the demand characteristics of the research design. Because none of the *S*'s in the faking control group verbalized awareness or tore up the papers, it could be argued that the demand characteristics of the design encouraged noncompliance with the posthypnotic suggestions. Except for the symptomatic reactions of the good repressor group, their behavior is similar to the control group and bolsters this interpretation. The contrasting behavior of the poor repressor group, however, becomes very interesting in this context. All the *S*'s in this group manifested some degree of awareness at some time, all displayed symptomatic behavior, and two tore up the papers. Could the demand characteristics of a research design be in conflict with the induced processes? Even though *S* perceives that *E* really does not want him to behave in a given way, the induced processes remain influential in precisely the way they were suggested. It seems possible that the compulsive quality of the suggestions per se might not be offset by the broader interpretive context of the research. This is consistent with the widely shared observation that a posthypnotic suggestion is often carried out despite the lack of an amnesia for the hypnosis. These *S*'s usually carry out the suggestion while rationalizing their behavior or with a frank confession that they must because the urge to comply creates too much discomfort.

The good repressor group highlights the necessity for keeping in mind that *S*'s bring to the research complex systems of values and conditionings that are descriptive of the culture but vary in the degree to which they characterize a given *S*'s behavior. In our middle-class culture, there are strong social pressures against acting upon hostile, destructive impulses as well as restraints built into the personality in the course of development. The complete lack of compliance by the control and good repressor groups may reflect a predisposition to react against the "induced" material, which might or might not be consistent with the demand characteristics of the research. If the demand characteristics of the design were in the direction of acting-out the induced material, they could be completely nullified by the restraints of subject variables. More precisely, hypnotically induced suggestions specifying behavior inconsistent with the cultural and psychological conditionings of *S* may produce anxiety and become inhibited by *S*'s characteristic mechanisms of defense. Because this restraint may also characterize control *S*'s, it may be impossible to ascertain fully the demand characteristics of the research; that is, *S* may perceive that *E* wants him to commit an antisocial act, but his own defenses restrain him. Thus, the demand characteristics can be in conflict with both subject variables and the intrinsic compulsive quality of the induced processes. In this case variance due to demand characteristic may be small or zero.

A comparison of the control, poor and good repressor groups indicates that the demand characteristics of the research design do not account for the symptomatic reactions of the experimental *S*'s, particularly the behavior of the poor repressors. If this analysis is correct, then the absence of verbalized awareness and paper-tearing in the good repressors indicates that the inhibition was probably due to subject or personality variables rather than to demand characteristics of the research design. The primary conflict seemed to have been between the induced processes and personality variables, and the reactions that were produced appear to be valid psychopathology.

The amount of evidence that is necessary to establish repression as a genuine phenomenon undoubtedly varies from one investigator to another. Some investigators will be satisfied by what has been shown already and others will not. For myself, I do not know of another concept that can even begin to integrate the data that have been considered so far. The skeptical investigator, however, can substitute another term or explanatory principle for every phenomenon in the text that is designated as a manifestation or function of repression. I am sure that he will be dissatisfied with the unwieldy, heterogeneous set of *ad hoc* hypotheses that he had to formulate.

An Index of Repression. If repression is assumed to be the opposite of verbalized awareness, then an index of repression can be devised simply by counting instances of verbalized awareness:

$$R = \frac{3 \sum (FA) + 2 \sum (PA) + \sum (CC) - \sum (CR)}{Tc}$$

where R is the average degree of repression over the experimental sessions; FA, full awareness upon c-word recognition; PA, partial awareness upon c-word recognition (awareness of either the hostility or the destructive impulse); CC, conscious correlates of the unconscious hostility upon *c*-word recognition, such as feelings of annoyance with the task of recognizing words; *CR*, complete repression upon *c*-word recognition (no instances of symptoms or awareness); and *Tc*, the total number of conflict words recognized.

In view of the omnipresent possibility of suppression of the verbalization of experienced affect upon the recognition of *c*-words, instances of full awareness were considered to be more important in assessing the average degree of repression than were partial awareness; therefore, the former were multiplied by a constant of 3, whereas the latter were multiplied by a constant of 2. Conscious correlates are assumed to indicate the mislabeling of the conscious representations of the relevant dynamics. The *S* is aware of some affect, but it is weak enough so that his cognitive appraisal of it may be distorted. Instances of *c*-word recognition with no verbalized awareness and no symptoms were assumed to be the outcome of complete repression and for that reason were subtracted from instances of the foregoing quantities. Because all of these quantities are divided by the total number of *c*-words, *R* is a term that expresses the average degree of repression per *c*-word recognized.

Classification of Reactions. The reactions of the *S*'s in the original investigation generated a number of different categories that seemed clinically meaningful and were determined to have interscore reliabilities ranging from Phi coefficient of .75 to .95. Categories 1 to 8 were ordered on a continuum of repression by computing Spearman rank order coefficients between *R* and the proportion of reactions in each category. The progressively increasing awareness of the induced processes determined the order of categories 9 to 13.

1. Symptoms characterized by the dominance of autonomic system enervation such as feelings of nausea, gastric distress, headache, tiredness, sleepiness, tachycardia, pressure in head, sweating, skin disturbances, flushing, organ dysfunctions, heaviness, temperature alterations, and such feelings as "queasy" and "antsy."
2. Symptoms dominated by enervation of the somatic or muscular nervous system such as stiffness, aches, pains, tension, tics, tremors, physical discomfort, and so on.
3. Disturbances of affect
   a. Flattening: lack of feeling, apathy, and the like upon the recognition of a *c*-word, when symptoms usually attend *c*-word recognition.
   b. Superego reactions: feelings of being alone, abandoned, ashamed, depressed, disgusted, guilty, worried, and so on.
   c. Inversion: definite feelings of well-being upon the recognition of a *c*-word.

d. Alienation: feelings that seem weird, strange, odd, unreal, unnatural, foreign, and so on.

4. Unspecified distress that cannot be clearly categorized as either physical or emotional in nature, in *S*'s frame of reference, and are expressed in such conventional terms as being upset, fidgety, jittery, nervous, on edge, restless, and bothered.
5. States of emotional agitation that reflect the reaction of the ego to the threat of complete breakdown of repression, such as feelings of anxiety, fear, apprehension, and terror.
6. States of confusion, doubt, and disorientation that include statements that one's thoughts are being pushed or pulled and that the content of thought cannot be specified.
7. Dissociative reactions
   a. Somatic and ideational delusions such as limbs feeling detached, "crazy" thoughts and intruding paranoid ideas.
   b. Strong compulsive urges not carried out in behavior, such as wanting to move hands around, scratch at something, and so on.
   c. Recognition light response (*LR*).
   d. Compulsive destructive urge acted out in behavior without awareness of the relevant hostile or destructive impulse, such as hitting or picking at the papers without knowing why, including destructive acts not directed at the papers.
8. Disturbance or distortion in perception of the tachistoscopic stimulus.
9. Derivatives of the induced conflict. These are symbols of the induced experience and/or the repressive forces themselves. Memories of personal experiences that are congruent with, or similar to, the induced experience frequently are activated in some *S*'s.
10. Conscious correlates of the unconscious hostility, such as feelings of irritation, annoyance, and frustration.
11. Delayed awareness of one or both aspects of the conflict.
12. Immediate awareness of one aspect of the conflict.
13. Immediate and complete awareness of both aspects of the conflict.

Shall we consider the reactions from 1 to 12 to be manifestations of psychopathology? What is more psychopathological, the few *S*'s who went through the research with hardly a symptom and no awareness of the induced processes or the *S*'s who had a wide variety of symptoms and variable degrees of awareness? What is the most adjustive way for an *S* to respond to the situation? If the reactions of the experimental groups that were not shared by the control group are defined as being psychopathological, then all the above reactions must be considered to be psychopathological. The one *S* with the fewest symptoms (she had one) also had a veritably flat GSR throughout both sessions and was one of the *S*'s who could not recall the paramnesia upon the posthypnotic signal. Outside the experimental situation she seemed to be quite colorless and bland, which suggests that much of her affective life was subject to repression. Such comprehensive and unrelenting repression may also be psychopathological. This possibility creates the apparent paradox of both the presence and absence of a reaction being symptomatic. This paradox can be resolved if we keep in mind that *c*-word recognition causes a sudden increase in the intensity of covert, anxiety-producing processes, which in turn trigger a defensive reaction. Most *S*'s react with a partial breakdown of repression, whereas some *S*'s react with heightened repression. The brief time that *S*'s defenses are put into disequilibrium presents an opportunity to observe the symptomatology that he will display whenever there is an insufficiency in his vital defenses, regardless of how it is brought about. This interpretation is supported by the observation that some of the *S*'s had a recurrence of symptoms that had accompanied an emotional disturbance earlier in their lives.

The above discussion is consistent with Freud's statement about the motive and purpose of repression:

> We recall the fact that the motive and purpose of repression was simply the avoidance of "pain." It follows that the fate of the charge of affect belonging to the presentation is far more important than that of the ideational content of it and is decisive for the opinion we form of the process of repression. (1948, p. 92)

Most research on the Freudian concept of repression has focused on the fate of ideas or percepts, rather than affect. If Freud was correct, which is suggested by the present data, it is understandable why the research literature in this area is ambiguous. The researcher who is interested in investigating Freud's concept of repression must keep in mind that the degree of energy, or charge of affect, will determine the point at which repression takes place as well as the remoteness of the derivative.

Degree of Repression and Type of Psychopathology. In the original study the relationship between *R* and the type of reaction was tested by obtaining the Spearman rank order correlation between *R* and the proportion of somatic complaints for the *S*'s. Because the categories designating awareness (11 to 13) and conscious correlates (10) entered into the computation of *R*, they were not included in the total number of reactions from which the proportion of somatic reactions was computed. The obtained correlation of .74 is significant at the .05 level. The same data were available in the replication study after the fourth count (overwhelming intensity) and the obtained correlation was .78, which is significant at the .01 level.

The main purpose of the counting procedure in the replication study was to test this relationship by attempting to reduce progressively the degree of repression in the *S*'s (poor repression group). The same sequence of symptoms should unfold that was generated in the original study by spontaneous fluctuations in the degree of repression, and that was determined objectively by ordering the categories on the basis of

Table 1
Means, Ranks, and Reliabilities of the Categories for the Poor Repression Group

SEQUENCE OF CATEGORIES	MEAN COUNT AND RANK: SESSION 1		SESSION 2		COMBINED		RELIABILITY OF CATEGORY
	Mean	Rank	Mean	Rank	Mean	Rank	
1	2.36	3	2.09	1	2.18		−.45
2	2.25	2	2.65	5	2.59	5	.24
3	2.52	5	2.48	3	2.50	2	.77*
4	2.20	1	2.85	7	2.58	4	−.30
5	2.62	6	2.76	6	2.71	7	.42
6	3.40	10	3.07	8	3.14	9	.16
7	3.10	7	2.42	2	2.64	6	−.43
8	2.40	4	2.60	4	2.50	3	.97*
9	3.17	8	2.83	9	2.95	8	.76*
10	3.55	9	3.14	10	3.25	10	.47*

* Significant at the .01 level.

the size of the correlations. Table 1 shows the putative sequence of categories and the average count and rank for each category for the poor repressor group. The rank order correlations between the putative sequence and sessions 1 and 2 were .67 and .61, respectively, and the correlations between the combined sessions and the putative sequence was .70. All three of the correlations are significant at the .05 level. Categories 4 and 7 were very unstable from session to session and category 8 seems to have been misplaced. Category 7, like 6, is a composite of allegedly related reactions, which may or may not occupy different places on the continuum; nevertheless, these reactions were combined because of their relatively low frequency of occurrence.

The similar scores for some of the categories make it unlikely that each category represents a discrete point on the continuum. Some of them may be alternative or equivalent reactions that are determined primarily by idiosyncratic aspects of *S*'s personality structure and/or small differences in the organization of underlying neurophysiological processes. Unfortunately, there is no way to resolve these problems with the present data. More data needs to be collected to stabilize the category means. When this has been accomplished, the true scores can be estimated more accurately and final decisions reached about the ordering of categories.

Both investigations showed that as repression weakens, there is an increase in the frequency of reactions and the number of categories used. The rank order correlation between *R* and the frequency of reactions to *c*-word recognition for the original and replication investigations were —.68 and —.80, respectively. These are significant at the .05 and .01 levels. The corresponding correlations between *R* and the number of categories were —.45 and —.79. Only the latter is significant at the .05 level. These findings suggest that as repression weakens, there is an increase in the kinds of reactions and, perforce, the frequency of reactions. Subjects who achieved some degree of awareness invariably manifested reactions in many or even all of the prior categories. In contrast, some *S*'s who did not verbalize any awareness experienced very few reactions, with all of these being in categories 1 and 2. Thus, as repression begins to break down, the first reactions are likely to be somatic in nature. With further diminution of repression, additional reactions are produced without there being necessarily a reduction in the absolute number of reactions in the prior categories.

Because the data strongly suggest that repression was activated by the stimulation of the induced processes, the presentation of the remaining data will be guided by the delineation of Freud's early views, which have not been cited in most secondary sources. He described repression as being "specific," "mobile," and "variable."

The Specific Nature of Repression. Freud described the "specific" attribute of repression as follows:

> We can lay down no general rule concerning the degree of distortion and remoteness necessary before the resistance of consciousness is abrogated. In this matter a delicate balancing takes place, the play of which is hidden from us; its mode of operation, however, leads us to infer that it is a question of a definite degree of intensity in the cathexis of the unconscious—beyond which it would break through for satisfaction. Repression acts, therefore, in a *highly specific* manner in each instance; every single derivative of the repressed may have its peculiar fate—a little more or a little less distortion alters the whole issue. (1948, pp. 88–89)

A considerable body of data favored the hypothesis that perceptual vigilance and defense are manifestations of the specific nature of repression; however, before getting into these data more information is needed about Freud's views. In regard to perception, Freud was both a one- and two-process theorist. He clearly delineated a one-process position in connection with the normal mental apparatus:

> Our perceptions are linked with one another in our memory. . . . It is clear, then, that if the *Pcpt.* system has no memory whatever, it cannot retain any associative traces; the separate *Pcpt.* elements would be intolerably obstructed in performing their function if the remnant of an earlier connection were to exercise an influence upon a fresh perception. (1960, p. 539)

He adopted a two-process position with respect to psychopathology:

> If the sexual component-instinct which makes use of sight—sexual "lust of the eye"—has drawn down upon itself, through its exorbitant demands, some retaliatory measure from the side of the ego-instincts, so that the ideas which represent the content of its strivings are subjected to repression and witheld from consciousness, the general relation of the eye and the faculty of vision to the ego and to consciousness is radically disturbed. (1959, p. 110)

The foregoing quotations indicate that the veridicality of perception should be affected only by active intrapsychic conflict, not memories per se. Furthermore, there must be a "miscarriage of repression" if psychogenic visual disturbances and symptoms are to be produced. Accordingly, it might be worthwhile if research in perceptual vigilance and defense used neurotic *S*'s rather than "normal" or nonclinical *S*'s, unless conflict of neurotic magnitude can be created in the latter.

Both of the hypnotic investigations support the hypothesis that perceptual vigilance and defense represent processes of facilitation and inhibition operating in the region of the psychophysical threshold of visual recognition. During the prerecognition trials near the visual recognition threshold, some of the *S*'s showed what seemed to be moment-to-moment fluctuations in the status of the conflict. At one moment the status of the conflict favored the recognition of a *c*-word and at another, it favored an *n*-word. Citations and excerpts from a number of the protocols of both investigations are given below that seem to illustrate that occasionally these processes could be verbalized.

Let us go back to the verbatim protocol of subjects A_1, H, H_1, and J. Discussion of subject A_1 will be deferred, but attention is directed to the prerecognition and recognition reactions of subject H_1 on set 5 (Paramnesia *B*). A similar reaction was elicited in another *S* by the same paramnesia. She said, after recognizing a *c*-word, "I got it but I didn't see it. Have you ever been thinking about things only just to get angry? [*Kind of angry feelings?*] Yes, only I can't think of what it is though."

Table 2 shows the protocol of one *S* in the original investigation who recognized only two *c*-words. In the latter third of the session his prerecognition behavior showed marked subceptual characteristics. The *LR* made its first appearance, and it occurred only when the position (top or bottom) designated as "brighter" coincided with the actual position of the *c*-word. He also began reporting symptoms before recognition. Because it seemed that perceptual vigilance and defense were strongly

Table 2
Reproduction of a Series of Trials Illustrating Perceptual Vigilance and Defense*

T-SCOPE SETTING TRIAL	ACTUAL POSITION OF *C*-WORD	POSITION CALLED "BRIGHTER"	WORD RECOGNIZED
39	T (top)	B (bottom)	"square" (*n*-word)
40	B	T	
41	T	B	
42	T	T	
43	T	B	"square" (*n*-word)
44	T	T *LR*	
45	B	B *LR* (getting edgy)	
46	T	T *LR*	"money" (*c*-word)-*LR*
	Q. [*How are you doing?*]	*A*. I'm getting flushed and warm.	

* Entries in the body of the table refer to that part of an ascending series of trials following the recognition of the *n*-word "square."

and consistently in evidence at this time, *E* decided to continue presenting the word pair on set 16—after an *n*-word had been recognized—just to see what would happen. Table 2 shows what happened following the recognition of the *n*-word "square." The *LR* occurred only when the aperture designated as "brighter" coincided with the position of the *c*-word, and a symptom was produced just before recognition, on trial 45. At no time in the research did this *S* ever verbalize awareness of the induced process, and almost all his symptoms were of a somatic nature.

Subject A_1 in the replication study produced an unusually compelling set of data (see protocol reproduced earlier). He was a tall, muscular senior who appeared to be quite deferential and motivated to please authority figures. In psychoanalytic terms, he appeared to have strong oral-dependent trends.

Although he recognized *c*-words in relation to food, there were many cues that strongly suggested the operation of perceptual vigilance and defense to the *c*-word "milk," such as hitting the arm of the chair when "milk" was presented but not recognized, large GSR's, and reductions in levels of confidence and brightness. Because of these reactions, "milk" and its paired *n*-word "gold" were reintroduced on three more occasions, with the recognition of "gold" and the same general pre-recognition reactions. It seemed that "milk" was able to activate greater threat and inhibitory reactions than other *c*-words near the visual recognition threshold. Instead of terminating after the last set, *E* decided to present "milk" alone without also presenting "gold." The reader should bear in mind that in the replication study the tachistoscopic procedure was modified. The paired words were not presented simultaneously in two apertures, but were singly presented in one aperture in random order at each level of illumination. Table 3 is a reproduction of this last special set of trials-to-recognition of "milk."

Table 3
Series of Trials for Subject A_1 Illustrating Perceptual Vigilance and Defense

WORD	T-SCOPE SETTING	LEVEL OF CONFIDENCE	BRIGHTNESS "BRIGHTER"	"SAME"	"DULLER"	GSR*	REMARKS
"milk"	38	D (doubtful)					
"	39	C (confident)			*x*	0	
"	40	C		*x*		0	
"	41	N (nothing)			*x*	0	
"	41	C	*x*			9	Smile
"	41	N			*x*	0	
"	42	C	*x*			0	
"gold"	42	C	*x*			41	Gold—mild feeling of hate
"milk"	42	N			*x*	0	
"	42	C	*x*			0	
"	43	C	*x*			0	
"	44	C	*x*			11	Shilling
"	45	N			*x*	0	
"quarter"	45	C	*x*			0	
"milk"	45	C			*x*	0	
"	46	C		*x*		0	
"	47	C	*x*			0	
"	47	C			*x*	0	
"quarter"	48	C			*x*	15	Quarter—slightly frustrated
"milk"	48	C	*x*				
"	49	C	*x*			0	Guild
"	49	C		*x*		0	
"	50	C	*x*			44	Mil—it was much brighter
"	51					57	Milk—MAD†

* The scores in this column represent 1/16 of an inch.
† See protocol for his complete reaction.

The shift in confidence to "nothing" at a setting of 41, after the prerecognition hypothesis "smile," indicated that perception was being influenced. To test this further, "gold" was inserted and presented at a setting of 43. It was recognized with an attendant feeling of "hate." "Milk" was immediately presented and it elicited a shift in confidence to the "nothing" level. After another "nothing" response at 45, the word "quarter" was presented and was not recognized. No further symptomatic reactions were elicited, except for the increasingly long delay in recognition, until setting 48 at which time "quarter" was again substituted for "milk" and it was recognized. He reported feeling okay. The comment on the next trial indicated that a defensive inhibition was still operating in connection with the word "milk." At the extremely high level of 50, the prerecognition hypothesis of "mil," which is structurally similar to "milk," was accompanied by a very large GSR. "Milk" finally was recognized on the next trial and was followed by the loud exclamation of "I'M MAD" and he violently turned in the chair, *away from the papers*. The rest of his reactions can be read from the protocol.

There is little doubt about the reality of perceptual vigilance and defense in relation to the word "milk." Not only was recognition delayed to a point 4.99 sigmas above the mean threshold for the session, but there is ample evidence that discrimination was occurring on some of the trials below this point. The most significant outcome of the session was the peculiar ability of the word "milk" to elicit greater inhibitory and defensive reactions than the other *c*-words in the category of food. This is particularly meaningful because the other *c*-words were eliciting reactions and hostile affect was being expressed. The destructive impulse, however, was not expressed directly but was expressed symptomatically (upon the recognition of "milk") by the violent turning away from the papers and the extreme muscular tension. As was observed in the original study, the joint awareness of both aspects of the conflict was avoided. Either the anger or the destructive impulse could be tolerated singly, but not together. Why the word "milk" should have greater activating properties in an oral-dependent personality cannot be explained in terms of the present data. A psychoanalytic interpretation is that "milk" is vitally involved in the organization of his drives, gratifications, conflicts, and defenses and is so charged with affect that the additional burden of conflict brought about by the paramnesia rendered ego-controls and defensive reactions less effective than for other *c*-words. Again it is evidenced that the management of affect is the primary motivation for repression, and the delay in perception of the word "milk" was commensurate with the intensity of the repressed affect and impulse. Also in agreement with the Freudian formulation of repression and the results of the original study is the conclusion from this protocol that emotional processes interfere with the veridicality of perception only under conditions of severe emotional conflict, and even then the impairment is likely to be infrequent and transitory for most *S*'s.

Because poor repressors often made prerecognition hypotheses in the area of conflict, they were considered to have a set favoring *c*-words and therefore should have lower visual recognition thresholds. Figure 2 reveals a significant interaction between groups and levels, confirming this prediction from the original investigation. The upward trend of the good repressor group is puzzling, because it is in the direction opposite to a practice effect. If this is something other than a chance aberration in the data, it may mean that the good repressor group, which was not nearly so upset psychologically, may have experienced more fatigue or a reduction in alertness to the task.

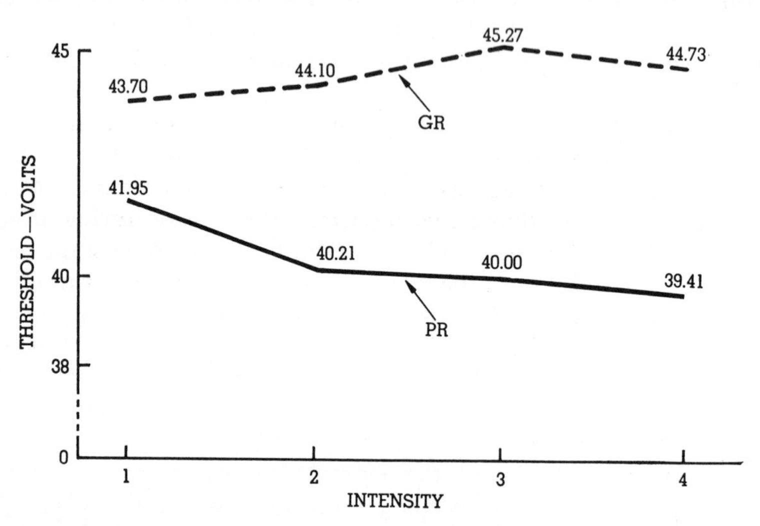

Figure 2. Visual recognition thresholds over levels of intensity for Good Repressors (GR) and Poor Repressors (PR).

The light response was a most interesting reflection of the specific nature of repression. In some sessions it made its appearance early, only to drop out later. Sometimes it would not occur until the end of a session. In other sessions, it occurred only once or twice or not at all. Although it frequently accompanied expressions of anger, it also occurred in their absence. It also occurred during prerecognition trials near the visual recognition threshold, and it was accompanied often by prerecognition hypotheses in the area of conflict. Although an extended analysis of these data is beyond the scope of this chapter, I have reason to believe that both recognition and prerecognition light responses appear to be sensitive indicators of alterations in a dynamic balance between forces of facilitation and inhibition brought about by spontaneous alterations in the status of the conflict, by prerecognition discrimination (perceptual vigilance), and by the recognition of *c*-words. An inspection of the protocols reveals that the light response is often dissociated from the hostility that it represents. For some *S*'s it often preceded the correct indentification of the nature of their distress by a number of trials, and, for other *S*'s, neither aspect of the conflict was identified (see subject *H*) despite its occurrence throughout the session.

The "Variable" Nature of Repression. Freud described this attribute of repression as follows:

> Special devices have been evolved, with the object of bringing about such changes in the play of mental forces that what usually gives rise to "pain" may on this occasion result in pleasure, and whenever such a device comes into operation, the repression of an instinct-representation that is ordinarily repudiated is abrogated. The only one of these devices which has till now been studied in any detail is that of joking. Generally the lifting of the repression is only transitory; the repression is immediately re-established. (1948, p. 89)

This attribute of repression received some support from the data. In both investigations combined, five *S*'s had relevant reactions. Subject *I* on set 19 is an example. The data are also consistent with the transitory nature of this attribute.

The "Mobile" Nature of Repression. Freud described this attribute as follows:

> The process of repression is not to be regarded as something which takes place once and for all, the results of which are permanent, as when some living thing has been killed and from that time onward is dead; on the contrary, repression demands a constant expenditure of energy, and if this were discontinued, the success of the repression would be jeopardized, so that a fresh act of repression would be necessary. We may imagine that what is repressed exercises a continuous straining in the direction of consciousness, so that the balance has to be kept by means of a steady counter-pressure. (1948, pp. 89-90)

The most convincing evidence in support of the attribute of mobility was the transitory nature of the disturbance generated by the recognition of a *c*-word. Despite the lack of an objective criterion for the cessation of the disturbance in regard to GSR activity and verbal report, the protocols typically revealed that disturbance would last from only a few seconds to several minutes. It seemed as if inhibition came into play shortly after the moment of recognition and sometimes during recognition as the protocols presented in the section on perceptual vigilance and defense suggest (subject *J* in particular).

The mobility of repression may account for one of the most interesting and puzzling facets of the observed phenomena. Over the course of a session in the original study both the degree of awareness and the symptomatic reactions of *S* were observed to fluctuate. The counting procedure of the replication study tended to mask this phenomenon. In my experience, these reactions are similar to events in psychotherapy when uncovering techniques are used (Reyher, 1963b). If a technique is used that succeeds in both increasing the strength of repressed material and reducing the effectiveness of the patient's defenses, repression often becomes unstable. This instability is reflected by the variable degree of representation of the repressed material in the continuous flow of the patient's affective states and conscious productions along with correlated changes in symptomatology. In the research being reported, the instability of repression is probably caused by the sudden and intense activation of the induced impulses, upon the recognition of *c*-words, which causes a short-lived period of disequilibrium between facilitative and inhibitory processes. The resultant shifting interplay between these processes proceeds with a variety of transitory outcomes until *S* either acts out the induced affect and impulses (Reyher, 1961a) or gains better control through greater repression and other inhibitory controls.

Antisocial Behavior. In both investigations combined, only three of the *S*'s tore up the papers and another *S* tore off a piece from the corner of the attached note. All of these *S*'s had experienced full awareness of both aspects of the conflict on one or more occasions. The three *S*'s who tore up the papers were also distinguished by the absence of symptoms that could be classified as derivatives of conscience prior to the commission of the antisocial act. Derivatives of conscience refer to feelings of guilt, anxiety, apprehension, depression, and remarks revealing the involvement of the superego. In an earlier report (Reyher, 1961a), the commission of the antisocial act was attributed to the repression of conscience or superego functions rather than repression of the id-dominated material. This line of reasoning was developed in the following way:

Hostile-destructive impulses are controlled by unconscious reactions to avoid severe qualms of conscience, which motivate *S* to behave in conformity with the norms of society. At some critical point, however, the pressure of the conflicting hostile-destructive impulses becomes so intense that qualms of conscience are repressed and *S* acts out the hostile-destructive impulses. The intrapsychic conflict is resolved and *S* experiences an extrapsychic conflict with society. The critical point probably varies from person to person. For some it may be nonexistent, and in these cases, superego development is considered to be very strong. Only *S*'s with undeveloped or weak superegos are able to repress qualms of conscience and feel comfortable while acting out their antisocial impulses. When the environment is supportive, such an individual may be able to function in conformity with prevailing norms, but any persisting situation that arouses intense anger and aggression is likely to build up these processes to a critical point. When this point is reached, conscience is repressed and he acts out the hostile-destructive impulses.

The *S*'s with strong superegos follow the Freudian model of neurosis while *S*'s with the relatively weak superegos follow the Mowrerian model (Mowrer, 1950). In terms of the present data, the latter model involves malformations in character structure and patterns of acting out id-dominated drives that bring the person into conflict with society.

NEW DIRECTIONS AND WIDER IMPLICATIONS

Now that I have completed the task of describing research relevant to the paradigm, it is clear that the research potential of hypnotically induced psychopathology is impressive. Both the artificial and natural methods of induction show much promise. In the long run, however, I suspect that the latter approach will be the most productive. The effect of artificial conflicts in "normal" *S*'s is transient and seems to lack the symbolic aspects of many naturally occurring symptoms. Also, there are ethical limitations in the nature of the processes that can be induced in volunteer *S*'s.

The term artificial may be inappropriate because a majority of *S*'s in my research experienced the induced hallucinatory experiences as real events. When *E* described the events of the paramnesia, *S* almost always hallucinated people and places from his own past. At the time of the posthypnotic cue to recall the paramnesia, most *S*'s remembered it as a real experience; some were not sure and became confused about whether it was a dream or a real experience; a few remembered it as something I told them. For the great majority of *S*'s, the paramnesia seemed to function as if it were a natural conflict.

There is evidence that a direct approach to the induction of artificial conflicts is ineffective. In a study completed recently (Rokeach, Reyher, and Wiseman, 1964), a deliberate and undisguised attempt was made to reverse or alter the beliefs of hypnotized *S*'s. These beliefs ranged from such significant matters as one's own name and death wishes toward parents to such inconsequential matters as whether it is better to bathe with soap that floats or sinks. While in hypnosis *S*'s were told that they would react with opposite feelings to a group of items, which they had rated shortly before in the waking state. Although meaningful data about belief systems were obtained, the procedure produced only a few isolated symptoms in thirty-two *S*'s. Unlike induced paramnesias, which seem to be regarded by *S* as originating in himself, direct suggestions contrary to significant personal matters appear to be regarded correctly as external in origin and, therefore, do not pose an intrapsychic threat. It is likely that the inherent, compulsive quality of the suggestions are easily offset by the defenses of *S*, which owe their superior strength to their anxiety-reducing properties.

Seitz's (1951, 1953) procedure for symptom removal is interesting. Because the pathogenic process in patients has already been induced naturally, the investigator can work backwards from the phenotype. When a symptom is removed by direct suggestion, without a suggested replacement, it appears that the pathogenic processes underlying it become activated and produce new, symbolically equivalent symptoms. When an equivalent substitute was suggested, the symptom disappeared, but when a nonequivalent symptom was suggested, it merely became a contemporary of the original. Unfortunately, symptom removal does not provide an objective description of the genotype, which, under ordinary circumstances, is not identifiable. Eisenbud (1937), however, has described a procedure for inducing parallel conflicts that might provide an objective identification. He reported a case in which the induction of a parallel conflict caused an exacerbation of the patient's symptoms. If this procedure proves to be reliable, it might be possible to identify an unknown genotype. With this procedure, a genotypic-phenotypic relationship is demonstrated if an inferred (parallel) genotype exacerbates the patient's symptoms or reproduces symptoms in remission. The inferred genotype is incorrect if it produces no symptoms or new symptoms. In this event a series of inferred genotypes must be induced until an exacerbation of existing symptoms occurs.

A case report by Ikemi and his coworkers (1959) suggests that the combined procedures of Eisenbud and Seitz might be employed to great advantage. On the basis of clinical data from a given patient, genotypes are inferred and induced until a genotypic-phenotypic bond is demonstrated. This could be the point of departure for a variety of investigations. One aspect of Seitz's (1951) findings is particularly provocative. He reported that a new but similar symptom occurred automatically whenever the original symptom was hypnotically removed. This procedure should be repeated until a great many substitute symptoms have been obtained. It would be of interest to learn if all the substitute symptoms found expression in the voluntary muscular and special organ systems, which, according to Alexander (1943), should be the case for all conversion symptoms. Perhaps some of the principles governing the so-called "language of the body" could be discovered. Another line of research could be generated by the induction of objectively determined natural genotypes in "normal" *S*'s. Would these *S*'s develop symbolic symptoms? If symbolic conversion symptoms occur, what nonhypnotic psychotherapeutic techniques achieve the best results? It may be that there is an interaction between genotypes and techniques.

The nonsymbolic or psychosomatic symptoms sorted out by the above procedures would receive no further attention. The induction of artificial conflict, however, is a method that lends itself to the investigation of these symptoms, which appear to be a joint function of the induced genotype, personality structure, and degree of repression. It is conceivable that this line of research could become instrumental in unraveling the nature of the transactions that take place between emotional and neurophysiological processes.

In most cases of natural psychopathology, symbolic and nonsymbolic symptoms probably coexist; in fact, there often may be symbolic and nonsymbolic components of the same symptom. The symbolic component may be either intrinsic or acquired. In the former case, the structure of a symptom is a vehicle to express the meaning of the genotype; in the latter case, the symptom is purely psychosomatic but meaning is acquired via experience (secondary gains). Crosscultural research would focus on the differences between symbolic and non-symbolic symptoms. If the same investigatory procedures were applied in different cultures, we might find that there are almost unlimited phenotypic possibilities, but relatively few genotypes.

The method developed by Kepecs *et al.* (1951) is very promising. They artificially created a symptom and then tried to discover what psychodynamic processes affected it. There is no reason this method could not be modified and applied to other organs or even in the realm of purely psychological processes. For example, a hand-washing compulsion could be induced by direct suggestion. The suggestions would include the instruction that this would simply occur from time to time during the course of a day for no apparent reason. After observing what happens to this response for several days, *E* interviews the *S*'s in the same manner as Kepecs *et al.* did while taking notes of what processes activate the compulsion. Or *E* can induce a series of genotypes and make detailed observations of *S*'s behavior following the induction of each one. Some genotypes should exacerbate the artificial symptom more than others, and many should not influence it at all. When the artificial symptom becomes exacerbated, it should function as a real symptom. The term "artificial" could be dropped, and the investigation of the principles governing genotypic-phenotypic relationships becomes possible.

White's (1956) hypothesis about the critical significance of the status of a conflict is consistent with the results of the posthypnotic stimulation of hypnotically induced conflict. He said:

> It may be that looking for a specific emotional constellation to go with each form of disorder, one should not rest content with describing impulses and defenses that are involved; one should rather pay particular attention to the status of the impulses. Are some of them trapped midway between being expressed and being repressed? Is it specifically this status of an impulse that allows it to activate autonomic pathways and spill its trapped energies into the viscera? (p. 441)

How does a conflict activate autonomic pathways? Although a detailed discussion of possible solutions is beyond the scope of this chapter, one possibility that has integrative potential will be mentioned. If levels of repression (or awareness) correspond to levels of cortical integration, then the phenomena of each degree of repression might be a function of the distinctive attributes of a particular level of cortical integration. Because each of these levels of cortical integration differ in the cytoarchitecture of its component structures and its connections with other cortical and subcortical structures, different patterns of psychological and physiological processes would be activated by each level. Regardless of the merits of this possibility, the laboratory production of psychopathology permits the unique incorporation on physiological and neurophysiological methods on investigation into research on psychopathology. Not only can a wide variety of symptoms be monitored, but they can be turned off and on by the presentation of critical and neutral stimuli (Reyher, 1964).

In this chapter I have defined psychopathology as the investigation of the relationships between psychodynamics and behavior. Although most behavior seems to have psychodynamic wellsprings, this relationship is observed most clearly in the phenomena of psychopathology. Like the two sides of a coin, they cannot be separated. Nonclinical investigators do not have the opportunity to observe these transactions, which are so visible in psychotherapy, particularly the intensive, uncovering varieties. The uniqueness of these clinical data has created a breakdown in communication between clinical and nonclinical investigators, but the laboratory investigation of hypnotically induced psychopathology offers the hope that these data can be lifted from their cloistered existence and exposed to the scrutiny of the scientific community. This would be a good beginning in laying a scientific foundation for psychopathology and, perhaps, clinical practice.

REFERENCES

ALEXANDER, F. (1943). "Fundamental concepts of psychosomatic research," *Psychosom. Med.*, **5**, 205–210.

DECKERT, G. H. and WEST, L. J. (1963). "Hypnosis and experimental psychopathology," *Amer. J. clin. Hyp.*, **5**, 256–276.

EISENBUD, J. (1937). "The psychology of headache," *Psychiatric Quart.*, **11**, 592–619.

ERICKSON, M. H. (1944). "The method employed to formulate a complex story for the induction of an experimental neurosis in a hypnotic subject," *J. gen. Psychol.*, **31**, 67–84.

FREUD, S. (1938). "The interpretation of dreams." In Brill, A. A. (ed.), *The Basic Writings of Sigmund Freud.* New York: The Modern Library.

——— (1948). "Repression." *In Collected Papers.* Vol. IV. Translated under supervision of Joan Rievere. London: Hogarth.

——— (1959). "Psychogenic visual disturbance according to psychoanalytical conceptions." *In Collected Papers.* Vol. II. Translated by James Strachey. New York: Basic Books.

——— (1960). *The Interpretation of Dreams.* Translated by James Strachey. New York: Basic Books.

IKEMI, Y. et. al. (1959). "Hypnotic experiments on the psychosomatic aspects of gastrointestinal disorders," *Int. J. clin. exp. Hyp.*, **7**, 139–150.

KEPECS, J., ROBIN, M., and BRUNNER, M. (1951). "Relationship between certain emotional states and exudation into the skin," *Psychosom. Med.*, **13**, 10–17.

LEVITT, E. E. (1963). "A comment on 'A paradigm for determining the clinical relevance of hypnotically induced psychopathology,'" *Psychol. Bull.*, **60**, 326–329.

MOORE, W. F. (1964). "*The effects of posthypnotic stimulation of hostility upon motivation*," *Amer. J. clin. Hyp.*, **7**, 130–135.

MOWRER, O. H. (1950). *Learning Theory and Personality Dynamics*. New York: Ronald Press.

ORNE, M. T. (1959). "The nature of hypnosis: artifact and essence." *J. abnorm. soc. Psychol.*, **58**, 277–299.

——— (1962). "On the social psychology of the psychological experiment with particular reference to demand characteristics and their implications," *Amer. Psychol.*, **17**, 776–783.

REYHER, J. (1958). *Hypnotically Induced Conflict in Relation to Subception, Repression, Antisocial Behavior and Psychosomatic Reactions*. Unpublished doctoral dissertation, University of Illinois.

——— (1961a). "Posthypnotic stimulation of hypnotically induced conflict in relation to antisocial behavior," *J. soc. Ther.*, **7**, 92–97.

——— (1961b). "Posthypnotic stimulation of hypnotically induced conflict in relation to psychosomatic reactions and psychopathology," *Psychosom. Med.*, **23**, 384–391.

——— (1962). "A paradigm for determining the clinical relevance of hypnotically induced psychopathology," *Psychol. Bull.*, **59**, 344–352.

——— (1963a). "A reply to Levitt's comments," *Psychol. Bull.* **60**, 330–332.

——— (1963b). "Free imagery: an uncovering procedure," *J. clin. Psychol*, **19**, 454–459.

——— (1964). "Brain mechanisms, intrapsychic processes and behavior: a theory of hypnosis and psychopathology," *Amer. J. clin. Hyp.*, **7**, 107–119.

ROKEACH, M., REYHER, J., and WISEMAN, R. (1964). "Further studies of the organization and the modification of belief systems." Unpublished study.

ROSEN, H. (1953). *Hypnotherapy in Clinical Psychiatry*. New York: Julian Press.

SEITZ, P. F. (1951). "Symbolism and organ choice in conversion reactions: an experimental approach," *Psychosom. Med.*, **13**, 255–259.

——— (1953). "Experiments in the substitution of symptoms by hypnosis, II.," *Psychosom. Med.*, **14**, 405–424.

WHITE, R. W. (1956). *The Abnormal Personality*. New York: Ronald Press.

WISEMAN, R. J. (1962). *The Rorschach as a Stimulus for Hypnotic Dreams: A Study of Unconscious Processes*. Unpublished doctoral dissertation, Michigan State University.

WOLBERG, L. R. (1947). "Hypnotic experiments in psychosomatic medicine," *Psychosom. Med.*, **9**, 337–342.

6

Hypnosis in Research on Psychotherapy

JESSE E. GORDON
University of Michigan

In the early days of clinical psychology's post-World War II expansion, the inclusion of training in psychotherapy in the ideal training program for clinicians was largely predicated on the belief that psychologists would make their major contribution to psychotherapy through research, for which training in therapy was a preparation. Since that time, the belief has become divorced from the training that was to justify the belief and that was in turn based on it. Training in psychotherapy has assumed a larger and larger place in the graduate careers of clinicians, but research in psychotherapy has not kept pace with this implied promise.

However, this is not to say that psychology has reneged on its promise; what well-controlled research has been done in psychotherapy has been done by psychologists, or stimulated by the hot breath of scientifically oriented psychology on the necks of other professions. The difficulty may more properly be ascribed to the incredibly complex nature of the phenomena to be investigated. It is rather a testimony to the good sense of psychology that in the relatively brief period in which the discipline has encompassed psychotherapy it has so fully and well understood the magnitude of the task and has moderated its expectations about what it may do in a short period of time. For a discipline whose sharpest tools do not yet go beyond exploration of single associative bonds, the exploration of what goes on between two people in a close and intimate relationship that endures for significantly long periods of time must necessarily be delayed by the search for appropriate means of study.

The challenge that the scientific study of psychotherapy sets may be divided into several categories. But first it is necessary to make clear that in discussing psychotherapy, my intention is to refer to the kinds of things that go on between people who practice therapy and their patients. This chapter is not concerned with what might possibly go on, if we knew more. That is, I do not plan to discuss the possibility for discovering more effective techniques or ways of modifying the behavior of patients, or of people who play the role of patient. Rather, I shall take it for granted that two people who spend considerable amounts of time (and money) in emotionally charged interaction cannot help but have effects on each other. Certainly all human research in psychology testifies to the sensitivity of humans to stimulation, and the incredible amount written by therapists testifies to the existence of effects on them by their experience with patients. It seems equally probable that therapists also have effects on their patients. The question is, what kind of effects, and what goes on to which these effects may be ascribed?

The successfulness of psychotherapy as an enterprise designed at least in part to "cure" people is a subset of the general question, and it is one that is of less relevance to a psychological frame of reference. Whether or not the effects of psychotherapy constitute cures tells us nothing about the specific nature of the relationships between the events of therapy and specific patient response. The curing power of psychotherapy is largely a question of economics, having relevance to the question of whether it is economically sound, in terms of costs and products, for people or institutions to devote their resources to such an activity, but it does not tell us much about human behavior and its determinants.

Therefore, the burden of this chapter will be to explore some of the problems in *psychological* research in psychotherapy, that is research that attempts to discover relationships between events in therapy and patient responses.

Economic considerations are, of course, important for practical clinical work, and cannot be dismissed altogether. But the notion of cure is often founded on the assumption that cure is a unitary state, which is essentially the same for all people. "Movement" toward "cure" is taken to be movement in the same direction for all patients. Patently this is not so. The impulse neurosis must move in a rather different direction from the overinhibited defense neurosis. Thus a movement in the direction of greater spontaneity in one patient constitutes desirable progress, whereas its reverse constitutes desirable progress for another. Are the same therapist behaviors likely to produce both kinds of movement, with the difference in direction solely a function of the patient? Or might it not be that different therapist behaviors are required for the two kinds of movements? Is the variance in the patient, or is it in an interaction between patient and the conditions of therapy? To the extent that the latter is a possibility, to that extent the practical question of economics (in what ways shall a therapist channel his resources, and for what will a patient trade his emotional commitment, time, and money) becomes identical with the question of what effects occur in what kinds of therapy relationships or interactions.

As one reviews the literature on psychotherapy research he is struck by a feeling approaching baffled futility. It is not only difficult to assess the progress of the enterprise; it is almost impossible to know even where to begin. There is a promising lead here, one there, and new ones with increasing frequency, but each lead seems as if it is on its own orthogonal plane in *n*-dimensional space, and we cannot even label the factors underlying that space. Every investigator and every conference of investigators is aware, so acutely, of the multiplicity of problems that face them at every turn and choice point, each one of which seems to be crucial from someone's point of view. We do not even have a classification for the problems in psychotherapy research, much less a means for converting them into the agencies for solving the riddles of psychotherapy. Thus as we modify our goals and concentrate our attention, not on substantive matters but on the problems of getting to the substance, we are equally baffled by an inability to even make order out of those problems and get to know their true dimensions. Like mercurial defenses, one puts his finger on one problem and it squirts away only to turn up somewhere else.

This is not to say that research in psychotherapy is prescientific. If anything, the concern about research methods and strategies is evidence for the high scientific status of the search. For among the other things a science is or may be, it is *prima inter alia* a method for knowing that focuses attention not only on what is known, but also on the means for producing that knowledge, and the effect of the means on the knowledge produced. Given such a context, it is not likely that we will cease discovering new problems in doing research on psychotherapy. Further, the discovery of a problem implies the creation of positive knowledge, in the sense that the institution of scientific controls assumes evidence that the controls involve significant variables.

This chapter is concerned with the role of hypnosis as a strategy for research in psychotherapy. To evaluate its potentiality as a research method, hypnosis must be measured against the kinds of problems that exist in therapy research, and the credits and debits associated with various solutions to these problems. Thus the chapter will first present a summary of what appear to be major logical and methodological problems in psychotherapy research. Following this, some applications of hypnotic techniques to psychotherapy research will be reviewed and described. These will then be evaluated with reference to the problems mentioned, to indicate the advantages and limitations of the hypnotic strategies, in terms of the kinds of substantive questions with which it is best suited to deal.

PROBLEMS IN PSYCHOTHERAPY RESEARCH

Some of the dilemmas of psychotherapy research have been reviewed elsewhere (Gordon, in press). Zax and Klein (1960) and Edwards and Cronbach (1952) also review some of these problems. Close reading of the discussions and criticisms of papers presented in both the first and second APA symposia on research in psychotherapy (Rubenstein and Parloff, 1959; Strupp and Luborsky, 1962) will also reveal some of the strategic difficulties. Such a discussion would be too long and out of place in this chapter, but some of the major difficulties can be briefly indicated. These include (a) problems in the specification of the appropriate variables deserving study and difficulty in measuring or isolating these variables so that they may be either statistically or experimentally controlled; (b) reduction of back-action effects of the research study qua research, in which the operations involved in doing the research result in modifications of the behavior of therapists and patients or subjects such that the research situation is no longer representative of what goes on in psychotherapy when it is not the object of research interest; and finally, (c) conflict between ethical considerations and the back-action effects growing out of needs to measure or control significant variables, or, if nontherapy analogues are used to avoid such conflicts, problems in the representativeness of the analogue.

There is no agreed-upon set of dimensions on which patient, therapist, and outcome variables can be measured. In general, the more theoretically significant a variable is selected for study, the less reliable will be the measurement of that variable and the more difficult it is to control the variable either statistically or experimentally. Further, operations designed to increase reliability of measurement involve increasing complexities, which tend to have back-action effects on both the measurement situation and the therapy, reducing the validity of both.

Because of the recognition that the direction of a patient's movement must depend on his initial status and the nature of the therapeutic goals, outcome variables must be measured by highly abstracted indices of "increased adjustment," greater "mental health," or "emotional maturity." But such highly abstracted variables are difficult to define, and equally difficult to measure reliably, much less validly. Thus the search for acceptable variables is most problematical.

Control of therapist and/or patient behaviors, or measures of both, produce awareness of the research in the subjects, which may operate to influence their responses to each other or to the measurement procedures, reducing the validity of the psychotherapy situation as an example of therapy as it is usually done. The presence of measurements before and after treatment, for example, focuses the patient's attention on aspects of the therapeutic relationship that might not otherwise have been salient, and produces modifications in the development of transference attitudes. Needs to control therapist characteristics by own-control procedure involve problems in the therapist's attitudes toward the experimental and control therapies, differences in amount of experience with the experimental therapy techniques, and differences in skill in their use, so that the control therapy may be different from what that therapy might be were it done by people who usually use it (Meehl, 1955).

The presence of back-action effects gives rise to ethical considerations in which the investigator must reach decisions about the extent to which patients will be exposed to procedures whose justification is in terms of the research rather than in terms of the patient's welfare, especially when these conflict. In experimental studies, for example, it is almost impossible to reconcile ethical considerations with the need to control significant therapist behaviors. The researcher is therefore limited in the range of variables that he can manipulate and control, thus also reducing the possibility of obtaining statistically significant differences. He is also limited by back-action effects in the complexity and fineness of measurements he can make of the patients at various points in the therapy process where the measurement operations are likely to alter drastically the relationships among the patient, his therapist, and the clinical agency.

The use of experimental analogues of psychotherapy offers the hope of finding ways out of some of these dilemmas. An experimental analogue of psychotherapy involves either the location of subjects or the creation in randomly selected nonpatient subjects of miniature neuroses—behaviors that are isomorphic with those of therapy patients in certain significant ways, and then studying the effects on these behaviors of other subject variables, therapy variables, or both. As an experimental situation in which patients are not involved, the experimenter has greater freedom to measure his subjects and to control significant variables in the therapist's behavior without fear of further damaging a patient's health. Analogues may also give to the experimenter a control over the miniature neurosis, which allows him to specify and standardize patient variables in a manner not possible when unselected patients are used in more naturalistic studies. In effect, the experimenter is thereby enabled to convert back-action effects from liabilities into useful tools of research by purposively controlling and manipulating therapy variables and measuring the extent of back-action (that is, alteration in subject behavior) as a function of those manipulations. Thus, what is a liability to naturalistic study of therapy as it is typically done constitutes the method and the advantage for experimental studies of the effects on behavior of certain controlling variables.

HYPNOTIC ANALOGUES OF PSYCHOTHERAPY

As indicated above, a laboratory analogue is a study in which the significant events are isomorphically related to their referents in the naturalistic setting. Verbal learning and attitude change experiments (Krasner, 1962) may serve as analogues, and have been used in this way. However, their use requires many inferences and assumptions, of unknown validity, to mediate the isomorphic connections. The fewer inferential links in the chains of logic that connect the analogues to real psychotherapy, the better is the analogue. Hypnotic analogues seem to possess this virtue of being relatively closer to the referents of real psychotherapy, and thus have much to recommend themselves. In this section such hypnotic analogues will be described and evaluated in terms of their closeness to real psychotherapy, as well as in terms of their ability to yield reliable data on questions of interest concerning psychotherapy.

Hypnotic analogues can be grouped into two general types. The first are those in which hypnosis is used to create, *de novo*, experimental neuroses in *S*'s, thus providing for standardization of at least neurotic contents. The second type is that in which hypnosis is used to activate some neurotic core conflict, which presumably already exists in normal *S*'s. In both types, experimental interest has been directed at the responsiveness of the experimental neuroses to therapeutic efforts in terms of particular outcome variables, which are theoretically and/or logically related to the miniature neuroses. There have been no experimental studies in which hypnosis has been used to obtain control over therapist variables, although such use is within the realm of possibility. Thus the major utility of hypnosis has been to provide control and standardization within the experimental sample of certain patient variables in such a way as to permit measurement of particular outcome variables associated with the content of the neuroses.

Hypnotic Analogues Involving the Production of Miniature Neuroses

Miniature Neuroses Produced by Paramnesias. The basic technique for producing hypnotic paramnesias can be observed in a training film used by Beck to communicate a conviction in students that unconscious forces affect conscious behavior. Beck's film, *Unconscious Motivation* (1949), still very popular for use in introductory psychology classes, is a documentary record of the induction of a miniature neurosis in two college students, of the manifestations of the neurosis in dreams, their projective test responses to an inkblot and a TAT–like stimulus, and of their own therapeutic-like analyses of their responses, which yield insights into the neurosis.

Beck's technique in the film is as follows. The two subjects, a male and female student, enter a hypnotic trance state upon the signal of Dr. Beck (heard but not seen in the film) who had previously trained them to do so. While in this state, the experimenter produces a paramnesia (that is, a "memory" of an event that did not really occur) for a mildly disturbing experience, following which the *S*'s are awakened with the posthypnotic suggestion that they will not remember the contents of the paramnesia, although it will influence their waking behavior. The paramnesia described the following event:

> While a child in elementary school, *S* was said to have been walking through a park when he (she) found a purse which he (she) recognized as belonging to a school chum. In the purse were two pennies. The subject picked up the purse with the intention of returning it to its owner the next day, but on the way home passed a candy store and was attracted by the display. Unable to resist the temptation, *S* bought some gum, but then felt too guilty to chew it, and when *S* arrived home, hid it. *S*'s mother found the gum and asked *S* where he (she) had gotten it, and *S* lied that he (she) had found it. *S* experienced intense feelings of guilt about the episode, and about not returning the friend's purse, and this experience is said to continue to bother *S*.

Following the production of this paramnesia, suggestion of posthypnotic amnesia for the event and a suggestion to dream about the event upon a signal, the *S*'s were awakened and interviewed about their feelings concerning the tension, which was apparent in their frowning appearance, hand-wringing, thoughtful expressions, and some slight psychomotor retardation in the female *S*. The *S*'s are briefly interviewed regarding their feelings, and then the signal for the posthypnotic dream is given. Both *S*'s fall silent, appear preoccupied and introspective, and then describe highly disguised and affect-laden anxiety dreams. The *S*'s were then given an inkblot and asked to report their perceptions of it, and later a picture modeled after the TAT. On the inkblot the female *S* reported seeing two spots, which were like round fish or discs, among other things. The male *S* interpreted the photograph of a younger and an older man in conversation as a quasi-treatment situation in which the older man was, as a wise and sympathetic counselor, helping the younger with some trouble. In the course of making these projective responses, the two *S*'s engaged in a three-cornered conversation with Dr. Beck in trying to understand their feelings and the meanings of their responses. Ultimately they acquire insight into the miniature neurosis, although the female *S* becomes convinced that she had not committed the crime; it is not possible to know whether this rejection was a true insight into its hypnotic source or a defensive denial. Experimenters unfamiliar with hypnotic paramnesias ought to study this film as part of their preparation for such research.

The first important research use of hypnotically implanted neuroses was by the Russian psychologist, A. R. Luria (1932), working in Moscow in the early and mid-1920's. As part of a series of laboratory investigations into mental structures and functions as revealed by conflict effects, Luria conditioned *S*'s to depress a kymograph-connected tambour with the preferred hand while giving verbal responses in word association tasks to both neutral and conflict-associated stimuli. He explored the disorganizing effects of conflict-associated stimuli on the verbal response-motor response linkage, and in other response systems (activity of the nonpreferred hand, and various chacteristics of the verbal associations, including latency and content). Working first with people who had experienced real trauma (students being investigated for purging from the university, and people recently arrested by the police for rather horrendous crimes, typically involving axe-murders, rape, and the like) Luria isolated some stable components of the affect responses and then continued testing with hypnotically induced conflicts. These were of two types: (a) production of paramnesias, and (b) production of more focused conflicts by giving posthypnotic suggestions for performances, which *S* would experience as illogical or embarrassing compulsions and/or inhibitions. The former type is of most interest here because the method attempts to engage *S*'s personality rather completely without placing any restrictions on *S*'s responses to the implanted neurosis.

Luria reports using four different paramnesias and apparently used some criterion of appropriateness in applying them to his *S*'s. For example, a female medical student *S* was made to believe that she performed an illegal abortion in which the patient died; a male student was made to believe that he had stolen money from a friend. The specific implantations Luria used are as follows:[1]

> . . . it is suggested. . . that a woman comes to see (*S*) with the request to produce in her an abortion, which (*S*) has no right to do. The suggestion meets in her an obstacle. The doctor: "You are sitting at home and there is a woman who comes to see you and is imploring you to perform an abortion on her and that nobody should know that. She offers you ($35.00). You hesitate because this is prohibited, but later you agree." The person under test (interrupting): "I will not do it." The doctor: "But I suggest to you that you should agree." (*S*): "I tell you I will not." The

[1] Quoted from Luria (1932).

doctor: "The woman is imploring. She has no other way out and you are agreeing." (*S*): "No." The doctor: "You have agreed and the woman has gone away."

Obviously this *S* had a good deal of difficulty in accepting this suggestion. Such difficulties will be discussed later in the chapter. It is also apparent here that the investigator varied his specific instructions to meet the needs of the moment.

In another use of the same conflict, Luria extends it:

You take your instruments, put them in a suitcase, and proceed to the sickbed. You ascend a narrow staircase, ring a bell, and an old woman opens the door. You are very excited and start the operation. But immediately a hemorrhage begins and you cannot stop it. You see a pool of blood on the floor. The sick woman is very weak, you have made an error in your operation and you fear for her life. . . .

Other paramnesias used by Luria are described as follows:

(Situation C) You are in great need of money. You go to a friend in order to borrow from him; he is not at home. You decide to wait in his room and suddenly notice on his bureau a fat wallet with money. You open it and find many five ruble notes. You make a decision; you quickly take the wallet and conceal it on your person. You cautiously go outside and look around to see if you are detected. You have stolen money and now you are afraid that there will be a search in your home and that they will discover you.

(Situation B) You are sitting in your room and are studying. A child of your neighbor's, a boy of about six, comes into your room. He shouts and disturbs your studies. You ask him to stop; he does not listen to you. . . . You get angry, and forgetting yourself, take a stick and beat the boy, first on his back and then on his head. There are some wounds on his head and he cries. You feel very much ashamed and you do not understand how such a thing could have happened to you, how you could beat up a child, and you try to forget it.

Luria apparently also used a fourth situation but this is not described.

Luria's research on the affects of these paramnesic traumas indicates disturbances in breathing, in verbal associations, and in hand pressure responses entirely analogous to those obtained from nonhypnotically traumatized *S*'s (that is, arrested murder suspects, students during purge). He indicates the advantage of the hypnotic method over the earlier studies:

We tried to rely on the objective analysis of the changes, which are brought into the neurodynamics of the subject analysed by the traumatic situation; however, we still worked largely in the dark, because the objective situation of the trauma naturally never quite corresponds to its reflection in the psyche of the personality, and that psyche, which is defined by the very complicated past experience, was entirely omitted from our record.

It is quite comprehensible, therefore, that only an artificial insertion of an affective complex into the psyche of the subject, which complex is known in all details, can create for the psychologist a situation where it would be easier for him to record all the factors forming the affective reaction. The course of our experiments has shown us that way.

He later concludes that the hypnotic production of affects in this fashion is a valid procedure:

We inserted into the psyche of the person under test definite affective contents, and were thus able to see how those contents were met by the personality of our subject under test, how they became obscured by certain details and were liable to certain changes, how they became affective traces, and how they continued to act on the behavior of the person deprived of the knowledge of them, and, as if becoming models of unconscious complexes, showed a number of extremely interesting symptoms, which were much more comprehensible to us than to the person under test. Having created the artificially affective traces, we were able to verify their symptomatology in pure form and their appearance in the state of sleep and in the state of awakening; discontinuing at our will the suggestion or making it deeper, we were in a position to follow up the special dynamics of the affective traces; and when we evoked analogies of the natural affective states formerly recorded by us, we could better understand the data, of which we were previously only passive observers.

Luria's is a highly creative and brilliant series of studies which, though lacking in sophisticated controls, standardization of procedures, and statistical treatment, are highly instructive and a goldmine of clever research strategies. Although his conclusions may not be acceptable today, considering the uncontrolled nature of his evidence, and the results of his studies in "neurodynamics" are irrelevant to the concerns of this chapter, we will have to return to his studies shortly to evaluate the validity and the utility of hypnotically induced neuroses for research in psychotherapy.

Huston, Shakow, and Erickson (1934) replicated some of Luria's findings, and extended their interpretations to include the hypothesis of alternative discharge systems, such that if affect is not discharged verbally, then the motor system would be involved. This conclusion was based on a tendency for disturbances following the hypnotic implantation to be shown either in verbal associations or in hand-pressure responses recorded on the kymograph. Like Luria, these investigators used several different paramnesias, and tested their *S*'s on the dependent variables before hypnosis, during hypnosis but before the production of the paramnesia, during hypnosis but after the paramnesia, in the waking state with the *S* amnesic for the hypnotic experience, and then following the removal of the neurosis, or "complex." They reported the following situations as the contents of the induced "complex":

One night, while visiting some friends, (*S*) met a girl to whom he was much attracted. During the conversation, attention was called to her new brown silk dress and she explained that although not able to afford it, she had bought the dress hoping to make a good appearance when applying for employment. He gave her a cigarette and lighted one also. While smoking he noticed the smell of burning cloth occasioned by contact of his cigarette with the girl's dress. Unobtrusively he withdrew his hand, noting with relief that the girl had not yet noticed the accident and that she held her own cigarette above the burned hole. The girl soon became aware of the damage. She attributed it, however, to a spark from her own cigarette. He tried to take the blame by assuming the responsibility of having given her the cigarette but the girl refused his apparent generosity. The next day, by which time he had summoned up enough courage to tell the truth in order to save his self-respect, he found that she had left the city.

The experimenters also reported using another situation in which *S* was said to have failed to mail a roommate's letter of application for a graduate school fellowship until after the final date for application had passed, while the subject mailed one of her own, and obtained the same fellowship.

Like Luria, these experimenters also experienced failure of the "neurosis" to "take." They report that three of their 12 subjects did not accept the complex, one of these reporting that the account of the experience as stated did not seem logical and that she felt it was artificial.

Two other reports of the use of hypnotic paramnesias are worth mentioning. The first of these was one used by Erickson (1944) in his work with a neurotic patient, and which he later explicated in an article in which he gave a rather detailed rationale for his particular choice of wordings in the instructions to his subject. Although there is little to support the validity of this rationale, other investigators have found no objection to the wording used, and have thus used Erickson's instructions in their own work. The instructions are as follows:

Now as you continue to sleep I'm going to recall to your mind an event which occurred not long ago. As I recount this event to you, you will recall fully and completely everything that happened. You have had good reason to forget this occurrence, but as I recall it, you will remember each and every detail fully. Now bear this in mind, that while I repeat what I know of this event, you will recall fully and completely everything just as it happened, and more than that, you will re-experience the various conflicting emotions which you had at the time and you will feel exactly as you did while this occurrence was taking place. Now the particular event of which I am going to tell you is this: (There follows an account, especially designed to elucidate the dynamics of the patient, of an occasion in which *S* accidentally broke a prized ash tray painted by a young and attractive lady as a gift, not yet presented, to her father, a professor to whom *S* was a petitioner in search of a fellowship). Now after you are awakened this whole situation will be on your mind. You will not consciously know what it is but, nevertheless, it will be on your mind, it will worry you and govern your actions and your speech although you will not be aware that it is doing so. I have just told you of a recent experience of yours, and as I recounted it to you, you recalled it in detail, realizing the whole time that I gave you a fairly accurate account of the situation, that I gave the essential story. After you awaken the whole situation will be on your mind but you will not be conscious of what it is, you will not even be aware of what it might be, but it will worry you and it will govern your speech and your actions. Do you understand? And you do feel badly about this thing.

Counts and Mensh (1950) used the hypnotic production of a paramnesia to produce an attitude of hostility toward a Rorschach administrator to test the effects of such affect on the responses. *S*'s had been given Rorschachs prior to the hypnotic implant. They were also tested by the same tester after the removal of the paramnesia, and also by the other experimenter. Immediately after the Rorschach in the experimental condition the five *S*'s were interviewed concerning their feelings toward the test administrator by the experimenter who had conducted the hypnosis. The paramnesia used was one in which the Rorschach administrator was said to have bumped into *S* in the college hallway. The incident was described as the fault of the test administrator, who almost knocked *S* down, and who then became sarcastic toward *S*, blaming *S* for the incident and threatening official reprisal. *S* became very angry but was unable to express it at the time. *S* was then instructed that he would not remember this experience, but that while taking the the Rorschach after awakening he would feel angry at the examiner without knowing why. *E* also added, "You will not feel angry with me and you will be hypnotized after the procedure as readily as you just have been."

Although the experimenters found no reliable changes in the Rorschach protocols, all *S*'s reported feelings of tension and discomfort during the Rorschach examination, usually rationalized by references to the examiner's ineptness or aloofness. One of these *S*'s was not amnesic for the hypnotic session, but had these reactions anyhow. Counts and Mensh apparently felt that the validity of the hypnotic procedures was unquestionable, so far as their effectiveness in producing the desired effects was concerned, for they interpret the lack of significant differences in the Rorschach data by reference to characteristics of the Rorschach rather than by criticism of the paramnesia technique.

Although not published until 1958, Bobbitt had done a doctoral dissertation in 1947 on repression using the Luria technique of hypnotically induced paramnesia and measurement of various aspects of verbal and motor response to word association stimuli under conditions of posthypnotic amnesia, partial awareness, full awareness, prehypnotic control, and after removal of the paramnesia. The paramnesia she used with her medical student *S*'s was described as follows:

In medical school, the *S* has had an experience so disturbing that he had to forget it. As it is recalled, he will re-experience it in detail. He was attending a party and volunteered to borrow a car and go for more beer. On his way back he drove rapidly around a dark corner and felt the car hit something. He feared an accident but did not want to stop since he was in a borrowed car and had been drinking. He rationalized that it had probably been only a bump in the road and drove on. Next morning his fears were confirmed in a newspaper story of a child, near death and hopelessly crippled as the result of a hit and run accident. The details of the account made it clear to him that he was the driver for whom the police were searching. He experienced great panic and conflict about what to do.

Bobbitt found disturbances in most of her measures, with maximum disruption occurring in the condition of partial awareness, and lesser disturbance in the conditions of complete amnesia and in the condition of complete recall. Because she hypothesized that amount of disturbance would be directly related to the effectiveness of repression, this last result was unexpected. She accounts for it by suggesting various alternatives, including (1) practice effects might have lowered disturbance and obscured what otherwise might have been greater disturbance in the full awareness condition; (2) rapid resolution of the conflict as soon as the conflict became fully conscious; (3) an error in the hypothesis, such that maximum disturbance is associated with incomplete repression, rather than with a complete failure of repression which permits the development of other defenses. She does not consider the possibility that disturbance may be a function of the extent of conflict between antithetical tendencies (to remember versus to forget) rather than a direct manifestation of anxiety stimulated by the thought of the "trauma."

These several studies provide precedents for the use of hypnotically induced paramnesias in psychotherapy research. The findings of Luria (1932), as confirmed by Huston, Shakow, and Erickson (1934) support an interpretation that the effects of such paramnesic conflicts on motoric and verbal responses are essentially like those of nonhypnotically induced traumas. Bobbitt's (1958) findings are consistent enough with a theory of nonhypnotic repression to suggest that hypnotically induced repression of a paramnesia is not fundamentally different from the natural phenomenon. Finally, Counts and Mensh (1950) indicate that the posthypnotic effects of an induced paramnesia are manifest in interview behavior, thus pointing to the possibility of their use for the study of psychotherapeutic-like interviews.

HYPNOTIC PARAMNESIAS IN PSYCHOTHERAPY STUDIES

The first use of a hypnotically induced paramnesia for the experimental study of psychotherapy was by Kesner (1954). This very original study ought to be read in its entirety, but its main features can be outlined here. Kesner selected therapist responsiveness to the factual versus the emotional content of *S*'s verbalizations as a significant therapy variable. Although he recognized that neither tactic can be thought of as typical of any particular school of therapy, he arrived at his decision to manipulate this variable after study of the similarities and differences between psychoanalytically oriented therapy and client-centered therapy.

Kesner's procedure was to hypnotize twenty carefully screened *S*'s, produce a paramnesia for an embarrassing situation, awaken *S* and administer a word association test, and then expose *S* to a therapeutic interview following one or the other tactic (factual or emotional content) until *S* either reached a decision regarding extricating himself from the embarrassment or indicated that he had no further use for continued interviewing. *S* was then rehypnotized, made amnesic for the paramnesia, awakened, and the word association test readministered. In a second session the entire procedure was repeated except that *S* was this time exposed to whichever of the two therapy tactics he had not had in the first session. Thus each *S* served as his own control, and the order of conditions was randomized. At the end of the second session, *S* was rehypnotized and the hypnotic conflict removed. Kesner used response time differences between neutral and conflict-associated stimuli as his dependent measures.

The paramnesia he used was as follows:

> (After the Erickson preamble) While riding to a house in a crowded vehicle you were discussing with a friend a fast deal that you pulled on an important acquaintance. You started to tell about some things which he had told you in strict confidence and then you began to joke about these things and him. Suddenly your friend stopped laughing. To your horror you realized that this person you were laughing about was in back of you. You tried to tell further stories mentioning another name in the hope that this person would be deceived. But it was an awkward attempt and only made matters worse. Now you are feeling very badly. This situation is very embarrassing and you may lose an important acquaintance. You must decide whether to speak to him and apologize or to hope that he will forget the incident. You must decide soon, but this is not an easy decision to make.

The experimenter also served as therapeutic interviewer, later submitting a sample of his interviews to two other psychologists and a psychiatrist for judgments on whether or not he realized his intentions in making the experimental conditions different on the fact vs. feeling variable. These judges were almost unanimous in their agreement with Kesner.

Kesner's data indicate the following: (1) the paramnesia produced a significant difference in response times to neutral and "charged" stimuli, lengthening the response to the latter items; (2) both therapies were effective in reducing the difference between the response times to the two types of words; (3) the lengths of the therapeutic interviews, which were determined by the *S*'s, were about equal in the two conditions, with a mean about twenty minutes and ranging from nine to forty minutes; (4) responsiveness to feeling was more effective in reducing the difference between response times in more *S*'s than was therapist attention to the facts, though neither technique was completely effective; (5) the production of amnesia for the hypnotic session and its paramnesia reduced differences in response times to the neutral and "loaded" stimuli to nonsignificant levels.

It is worthwhile to point out some significant features of Kesner's design. His use of the same *S*'s in two experimental conditions solves the difficult problem of ensuring comparability among *S*'s in the two treatments. However, this procedure rests on the shaky assumption that the hypnotically induced amnesia effectively "erased" *S*'s experience in the first condition, or that any residuals of this experience in their effects on the second condition would be identical for the two orders. The data in fact argue against this; if the "feeling" therapy produced greater relief of the conflict than the "factual" therapy, then *S*'s who had the "feeling" therapy first may have brought different expectancies or attitudes regarding the interview in their second sessions than *S*'s who had the factual condition first. Kesner does not report an analysis of his data for order effects, although his data permit such an analysis.

It should be noted that the hypnotist was also the therapist. This arrangement has several implications. *S*'s attitudes and responses to *E* in his role as interviewer must certainly be conditioned by their experiences with him as hypnotist. In addition, the therapist was thus intimately familiar with the uncomfortable decision *S* was trying to make, and this familiarity could have provided him with opportunities to bias the findings, unconsciously or otherwise, in favor of his preferred technique. It also makes the therapy nonrepresentative, because most therapists do not begin with such a clear idea of the "reality" choices their patients must make. In addition, the therapist seeing the same *S* in the second session has a good deal more information about him than he did in the first session, further strengthening the possibility of order effects and the possibility for biasing the data by selective reinforcement. Although raters agreed in their judgment of the interviews as being factual or feeling oriented, this still allowed the therapist freedom to select which facts and feelings he would respond to, and if this bias were in favor of the "feeling" therapy, it would not have been difficult for him to concentrate the feeling therapy on significant feelings but the factual therapy on irrelevant facts. That this might have happened is suggested by some quotations from the interviews reported by Kesner, in which he quite succinctly recognized *S*'s feelings in the first session, but seemed to respond to less relevant facts in the second.

Another point worth noting is that the miniature "neurosis" used appears to be rather superficial and nonrepresentative of the kinds of problems brought into psychotherapy. His model of a neurosis as implied in his selection of a paramnesia, is that patients have reality problems to solve concerning interpersonal relations and guilt over past actions. Problems in impulse control and expression, conflict between impulses and their inhibition, repression and defense seem to be outside the scope of this model.

Despite these criticisms, Kesner's experiment does have validity as a study on the helpfulness of two kinds of interviewer tactics in aiding the reaching of decisions in emotionally toned choice situations. The study demonstrates the feasibility of the use of hypnosis to produce laboratory neuroses to serve as grist for the experimental therapies, contributes to the solution of the problem of ensuring comparability among *S*'s in the experimental and control treatments, which is so difficult to achieve in naturalistic research. The study also demonstrates the utility of verbal reaction time as an index of the effectiveness of the experimental therapies.

The only other psychotherapy research in the literature using an hypnotically induced paramnesia was a study by Gordon (1957). Like Kesner's, this study compared two kinds of therapy tactics for their effects on hypnotically induced paramnesic *S*'s. Because schools of therapy vary in the kinds of therapeutic effects that they establish as meaningful goals, and are likely to discount any studies concerned with variables that are only peripheral to their theoretical structures, an effort was made to test for therapy effects that would be considered meaningful to proponents of different therapies.

At the time of this research it seemed that therapists' behaviors could be differentiated as "leading" versus "following" and that these two styles represented meaningful points of difference between client-centered and psychoanalytically oriented therapy, a view supported by the findings of Strupp (1955a), Danskin and Robinson (1954), Snyder (1948), and Gump (1944). "Following" refers to therapist activity that does not go beyond material already expressed by a patient; "leading" refers to therapist activity in which the patient's attention is directed to phenomena, events, or material that were not explicitly dealt with by the patient. Thus recognition or reflection of feeling and restating content are "following" while asking questions, making suggestions for things the patient should do or talk about, and offering interpretations are "leading" therapist activities.

It often happens in psychotherapy research that the outcome variables chosen for study are so solipsistically related to the school of therapy being studied that the results are dismissed by proponents of other schools as being irrelevant. Thus demonstration that acceptance of self is altered by client-centered therapy (Rogers, 1951) may be considered quite unconvincing by analytically oriented therapists for whom self-acceptance is a more peripheral or epiphenomenal variable, compared with events such as the lifting of repressions, which occupy a more central role in analytic theory. Thus an effort was made to design an experiment in which dependent variables relevant to both experimental therapies could be used. Lifting of repression (that is, recall of previously repressed material) was selected as one dependent variable of particular interest to historically oriented therapies such as psychoanalysis, in which leading techniques are commonly used. Measures of interpersonal attitudes (that is, hostility toward the therapist) were selected as appealing particularly to client-centered therapists (who use "following" techniques), to neoanalysts such as Alexander who stress current adaptation and interpersonal relations, as well as to classical analytical concern with transference events. Although many investigations have used measures of attitudes toward the therapist, only one study has treated lifting of repression as a function of therapy, despite the centrality of this idea in psychoanalytic theory; and that study (Keet, 1948) involves a biased design (the experimenter also served as therapist) and has been refractory to replication despite several efforts (Merrill, 1952; Grummon and Butler, 1953).

Hypnotically induced paramnesia provided the means for testing the relationships among these therapy and outcome variables. Obviously, the measurement of the lifting of repression requires that the experimenter know what is repressed, and this knowledge is provided by the control hypnosis given him over the production of amnesia. For comparability among *S*'s subjected to the two therapies, experimental rather than natural neuroses are required, and ethical considerations regarding freedom to define therapist behaviors narrowly underscores this necessity. The production of paramnesia offers the possibility of providing these controls without destroying the validity or the representativeness of the experiment as an analogue of psychotherapy. The use of such an analogue also permits outcome measures on the behavioral level, thus avoiding reliance on inferences drawn from tests, the validity of whose interpretation is still problematical.

The experimental procedures were as follows. *S*'s were college males recruited from volunteers, who were screened in small group sessions for ability to enter a light trance. Those who passed this screening-practice session were invited to another small group screening-practice session; the criterion for passing in this session was positive response to a posthypnotic suggestion to enter into hypnosis upon a verbal signal. Those who passed were given individual appointments for further screening and practice, in which they were instructed, while hypnotized, to have a dream posthypnotically upon a signal. They were instructed to dream about an occasion in high school on which they had been unfairly blamed by a teacher and to be amnesic for the trance events.

This session served several functions beyond training and screening. The selection of the dream subject was intended to rehearse *S*'s fantasy regarding such events, in preparation for the experimental paramnesia, which was about false blame by a teacher. It was reasoned that individual differences in ability to accept a paramnesia might be affected by the nature of the paramnesia. Thus, *S*'s who could accept such a dream suggestion might be more likely to accept the paramnesia in the experimental session. *S*'s who indicated, after the dream, that the dream seemed false, or that such a thing never happened to them, were therefore disqualified from further participation.

The fourth session with *S*, again an individual one, was divided into four parts. In the first part, *S* was hypnotized and the paramnesia described to *S* as something for him to imagine. He was then instructed to dream the situation posthypnotically. This provided *S* with practice in the experimental neurosis, as well as a check on his ability to carry out the hypnotic instructions. One *S* who had passed the screening up to this point was disqualified because he indicated, after the dream, that such a thing could never have happened to him. (The paramnesic dream concerned a physical education teacher in high school who unjustly blamed *S*, but this *S* indicated that he had been the school's star football player, and the physical education teacher-coach about whom he dreamt was also his uncle. The situation as described was therefore preposterous; no coach would treat his star player—and nephew—in that manner.)

Following the dream, the therapist to whom *S* was to be assigned was brought into the experimental room briefly and introduced to *S*. This was done so that during the paramnesia induction, *S* could be instructed to "remember" the physical education teacher as looking like the therapist. This prescribed similarity had two purposes: (1) to generate transferencelike phenomena, making measurement of *S*'s hostility toward the therapist meaningful as measures of the extent to which the therapy reduces inappropriate interpersonal perceptions arising from the experimental neurosis, and (2) the discomfort experienced by *S* in the therapy interview could serve to motivate *S*'s engagement in the therapy process, and provide material for him to deal with.

After the introduction of the therapist, who then left the room, *S* was rehypnotized and the paramnesia induced.

The paramnesic instructions which used Erickson's (1944) prologue, were modeled on the paramnesia used by Counts and Mensh (1950), described earlier:

> This happened to you when you were in high school. You were just getting out of a class. As you were walking down the hall, a physical education teacher, who looks like Mr. (*name of therapist*), the man who will be interviewing you soon, came rushing out of one of the rooms. He bumped into you. It was obviously his fault as he was not looking where he was going. He was walking so fast that you were almost knocked down. As you were recovering your balance and dignity, he said sarcastically that

you were very clumsy to bump into him, that if you didn't watch what you were doing he would make trouble for you. You immediately felt very angry but realized that you could say nothing. As you walked away you felt more and more angry, and thought of many sarcastic things you might have said but didn't.

Now when you awaken, you will not remember this event consciously but it will be preying on your unconscious mind. Though you will not consciously know what it is, it will nevertheless be on your mind, because of the way Mr.______ seems somehow to be like that physical education teacher. It will worry you, and govern your actions and speech, although you may or may not be aware that it is doing so. I have just told you of an experience of yours. As I recounted it to you, you recalled it in detail, realizing that the whole time I was giving you a fairly accurate account of the situation, that I was giving the essential story. After you awaken the whole situation will be on your mind, but you will not be conscious of what it is. You may not even be aware of what it could be, but it will worry you, and it will govern your speech and actions towards Mr.______. You will feel upset and uncomfortable. After you awaken, you will spend fifty minutes with Mr.______ in an interview. Because of the way this experience will be on your mind, and will bother you, you will want to use the opportunity to talk about your feeling of discomfort, or about how you feel toward Mr.______. Use the interview situation with Mr.______ to figure out what it is that is on your mind and is bothering you; you might be successful at it, and then you will know consciously what was bothering you, and you will feel better.

Following this, amnesia for the trance and for the introduction of the therapist was induced, and *S* awakened. These hypnotic instructions are based on a neurosis model that characterizes neurotically inappropriate behavior as resulting from an unconscious identification of the patient's present situation with an unpleasant and often unremembered and incomplete or unresolved experience in the patient's past in which his impulses threatened his functioning and integrity.

Both the Keet and the Kesner studies have been criticized for their handling of the therapist variables. In both studies the experimenter was the therapist, and although Kesner took care to have his behavior during the interviews rated and examined by independent experts, there is obviously much opportunity for the experimenter's implicit theories and expectations to produce subtle biasing of their responses to *S*'s. Further, when only one therapist is involved, the experiment is no more generalizable to therapists in general than is the study in which only one *S* is involved. Therapists are, in a certain sense, subjects in psychotherapy research, which must in its very nature be concerned with the interaction between subject and therapist; this is especially true because such large individual differences in style exist among therapists. This criticism cannot be limited to psychotherapy research (see the chapter by Rosenhan on the social psychology of hypnosis research in which he reviews some of the evidence pointing to the biasing effects of experimenter characteristics), but it is nevertheless particularly cogent in this area.

The solution to these problems requires a sample of therapists. The study described here used such a sample, with the same therapist in both experimental conditions. Pains were taken to keep the experimenters ignorant of the subject and outcome variables being studied. The therapists were nine graduate students in clinical psychology who were trained in the application of the independent variables by the experimenter in group meetings. The order in which the therapists appeared in the two conditions was randomized, so that some used the "leading" techniques with their first *S*'s and some used "following" with the first, using the other technique with their next (and final) subject. Although the therapists knew that somehow hypnosis was involved in the study, and that the *S*'s had been hypnotized, they did not know of the paramnesia induction, or any details of the hypnosis. They were instructed to deal with their *S*'s as they do with any client who comes to the clinic on a first contact (the practice at the Psychological Clinic in which these students were trained did not include diagnostic examination of clients as a routine matter, except for practicum training for students in the diagnostic courses).

As a check on the validity of the experimental conditions, typescripts made from the tape-recorded interviews were scored by independent scorers who were familiar with the definitions of the therapy variables being studied. These scorings indicated that about 65 per cent of the therapist activity in each condition consisted of the kind of therapist behavior for which the conditions were named, that about 20 per cent of each condition consisted of therapist statements characterizing the opposite condition, and that only 15 per cent consisted of other miscellaneous therapist remarks. These remarks were largely pleasantries. Although there was a good deal of variability among therapists in their total activity, and in their levels of usage of the individual techniques, these differences were relatively constant across the two conditions, so that the differences between the results obtained by a particular therapist in one condition and the results he obtained in the other could be compared with the differences obtained by the other therapists. These variabilities among therapists, incidentally, justify the use of the same therapists in both conditions, permitting analyses of the data in terms of differences between each therapist's two interviews.

Therapists' ignorance of the purposes of the research was cited earlier as an important consideration. Some check was made on the effectiveness of the experimenter's secrecy by informal interviews with the therapists after each of their interviews. In no case did a therapist correctly guess the existence of a paramnesia, or the nature of the significant "neurotic" element after the first interview. Although *S*'s did talk about the paramnesic experience, no therapist identified it as the focus of the research, nor did any therapist suspect that the experience was artificial, or in any way "special." Naturally, when the therapists worked with their second *S*'s they did realize what was going on, because of the coincidence of the same thematic material in their two clients. However, as will be indicated below, this realization came too late to bias the results. If anything, one would expect that such a realization would have facilitated the therapist's exploration of the "neurosis" and thus result in greater recall of the paramnesic elements. But in fact, therapists' second interviews were inferior to their first on the measures of subject recall, regardless of whether the second interview was "leading" or "following."

Dependent measures in this research were designed to tap the lifting of the hypnotically induced repression. The specific measures included the amount recalled (measured as the number of separate items of the paramnesia recalled), latency of recall (amount of time elapsed before *S* had recalled at least three scorable items of the paramnesia, indicating that active recall was underway), and recognition time (amount of time elapsed before *S* verbalized an awareness that the therapist or someone like him was familiar to *S*). Measures of hostility toward the therapist were based on rankings of the interview typescripts on extrapunitiveness, passive hostility, and disguised hostility.

Tests of the differences between the means of the two conditions on these measures were generally inconclusive, with amount recalled being most clearly affected by the experimental variable. Significance testing was in terms of the differences between each therapist's "leading" and "following" interviews. Six differences showed greater amount recalled in the "leading" condition, two differences favored the "following" condition, and one difference was of zero value. A randomization test indicates that this distribution of differences just falls short of significance at the 5 per cent level with a two-tailed test. Recall time and recognition time measures did not approach significance.

However, the three recall measures were significantly intercorrelated (Amount Recalled — Recall Time $r = -.78$, Amount Recalled — Recognition Time $r = -.55$, and Recall Time — Recognition Time $r = +.50$). On the assumption that these correlations represent the extent to which they are all measuring *S*'s ability to repress and to conform to the hypnotic suggestions, analyses of variance of errors of estimate were done. In effect, this procedure parceled out intersubject variability in conformity to the hypnotic suggestion. The analysis of the errors of estimate in the regression of recall time on amount recalled yielded differences between treatments significant at the .01 level and among therapists significant at the .05 level. This analysis was interpreted to indicate that amount recalled could be better predicted from recall time in the "leading" condition ($r = -.93$) than it could in the "following" condition ($r = -.63$). It thus appears that in the "leading" condition *S*'s tended to verbalize the "repressed" material more nearly to the limits of their ability and understanding of the hypnotic instructions, as estimated from their recall time scores; whereas in the "following" condition other variables beyond the basic recall factors entered into the determination of how much recalled material was verbalized. Study of the typescripts suggested how this happened. In the "leading" condition, therapists were able to limit *S*'s to topics. When *S*'s began to recall the neurotic experience, therapists were able, by means of questions and suggestions, to continue them along the lines they had started. However, in the "following" condition, the therapists were less able to impose such limits. Thus *S* might start recalling, but not continue to develop the theme, either because of defensiveness, unwillingness to verbalize to the therapist, or the pressure of other thoughts.

Other findings in the study were that therapists' second interviews produced significantly less recall than their first interviews ($p < .05$). This result has the rather surprising implication that therapist practice decreases his efficiency, at least in lifting repression, but such an interpretation would not be justified. Rather, it is more likely that the result reflects the dangers of incorrect diagnosis. As indicated earlier, although no therapist gave a correct account of the research after his first interview, every therapist did have some hypotheses about what was going on, and these hypotheses were all in error. It is likely that these hypotheses guided the therapists' expectancies regarding their second interviews, making them relatively less sensitive to the true state of affairs as they concentrated their attention on looking for other things in their *S*'s, which did not appear. There is thus some reason to support Rogers' suspiciousness of diagnostic evaluations; to the extent that such evaluations may be misleading, to that extent may the therapist be rendered less able to respond appropriately to the cues presented by his clients.

Interjudge agreement in rating the interviews for hostility toward the therapists were satisfactory for Extrapunitiveness and Passive Hostility, but not for Disguised Hostility, which was therefore discarded from further analyses. Extrapunitiveness was significantly related to recognition time (rho $= .44$, $p < .05$) but Passive Hostility was not, and neither hostility measure was significantly related to the other repression measures. The significant correlation obtained suggests that *S*'s who "recognized" their therapists early were also more aggressive toward their therapists (or had more time to express aggression in the course of the interview, producing judgments of greater extrapunitiveness). It was also found that *S*'s were significantly more hostile (extrapunitive) in the therapists' second interviews than in their first ($p < .01$). It will be remembered that there was also significantly less recall in these interviews.

Although the bulk of these findings stem from relatively unreliable data, they do demonstrate the fruitfulness and the potential utility of the experimental strategy. The procedures appear practicable, and they appear capable of adaptation to a variety of experimental questions. But before assessing this utility further, some examination of qualitative aspects of the results is in order. The experimental stimulus was a standard "experience" to which subjects were free to respond in their own ways. Some became openly hostile to their therapists; some were passively resistant and negativistic. One *S* was superficially friendly and polite, though distant, but complained of a headache, which disappeared when the neurosis was repealed in the posttherapy debriefing. Of particular interest are the *S*'s associations to the repressed experiences as revealed by their choices of topics for discussion with the therapists. An example is one *S* who, while trying to recall where he had met the therapist before, wondered when they had "bumped into" each other around campus. Another *S* felt that he and the therapist must have had an argument some time before, which he described metaphorically as a "collision." These word choices strongly support the validity of psychic determinism in word choice. The control over the antecedent experiences provided by the hypnotic procedures makes it possible to place more faith in the relationship ascribed to such word choices and previous experience.

An interesting suggestion emerging from the data concerns the relationship between therapy and insight. As was indicated earlier, therapists were generally incorrect in their explanations of the nature of the research following their first interviews, despite the fact that many of their *S*'s did recall the "experience" during those interviews. In effect, repression was lifted, or therapy was done, without the therapists understanding what had gone on. This suggests that therapists' understanding may not be related to their actual therapeutic effectiveness. Indeed, one possible application of this experimental design is the study of individual differences in therapist effectiveness in dealing with various kinds of implanted "experiences."

On the other side, it sometimes happened that *S*'s experienced feelings of relief and relaxation of their tension in the interviews when in fact they did not achieve insight. For example, one *S* who was bothered by a feeling that the therapist was familiar to him eventually ascribed this feeling to what is probably analogous to a screen memory: a possible meeting near the offices of the student academic counseling service, where the therapist worked and which the subject had visited on occasion. He followed this "insight" with many verbal and behavioral signs of relief, and was much more comfortable during the remainder of the interview. Both he and the therapist were convinced that this was the source of the therapist's familiarity to *S*.

Both of these observations suggest that neither the patient's nor the therapist's insight may be necessary for therapy to be effective, and that the effectiveness of the therapy may not require that either of the participants be correct in their understanding of what goes on. Certainly we are accustomed to thinking of this in connection with the undeniably therapeutic effects some people have experienced with faith healers and the like, but it is not often recognized that the same may be true of professional psychotherapy. It does seem possible to conclude from the experiences of the therapists and *S*'s in this study that as long as both feel that they have a rational explanation, or an explanation that is acceptable to themselves, then the truth of that explanation may be irrelevant. It is also therefore suggested that patient reports and evaluations of their therapy, as well as therapists' reports and evaluations of patient progress, may have little to do with the real effects of the therapeutic experience. Patients may be satisfied with nonveridical explanations and understandings, which produce feelings of relief and well-being, and therapists may have understandings of what went on which are clearly incorrect, rendering evaluations from both sources suspect, and underscoring the need for behavioral and objective outcome measures in psychotherapy research.

The following are summaries of some of the therapy sessions, together with a complete typescript of one of the sessions. These are presented here to convey some sense of the kind of realism that the experimental procedures generate.

Subject 2: This subject, a graduate student, began by discussing the role of a psychological clinic in a college. Some implied criticisms of clinical psychology may be expressions of hostility related to the experimental procedures. He expressed doubt during the interview that he had been hypnotized. He followed this by mentioning that if the therapist were a little more stocky, he would remind the subject of a former physical education teacher whom he later described as a dirty basketball player and poor sport. The subject related the interview to a basketball game and implied that the therapist might use his position to "play dirty." Following this the subject changed the topic to an intellectual discussion of professional matters.

Subject 4: This subject responded to the therapist's opening lead by telling the therapist to do the talking. In response to continued leading, the subject told of a high school experience in which he was knocked down and insulted. In response to the therapist's attention to the subject's reactions to this experience, the subject described intense hostile reactions in which he almost loses control over his impulses to kill. He described several instances in which unreasoning and illogical hatred threatened his self-control. From there he spontaneously spoke of experiences he has had which aroused strong feelings of diverse natures. His interview seemed to be a very cathartic experience for the subject. During the interview he grudgingly admitted that he felt better as a result of talking out his experiences and feelings. He spontaneously mentioned this to the experimenter after the last trance induction, which gave him an insight into the purpose of the experiment. His attitude toward the therapist during the first half of the interview seems to be one of minimal cooperation, expressed through short answers to the therapist's questions, and a reluctance to give any information spontaneously. This seemed to disappear when he began talking about the experiences that had aroused his hostility in the past.

Subject 5: This subject thought that the therapist looked familiar at the very beginning of the interview. He asked questions of the therapist at various points throughout the interview, in an attempt to place the therapist. He was not successful. It annoyed the subject that he could not identify the reasons for the therapist's familiarity, and in an effort to relieve the anxiety this caused him, he talked about various innocuous subjects. However, each subject he talked about turned out to involve an argument or dispute with someone. The subject recognized this, and then suggested that he and the therapist must have had an argument before. He had a vague feeling of annoyance with the therapist. In response to a suggestion by the therapist to think about possible reasons for the subject's annoyance with him, the subject mentioned that being unjustly blamed for something is a pet peeve of his. He related this to the therapist, blaming himself for feeling hostile to the therapist without any justification. The subject then wondered if he had ever almost run the therapist down with his car when the therapist was jaywalking. The subject then associated a school hallway with an argument with the therapist, but thought of the university as the locale of the hallway. The subject followed this with talk about a mathematics teacher in high school who had lowered the subject's grade because of the subject's absence from class due to illness. The subject described this as an instance when he was blamed for something he did not do, or could not help. The subject then implied a comparison of the therapist with an Army sergeant who had treated him unfairly. Following this the subject thought of his high school swimming teacher, whom he liked, and who he associated with a particular hallway in school. He was unable to discover the relationship between the therapist, the swimming teacher, an argument, and the hallway. Although this subject wondered where he and the therapist had "collided," he did not associate any incident with the high school hallway, and otherwise did not mention any occasions of bumping into someone, and so on. The subject did mention the therapist's eyeglasses as a possible source of the association with the swimming teacher, and then mentioned "it might flatter you to know that he went to a mental hospital."

The subject's most characteristic feeling during this interview was annoyance with the therapist and with himself. He repeatedly verbalized his awareness of this annoyance.

Subject 6: There are several interesting aspects of this interview, aside from the subject's chain of associations in his attempt to understand why he felt resentful toward the therapist. At one point in the interview, after expressing resentment toward people who in various situations have attempted to make the subject feel inferior, the subject began to express positive feelings toward people. This may be an example that supports the notion that "working through" hostile feelings results in improved attitudes toward others. Another interesting aspect of this interview is that the subject did not focus on the experimental experience, when he described it, but fit it into the context of the feelings associated with the experience and integrated it with similar experiences in his history, which he explored so thoroughly that he expressed relief, and noticed that he no longer felt resentful toward the therapist. However, the subject did not discover why he had felt resentful toward the therapist, and finally resorted to a logical explanation, although an incorrect one. However, both he and the therapist accepted this incorrect explanation. This is an interesting development, suggesting that some "repressions" or justifications "discovered" during therapy may really be contrived and incorrect, but still be accepted as true, and they may still have a salutary effect on the patient's feelings.

Subject 13: This subject began to speak of his high school physical education teacher early during the interview. He described several incidents to validate what he described as real hatred for the teacher. However, he did not mention the specific experimental experience, although he did discharge a great deal of feeling. From the wealth of detail in the incidents involving the physical education teacher, it seems apparent that for this subject there had already been a strong antipathy toward a physical education teacher prior to the hypnosis. There is some possibility of fabulizing, however. Following the first hypnosis of the fourth session, when the subject had been instructed to dream the experimental situation, this subject presented a distorted version of the dream, in which he described the physical education teacher as anti-Semitic, and reported that the "collision" incident ended in a fist-fight between him and the teacher which was broken up by the principal. The subject's interview behavior suggests that this overdramatization continued in his discussion of the physical education teacher.

The remainder of the interview was spent in a discussion of various personally relevant topics, such as the superiority of the subject's interests (philosophy) over those of technical specialists, his grandfather's and father's business successes, his own nature as a nonconformist, and his feeling of loyalty to Jewish people in general. It is apparent from this interview that the subject has very disturbed interpersonal relations, involving great hostility toward others and strong needs to feel superior. The subject reported having been in counseling for two years. Because of this subject's poor adjustment, strong needs for self-justification, and tendency to fabulize, it is difficult to determine the extent to which his interview behavior is a reaction to the experimental procedures, and the extent to which it is a reaction to a real situation. Nevertheless, the interview gives a good picture of the general pattern of this man's responses to others.

Subject 14: This subject appeared superficially friendly toward the therapist throughout the interview, which was spent in a fruitless attempt to identify the source of the subject's feeling of familiarity with the therapist. However, the subject suffered an intense headache throughout the interview. It disappeared once during some idle conversation, but returned when the subject returned to a discussion of the therapist's familiarity. The headache disappeared following the hypnosis at the end of the interview, when the hypnotic "experience" was recalled to him and the experiment described. There was some disguised hostility expressed toward the experimenter in the form of questioning the therapist about his opinion of the experimenter's skill in hypnosis, and some implied criticism of psychology in general. Most of the interview was spent in "small talk" and attempts at humor, which the subject used to fill in time while he tried to recall an earlier experience with the therapist.

Subject 16: This subject was outright hostile and negativistic toward the therapist throughout the interview, referring to him afterwards as "a sarcastic son of a bitch." He refused to accept any therapist reflections, regardless of their validity. At one point he asked the therapist if he taught Psychology 15, and then breathed an exaggerated sigh of relief when the therapist said no. He then explained that he was going to take the course the following semester.

The subject told the therapist that he reminded him of the military high school he had attended, which he described as an extremely unpleasant place in which he was always getting "shoved around." This was the extent of his verbalization of the experimental "experience." It seems likely that the subject recalled more, but because of his negativism and antipathy toward the therapist, he refused to discuss his high school experiences any further. Here, then, is an example of therapy being blocked as a result of transference from the anxiety-producing situation.

Subject 20: This subject appeared to be embarrassed and self-conscious throughout the interview, avoiding eye contact with the therapist, remaining silent for long periods, and giggling in an embarrassed manner frequently. The subject associated the therapist with a high school physical education teacher whom he described as one who used his status as a teacher as a "club." The subject felt that his memory for specific details and experiences was very foggy, although he finally did describe the experimental experience. The subject was greatly impressed by the similarity between the therapist and the teacher, and seemed to become more embarrassed each time he mentioned the teacher or the experience. He began to feel very uncomfortable, remarked on the slow passage of time, and tried to change the topic of conversation several times. However, he was unable to remain on any other topic for very long, and each time returned to the similarity between the therapist and the teacher with renewed discomfort.

The following typescript is of particular interest for the way in which *S*'s affects aroused by the paramnesia mediate his associations and influence his perceptions of the interviewer and his attitudes toward him. This *S* is also interesting because these dynamics occurred even though *S* did not really accept the paramnesia as true, as it turns out at the end of the interview. He recalls the hypnotic instructions and the fantasy situation, and although he recognizes that the situation was not real, he does accept it as approximately real in that it mirrors feelings and experiences that he has had and that are important to him.

(The first minute or two of this interview did not record.)

S. It doesn't mean anything and ah—I think of the name Frances Wadman. I don't know any Frances Wadman—I never (pause) although—I wrote a—I wrote a story. I think I used Frances Wadman as a character in it.

T. Can you remember anything else about this name?

S. Well, I remember what it reminds me of; it reminds me of a person in junior high school, and partly in high school, that I had a fight with, and his name was Frances Wadman. And I think when I wrote this story, I was—I was referring to this fellow. Yeah. That's all it means to me. I don't know why I happened to think of it.

T. You say you had a fight with this person.

S. Yeah, after a—in junior high school we became sort of wild in class, I don't know exactly why, and somehow or other, the talk started around about a fight, and ah—I wanted to have a fight in the gym, you know, on the mat, wrestling or something, because I didn't—I was kind of scared of the idea of actually fighting, and ah—but he wanted to fight outside, so it wouldn't get involved with teachers and everything. So we went outside after class, and then he didn't want to fight. He started walking away. And we started calling him a coward, and then he came back and he started fighting, and I was scared of him, and I didn't fight back. I just let him hit me. That's all there is about him.

T. Do you have any ideas why this comes to your mind?

S. (pause) Well, just a feeling I got about it, when I fought—when I was—before, or afterwards—the feeling I had, kind of a weak, scared feeling, like I should have fought back and I didn't. And I feel that I should have beat the fellow up and I didn't, and I was kind of ashamed of myself for not doing it. (pause) But, why I thought of him—it came to my mind, when I was walking out of the room, I thought of Frances Wadman.

T. I imagine that there was some sort of rivalry between the two of you?

S. Yeah.

T. Do you have any idea what this rivalry was about?

S. Well, I'm not sure. I think it probably had something to do with women, or girls, you know. Impress the girls, I guess, or—he—in a sense he was a rival for the attention of the girls. He was considered very attractively handsome, I guess, and I—I just felt very inferior about my appearance. I always envied him because he had all these girls, and I didn't. And ah—he used to be my friend, and then, in class—it seems to me that we were fooling around, and he said something—I don't know what I said, but he said, "That's pathetic" in reference to my action, and I was hurt that he said that; I thought that he had turned against me. It wasn't called for, that he should say something like that. And I think that's where it started. And he—he was acting kind of wise—what I would call wise. And from then on I guess we were kind of rivals.

T. Was that the particular incident that led up to the fight?

S. I—I'm not sure. I think it was. It came before the fight. It was in this particular—it was—I think it was the early part of the school year, in the Fall, and he ah—ah we had been friends before this, and he wasn't—he hadn't been in my room before this, my homeroom. But he was in my homeroom this particular time. And I was kind of looking forward to being friends with him, because we would be together, in the same room. I felt he kind of—rebelled against me, or betrayed me, or something like that. 'Cause I did like him till then. But—I think—I keep thinking of the weak feeling I get in my knees when I—when I ah—before I fought him or right—the feeling I get whenever I witness somebody fighting, or think about fighting. I get a very weak feeling. I'm very excited and I start trembling a little. And if I get mad, I fight, but if I'm not mad, if I don't think I'm in the right particularly, why I have a hard time starting a fight. But if I really get mad, I can start a fight. But I'm hardly ever mad.

T. This weak feeling always occurs when you see a fight?

S. Usually when I see a fight too, yeah. If it's a real fight, yeah—I mean, I can watch fights on television and—and although I get a little excited with it, and sometimes if I'm really interested in the fight, I get kind of a weak feeling, but if it's a—if it's a real fight, where it's a clash of personalities or something like this, why, I really get excited. I remember, I was down in the diner last—I guess it was early this year, and two fellows got in a fight outside, and I watched them. I shook for about fifteen minutes afterwards. I just trembled. And I felt kind of sick. It's not so much the actual fight, because—I boxed, when I was in the Navy, I boxed, and it didn't bother me. I didn't mind getting hurt, and I didn't mind hitting. In fact, I liked to. But when the fight involved an actual clash of the people, not just sport, why it bothers me. It's just like a—I hate to have a showdown with someone, too.

T. When did you first notice this feeling that you get when you see this fight, this clash of personalities?

S. You mean when in my life did I first notice it, or when today?

T. In your life—when was the first time you ever noticed it?

S. I don't know. (pause) As long as I can recall, I've always been afraid of being hurt, with bodily contact, or being hit, or being held down, and not being able to get up. But I can't recall when it first occurred. (pause) I was just thinking about—about—well, it's irrelevant, I mean—I was just thinking about it. When I was on the track team in high school, and ah—I got my letter in my senior year.

But—they have an award for somebody every—for the graduating seniors, about 2 or 3 weeks before classes end, and ah—most of the people—almost everybody that gets their letter gets—also gets what they call a citizenship key. This is presented along with the letter. And someone—an instructor black-balled me, for—not getting my key. One thing—he found me wandering around the halls, quite frequently. I had got permission from my track coach to cut my study hour, which I had the last period of the day, so I could practice, for track. And whenever the weather wasn't good, or I wasn't feeling like running, I would just walk around the halls; and this one instructor I had in chemistry was always catching me, and I think it was him that black-balled me. Anyhow, I wasn't allowed to get my award.

T. How did you feel about that?

S. Oh, I felt extremely burned up about it. And I felt it was very unjust, they shouldn't do this. It wasn't fair. I felt at first that he shouldn't have black-balled me, and even if I didn't get my key, I should at least have gotten my letter. And I thought—with all the work I did in track, and no one knew that I really got my letter. In fact, everyone would have assumed from that that I didn't get my letter. And that really hurt me. I was really annoyed. (pause)

T. Did you do anything about this?

S. Well, I went up and talked to my track coach about it—Mr. Ware. But ah—he was sympathetic, but he didn't do anything about it. He gave me my letter. I remember a couple of years after I came back—to him—and I was just talking to him—I was visiting the school. And he was giving me a little of his philosophy of life. And I was a little disappointed, that the person who I had liked quite a bit, then, I was a little disappointed that he was a—he was as shallow as I found him to be later on. On the other hand, my—there was a fellow who was an instructor in phys ed (Mr. Smith) who nobody liked, because he was always biting everybody's head off. And then when I came back, I was talking to him, accidently—I just happened to run across him—and I found out he was really a hell of a swell guy. And my other instructor in phys ed—he wasn't much of anything—a guy with a real high voice that looks something like Eddie Cantor.

T. What was it that was shallow about the philosophy of this person, this teacher you mentioned?

S. I don't know. I can't really think what it was. Sort of a Sunday School teacher kind of a thing. I—oh—he had a few pet sayings and ideas which he picked up somewhere, decided that this was for him, and didn't bother to think about it any more. And—I mean, evidently he picked this up somewhere along in his life, decided that this suited him, and it would save him from thinking about it any more. And ah—I didn't feel like arguing with him because, I mean, I didn't want to hurt the guy's feelings. I felt like turning away and walking out, because he talked about it almost—for a long time. When I was coming here, I also thought about (Mr. Smith) and when I think of him, I think of him in a sweat suit and sort of a reddish shining face. He had glasses. And I sort of had the—sort of embarrassed when I came here. I don't know why. I can't explain it.

T. That is, you experience sort of an embarrassed feeling now that you think of him?

S. Yeah, I sort of feel embarrassed about *him.* I don't know why. Just like—you would have a—you would get a friend, see, you become friends with someone, and ah—they—they feel a little ill at ease with him, or something. Now why? Maybe because of the way they look at you—I don't know. It's hard to explain. But there's—it's embarrassing to be friendly with them, for some reason. I can't—can't think of why it is, that would be embarrassing.

T. And that's the same feeling that you have now as you think of him.

S. Yeah. It—it's something like—like telling a dirty joke—hearing a dirty joke told, when you're around your father. Something like this, I mean, if you're not used to this kind of conversation with your father. Ah—or talking about sex to your father, if you've never done it before. You feel that this is a topic you just don't share with this person for some reason. And ah—I can't see why this would have any effect on me, and him.

T. How did you usually get along with him?

S. Oh, well, I didn't know him that well. I had him for boxing, when I—I took boxing in high school. And he—he didn't really get personal with many people—I—I disliked him eventually at first, and then I think I got to like him just a little. He calls me (name of *S*)—I think he knew me when I was in boxing. And he—he's sort of a—it seems to me now that I think of it, he was—from my last year there, he was sort of grouchingly affectionate, you know what I mean. He almost seemed like a father figure. He doesn't really look unlike my father, but—there is some similarity, I guess, but I never thought of him as one before. (pause) But I think I would feel uncomfortable in his presence, for some reason. I don't know why.

T. What's been the character of your own relationship with your father?

S. With my father? Well, the way I—I've had some counseling—and the way I had it figured out is that ah—I rejected my mother, somehow, fairly early, because she's—she constantly nags—gives you heck about just about everything, and was completely unpleasant to me. I didn't like her. And I think it became very important to be accepted by my father, and he was kind of demanding. He expected a lot from me. And—and I didn't—I couldn't live up to what he expected. And I kind of resented him for not—not coming more my way, instead of expecting me to come his way, and ah—or ah—there was something else. I went blank for a moment there. I don't know what happened—I went blank for a moment there. I just can't think of it—I was thinking about my father—oh. He has a tremendous amount of pride, and ah—I think I set up pretty high standards for him, too, and ah—we could never get along. I enjoyed him at times, but he was inconsistent. I didn't know what to expect from him. I mean, sometimes he was a hell of a swell guy to be around, but when I would do something, in keeping with the mood of him and then he would maybe jump down my neck for—doing it, because it wasn't—I was stepping out of my place. Even now he hasn't allowed me the privilege of an adult, as far as our relationship goes. I mean, he still—he still treats me like I should give reverence to his—to him—that he is my father, you know. He wouldn't let me speak back to him—at least he would object, you know. And I always feel like—there were several times I wanted to hit him, you know. Just slug him, or something. But I always felt—extremely—almost choked up when I thought about it, because I just couldn't stand to hurt him. I couldn't—I couldn't stand the idea of a—of a guy being hurt by his son, because, I mean, it meant so much to him. I would picture how I would feel if my son would do this, and I—I just couldn't—I refrained from talking back to him many times, because I didn't want to hurt his feelings. I didn't want to destroy his tremendous pride, I guess it was. But our relationship's better recently. I've been able to accept him for what he is. I mean, we get along better. And I—I'm very careful how I act to him so that he can't criticize me so very much.

T. You said that several times ah—you felt like hitting him, you got this choked up feeling. Could you tell me more about this feeling?

S. Well, I remember once—this is—I don't know if it's irrelevant or not—this was—I guess this was at Christmas when I was home. The fights were on television, and I like to look at fights. In fact, it's the only program I even care about. And ah—all evening I didn't pay any attention to the television set or anything, and it came time for the fights. My brother was at home—he's 21, and wanted another program on, and so did my mother. And I had the fights on the station—they just happened to come on the station it was already on, and I told my brother not to touch the station—I wanted the fights. I felt justified in seeing the fights. And I felt at least these people could—I'm their guest—at least they could let me see the fight—that's all I wanted the entire evening. And I stayed home, because when I visit them they like me to stay home, so you know, so they can participate in my company. And this was my reward for staying home. So I was very annoyed, and I threatened my brother that if he touched it, I was going to hit him. And he came over and touched it, and I threw a jab at him, and he jabbed back, and it caught me in the nose a little, and it really made me mad—I was going to slug him. I mean, I was poised, ready to throw a right—really, I saw red there for a minute, and Dad interfered, and I felt like slugging him too. I almost turned around and slugged him, and then I—I calmed down, and then I had to go over and sit in a corner because I know that I shouldn't do it. I mean, if I did, I would regret it, because I would feel bad about hitting him. And I felt very, very bad about the whole thing. And I had no way to express my feelings about it at all. They couldn't come out. In fact, I came home about three days early on my vacation. I came back up here, because I didn't—we weren't getting along.

T. Was your father there at the time?

S. Where?

T. When this event happened with the—when you want to slug your kid brother.

S. Yeah. He interfered. Yeah. I almost hit him. I mean, he's a—he's a little guy, that is, as far as height goes. He's very muscular. He's kind of small, and he got a little mad, and that was kind of ridiculous, and I felt—I could have poked him one and set him on his ass. But I—couldn't have done it. (pause) But I remember, I felt I was really—something had really been done to me, that was completely unfair, and I couldn't get back. There wasn't a thing I could do—I couldn't argue about it, I couldn't say anything, I just had to go in the corner and swallow it. (pause)

T. Sort—sort of, you had the feeling it was unfair. Was this anything like the feeling that you had about the missing out on the citizenship key?

S. Yeah, there's a similarity, yeah. Of course I wasn't—I was—I was more hurt in that citizenship key business than I was angry. I was angry of course, but I was more hurt than angry. Because this was something I really—expected—I didn't know it was going to happen until the morning of the assembly. I even went on stage. The curtain closed and we were supposed to go on stage and sit down on these bleachers and wait, and I was actually sitting down and waiting for the curtain to open and somebody—one of the instructors told me that I wasn't on the list, and I had to leave. And this really cut me down. Whereas with my father, ah—this wasn't actually a disappointment too much, because it was the kind of behavior I would expect. It would be characteristic of my home life. The other was—was really painful. And I've had unpleasant memories of high school ever since then I think. (pause)

T. This fellow that you mentioned in the beginning—Wadman—

S. Wadman—Frances Wadman. Wadman I made up—the name Wadman.

T. This name was like someone that you knew, and ah—was just that person receiving one of the keys and letters?

S. No, because he dropped out of high school, I think in his junior year. Went to a private school. But he was—he was fairly athletic, and he—he was pretty much of a favorite of the instructors—of the phys ed instructors, I think. I think—I think he and (Mr. Smith) got along pretty good, as I recall. I know that he and at least one of the instructors got along pretty good. I think it was (Mr. Smith). (pause) I was just thinking that you look like a history instructor that I had in college. At least that's the first impression I got of you, when I met you. But you don't look too much like him, when I look at you closer. You probably know the fellow up here. ——— I think his name is. Teaches history. There's a—there's just a similarity of first impression, when you—you look at your face and features and his, why there's not too much similarity. But the front view, and along in here, and the eyes, I guess, more than anything else. Your head is shaped differently than his.

T. How did you get along in that course?

S. Oh, I liked him. I got along fine, in the course. He's a pretty fine fellow. (pause) I'm just—I'm just trying—there's something that I just want to picture you in a sweat suit.

T. Like the one that (Mr. Smith) was wearing?

S. Something like that. Of course, you do have glasses on. So did he. I think that was what was funny about it—that he would have a sweat suit on and glasses—incongruous. (pause)

T. Do you have any idea why that should occur to you?

S. No, When I—when I look directly in your eyes, there is a similarity to your—it's fleeting—it's not all the time—but you and (Jack Smith) the way he looks at you. There is a similarity, because he does look directly at you. And through here, it isn't unlike him. I don't recall what his nose is like, so—how far that goes. But when I look straight at you, I see your suit. It looks—not exactly like a sweat suit, but you could imagine like a one-colored outfit, like a sweat suit. But—I don't know—it's kind of irrelevant. (pause)

T. Is that why you felt embarrassed here?

S. Uh—not exactly embarrassed. I—I remember when I first came in, you looked at me. I didn't feel like—I looked at you, and then I didn't feel like looking, you know, I felt like looking elsewhere around the room. But I don't mind looking at you. I don't feel embarrassed. I felt kind of uneasy, and I noticed that I was pinching my hand, because I got a little cramp here—all through here. (pause) I feel a little excited or something—like—like just like the effects of a benny, like I had taken a pill an hour and a half ago, and I was just starting to feel it, starting to tense up a little, a little excited. (pause) I noticed something else too, which I—I just became aware of, I don't know why. This I do occasionally. I don't know why I just became aware of it, because it's—it's insignificant. But sometime I tend to withdraw, like, go back like this in my seat a little. I know I've done it before—I don't recall that I've ever paid attention to it, but just now, I was doing it—I guess I'm trying to see how I feel. And I noticed how I automatically—drawing back.

T. Could you tell me more about this kind of keyed-up feeling that you have?

S. (pause) I just realized something else—now—I don't know how much truth there is to this, or how much there is to it, but when I first came in, you were looking at me, and I kept looking away, and I felt very tense. Since then, I've been looking at you pretty much, and I've found you looking away. And it seems to have changed my attitude. It seems to have—I don't mean put me in command, you know, but give me a more superior position than I had before. And you don't appear—not that you ever appeared foreboding to begin with, but you don't appear as foreboding on the continuum as you did before. And I felt that I could—I could get up and push you down, or something. I don't know why I would want to push you down, but I could get up and do it. (pause) And ah—now that I think about it, I think I'm a little embarrassed too, about—about ah—oh, first of all, how do you interview. I don't know exactly why—what it's about. But you occasionally seem that you ah—that you're uncomfortable in it, that you don't know where it's going, or that—what's or that we're not talking about the thing we're supposed to talk about or something. And I feel a little embarrassed for you that we're not doing it, or something. (pause)

T. So what you've been noticing here now is a shift in the way you feel about having command of the situation.

S. Yeah. There is a definite shift. I'm—I definitely feel now that I—I don't like to use the word that I can handle the situation, or that I'm in command of it, because, well, it's hardly the case, I mean, we're—there's nothing to justify me stopping. I mean, we're having an interview, and I could get up and walk out if I wanted to, or anything else. That's beside the point. But I have a definite feeling now that I'm more in command, or something—I don't know exactly what it is. (pause) These feelings are things that I wouldn't bother to talk about, except that—that you apparently want me to talk about whatever comes to my mind, and that's what comes to my mind.

T. You still having that embarrassed feeling?

S. No. I don't seem to have it now. I still feel a little tense though. (pause)

T. And you felt embarrassed for me.

S. Yeah. I didn't—somewhere in between. I mean, that's the—that's the—as the interview wore on. I felt sort of embarrassed for you. And then I seemed to come into command or something. I seemed to be trying to help you to do something. I don't know what. But ah—I mean—I wasn't exactly—it wasn't embarrassment. I think it wasn't—I don't know whether I was embarrassed before or not. I felt ill at ease. But when you would look at me, and I was looking at you, then I would turn away. I was—I didn't feel that I had to turn away, but I was embarrassed—I was conscious of that fact that I was—I wasn't looking at you. And now I don't mind. I feel—I guess I do feel more secure than I did before, for some reason. I feel like I got something off my mind in the past five minutes. Although I still feel a little tense about it. But I felt before like—I felt bothered by something, and now I just—got it out of my mind.

T. When you noticed this shift—was there any change in your feelings at the time?

S. Well, I didn't notice the shift as a current—that is, I wasn't aware that it was a shift. I wasn't aware that it was a shift until I looked back on it. So I felt—I'm not too clear on what happened. I know what ah—when we were talking about this situation with my father, I knew that—I knew that I became very emotionally involved in it, because I was—I was on the verge of crying. I think not—it's usually crying. I felt choked up, definitely. And it's unusual that I should feel choked up, because, although it is a sensitive situation, I don't usually become involved if I should tell about it. (pause) I feel like—I feel like Jack Smith disappointed me or something. I feel like Jack Smith—I feel the way about Jack Smith just like—like I felt about Mr. Ware, my track coach, who disappointed me when I came back and talked to him and he was such a shallow person. I feel disappointed in Jack Smith, because I did like him. I guess I still do, although I feel embarrassed at something. I feel somewhat also—like—I'm—I think a closer feeling of embarrassment—it's like, when I'm driving with my father, and he made a mistake in driving, and he blames the other fellow for doing it, and this embarrasses me very much. I feel that way about Jack Smith. (pause) Boy, this is the first time I've thought about Jack Smith since,—well, since I saw him the last time, which was three or four years ago, anyhow. I don't know why I should think about him. (pause) I feel like (words lost—something about a spot), I feel like I'm back on the spot again or something, like there's been a slight shift again. Because I was talking and I was very involved in talking (words lost—something about embarrassment). Suddenly there I have this thought which—the only relevancy I can see to it is that it happened in high school, when it is not very significant, except that in my homeroom—my homeroom instructor was the—the ex-football player. And he went over to the window once, and put it up. And he tried to put it up. Then he said, give me a hand here, to someone I don't know who it was—but they went over and with one hand, lifted up the window. There wasn't any weight to it at all. And this struck me as funny that he should call someone out to help lift the window up and there wasn't even any weight to the window at all—a baby could have pushed it up. I don't know why I thought of that.

T. Who was it that did the calling?

S. This homeroom instructor of mine, who ah—was a fairly nice fellow, and he had played football, among other—there was certainly no reason to believe that he was weak. Nobody could be that weak. And this baffled me for some reason, that he should do this, (pause) I—I've got a funny feeling that—like ah—like I was running down the hall, and I got hit—somebody suddenly opened the door, and I got hit in the face with it. I've had this—almost happen to me, cause I was running down the hall, right close to the rooms, and somebody opened the door, and I almost ran into it. I don't know why I thought of that, either. Except that it's a little frightening, because it could be—it's an unpleasant experience to run into a door. (pause)

T. You say this *almost* happened to you?

S. Yeah, at least I think it did. I mean, at least I thought about it, anyhow. It seems to me that—that I have run down the hall, and someone—either someone opened the door and I just almost ran into it, or at least I thought about it, when I was running down the hall—sometime or another I thought about it, what if someone opened the door, I'd run into it. I don't know which is the case. I can't actually recall anyone ever doing it.

T. If you did this, how would you feel?

S. If someone opened the door?

T. If you ran into the door.

S. I don't know. All I can think about is it would hurt. It would be pretty unpleasant in that respect. I can't imagine anyone opening the door, though. I can just see the door opening—I can't see anyone opening it and coming out. (pause) I just remembered. I never—I just remembered that he told me, when I was asleep. I remember that—it just came to me—that I was running—I don't know if I was running or not, but I was going down the hall, and this guy came out of the door, and bumped into me, and it was a phys ed instructor, and he gave me hell for doing it, when it was his fault. And I was mad at him, but I couldn't do anything about it. But I remembered—I remember him telling me, now. I mean, I remember—I can remember hearing him say that I would imagine this—I just remembered. I also remember that it was funny I—when he said one of your phys ed instructors in high school, I was trying to think of these three men—Mr. Ware, my track coach, and Jack Smith. I couldn't think who—who would have done this—who would have gotten mad. I tried to think—I liked Ware. He wasn't thc kind that would get mad at all. And I didn't want Smith to get mad, because I liked him. I didn't think he would do something like this. But then I couldn't see Baker getting mad, because he had this Eddie Cantor way of talking, you know, kind of high-pitched, and he just sort of reminded of Eddie Cantor. I couldn't picture him getting mad. It would sound ridiculous—kind of squeaky, and I—I was left with Jack Smith, I think. Because he does—he does get mad at people, but I don't think he would do something like this—he wouldn't get mad in a situation like this, where he was definitely at fault. (pause)

T. What do you think is the significance of these events and things that you recalled? This particular story?

S. I know that I talked about—I talked about Smith and Ware, didn't I? I talked about those two. Obviously I guess I was—it was—I was thinking about—maybe my embarrassment about Smith was I thought that he did this. I must have felt—I mean, I don't think that I was normal—I mean, I don't feel—I don't know how I feel about him. Now. But it surprised me. I know that I felt embarrassed about him, because I never had this feeling before. And I don't really see how my father fits in any of this. Oh, I can see—I can see in a way how I felt. I mean, I felt that this wasn't fair. At home, I said about the television, I felt that wasn't fair. And I would see where I would think that this wasn't fair. I wouldn't hit Smith I mean, I wouldn't get mad at Smith, either. I wouldn't feel that I could do this, because (words lost) and I wouldn't feel—I wouldn't feel that I could do anything about it. And it would be the same way with Dad. I couldn't tell him off. I don't know where this Frances Wadman came in, though. Except that it occurred in high school. The only thing that I could think about that might have any relationship to it is the fact that—that's the way I felt—kind of scared and weak, about when this friend fought me. I don't know whether I would have felt scared and weak when Smith fought—when Smith would have bumped into me. I may have—I don't know whether I was going to fight Smith or not—whether—even for a second when he bumped into me, whether I thought about fighting him. It didn't seem to me that I would. It seems to me that if he came out and gave me hell, I wouldn't think of hitting him. I just wouldn't imagine hitting him, or even think about hitting. And I would only get this weak feeling if I thought about hitting him, or fighting. Maybe I did think about it. I don't know. That's the—the only development I could see. (pause) Funny that I just remembered it. (pause) It almost seems that I knew it all along, except that I wasn't thinking about it. And I suddenly remembered, and I thought, well, I knew this. But I didn't think about it. And I can't remember when I stopped thinking about it. Because I can remember him telling it to me, and I was wondering if I was going to remember, and the next time I remembered it, I just suddenly remembered it, and I can't think of when I—stopped thinking about it. (pause) That's about it, I guess.

T. How do these reactions, which you felt toward me, tie in with this?

S. (pause) You were sort of—when I first came in, you—you kind of embarrassed—not embarrassed, I mean—I guess the way I felt about Jack Smith. I felt uncomfortable. I felt like—that—he was looking down at me—he had no right to, or something like that. I felt on the spot. And then I felt like I wanted to get the guns on him or something. And yet I was embarrassed, because I mean—like, when I wanted to hit my father. Yet if I had hit him, I would have felt sorry about it. And then—and then—then when you ah—when I felt—when that shift came, when I felt a little more in command or something, it was as though, either I had forgiven you or, or I had decided that it was a weakness in your character that made you do this, and that I shouldn't be mad at you, I should feel sorry for you, rather, I guess that's it. And that's how I come to accept my father, now. Now I feel sorry that he has these particular weaknesses. I don't feel angry at him any more. I feel just a little superior about him, that I can see them, and I can forgive them, or overlook them. And I think that's how I felt about you, too. I mean, the feeling that seems to be connected with this thinking seems to be similar to the feeling that I felt about the situation here in this office. But I didn't—I wasn't thinking these things about you. (pause)

T. I imagine that's it now, I think.

Evaluation of the Paramnesic Analogue Design. The evaluation of this kind of psychotherapy research strategy involves two related questions. The first to be discussed is the question of how well the strategy solves some of the problems involved in psychotherapy research, including a consideration of the range of therapy questions amenable to exploration through this strategy. The question to be discussed second, because the evidence bearing on it is so inconclusive, is the question of the validity of hypnotically induced paramnesias as analogues of neuroses.

One of the obvious advantages of this kind of design is that it permits multiple outcome measures, which either cut across theoretical lines, or which are relevant to several different schools of therapy, making it possible to compare the therapies for specific effects of interest to each school. This permits us to move toward the day when it will be possible to say that a particular kind of therapy is the appropriate one for achieving a particular outcome. Because these multirelevant variables can also be directly measured from *S*'s behaviors, we are able to reduce errors of inference arising from the use of psychometric devices of doubtful validity. A further advantage is that the measurements can be directly tied to the status of the patient-subjects, which is experimenter controlled. In naturalistic research, in which the characteristics of the patients are at best incompletely known, outcome measures must be general enough to be relevant to a wide variety of patient characteristics, thus inclining researchers to measures of such global variables as overall adjustment, emotional maturity, and the like; measures of such variables lack the reliability and validity possible for direct behavioral observations, and are much less meaningful because they are so ambiguous.

The ability to control important patient variables has several advantages, in addition to permitting the precise focusing of outcome measures already cited. It also allows one to test specific therapy variables: because the therapist is not dealing with a heterogeneous population, which makes it necessary that the therapy be global, or almost all things to almost all men, it is then possible to focus the therapy variables more precisely without making them irrelevant or inappropriate to a portion of the patient-subject sample. The standardization of at least one significant dimension of patient variables also reduces error variance, so that differences among treatment effects can show up in the analyses. A further advantage of this control is that it permits the study of the relative effectiveness of the same therapies with different kinds of patient problems. One can investigate the question of whether different results would have been obtained in the experiment described above had the paramnesia been concerned with erotic rather than aggressive impulses. This kind of investigation can also move us closer to the day when specific therapies may be recommended for specific problems as well as specified desired outcomes.

Although the use of hypnosis to provide standard "neuroses" has its advantages in reducing variance, it also leaves the subjects free to cope with the hypnotic implant in their characteristic ways. Thus the therapy variables are tested in a realistic situation, with the egos of the subjects functioning integratively and/or defensively, as is the case in natural psychotherapy. Thus the data are not limited to highly artificial imitations of people with problems.

The use of a sample of therapists has great value. It allows the results to be generalized to therapists not included in the sample. Such generalization is at best a highly riskly procedure when the research is based on the behavior of one, possibly highly atypical, therapist. Several different therapists operating in each of the experimental conditions also diffuses the operation of therapists' expectancies and biases, which are likely to vary among the therapists, and thus to be distributed more randomly than they possibly can be when only one or two therapists are used. In the latter case, it is difficult to know whether the variance ought to be assigned to the therapist's technical operations or to his implicit hypotheses and "demand characteristics" (Orne, 1959), which can become confounded with the experimental treatments. Keeping the therapists ignorant of the purposes of the research ought also to attenuate the selective effects of the therapists' biases and expectancies. When they have no ideas about what response classes in their patient-subjects are being measured, it is quite difficult for them subtly to influence that response class in accordance with their hopes or expectancies regarding the research. They are thus no better able to bias the results than are therapists in actual practice, and so the experimental analogue becomes more representative of actual practice.

Such representativeness, so far as therapists' expectations are concerned, was also furthered by allowing the therapists in the study to believe that their subjects might also be regular patients of the Psychological Clinic. The therapists knew that the subjects had been hypnotized; but they did not know that the subjects were not also patients, and when some of the therapists asked the experimenter directly about this, they were given an ambiguous reply. Thus the therapists could not allow themselves to think that their behavior during the interviews did not really "count" as far as the patient's welfare was concerned. The result of this is that the therapists were not likely to behave toward the experimental *S*'s in ways fundamentally different from the ways in which they behaved toward clinic patients (whose verbal behavior during interviews is routinely recorded at the clinic in which this research was done). In effect, another aspect of back-action effects of research on the therapy was thereby reduced.

The use of a sample of therapists, each of whom appears in the two experimental treatments, has the advantage of reducing error variance by permitting the variance associated with individual differences among the therapists to be set aside from the error term. Thus the personal characteristics of the therapists that might be confounded with experimental treatment are represented equally in the treatments. However, this solution is not without its difficulties. It is important to be sure that the therapists appearing in the experimental and control conditions are of equal competence in their use of the techniques demanded by the experimental variables. Short of obtaining a sample of experienced therapists for each technique, the typical solution is to use graduate students who are relatively unskilled in any kind of therapy, and thus not greatly more skilled in one than the other condition. Certainly this makes some conditions of the experiment nonrepresentative of professional psychotherapy, but it does solve the problem of comparability of skill. The alternative solution, the use of samples of experienced therapists, makes it impossible to use the same therapist in both experimental conditions, because obviously the experienced therapist who has worked for years with his preferred techniques cannot function with equal skill in the alternative condition. And if one cannot use the same therapists in the two conditions, then personal variables in the manners of the therapists, which are likely to be correlated with their therapy-school preference, will be confounded with the experimental techniques. Strupp (1955b) has shown that there are reliable differences in background, for example, between analytically oriented and client-centered therapists, and it is reasonable to suppose that there may also be more subtle personality differences between the adherents of the two systems, especially when one considers how pervasively occupied schools of therapy are with their own particular philosophies, ethics, and *Weltanschauungen*. It would then be impossible to discriminate between the therapeutic technique and the personalities of the therapists who use that technique in the assignment of the variance. Thus, both the use of the same therapists in each condition and the use of different but expert therapists in each condition has its own problems. The difficulty with the former strategy, which was used in the study described above, became apparent in the course of the data analysis. Even relatively inexperienced graduate students do have preferences, and it was noted in connection with one of the therapists in the study that he was quite unskilled in "leading" techniques, in which he always seemed to ask the most irrelevant questions, or to direct the subject away from what appeared to be promising, although affect-laden areas. On the other hand, another therapist who was quite opposed to client-centered techniques managed so suffuse his "reflections" with such aggressive and accusatory tone as to cast serious doubt on his ability to play the role demanded by the experiment. Nevertheless, the use of the same therapists in both conditions helped to minimize contributions of therapist personalities that were not of experimental interest (the aggressive therapist described was only a little less aggressive in the other experimental condition), and the method does not seem particularly less valid than the alternative available. Finally, the dilemma posed by this problem is not unique to research using hypnotically induced analogues; it exists for all research in psychotherapy, and no completely acceptable solution to the problem has been found in any experimental design.

One contribution to methodology in analogue studies is specific to the use of the hypnotic paramnesia in the study described. The paramnesia was specifically designed with a built-in transference problem, which makes the miniature neurosis rather closer to natural events in therapy than can otherwise be obtained. The feelings of discomfort and parataxic distortions that motivate real patients to engage in therapy, and that provide them with the subject matter of the therapy, were also present in the hypnotically paramnesic subjects. Thus these *S*'s were provided with an internal source of motivation, which guided their behavior with greater parallelism to the behavior of patients in therapy than is the case in which experimental subjects are motivated solely by a wish to help the experimenter, or to fill up some idle time in an intellectually satisfying manner. The neurotic analogue provided by the hypnosis provided the subjects with internal motivations, affects, and problems with which they felt impelled to deal in much the same ways, and with much the same defensive operations, as patients in actual therapy. And most important, this was achieved without creating a situation of such magnitude that ethical considerations would limit the experimenter's ability to manipulate and control the therapy variables. The hypnosis that provided the experimenter with the miniature neurosis also provides him with the means for removing it in short order, so that he does not risk grossly violating the integrity and personality of the subject by his restrictions on the therapists' activities. This is an important consideration; it is generally true that the more like the real thing one is able to make the experimental neurosis, the more this defeats the purpose of using experimental neuroses as means for avoiding ethical commitments to patients. Hypnosis provides a reasonable solution to this dilemma, permitting the maximization of realism with a minimum of ethical risk. Obviously, some ethical risk is still involved, and the realism is not perfect, as will be indicated, but its imperfections may not be significant ones for the validity of the research.

This discussion brings us to the general problem of the validity of hypnotically induced paramnesias. This involves the question of the specific paramnesia used, as well as the more general problem. The research used several techniques to ensure the acceptance of the paramnesia by the subjects who were retained in the project. These techniques included the posthypnotic dream in the last training-screening session, and the instructions to imagine and then dream about the imagined situation in the first part of the final session. These procedures enabled the experimenter to eliminate some *S*'s who could not accept this particular paramnesia. It seems likely that those *S*'s who passed these criteria were ones with a potentiality for feeling, and suppressing, anger over being unjustly blamed. Although there is no evidence on this point at all, it does seem possible, then, that the selection procedures resulted in a situation in which the experimental neurosis was not entirely imposed on the *S*'s, that it was not false to their own experiences. One might argue then that the hypnotic procedures did not actually produce a paramnesia, but that rather they provided the *S*'s with an archetypical situation or screen memory for real events in their experience. The fact that some *S*'s accept the paramnesia while others reject it, noted in this study, in Luria's research, and in the experiment of Huston, Shakow, and Erickson, indicates a selective factor in acceptance other than hypnotizability; the explanation given for rejection by the football-player subject in the Gordon study suggests that this factor is one of compatability between the content of the paramnesia and the subject's previous experience. The fact that many *S*'s were able to describe in the interviews apparently real situations in their experience, situations similar in thematic content to the paramnesia and probably stimulated by a common mediating affect, further supports the notion that acceptance of the paramnesia is at least in part determined by its congruence with *S*'s experience. Thus the acceptance may function as evidence of at least a latent capacity to experience the affects associated with the paramnesia, a capacity which indicates that such affects have in the past played a role in *S*'s psychic life. If this is so, then the use of such paramnesias perhaps ought not to be considered as "laboratory" neuroses that are merely realistic; rather they might be thought of as real, albeit small, neurotic cases, and the question of validity of the hypnotic induction procedures ceases to be relevant. Certainly much of the behavior of the subjects during the interviews is consistent with this interpretation; several of the subjects, such as the one whose typescript was reproduced earlier, reported more than one event or time in their lives in which they felt unjustly accused and yet unable to retaliate. Some of the reported associations in the interviews were also along these lines, indicating that the therapists were dealing with real affects and experiences that were meaningful in the lives of the subjects.

One implication of this interpretation deserves special mention. One might argue that to the extent that therapy works it does so by its effects on underlying symptom-producing and symptom-maintaining dynamic factors, rather than through superficial changes in the overt behaviors of the patients directly produced. This notion is consistent with psychoanalytic theory, in which one of the roles of the transference is described as the reorganization of the neurotic conflict dynamics through their attachment to the analyst, thus making the interpretation of the patient's transference the means for the therapy. Although such an interpretation of therapy is usually made by dynamic theorists, this viewpoint is not inconsistent with learning-oriented therapy, in which the therapist could account for the effectiveness of his efforts in terms of their effects on such intervening variables as response hierarchies, expectancies, drive strengths, stimulus generalization widths, and so on. If therapy does work through its effects on underlying dynamic factors, that is, if it operates on genotypes rather than phenotypes, then artificial therapies directed at neuroses that are produced by means other than these underlying "natural" dynamics can have no relevance to therapy of real neuroses. However, if it is true that the acceptance of the hypnotic paramnesia depends on its concordance with already existing dynamics, then this criticism is not applicable to the procedures described in the study reported.

It must be admitted that this argument rests heavily on unverified supposition, and although many subjects did report associations consistent with the genotypic interpretation of the experimental neurosis, it is also true that many subjects did not. Thus, it is still necessary to examine whatever evidence exists for the validity of the hypnotic procedures. Unfortunately, this evidence is meager, much of it based on very old and quite unsophisticated studies; and more important, the evidence largely refers to phenotypic identities between natural and hypnotically induced states rather than genotypic identities. The studies of Luria (1932), and Huston, Shakow, and Erickson (1934) described earlier, support the hypothesis of at least phenotypic identity between the effects of hypnotic and natural conflicts. Other studies, such as those of Gidro-Frank and Bull (1950) also report evidence for the reality of hypnotically induced affects, and the studies reviewed by Barber in Chapter 14 and by Edmonston in Chapter 12, as well as in other chapters, strongly indicate that the phenomena produced by hypnotic means are not unique to it, but are similar to behaviors that are brought about in nonhypnotic situations in which subjects' motivation, perceptions, and past experience are the determining factors. Thus hypnotic phenomena appear not to be "artificial" events different from phenomena that can arise naturally in peoples' interactions with their environment. It would be inappropriate to review in this chapter all of the relevant research, which is reviewed extensively in other chapters. It is probably fair to say that although a great deal of research is now available for interpretation, an unambiguous answer to the question of validity cannot yet be given, and the problem must remain open.

To some extent, part of the question of validity rests on the question of who is hypnotizable, and why. It might be argued that because the use of hypnotically induced paramnesias requires hypnotizable *S*'s, who are by that fact selected according to criteria different from those used in the selection of patients, then the results of such research are of only limited generalizability. I believe that this is a legitimate problem, and one that only future research can clarify; present research on the personality variables associated with hypnotizability is too internally contradictory and ambiguous for any accurate assessment of the extent to which hypnotizable persons differ from people who become patients. However, this is not a severely limiting problem; many patients are hypnotizable, so that the data derived from psychotherapy studies using hypnotizable *S*'s is at least generalizable to natural therapy with this group of patients. And in the absence of evidence to the contrary, it might as well be generalized to others at least on a tentative basis, on the principle that a little, possibly inaccurate, knowledge may be better than absolutely no knowledge, particularly as the existence of *significant* personality differences between hypnotizables and nonhypnotizables has not been proven.

Thus, many factors recommend the use of hypnotically induced paramnesias as a strategy for psychotherapy research. Some of the problems of research in this area, which the paramnesic analogues fail to solve, are not solved any better by other available strategies. However, limitations to the use of this strategy must be recognized. Some of these limitations are inherent in the merely suppositional nature of some of the arguments presented, which therefore require skepticism and a sensitivity to new evidence, that might be brought to bear on the problems. It should be noted, however, that the need for skepticism need not be paralyzing; in the absence of other solutions of better demonstrated validity, the charisma of hypnotism should not be allowed to disbar it from the attempt to obtain at least approximate knowledge in an area in which definitive knowledge is so scanty.

Of the other limitations in the use of the design, one of the most important is that is appears to be restricted to research on the initial phases of psychotherapy. Certainly patients, and subjects, react differently to therapist activities at different stages of the treatment process, whereas the use of hypnotic analogues probably cannot go beyond three or four therapist-subject sessions. The longer and the more frequently therapists interview research subjects, the greater is the likelihood of the development of transference attitudes in the subjects, and their conversion of the experimental situation into an actual therapy experience. And as this happens, the therapists' ethical commitments to the subjects as patients become more strongly involved, thus eliminating the major advantage of the research strategy. Once the therapist is committed to the subject as a patient, he is no longer free to control his therapeutic techniques in the interests of the research, and the experimenter is no longer free to impose measurements on the subject that might significantly alter or interfere with the course of the therapy.

A second limitation in the use of the design is inherent in the use of paramnesias, which are concerned with cognitive contents and their associated affects. These procedures do not appear to be applicable to the control of stylistic patient variables, such as character structure, defensive patterns, ego processes, and other structural aspects of personality. It does not seem as if these aspects of functioning are as amenable to hypnotic manipulation as are memories for specific events. Although one can bring a subject to believe that he has had a particular experience that is similar to experiences that he has in fact had, it is not so likely that one can create paranoid or obsessive character traits in most nonparanoid and nonobsessive subjects. To be sure, one can alter specific ego functions, as in the research of Blum and his students (1961), but the direct suggestion method for doing this eliminates the genotypic validity, which may be highly relevant in the total validity of the behavior as an analogue of therapy with neurotic disturbances. However, it might be possible to select *S*'s of known character structures, defensive types, and so on, for use as experimental groups in paramnesic analogue studies. Such selection would depend on fairly extensive diagnostic testing of the potential *S*'s. Although such extensive testing might not be possible or feasible with applicants for psychotherapy, because of possible back-action effects of the testing on the patients' attitudes and expectations regarding the eventual therapy, it is more feasible in analogue studies, which require less sensitivity to possible distortions of the therapeutic relationship.

In sum, with a limited range of applicability, the use of hypnotic analogues involving the production of paramnesias provides psychotherapy researchers with means for circumventing some major difficulties in research design, through the acquisition of control over some significant variables without invalidating back-action effects and without generating conflict between the ethics of commitment to the patient's welfare versus commitment to the needs of the research.

Psychotherapy Research Using Real Conflicts Hypnotically Aroused

The use of hypnotically produced paramnesias reduces the pool of potential subjects to those who can accept the particular paramnesia used. Even with these subjects, it is possible to question whether the paramnesia is "real" in the sense of touching and involving the underlying dynamics of the subjects' personalities, or only a superficial role-playing by the subject having no further meaning beyond his ability to imagine the role and his willingness to play it to satisfy the demands of the experiment. Although I have argued against such an interpretation in the discussion of subject acceptance or rejection of the paramnesia, the possibility of such superficiality remains as an issue.

If the validity of the data on psychotherapy coming from research using hypnotically induced paramnesic analogues of neurosis hinges on the reality of such neuroses, then other strategies, which are not threatened by this possibility, might be employed. A study by Gordon, Martin, and Lundy (1959) illustrates the use of hypnosis to produce a laboratory neurosis in which real conflicts within nonpatient subjects are used in the place of paramnesias. The concern of the experimenters was again with repression as it is affected by psychotherapy, except that in this study the experimenters were interested in the relationship between levels of consciousness of conflictual material and affective responses. Conflict with parents was selected as a focal example of a neurotic core, which could be presumed to have unresolved residuals in most college student subjects. Hypnosis was used merely to activate this core through revivification of the subjects' neurotic fantasies concerning such conflicts. GSR's were measured continuously through the course of posthypnotic interviews with the subjects, who had been given posthypnotic suggestions designed to produce repression, suppression, and verbalization of the conflictual material. Therapeutic techniques were not an independent variable; these were standardly nondirective for each *S*.

The major hypothesis of the study was that as verbal cues related to the conflict are produced, the anxiety associated with those cues will be elicited. The more fully constituted the verbal cues, the stronger the anxiety should be. Repression was conceived to be a condition in which (verbal) thought of the conflictual material is absent, even when cues for such responses are present. This concept is based on the Dollard and Miller (1950) definition of repression. Repression in the study was produced by posthypnotic suggestions "not to think about" the conflict with parents which *S*'s had just fantasized. There are some points of difference between this definition of repression and the psychoanalytic concept in that no mention was made to the subjects of any particular motives for not thinking about the conflict. However, on the phenomenological level the experimental operations approximate the psychoanalytic interpretation of repression in that some material, available to the consciousness of the subjects, is rendered unconscious. The distinction between these operations and forgetting or extinction rests in the fact that subjects were also instructed, in a later period, to talk about the material, thus demonstrating that the material can be made available again to consciousness without the benefit of interpolated learning trials. Psychoanalysts agree in defining such posthypnotic amnesia as dependent on the repressive resources of the ego. As far as defensive motivation is concerned, it was assumed that the unpleasantness associated with conflict with parents, as a fairly common experience among college students, would participate with the instructions for posthypnotic amnesia as at least one component of the subjects' motivations to not think about the conflict. Thus the instructions not to think about conflict with parents may be considered to be an analogue of repression, including the presence of avoidance motivations, and thus providing the experimenters with a known conflict-source of repression without that source having to be unreal or artificial, as might be the case with paramnesias.

Suppression was defined as the covert production of (verbal) thoughts concerning the conflictual material, together with an avoidance of talking about it. The experimental manipulations to produce suppression involved instructions to think and recall posthypnotically the conflict with parents, but to not talk about them.

Verbalization, which was hypothesized to produce the largest GSR reactions (although the experimenters considered the possibility that extinction might rapidly occur, lowering GSR's during verbalization), was produced by instructions to talk about the conflict with parents during the interview.

The specific procedures involved group and individual screening sessions of female volunteer subjects, much as in the previously described paramnesia experiment. After the third session, 12 subjects had emerged as meeting the criteria for posthypnotic amnesia, and were given appointments for the final experimental session, which contained four parts. In the first part, electrodes were attached to *S*'s fingers and connected to a GSR recording apparatus while *S* was nondirectively interviewed for 15 minutes, the purpose of which was to establish her acquaintance with the interviewer, allow adaptation to the GSR device, and to obtain base level GSR readings. Following this interview, *S* was asked by another *E* to fill out an attitude questionnaire designed to tap defensive reactions and positive or negative attitudes toward the interviewer. *S* was then hypnotized by the same *E*. *S*'s had been assigned randomly to two experimental groups, the only difference between them being the order of the experimental conditions. The RVS group was to receive instructions to produce repression, verbalization, and suppression in that order. The other group, designated RSV, was to be given instructions for repression, suppression, and verbalization in that order. Thus suppression and verbalization were counterbalanced. It did not seem reasonable to counterbalance repression; repression occurring *after* suppression or verbalization in a psychotherapy session seemed meaningless and unrealistic.

The second stage of the last session consisted of *S*'s hypnosis, in which the following instructions were given:

Now, as you continue to sleep, I want you to recall in your imagination some of the occasions on which you have come into conflict with either or both of your parents. Think of times when you might have had arguments, or when you felt either your mother or your father were too strict, or when you might have felt that you were unfairly treated or not being understood. Review some of these occasions in your memory. See them in your mind's eye. You don't need to talk about them—just think about them yourself. I'll give you a minute or two in which I'll be silent to give you a chance to envision yourself in those situations. Feel just exactly the way you felt at those times. Kind of relive those experiences in your imagination now. Just think about them for a little while.

Following these instructions, *E* remained silent for one and a half minutes, and then continued with the instructions. If *S* were in the RVS group, she was instructed as follows:

Now, when you wake up, all those experiences you've been thinking about will have completely left your mind. You won't be thinking of them at all. They'll be the farthest thing from your mind. In the beginning of your interview with Dr.______, he'll click a key three times. Just ignore that. It doesn't mean anything. But later on, when he clicks the key again, all these thoughts and experiences with your father or mother or both, and your feelings about those experiences, will come to mind. You'll begin to think about them again. You can talk about the feelings and experiences that are on your mind. You'll want to talk them over with Dr.______. Later on, Dr.______ will click the key again. When he does, it'll occur to you that you shouldn't really talk to him about your experiences and feelings toward your parents, and you won't want to talk about them any more, although they will still be on your mind.

These instructions were then summarized for *S*, posthypnotic amnesia for the instructions produced, and *S* awakened. For the RSV group the instructions were substantially the same, except that the instructions for the suppression were given before the instructions for verbalization.

Upon awakening, the third stage of the session began. *S* was brought into the interview room, the electrodes attached, and instructions given to talk about anything she cared to, as she had done in the control interview. The interviewer began each interview by telling *S* that the interview would be about the same as the one she had before, and she could start off by telling something about herself. From that point on, the interviewer responded nondirectively. All interviews were tape-recorded. The interviewer clicked a telegraph key (which also made marks on the GSR record and produced clicks on the tape recording, to allow the two records to be matched in time samples) at the beginning of the interview, again after 15 minutes had gone by (more or less, waiting until *S* finished whatever she was saying when the 15-minute period elapsed), and again after another 15 minutes, more or less. These clicks served as further means for matching the records, and were also signals for *S* to suppress or verbalize, depending on the condition.

It is important to note that the interviewer, although aware of the nature of the hypnotic manipulations, did not know which of the two conditions each *S* was in. This provided some control over the operation of interviewer biases, which might be expressed through subtle reinforcements and the like.

At the end of the interview, *S* was disconnected from the GSR apparatus and returned to the hypnotist who asked her again to fill out the questionnaire of attitudes toward the interviewer. This concluded the third stage of the session.

The fourth stage consisted of a final hypnosis in which *S* was disabused of the previous instructions, and was allowed to recall the events of the previous trance state.

As a check on the validity of the experimental instructions, the interviews were scored for the presence of references to parents. Thirty-second intervals of the tape recordings were scored for the presence or absence of reference to parents during the intervals. Figure 1 shows the distribution of such references for the two experimental groups. One *S* in each condition failed to talk about parents in any sections of their interviews; one of these *S*'s was in the RVS condition and the other in the RSV. These two *S*'s were dropped from further analyses. Figure 1

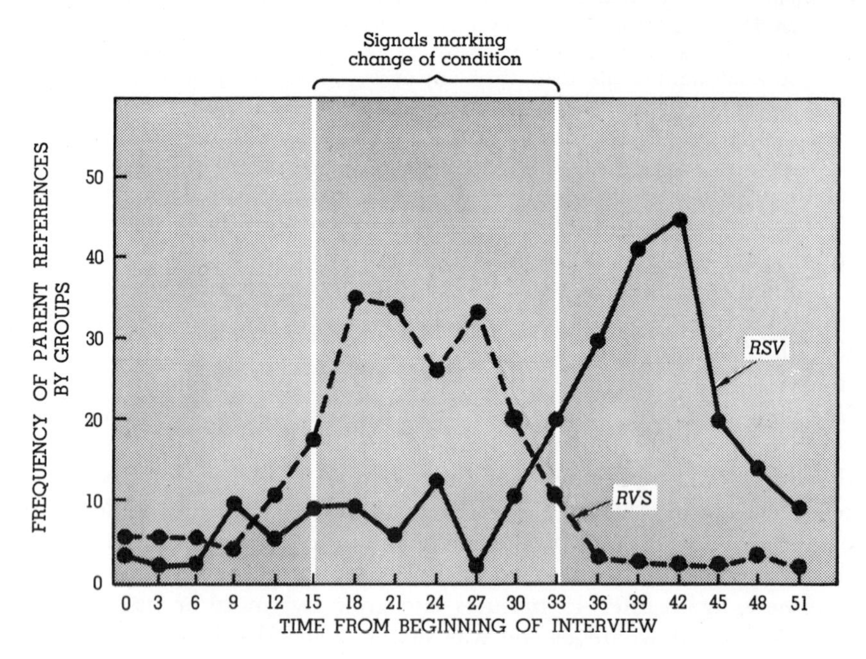

Figure 1. Distribution of references to parents and conflict with parents.

makes it apparent that *S*'s did follow the hypnotic instructions, as far as verbalizing is concerned.

The reader is referred to the original report of the research for a more complete presentation of the results. It is appropriate in this chapter only to indicate that the procedures were able to produce meaningful data: during repression, conductance increased significantly at a faster rate than during the control interviews; there were no reliable differences in the slopes of conductance in the repression and suppression interview sections; neither were the repression and verbalization curves significantly different in slopes; there was a significant difference between the slopes of the suppression and the verbalization conductance measures, with the suppression being associated with much sharper increases in conductance than verbalization, the curve for which, although higher than the curve for suppression, was almost flat; although the questionnaire did not differentiate significantly between the groups, the RSV group tended to change in the direction of more positive feelings toward the interviewer, whereas the questionnaires of the RVS *S*'s showed a change from the preinterview scores in the direction of more negative feelings toward the interviewer.

These data raised many questions. One anomalous finding was the fairly consistent increase in conductance throughout the entire interview for all *S*'s, except for those two whose data had been eliminated because of evident failure to follow the hypnotic instructions by talking about parents during their verbalization sections. The failure to find an adaptation to the GSR thus made it impossible to test the main hypothesis about the relationship between levels of consciousness and strength of GSR. However, the analysis of slope differences did permit some conclusions concerning the rate at which physiological arousal increases as a function of level of consciousness. The results obtained are consistent with those of Bobbitt (1958), who found relatively less disturbance in word association responses during awareness (that is, verbalization) than during partial awareness (that is, suppression), and more disturbance in repression than in the control condition. Our finding that verbalization produced less increase in anxiety than did suppression may be interpreted as either a reduction of arousal in association with a reduction in the dissonance (that is, conflict) between what *S* had to say and what *S* was thinking, or as an effect of extinction of the GSR during the permissive interviews, an interpretation that receives some support from the tendency for *S*'s who verbalized last in the interviews to feel more positively toward their interviewers than did *S*'s whose last interview segments were for supression.

Qualitative impressions of the interviews provide further evidence for the validity of the research strategy. *S*'s verbal behavior always appeared natural, and it is unlikely that any psychologist reading the typescripts would doubt that they are representative of patient behavior in psychotherapy. At no point did any *S* act as if she were automatically responding to hypnotic instructions. No *S*'s, for example, gave direct verbal responses to the clicks of the key marking the beginning of interview sections. Some *S*'s lapsed into silence momentarily, as if they were mulling something over. Some *S*'s made natural remarks, such as "Well, let's talk about something pleasanter," when shifting from verbalization to suppression, or "I guess I shouldn't bore you with these personal matters."

One notes frequent references in the suppression sections to the parent-conflicts of friends and relatives, and on occasion a spontaneous denial of personal conflict with parents. One record was particularly interesting in showing the development of *S*'s associations to conflict with parents. This *S* was in the RSV group. Her major topic of conversation during repression was a film on intellectual deficiency and brain damage, which she had seen in her psychology class. When the signal for suppression was given she indicated that the film reminded her of her friend's mother, who suffered from multiple sclerosis. During this section she talked about the emotional climate of her friend's home, which was characterized by tension, guilt, and unexpressed aggression. *S* noted that she was glad that her home life was not like that. When the signal for verbalization was given, *S* remarked that of course, her own home life was not all sweetness and light, either, and that "lots of people have problems with their parents, even when there isn't that kind of sickness and tension." From this point on she elaborated about some of her conflicts with her parents. The striking thing about this interview is that one is able to see how a conversation about a film on brain damage is related associatively to more personal concerns of the *S*; such behaviors only become intelligible when the experimenter has knowledge and control over the antecedent conditions, allowing him clearly to see associative connections that might not otherwise be apparent.

This experiment demonstrates the utility of using hypnosis to arouse neurotic conflicts that are real to the subjects, thus eliminating one source of objection to the use of hypnotic analogues. The technique could well be used to study the effects of different kinds of conflicts (provided the experimenter limits himself to conflicts that are likely to have been experienced by enough potential *S*'s to provide an experimental sample). One could study the outcome effects of different kinds of research strategies, as well as process variables. The use of the same *S*'s in the three kinds of conditions: repression, suppression, and verbalization, could be managed with the conditions more spread out in time, which might mitigate cumulative effects within interview sessions.

THE GENERAL VALIDITY OF ANALOGUE RESEARCH

Two examples of research in which hypnosis is used to create experimental analogues of neuroses for use in psychotherapy research have been described, together with a discussion of the value of the first design presented, which applies equally to the second design. A few remarks about the validity of analogues per se should be added. Analogues are not unmitigated blessings, and their liabilities must be recognized. Their greatest liability is involved in the question of their representativeness, their similarity to the real thing, which defines the validity of the analogue.

To answer the question of validity, one must know whether all factors in the analogue operate in the same way as their counterparts operate in real therapy. The problem is that the final answer to this question requires perfect knowledge of what goes on in real therapy. It requires a complete understanding of how all the factors operate in both the analogue and the referent of which it is a model; and of course, if this knowledge were available, there would be no need for analogues.

There is the further paradox that the more representative of therapy the analogue is, and the more it includes the kinds of dynamics present in therapeutic interactions, the less advantage it will have in offering controls not available to research using actual therapy. The more realistic the analogue, the greater will be the back-action effects on the measurements and on the experimental therapy process itself, and the more the analogue will be in danger of violating ethical considerations. Experimental subjects have personalities and feelings, which are as immediate and precious to them as are the feelings of those in therapy, and when one considers the increasing popularity of psychotherapy and the selectiveness of therapists in accepting patients (above average intelligence, high verbal ability, at least middleclass orientation and values, relative youth, and so on) the similarity between college student subjects and patients in therapy becomes closer and closer, until there is only a fine line separating the two. Even this line may be only a matter of time and accident; many *S*'s might just as well be in therapy, if they knew of its availability or had the money, and many of them probably will be in therapy in the not too distant future. Thus, analogues may approach true psychotherapy more and more closely, and so acquire the limitations of naturalistic research.

Almost by definition an analogue must be different from the thing that it represents, to have any advantage over the thing it represents as a research device. Laboratory research may be perfectly useful for model building in which the purpose of the model is to represent the events of laboratory research. But when the research is intended to provide information on nonlaboratory events, as in the case of engineering and psychotherapy research, the paradox inevitably arises that the more the laboratory increases its validity by becoming representative of the real situation, the more that such representativeness eliminates the control advantages of the laboratory and so interferes with the needs of the research. Thus, inevitably, critics of analogue research can always point to differences between the analogue and the real thing, and the products of such research are likely then to be consumed only by those who are in the market for the findings, and to be quite unconvincing to those who do not desire such products. Any needs to protect dearly held theories and conclusions about psychotherapy from discomforting evidence arising from analogue studies can always be supported by citations of the inevitable and necessary differences between the analogue and the real thing. When one considers the extent to which the personality theories underlying psychotherapeutic schools are pervaded by ethical world views, philosophies, and assumptions regarding the nature of man, the sources of the needs to protect theories from evidence become clear and the power of these needs impressive. Thus, as heuristic devices, analogue experiments are not likely to be universally successful. But then neither are naturalistic studies, which are always open to charges of distorting back-action and lack of controls. Thus, it is impossible in both principle and practice to perform the perfect psychotherapy experiment, analogue or naturalistic, whose results would therefore be compelling for all scientist-practitioners.

The advantage of analogue studies does rest on the extent to which they can eliminate *significant* differences between the analogue and its referent. Some differences may account for only negligible amounts of variance, and so can be sacrificed in the interest of experimental rigor. Although the use of hypnosis in the experiments described here does seem to do this, it must be kept in mind that what is significant for one man may not be for another, thus always leaving room for a rationalized denial of the evidence. Nevertheless, the techniques for the research are open for all to use, and are capable of many variations to provide the significant controls demanded by consumers who can also be producers of research.

REFERENCES

Beck, L. (1949). *Unconscious Motivation* New York: American Films.

Blum, G. (1961). *A Model of the Mind.* New York: Wiley.

Bobbitt, R. (1958). "The repression hypothesis studied in a situation of hypnotically induced conflict," *J. abnorm. soc. Psychol.* **56**, 204–212.

Counts, R. and Mensh, I. (1950). "Personality characteristics in hypnotically-induced hostility," *J. clin. Psychol.*, **6**, 325–330.

Danskin, D. and Robinson, F. (1954). "Differences in 'degree of lead' among experienced counselors," *J. couns. Psychol.*, **1**, 78–83.

Dollard, J. and Miller, N. (1950). *Personality and Psychotherapy.* New York: McGraw-Hill.

Edwards, A. and Cronbach, L. (1952). "Experimental design for research in psychotherapy," *J. clin. Psychol.*, **8**, 51–89.

Erickson, M. (1944). "The method employed to formulate a complex story for the induction of an experimental neurosis in a hypnotic subject," *J. gen. Psychol.*, **31**, 67–84.

Gidro-Frank, L. and Bull, N. (1950). "Emotions induced and studied in hypnotic subjects," *J. nerv. ment. Dis.*, **3**, 91–100.

Gordon, J. (1957). "Leading and following psychotherapeutic techniques with hypnotically induced repression and hostility," *J. abnorm. soc. Psychol.*, **54**, 405–410.

——— (in press). "Some dilemmas in psychotherapy research," *J. Psychother.*

Gordon, J., Martin, B., and Lundy, R. (1959). "GSRs during repression, suppression, and verbalization in psychotherapeutic interviews," *J. consult. Psychol.*, **23**, 243–251.

Grummon, D. and Butler, J. (1953). "Another failure to replicate Keet's study, 'Two verbal techiques in a miniature counseling situation'," *J. abnorm. soc. Psychol.*, **48**, 597.

Gump, P. (1944). *A Statistical Investigation of One Psychoanalytic Approach and a Comparison of it with Nondirective Therapy.* Unpublished M.A. thesis, Ohio State University.

Huston, P., Shakow, I., and Erickson, M. (1934). "A study of hypnotically induced complexes by means of the Luria technique," *J. gen. Psychol.*, **11**, 65–97.

Keet, C. (1948). "Two verbal techniques in a miniature counseling situation," *Psychol. Monogr.* #294, **62**.

Kesner, L. (1954). "A comparison of the effectiveness of two psychotherapy techniques in the resolution of a posthypnotic conflict," *J. clin. exp. Hypn.*, **2**, 55–75.

Krasner, L. (1962). "The therapist as a social reinforcement machine," In Strupp, H. and Luborsky, L. (eds.) *Research in Psychotherapy, Vol. II*, 61–94. Washington: American Psych. Assoc.

Luria, A. (1932). *The Nature of Human Conflicts.* New York: Liveright.

Meehl, P. (1955). "Psychotherapy." *Annual Rev. Psychol.*, **6**, 357–378.

Merrill, R. (1952). "On Keet's study, 'Two verbal techniques in a miniature counseling situation'," *J. abnorm. soc. Psychol.*, **47**, 722.

Orne, M. (1959). "The nature of hypnosis: Artifact and essence," *J. abnorm. soc. Psychol.*, **58**, 277–299.

Rogers, C. (1951). *Client Centered Therapy.* Boston: Houghton Mifflin.

Rubenstein, E. and Parloff, M. (eds.) (1959). *Research in Psychotherapy.* Washington: American Psych. Assoc.

SNYDER, W. (1948). "Client-centered therapy." In Pennington and Berg (eds.). *An Introduction to Clinical Psychology*, 465–497. New York: Ronald Press.

STRUPP, H. (1955a). "An objective comparison of Rogerian and psychoanalytic techniques," *J. consult. Psychol.*, **19**, 1–7.

——— (1955b). "Psychotherapeutic technique, professional affiliation, and experience level," *J. consult. Psychol.*, **19**, 97–102.

STRUPP, H., and LUBORSKY, L. (eds.) (1962). *Research in Psychotherapy, Vol. II.* Washington: American Psych. Assoc.

ZAX, M. and KLEIN, A. (1960). "Measurement of personality and behavior change following psychotherapy," *Psychol. Bull.*, **57**, 435–448.

III

CLINICAL APPLICATIONS

7

Hypnodiagnosis

JOHN J. BROWNFAIN
Veterans Administration Hospital, Dearborn, Michigan

No systematized body of knowledge in clinical psychology or in the entire field of applied hypnotism might fairly be described by the label "hypnodiagnosis." The term itself has never had general currency. Jenness (1944) does not refer to it at all in his comprehensive review of hypnotism, nor do subsequent reviews make more than incidental mention of it. Yet from time to time psychologists use hypnotism not in the interest of formal research nor as an adjunct of psychotherapy, but simply as an investigative method in the exploration of personality. This exploration may be broad enough to constitute an assessment of the total personality and its interpersonal functioning, or it may be narrowly confined to a single issue of psychopathology or differential diagnosis. In either event, the clinical psychologist is likely to refer to the totality of this process as psychodiagnosis. He may use projective and psychometric techniques, which are unique to clinical psychology, along with a method of interview that is probably not unique. The repertory of methods will vary considerably from one psychologist to another, depending upon training, theoretical orientation, and the patient population. His goals may vary less and, whatever his method, he will generally be interested in describing and explaining his subject in psychodynamic and structural terms according to the context of the practical questions he addresses to his theory and his materials. If, at any stage of this psychodiagnostic enterprise, the clinician uses hypnotism to add a dimension to his study or to facilitate his work, then he may wish to identify this activity as hypnodiagnosis.

Hypnodiagnosis, then, is hypnotism used in the context of psychodiagnosis. Like most other methods of psychodiagnosis, its value cannot be greater than the competence of the clinician who uses it. It cannot stand alone as a discrete laboratory method. It has much more in common with such complex projective methods as the Rorschach, or even more, with the clinical interaction itself, which imposes its own meanings upon all that transpires within it.

It is important to note that clinical psychologists do not have a proprietary interest in hypnodiagnosis. Clinicians in the fields of medicine, psychiatry, and dentistry also make use of the concept from points of view related to their own needs and practices. As one would anticipate, there is much similarity in usage in the fields of psychiatry and clinical psychology and one characteristically finds in the literature of the two disciplines common citations relating to the theory and practice of hypnotism.

I have written this chapter from the point of view of a clinical psychologist who has found in hypnotism a valuable adjunct in his everyday work as a diagnostician and psychotherapist in a VA General Hospital and in private consulting practice. I have emphasized my own experience in the practical clinical situation to encourage my fellow clinicians of comparable training to discover for themselves what a valuable addition hypnotism makes to the conventional repertory of methods and skills in clinical psychology. Although I regard myself as an advocate of hypnotism, I would not want to convey an uncritical enthusiasm for the method. It is one method among many, and I would no sooner use hypnotism in a routine fashion than I would administer a Rorschach to every patient on a routine basis. Indeed, I have used hypnodiagnosis in a minority of cases. Yet its selective application has yielded such ample rewards over the years that I can only deplore the fact that hypnotism is so rarely regarded as an ordinary interest and skill of the well-trained clinical psychologist.

There are undoubtedly many reasons for the reluctance of the psychologist not merely to use hypnotism but even to know about it. The psychologist's training is heavily academic and he hesitates to use clinical methods that intervene actively in the patient's psychological functioning. He has not learned how to "touch" patients and he is wary of leaving the security of his passive methods. He is likely, too, to be under the psychoanalytic spell, which all but interdicts hypnotism.

Of course, much of his resistance comes from his fear of being tarred by the charlatan's brush, but, paradoxically, perhaps as much comes from his own irrational belief in magic. He loses interest in hypnotism when he discovers that it produces no miracles, that it may fail to do in two sessions what psychoanalytic investigation may also fail to do in a hundred.

The clinician often explains his resistance to the use of hypnotism as a concern over the patient's untoward transference reactions instigated by the hypnotic state. Although transference (or relationship) phenomena must be taken into account in all clinical work, it seems reasonable to suppose that when a clinician is unduly worried about "the transference," he might more realistically be concerned about the countertransference. If, for example, he is anxious about wayward erotic impulses in the patient, then he should also be anxious about similar impulses in himself. If he is concerned about the danger of too zealous an intrusion in the patient's personality, then he ought to be equally concerned about the vacuum and waste of an undue passivity. The concept of transference is in fact broad enough to accommodate such an innovation as hypnotism in diagnosis and therapy. The clinician needs only to be aware of what is going on in the patient and in himself to turn the so-called problems of transference to his advantage.

Still another basis for rejection may be found in the unfamiliarity and tedium of the hypnotic induction. In clinical interactions, as in most other interpersonal relations, one finds gratification in the mutual play of intellect. To say that a patient is interesting is, often enough, another way of saying that he has found the clinician interesting. In the process of hypnotic induction one must reverse this process of stimulation. In many inductions one is most successful with the patient when he is also most boring to himself. For a brief period, at least, one passes from dialogue to monologue. The skill of inducing hypnosis does not come naturally; it must be patiently learned until it does come naturally. But here, as in the transference—countertransference objections, many clinicians may be placing their own needs and preferences over the needs of the patient to have the clinician use the most efficient and effective techniques available.

Another approach to understanding the attitudes of clinicians toward hypnotism is to study their behavior as hypnotic subjects. Wagner (1959) observed the reactions of a group of psychiatric residents who were invited to volunteer as subjects for hypnotic induction. Many who volunteered failed to keep their initial appointment. Of those who did participate, the greater number demonstrated a marked resistance to experiencing the hypnotic state. To say the least, they were reluctant volunteers. The basis for resistance appeared most frequently to be a perception of hypnotic induction as a "battle between minds."

Although other sources of conflict were suggested, this phrasing of the hypnotic experience as a struggle for power is undoubtedly implicated in the rejection of hypnotism as a modality of treatment and diagnosis. Although one might argue that the interpersonal situation in hypnotism does violence to one's equalitarian value system, behind this rationalization lurks both the fear of submission and the fear of exposure. Of course, these fears are merely exaggerated instances of defensiveness, which one so often finds in intercolleague situations, a defensiveness all the more pronounced in the fields of psychology and psychiatry where one may so readily attribute to colleagues one's own proclivities for probing.

It may be instructive to recall my own first experience as a hypnotic subject. The psychiatrist who was Chief of the Mental Hygiene Clinic to which I was assigned during World War II had just completed a course of training with an eminent teacher of hypnotism of that time and was eager to demonstrate his skill. Although we enjoyed a congenial relationship and I "volunteered" for the experience, still I could not respond in spite of his most artful and zealous efforts. Years later, in a group demonstration where I was not the subject, I responded to induction with a moderately deep trance. My failure to respond in the first instance may of course have been related to an unconscious motive beyond my ability to fathom, but I believe it was more likely due to an omission on the part of the psychiatrist. Although he had learned his induction lessons well, he failed to prepare me for the experience, to educate me about hypnotism, and to answer my many questions. Consequently, I was too much the observing ego to be the responding ego. Certainly this healthy curiosity is still another obstacle in the way of the would-be hypnotic subject who is also a professional worker in the psychological field. And it is only a short step from a consideration of his own experiences and feelings about hypnotism to a projection of such feelings onto patients as a rationalization for not using hypnotic techniques.

Whatever the reasons for resistance to using hypnotism, the clinician is the poorer for it. Among the professional groups with a legitimate interest in hypnotism, surely the clinical psychologist, like the well-trained psychiatrist, is preeminently suited to apply hypnotism in his clinical work. He is already well informed in the realms of personality theory and psychodynamics, and well experienced in psychodiagnosis and psychotherapy. Indeed, the only thing that separates him from a useful knowledge of this readily available tool of diagnosis and therapy is his own attitude of avoidance.

HYPNOTIZABILITY AND INDUCTION

The topics of hypnotizability and induction are treated in detail elsewhere in this handbook, but some preliminary remarks are in order here about their relationship to hypnodiagnosis. Most patients come to the psychologist without expecting to be hypnotized. Their response to such a suggestion depends a great deal upon how it is presented. Indeed, sometimes it is wise not to refer to the process as hypnotism at all. Many anxious, fearful patients who would reject hypnotism are nevertheless ready to be taught how to relax, and, having accepted this euphemism, are later able to identify the experience accurately and securely as hypnosis. Ordinarily, however, the psychologist who has a conviction about the diagnostic utility of hypnosis, who respects the hypnotic state as a resource of personality, who can in a simple, matter-of-fact way educate his patient to appreciate the value of hypnotism as he appreciates it, can establish a rapport with his patient, which in itself is the initial phase of hypnotic induction. As the patient learns from the clinician, he is engaging in a sequence of affirmations that will gradually lead him to the deepest trance of which he is capable. Generally the clinician is on firm ground in conveying to the patient that he is capable of experiencing, at some level, some of the phenomena of hypnosis, if he wishes. If this turns out not to be so, then it is important to assure the patient that at some other appropriate times and under other conditions, he might still be capable of experiencing these phenomena if he desired. In taking such a stance, the clinician is aware that, although the potentiality for hypnotic experience lies within the patient, the likelihood of its fulfillment will depend upon the ability of the hypnotist to educate and motivate his patient within the context of their personal relationship. With this frame of reference, failure is not possible either for the hypnotist or his subject and face-saving is not necessary.

As we shall see, whatever the response of the patient to hypnosis proper, there is still value in exploring his concept of hypnotism and his reaction to its proposed use. Nevertheless, a trance state of a certain depth is necessary to accomplish certain kinds of diagnostic objectives. For example, if the patient is to respond to a Rorschach inkblot or other visual stimuli under hypnosis, he must be capable of a somnambulistic trance. A trance not as deep might be sufficient to allow a verbal response to auditory stimuli such as a word association test. And to facilitate responsiveness or to affect an attitude toward tests administered in the normal waking state, it may be enough to offer suitable suggestions in a light trance. Although the varying depths of trance have different kinds of clinical utility, the significance of the response is not necessarily related to the depth of trance. Certainly many authorities are in agreement that it is not necessary to elicit the classical signs of deep trance to do effective clinical work, that the light trance will in many instances prove to be quite sufficient. The issue of trance depth is complicated by the fact that subjects may not conform to the normative sequence of hypnotic phenomena, which define various scales of hypnotizability. Furthermore, subjects may show fluctuations in trance depth at various times, which have diagnostic significance of their own. The hypnotic state appears to be as dynamic as consciousness itself, and may be subject to as many vicissitudes.

The clinician will naturally wish to be informed about the distribution of hypnotizability in various populations (see Chapter 13), but he should not be too much influenced by such knowledge in overestimating or underestimating the susceptibility of a particular patient. Various studies show that younger, healthy, intelligent subjects who volunteer have higher susceptibility scores than do clinical groups. On the other hand, the closer relationship of the patient with the clinician and his greater need for help are powerful motivating factors, which are likely to enhance the patient's response to hypnotism. In any event, each patient is a unique individual and his potentialities remain to be discovered in the clinical situation. This is true no matter what his diagnostic label. It is commonly said that hysterics are more responsive than obsessives, that psychotics are not suitable subjects, that latent homosexuals are prone to panic reactions, and so on. There is some truth in these clichés but not enough to use them as guidelines. In assessing a patient's suitability for hypnodiagnosis, the clinician is on safer ground to apply the broad, familiar criteria that he uses in his everyday clinical work: ego strength, anxiety level, capacity to relate, and the like, as well as attitude toward hypnotism. Diagnostic stereotypes have their uses, but it is sounder to follow the principle of uniqueness of the individual and to judge each patient on his own merits.

Although hypnotizability is a resource of the individual, a patient's response is apparently more likely to be realized by one induction method than by another. Thus, Pascal and Salzberg (1959), using a method derived from a Skinnerian model of operant behavior, estimate that about 50 per cent of their sample (of college students) achieve a somnambulistic level. Their results are extraordinary and surpass by far all others reported in current literature. Giles (1962) verified their experience with the qualification that the inductions must be accomplished by a *trained* experimenter. This last point is of utmost importance in its implications for clinicians. The clinician will be most effective when he feels as natural carrying out an induction as he does in ordinary conversation. During the learning phase, he might wish to explore methods of induction that have research underpinnings and a normative frame of reference, such as the Pascal method and the Stanford Scale (Weitzenhoffer and Hilgard, 1958). He might feel more secure by following a script, but as he gains in comfort he will want to discard the script along with the formal and didactic elements in his method. With practice he will find himself evolving an approach that is reliable yet modifiable enough to take account of the individual needs of his patients. His methods will eventually have an authority that grows out of an easy stylistic fit with his own personality. However methods may vary in efficacy, it is likely, as Giles' study suggests, that the method is transcended by the personal qualities of the hypnotist, most important of which is that growing out of his own experience: his level of security and comfort.

APPROACHES TO HYPNODIAGNOSIS

Let us suppose that the clinical psychologist is already acquainted with the peculiar properties of the hypnotic state and is versed in the induction of hypnosis, the question remains why use it in diagnostic work. The answer is simply that one uses hypnodiagnosis to gain significant information that is either not as easily available or perhaps not available at all by other more conventional means. In other words, one would use the special properties of hypnosis to explore the meaning of behavior, thoughts, and feelings that the patient cannot explain (or, in some instances, will not) for reasons of repression and other ego-defensive mechanisms and maneuvers. Hypnotism provides the means to penetrate repressions, to stimulate fantasy, to intensify feelings, to encourage responsiveness, to decipher symbols, to do all those things that make it, in a word, a catalyst par excellence of the diagnostic endeavor.

The signs of repression that invite the use of hypnotism—low productivity, stylistic rigidity, sterile content, blocking, amnesias, perceptual distortions, esoteric responses—are too well known to clinicians to need elaboration here. What will concern us primarily is not why but how the clinicians use hypnodiagnosis. In the sections which follow we shall deal with the question "how" by discussing approaches to hypnodiagnosis under four categories:

1. Hypnotism as a projective technique: the patient's concept of hypnotism, and his response to its induction.
2. Administering psychological tests under hypnosis.
3. Other hypnodiagnostic techniques: projective tasks, age regression, scene visualization, and so on.
4. Clinical illustrations: the use of varied phenomena of hypnosis to explore personality and test specific diagnostic hypotheses in everyday clinical work.

Hypnotism as a Projective Technique

For most people hypnotism has qualities of ambiguity and mystery, the essential attributes of a projective technique. Almost everyone knows something about hypnotism, but few people have actually experienced it in the clinical setting, and fewer still are able to contemplate it as they would other fields of knowledge. The gap between the imagined and the experienced is fertile breeding ground for myths and fantasies. Each patient has his own myth about hypnotism made up of a stereotype common to his group and colored by a blend of impulse and defense peculiar to himself. Of course, one does not propose the use of hypnotism just to explore the patient's idiosyncratic concept of hypnosis; the sights are higher. The point is that, whatever the patient's response to hypnotism as such, his response to the idea of hypnotism, to the induction itself, and finally to the hypnotic state may all offer sources of inference for the diagnostician similar to the patient's reactions to any projective technique. Psychologists are not interested in content alone, but also in style of response, the test-taking attitude, and the set or structure of meaning that the subject imposes upon the material quite aside from the explicit directions that he appears to be following. In this sense the hypnotic situation can be looked upon as a projective task. In the subject's response may be expressed his fundamental attitudes toward authority, toward novel experience and risk-taking, and toward the possibilities of passivity and activity. He may reveal the autonomic pattern of his anxiety, the disparity between his avowed wish to experience the hypnotic state and his unconscious resistance, or between his conscious reluctance and unconscious readiness to experience the trance. One might differentiate his reactions to the induction from his behavior in the trance itself, as Gill and Brenman (1959) do, or even his reaction to the idea of induction from both of these, without making further clinical use of the hypnotic state, and still be impressed with the richness of the psychological yield. The yield is not simply in what is observed, but also in what is reported by the patient in the inquiry that follows. If the subject is capable of a deep trance, other kinds of explorations of personality also become possible. Even if he is not capable of trance experience, he may, nevertheless, react to the hypnotic situation with a uniqueness that may be generalized to other significant interpersonal situations. As with all good projective techniques, the patient's response always has meaning, and nothing is wasted.

Whether the patient or the psychologist proposes the use of hypnotism, it is equally important to understand the patient's concept of hypnosis and his anticipation of the trance experience. Many subjects, of course, have seen a stage hypnotist at work and may even have participated in the entertainment. If, as in the case of one of my patients, he had gone through the audience "braying like a donkey," he will be aware both of his successful response to hypnotic induction and also of his anxiety about being victimized and made ridiculous. Whatever his level of education, and whatever books he may have read about hypnotism, he will very likely have rather serious misapprehensions about the hypnotic state. He will in most instances expect to enter into a state of unconsciousness akin to sleep that will render him oblivious to all stimuli, including, paradoxically, the voice of the hypnotist. Many nuances, both of the patient's expectancies and his misapprehensions, tell more about the patient than he knows how to tell about himself. Some subjects yearn for a complete blotting out of consciousness, for a kind of transcendental experience approximating the Nirvana of the East. Others fear hypnosis as they fear death, and for the same reasons. Some expect "just to feel good all over," and convey the anticipation of erotic fulfillment somewhere between a warm bath and an orgasm. Others, mindful of the Svengali-Trilby model, emphasize the giving up of control and the complete submission to the hypnotist; whereas still others anticipate with negativistic glee a struggle for dominance in which they must prevail. Thus, the question, "What do you think it feels like to be hypnotized?" serves in its own right as a very good projective device. In the expectancy of the subject may be found his desires, his fears, his conflicts over sexuality and impulse expression, and his resistance to the experience of hypnosis itself.

Casual remarks by the patient may reveal as much as a direct inquiry. There is a tremendous distance in attitudes about sexual expression between the woman who said, "I'm sure it feels good to be hypnotized, but I don't expect anything to happen until I wriggle out of this girdle," and the woman who said, "I'm sorry but I couldn't possibly relax unless I keep my legs crossed," but both reveal themselves unmistakably in a single remark. We can see in the spontaneous remarks of two young men referred for diagnostic study the core of their neuroses. Mr. B., barely five feet tall, had developed an anxiety state following a broken engagement with a girl who happened to be much taller than himself. He anticipated that he would find in hypnosis "a way of getting out of my skin . . . an expansive experience." He looked upon the hypnotic experience as an escape from the chrysallis of an inadequate, confining body-image. In his few prosaic words he expressed a yearning for a new identity and a new physique, which was at the heart of his self-rejection. Mr. K., beset by many fears including a phobia of enclosed places, refused to be hypnotized because he imagined it would feel "like being suspended in midair." In his childhood his father had committed suicide by hanging. Other than this fact itself, he recalled nothing of the event, but his remark about hypnosis suggested how alive it is for him. The dynamic behind his phobia was the anxiety that he would seek out his father's fate.

Just as it is useful to explore the patient's concept of hypnosis itself, on occasion it may be valuable to inquire into his prescription of induction. Thus, one might ask the question, "If you wanted to relax yourself very deeply, or even to hypnotize yourself, how would you go about it (or what would you say to yourself)?" I recently saw a patient who brought with him his own script for hypnosis, which was deeply revealing of his psychodynamics. The lengthy script was characterized by a religio-mystical aura invoking a complete surrender to some quintessential universal peace. The following brief excerpt gives something of the flavor of the induction script:

> You cannot find yourself unless you first lose yourself. Think of something much bigger, much more beautiful, much more worthwhile than yourself. Let yourself be attracted and gratefully drawn into it. Think of the blessed Virgin Mary. She is the Mother of God. She is pure, loving, understanding, and secure, pure and clean as mountain air, a beautiful young girl, with clear loving eyes. She is called the star of the sea. As you think of her you are breathing the purest most fragrant mountain air. She beckons you like a beacon over the bosom of the sea. You are floating in fragrance and freer than you have ever been before. You know you can trust her for she is full of grace and the Lord is with Her. . . .
>
> The Virgin is dissolving and you want her to dissolve. She is dissolving in love and truth. Her beautiful and peaceful mind is like your mind. It is very little compared with the mind of God. She can dissolve into a higher self. So can you. You are beginning to experience a peace like nothing you have ever known before. It is the most beautiful and peaceful thing in the world. It is very dark, very strong, very secure. You are dissolving yourself and you become one with the strongest love, peace, and power. You are in absolute truth. . . .

The fact that the patient consulted the writer concerning a serious work inhibition, and that he later revealed much confusion and conflict in psychosexual functioning come as no surprise in light of the patient's self-confessed overwhelming enchantment with passivity and with a regressive reunion with the mother of his infancy. To be sure, very few patients will have explicit scripts but many more will have implicit ones contained in fantasies available for exploration.

Because it is likely that the patient may have been given psychological tests before hypnotism is discussed, it is appropriate to consider the possibility that the test protocols might contain favorable or unfavorable indicators for response to hypnotism. Although many projective and psychometric tests familiar to clinical psychologists have been correlated with hypnotizability, unfortunately their correlations are too low and the findings too often contradictory to be useful to the clinician. The projective test most commonly used to predict responsiveness to hypnotism has been card 12 of the TAT (Thematic Apperception Test). This is often called the "hypnosis card," and the themes that it produces invite inferences about attitudes toward authority, vulnerability in the passive position and, by face validity, about hypnotism itself. The early studies by White (1937) and by Sarason and Rosenzweig (1942) showed that subjects producing a positive theme about hypnotism are more susceptible to hypnosis. The remark is made in a later study by Ventur, Kransdorf and Kline (1956) that

> . . . The ability to see hypnosis in Card 12M may be related to a willingness to regard hypnosis as a useful therapeutic technique. It might also be argued that the reluctance or inability to recognize the two figures as parties to any hypnotic relationship implies an unwillingness to accept hypnosis in this sense.

Although this is a perfectly sensible assumption, a recent study by Secter (1961) failed to show a relationship between the response to Card 12M and hypnotizability in a series of 48 subjects. The clinician who uses hypnosis will obviously be interested in the patient's response to Card 12 but he should not be unduly influenced by it.

Among inventories devised specifically to infer hypnotizability, one of particular interest to clinical psychologists was developed by Shor (1960) to measure the incidence and intensity of response to the hypnotic phenomena of everyday life. It contains such representative items as: Have you ever been lulled into a groggy state or put to sleep by a lecture or concert even though you were not otherwise fatigued or tired? Have you ever tended to be lulled to sleep while you were driving your car on a quiet, level stretch of road? Do you know of ever having had the experience of sleepwalking? The rationale of this promising approach is convincing: individuals who spontaneously react to prosaic stimuli with autohypnotic signs will, to that degree, react to the formal induction of hypnosis. Similar information elicited in the clinical interview would of course encourage the clinician to consider a hypnodiagnostic approach. However, whatever the indications in test protocols and in the interview, the best prediction of hypnotizability remains the patient's response, first, to the concept of hypnotism, and second, to the induction of hypnosis itself.

Using Psychological Tests in Hypnodiagnosis

Projective and psychometric tests have frequently been used in conjunction with hypnotism, both in research and psychodiagnosis. Their value in research is obvious. They are potentially useful measures of the hypnotic state; they throw light on the developmental process, on the nature of regression; and they may be objects of study in terms of their own meaning, reliability, and validity. The Rorschach, TAT, Bender-Gestalt, tests of intelligence, personality inventories, word association tests, and so on, have all been used in this way. Looked at in another way, these same studies shed light not only on the nature of hypnosis per se, but also on the effects of hypnosis on patients' responsiveness to diagnostic tests and procedures. As an example, Schneck and Kline (1951, 1952) report a series of investigations using such devices as the Word Association Test, the House-Tree-Person Test, and Card 12M of the TAT administered to individual patients and to small groups of patients to measure various psychodynamic factors. The Word Association Test was given under usual conditions and then in the hypnotic state. The hypnotic presentation produced an increase in the proportion of fast reaction times, a decrease in slow reaction times, and an increased proportion of disturbed reactions to traumatic stimuli. The associative changes appeared to relate meaningfully to other available clues to psychodynamics. These findings are similar to those suggested by other studies contrasting test responses obtained in the normal and hypnotic states. The presentations under hypnosis show these general trends: increased productivity, a freer expression of conflict- and affect-laden material, and a coloration of response by primary process, all of which suggest a relaxation of defenses against the emergence of phenomena dominated by the unconscious. Thus the hypnotic administration of projective techniques may provide insights into the sources of the defensive structures manifested in protocols obtained under conventional conditions.

In spite of the obvious value of using tests in hypnodiagnosis, several practical and theoretical considerations argue against its routine application. As I have pointed out, only a minority of patients can achieve a trance deep enough to allow a response to psychological tests. Indeed, projective tests are so valuable for this very reason. If we could have the direct access to the preconscious and unconscious of all patients that we have with the minority who are capable of a somnambulistic trance, we would have rather less use for projective tests. As it is, projective tests conventionally administered are still the best techniques available to psychologists for investigating personality in its complexity of structural layers, and in the dynamic interplay of impulse and defense, even if they have not altogether fulfilled their early promise as X-rays of personality.

Another limitation upon testing under hypnosis is that tests for the most part derive their value from a normative framework that regulates their administration and defines their results. This is particularly true of psychometric tests such as the Minnesota Multiphasic Personality Inventory. The individual profile is based upon normative scales derived from administering the test to large groups in the nonhypnotic state. It follows that the test should be administered under the same conditions if the normative scales are to be used. Projective tests are to a large degree free of these normative strictures, but they too are designed to be administered under standardized conditions to nonhypnotized subjects. True, at times the clinician may want to test his somnambulistic patient under hypnosis, but he will get his most meaningful results when he contrasts the protocols of the hypnotic state with those of the normal state, and takes into consideration the effects that the hypnotic relationship, with its overtones of sexuality, submission, relaxation of inhibition and ego controls, and escape from reality, might have on the protocols, and adjusts his interpretation in the light of such factors. Furthermore, he must keep in mind that differences in response will be influenced by the sequence (waking state followed by hypnosis, and, more rarely, the reverse) as well as by the repetition itself. A second administration of any test will yield additional and different responses even in the normal waking state.

The administering of complete batteries of psychological tests under varying conditions to patients may serve a valuable research function but as a clinical practice it is simply a tour de force. The busy clinician does not have the time or the energy to work in this way, and it is doubtful if his patient has. In my own work I have found it valuable at times to administer a particular TAT or Rorschach card under hypnosis to test a diagnostic hunch, to stimulate productivity, or to decipher an obscure response. The following illustrations present several variations of this approach. In the first case Card 13MF (young man in foreground, head buried in arm; in background, a woman lying in bed) was presented under three different conditions to the patient, a young man of rigid fundamentalist religious background. He had developed an anxiety state upon transferring from a small sectarian college to a coeducational state university, which afforded him a freedom he was not prepared to cope with. He produced the following themes:

Conventional: That's a man and his wife. He had a long hard day and so did his wife. She's tired and is sleeping soundly and he is thinking he better go to sleep himself. He's got a busy day in the morning.

Under hypnosis: That's a young guy who picked up this girl and went to her room. But now he feels guilty and disgusted about being there. He wanted to do something with her but he knew it was wrong. He'll go home now and be glad of it.

Presented as a stimulus for a dream under hypnosis: I went to a drive-in with my buddy and saw this girl. She was real friendly and came over to talk to us. She wanted me to take her for a ride. Then we end up somewhere and she doesn't have any clothes on. I feel real excited and I want to touch her but my buddy is around somewhere and I can't do it.

The stories, simple as they are, show the interplay of impulse and inhibition and suggest, in the third theme, that the overwhelming repression of sexuality is in part a defense against homosexual temptation.

In another instance involving the TAT, the patient, a bright, articulate college graduate was referred for diagnostic study prior to his starting psychotherapy. He was as productive as one would expect on all cards with the notable exception of Card 6BM (the "mother-son" card). This card was presented to him again under hypnosis. The contrasting themes under the two conditions follow:

Conventional: Looks like an older woman and a younger man. . . (Pause) [*Yes, and what is going on?*] Why, nothing much . . . they are just standing there. [*What is their relationship?*] Why, I don't know. It could be one of several.

Under hypnosis: That's a mother and her son. She looks like an awfully nice woman. She seems sad. (Pause) [*What is going on?*] She's saying something, but I don't know what it is. [*Listen carefully and you will hear. . . .*] (The patient breaks into tears. . . .) [*What did she say?*] You are my son! (with a poignant cry).

Upon his return to the waking state, the patient had an amnesia for this experience. His mother was committed to a state mental hospital when he was 11. He lived with an aunt for the next ten years, and he saw very little of his mother during this period. He admitted in a detached way that he had no wish to see her and avoided every opportunity to visit her in the hospital. She died unmourned by her son shortly after his graduation from college. In his relations with women he was cold and aloof. He felt lonely and dissatisfied and on this account he turned to psychotherapy. He had never forgiven his mother for leaving him, nor could he forgive himself for having turned away from her. This seemed to be at the core of his neurosis. The extended therapy that followed fully supported the diagnostic formulation so clearly revealed by these fragmentary responses to a single card of the TAT.

In the foregoing illustrations it was necessary for the patient to achieve a somnambulistic trance to respond to the visual presentation of the TAT. Rather few patients are capable of achieving this depth of trance, but a larger number are able to respond verbally to auditory stimuli. This suggests a variation in technique that enlarges the possibilities of using test data hypnodiagnostically. In the following case the Rorschach was not presented under hypnosis, but a modified inquiry was conducted under hypnosis to unravel the significance of a condensed, symbolic percept.

A young man referred for diagnostic study because of sexual exhibitionism produced this reponse to the bottom detail of Card 6, which is often perceived in vaginal terms: "That's a narrow passageway. Looks like light is going through it so you can see the business at the top." (Note: the "business" at the top is commonly seen as a variation on a phallic theme.) In contrast to his abbreviated and meager responses to other Rorschach blots, this response seemed to emanate from an actual experience. To explore this hypothesis, the patient was hypnotized and the following instruction was given to him:

Examiner: On one of the inkblot cards, you saw a narrow passageway with a light going up through it, and so on. This is connected with something that once happened to you. It may have been a long time ago, but it's going to come back to you now. Just let yourself drift now very peacefully and without making any kind of effort, a memory is going to come to you that's connected with what you saw. . . . The narrow passageway and the light. . . .

Patient: I'm in bed with my aunt . . . She's sound asleep. I feel real hot. . . . I take my searchlight and get under the bed clothes. I want to shine it up her so I could see it. . . . I'm lifting her nightgown up and she's spreading her legs for me. . . . (The patient is visibly upset.) [*How do you feel?*] I feel scared. . . . Like I might get caught.

The patient was reassured and was advised that he might talk about this if he felt he could remember it without being upset. In the waking state, he filled in the gaps. The reported event occurred in his thirteenth year. His aunt had come for an extended stay. Because his parents occupied the only other bedroom, it seemed suitable that the aunt share a bed with her young nephew. He kept a searchlight beside his bed because he liked to examine his genitalia during the night when his parents supposed he was sleeping soundly. What he had not reckoned with in his stealthy gynecological examination of his aunt was her ready cooperation. His success had unnerved him and he failed to find what he was looking for. It is interesting that the Rorschach reponse expressed the voyeuristic side of his conflict, although his exhibitionism is implicit in "the business at the top."

Might subjects who are resistant to taking tests be more likely to respond to tests in the hypnotic state? Wilkins and Adams (1947), working in a psychiatric military setting, found that patients who were anxious about and resistive to testing were able to repond to the Rorschach under hypnosis with a greater number of responses, fewer rejections, increased movement responses than in the normal waking state. Spiegel, Shor, and Fishman (1945) in another early study also found that their subjects were more productive on various psychological tests administered in the hypnotic state. However, it is a reasonable assumption that the rapport necessary for the induction of hypnosis is hardly different from the rapport necessary to give psychological tests, and clinicians who would prepare their patients for testing as sensitively and as thoroughly as they would prepare them for the hypnotic state might find little difference in productivity under the two conditions. Of course, hypnotism might be used to suggest a freer response to psychological tests, which would be administered later in the conventional way. Hammer (1954) found that posthypnotic suggestions had a facilitating effect upon a wide range of motor and intellectual functions and so enhanced test performance. Thus, hypnosis lends itself as a method of motivating the patient to greater effort on psychological tests, but in this usage it is simply one among many methods of motivation.

The facilitating effects of hypnosis on test performance may not necessarily be unique to hypnosis, and comparable performances might be elicited by other means. Nervetheless, this property of hypnosis together with its ambiguity and "mystique" provide useful sources of diagnostic information. Like any other method that has similar results, such as manipulation of the transference, use of verbal encouragement, and so on, hypnotism has drawbacks. However, as in these other methods, drawbacks can be minimized and, through later use as foci for interpretation, they may even be converted into diagnostic and therapeutic assets.

Other Hypnodiagnostic Techniques

The ability of hypnosis to penetrate the unconscious, to reclaim the dissociated, to provide new dimensions for self-experience has stimulated the creation of a host of ingenious techniques useful in diagnostic work. Some of these methods have been devised primarily to serve research purposes, but they too are of interest to us because they lend themselves readily to clinical application. Among the clinically oriented approaches are brief, experimental projective methods, such as specially devised word association tests, scene visualization, hypnographic techniques, and so on, which are designed to explore fantasy life, unconscious conflicts, defensive structure, and the like in the hypnotic state in the same way as the more elaborate projective tests are used conventionally.

Scene Visualization. Schneck and Kline (1952) describe a hypnotic scene visualization technique in which visual imagery is the called-for response. The scenes elicited throw considerable light upon unconscious motivation and experience. The technique has considerable flexibility, because it may be applied to individuals in varying states of trance, and may be used in association with various projective techniques, such as Word Association Tests, TAT, and Rorschach. When it is used with Word Associations, the stimulus words may be tailored to suit the diagnostic requirements. Kline and Schneck (1952) have applied this technique to the exploration of vocational interests in several interesting studies. The scenes elicited were valuable in clarifying the unconscious sources of vocational choice, although they could only be interpreted in relation to other psychodynamic material derived from personal history and transference aspects of psychotherapy.

The following example taken from Kline (1963) illustrates how he uses the scene visualization approach in conjunction with the TAT. The responses are those of a young married woman referred for diagnostic study because of intense depression and a variety of somatic complaints.

Waking visualization: This is a pretty house. Right near it here is a rose arbor which is very nice to sit under and relax. It has a pretty cobblestone path and it's a cute little house. It has flowers and is generally associated with good things and good weather and prosperity.

Under hypnosis: This is a witch's house. It's very old and musty and very bad. It's a very unhappy house and it keeps people locked inside. But in the meanwhile it has a lot of windows so that people can look inside and criticize you. Everything around the house is dead. There's only rocks and a dead tree and a cold moon.

The contrast between the two themes is obviously diagnostic and suggests the necessity of obtaining responses under both waking and hypnotic conditions. Although the instructions differ, the material obtained in the above scene visualization method is quite similar to the earlier illustrations of responses to the TAT administered under hypnosis. In both instances the underlying conflict and affect are sharply revealed in the hypnotic state, whereas the defensive facade is apparent in the waking state.

A variation of the scene visualization method appears to be useful in resolving amnesias. I recall an amusing instance of this during a demonstration of the value of hypnosis in reviving lost memories. The subject, a single young woman, declared her interest in remembering the name of a lake where she spent many enjoyable summers during her adolescence. Because these visits had occurred not too many years before, she was puzzled by her inability to recall the name. She still was unable to recall it in a moderately deep trance. She was asked to visualize the lake and the surrounding terrain, which she was readily able to do. She was told that as she approached the lake she would see a sign with the name of the lake. She smiled and said, "I see it. Why it's Schroon Lake." One might speculate that the name of the lake was only too suggestive of forbidden activities first experienced in adolescence, and for this reason had been repressed.

In still other related techniques, the subject might be asked to observe a stage in a theater and report the scene that appears when the curtains are drawn, or to turn on an hallucinated TV set to a program that will reveal some significant personal facts of which he ordinarily is not aware, or to open a door upon a secret room that contains forgotten images of the past. The mechanism of these similar approaches is essentially free association by visual channels. Unlike the earlier examples of scene visualization, the external stimuli are missing and the subject is encouraged to structure his own scenes out of the material of buried desires and dim or forgotten memories.

Graphic Methods. Graphic methods have also proved of value in hypnodiagnosis. Meares (1954) describes a technique of obtaining drawings from hypnotized patients, which he calls hypnography. While he presents this as an aspect of hypnoanalysis, it may also be used purely as a hypnodiagnostic device similar to automatic writing, or to the somewhat more structured task of drawing the human figure and other objects under hypnosis. Meares suggests that painting with black paint on white paper is the most satisfactory medium. He believes that the main value of the method lies in the patient's associations to the paintings obtained while he is still in the hypnotic state. Meares finds his hypnographic method more effective than verbal responses in circumventing repressions. For this reason he advises that measures be taken to shore up the defensive structure against too overhwelming a cathartic effect.

Automatic writing is a dissociated response in which the subject in a deep trance literally does not know what his right (or left) hand is doing. The suggestion is given to the subject that without his awareness and even while he is concentrating on other matters, his hand will guide his pen in writing a message from the unconscious. Harriman (1942) reports a case in which a student under hypnosis wrote his name and linked it with the name of a girl other than the one he was engaged to, revealing among other things a romantic conflict of which he was not consciously aware.

The writer still recalls vividly his first experience with automatic writing during World War II. A young soldier had been picked up in a confused condition by military police and brought to the Mental Hygiene Clinic for psychiatric study. He had been AWOL for several weeks but had an amnesia for the events of that period. He easily entered a deep trance and was able to relate all that had occurred during his AWOL, but he could offer no explanation for his behavior. He insisted that he had no personal problems and that he was more content in the army than he had ever been before. While still in a trance, he was given paper and pencil and told that his hand would write out for him the real reasons for his AWOL. Even while responding to other unrelated questions, his hand, as though it had an existence of its own, wrote out in a childish scrawl, "I wanted my mommy." His performance was especially impressive, because it was known that his mother had died in his fourth year and that he had been raised in an orphanage. Despite his brave front, he was essentially dependent and inadequate and the rigors of army life had reawakened in him a longing for a mother he had never truly possessed.

Vivification of Emotions. Hypnotism has been used to engage the emotions more directly than do the verbal and graphic methods already described. Rosen (1952) has used the hypnotic state to intensify and identify the "emotion of the moment." The suggestion is given that the patient will experience with the greatest intensity possible whatever emotion is available to him at the moment. Patients who ordinarily blot out feelings are able to experience profound emotional reactions; their verbalizations in these states provide rich diagnostic material for therapeutic investigation and working through. The author speculates that the intensification of unrecognized emotions frees anxiety from its somatic binding and allows forbidden sexual and aggressive impulses to approach consciousness. This method is illustrated in the following case of a veteran with hysterical blindness who was referred to the Psychology Service at the Dearborn Veterans Administration Hospital for diagnostic study. He appeared to be quite complacent about his symptom and made no effort to explain it. Under hypnosis he was told,

"Something has happened to upset you recently and whatever it was caused you to become blind temporarily. Even though you are feeling much better now (the blindness had been "cured" prior to the diagnostic study), you still have some of the same feelings deep down inside of you that caused you to lose your sight. As you relax very deeply, this feeling is going to become stronger and stronger, stronger and stronger, and now you can feel all of it and tell me what it is about." The patient sputtered in more or less comprehensible fashion: "I want to kill the bastards. Why did they do it? They put me on that welding machine. It wasn't my turn. My eyes hurt me. I can't take it. I'll kill the. . . ." The patient had responded to the strain of the glaring light of the welding arcs by the primitive defense of refusing to see what was painful to him. His symptom had a secondary utility of extricating him from the threat of being overwhelmed by his own destructive impulses and placing him in the safe haven of a VA hospital. Interestingly enough, although the patient was able to talk freely about a number of distressing personal and domestic problems, the dynamics responsible for the symptom did not come to light until the intense feelings behind the belle indifference were released and examined.

Other Techniques. In the research literature which has implications for hypnodiagnosis are the early studies of Luria (1932), the classic experiments of Wolberg (1947) which relate the specificity of symptom formation to personality reaction systems (hysterical, anxiety state, psychosomatic), the report on symptom substitution by Seitz (1953), and the more recent studies of artificial neuroses by Levitt, *et al.* (1960), and Reyher (1961), to name a pertinent few. A work of particular fascination is Erickson's (1939) experimental demonstrations of the psychopathology of everyday life. In this series of ten ingenious and imaginative experiments is a panoply of hypnotic phenomena: dissociated states, implanted conflict, hallucinated multiple personality, elaborate defensive maneuvers, all of which have obvious diagnostic applications. The film by Beck (1949), which fortunately is easily available, is an excellent summing up of the method of implanting an experimental neurosis in hypnotized subjects, investigating its course, working it through, and resolving it during the posthypnotic interview period. The subjects are healthy ones, and the implanted neurosis is benign, but similar techniques may be used in the clinical situation, in hypnodiagnosis as well as hypnotherapy.

Displacements in Time. A number of studies have exploited the unique property of hypnotism to facilitate age regression. Biddle (1957) regressed a series of 100 subjects to the third year of life to interview them concerning their oedipal fantasies. He concluded that the Oedipus complex as posited by Freud is not found regularly but that children of both sexes "strive for a shared spiritual union with both parents."

Biddle does not tell us enough about his procedures and results to convince us about his conclusions, but his method is of interest. The regression method can be used not only to explore actual events and fantasies of the forgotten past, but also fantasies of life before birth and after death. Israeli (1953) asked his subjects for their outlook upon the remote future extending "through the quintillionth year," and Rubenstein and Newman (1954) asked their subjects to live out "future" experience according to an age or date suggested to them. At the other end of the time continuum, Kelsey (1953) investigated fantasies of birth and prenatal experiences in his patients and concluded that the fantasies represented actual events, which had been repressed. Although we are not prepared to accept his postulation of telepathic communication between mother and fetus, we can nevertheless appreciate the value of these fantasies for elucidating psychodynamics. Zolik (1958) studied fantasies about a previous existence in a college student with a background as business executive, who produced responses reminiscent of the "Bridey Murphy" story. Zolik labels this phenomenon the "progignomatic fantasy" (from the Greek, meaning "to have been born before"). The principal character of the fantasy, a British officer born in 1850, had a significant emotional relationship with the subject's grandfather, who, in turn, had played a major role in the subject's childhood and adolescence. The "progignomatic fantasy" was based upon stories the grandfather had told about his friend, the British officer, who became for the subject an ego ideal fashioned by the grandfather. To be sure, there is dispute among these writers and other authorities about the validity of hypnotic age regression, but there is no question about the usefulness of the fantasy material obtained in this way for an understanding of the dynamics of personality.

Differential Diagnosis. Most of the foregoing examples of hypnodiagnosis use the case method on a small series of subjects. There are, in addition, a handful of studies, using larger samples and satisfying more rigorous methodological criteria, which have direct bearing upon diagnostic problems of interest to clinical psychologists. In the several studies cited here we shall be interested in findings rather than in the hypnodiagnostic methods themselves. Kiersch (1962) surveyed a series of 98 cases of amnesia in which hypnosis, along with other procedures, assisted in differentiating feigned from psychogenic and organic cases. Sumner, Cameron, and Peterson (1952) used hypnosis to differentiate epileptic from convulsivelike seizures. They found that the epileptic has complete amnesia for the seizure both while hypnotized and while conscious, whereas the nonepileptic is able to recall the details of his seizure under hypnosis. Dorcus (1956) reports an additional criterion to assist in distinguishing between idiopathic and hysteroepilepsy. Both types of seizures can be induced under hypnosis, but the idiopathic seizure seems to run its course and cannot be interrupted, whereas the hysteric seizure can be interrupted and terminated. Kodman and Pattie (1958) were able to demonstrate the psychogenic nature of some forms of deafness in children by the simple procedure of ameliorating the condition by hypnotic treatment.

Clinical Illustrations

As valuable as are the research reports on hypnodiagnosis, the clinical psychologist and the psychiatrist will be more interested in the clinical literature that describes the applications of hypnosis to the practical everyday clinical situation. In getting down to cases, we must recognize that only in an artificial sense may a sharp distinction be drawn between hypnodiagnosis and hypnotherapy. One so often merges with the other. Diagnosis well done is frequently the beginning of therapy, and the response to psychotherapy often provides the answer to diagnostic questions. And of course, uncovering therapy is in itself an elaborate procedure of finding out—diagnosing in the service of treatment. The difference is more often a matter of focus than of kind. Let us say that in hypnodiagnosis hypnotism is used in the interest of investigation and assessment rather than influencing personality. If personality is influenced, as it often is, that outcome is incidental rather than primary to the hypnodiagnostic endeavor. The psychotherapist, whether he is a psychiatrist or psychologist, will often regard diagnosis as the initial phase of treatment which both explores personality and assesses readiness and suitability for psychotherapy. Thus, Rosen (1953) illustrates the process of hypnodiagnosis as an early and ongoing feature of hypnotherapy in his text. Many psychologists in their roles as psychotherapists will conceptualize hypnodiagnosis in a similar manner. However, the psychologist functioning as a consultant to the physician, the psychiatrist, and to other psychologists, will more likely use hypnotism in combination with the traditional tools of clinical psychology: the battery of projective and psychometric tests and the clinical interview. His participation in the case will end with his report to the referring source. Dorcus (1956) presents hypnodiagnosis primarily in these terms and demonstrates its value as a means of differentiating organically determined symptoms from hysterical and other psychogenic states, a diagnostic aid in determining glandular functioning, a motivational aid as well as diagnostic tool in speech retraining, a means of detecting malingering, a tool for determining the nature of pain, and a means of investigating the meaning and the importance of a number of psychological factors.

The cases that follow are not intended to illustrate the full range of clinical applications, but to illuminate several rather representative problems in psychodiagnosis, which confront the clinician on a daily basis. They are cases drawn from the author's practice or from that of his colleagues. Several cases are presented in some detail because of the inherent complexity of the diagnostic problem and because it must be emphasized that hypnotism cannot generally be used as an isolated technique yielding definitive answers. It is embedded in the clinical process and the data it yields must be sifted and scrutinized according to the rules of clinical inference growing out of personality theory, and in the light of all the other information coming from the patient.

Hypnosis Used in Differential Diagnosis. When a somatic symptom can be removed, displaced, or significantly modified as a result of hypnotic intervention, one may be reasonably sure that the symptom is psychogenic. Thus, hypnotism may prove to be valuable in identifying quickly presumed neurological and medical disorders presenting obscure findings. Psychologists working in hospitals and other medical settings are likely to be consulted about many cases in which medical findings are negative and minimal, and, often enough, using hypnotism as an adjunct to their usual clinical procedures, will be able to present a definitive answer. If in the hypnotic state, the patient with a tentative diagnosis of multiple sclerosis loses his spastic gait; the patient with intractible torticollis turns his head; the patient who formerly could not bend his back because of incapacitating pain, can touch the floor; the patient who claimed a limitation in his ability to raise his arms above shoulder level can reach straight up; then we have a sound basis for presuming a psychogenic contribution to the symptom, if not a psychogenic origin for it. The effect of hypnotism in such cases goes beyond the diagnostic. Such demonstrations of the restoration of a function presumed lost by a patient are likely to have a dramatic effect, which can be turned to good therapeutic account. Many cases similar to those illustrated have come to the writer's attention but most cases do not present unitary symptoms that are so classical as to diagnose themselves. More often than not there is an interplay between the psychic and the somatic so that the task for the psychologist is to define the psychogenic contribution and its background rather than merely to decide in favor of a psychogenic hypothesis. In doing his work, the psychologist will want to remember several principles:

It is never safe to diagnose by exclusion. The absence of medical findings is only the absence of findings discoverable at this stage of the evolution of medicine. It does not inevitably invoke the psychogenic hypothesis.

The formulation of a plausible psychogenic hypothesis does not rule out a somatic basis for a disorder. Neurotics get somatically ill at least as often as do other people.

Certain organic disorders have periods of remission, which are presumably unrelated to psychogenic factors.

Patients who are infused with hope in the hypnotic state (or out of it) may develop a different attitude toward their symptoms. Pain may for a time be obliterated, the appetite may improve, a motor function may be partially restored—all as expressions of remotivation, even while the disease process continues in its relentless course.

The following case illustrates these points along with the complexity of factors that must be reckoned with in partialing out psychogenic from organic effects.

This patient was referred to the Psychology Service of the Dearborn VA Hospital in June 1962, with the following note:

> 40 y/o male with chief complaints of vomiting and burning abdominal pain for three weeks. History of radical neck dissection in October 1961 for malignant melanoma. Thus far, work-up has not revealed an organic basis for his complaints. He does seem emotionally upset and we wonder how big a part this plays in his symptoms.

The patient, Mr. V. B. was seen initially for interview and history taking and then was given a battery of psychological tests. Hypnosis was used both as an adjunct to diagnosis and also as a suggestive therapy. He responded warmly and well to the interview and spoke easily and at length about his background and current problems, an account of which follows:

Mr. V. B. grew up on a farm in Indiana. He was the only child of his father's fourth and last marriage. The father was widely regarded in the area as a mean, violent man and treated his son with calculated brutality. Mr. V. B. described many traumatic experiences at his father's hands. During his adolescence his rebellion took the form on several occasions of physical attacks upon his father. His intent was murderous, and he believes that were it not for chance interventions he would have killed his father. The father unceremoniously turned his son out of the home in his seventeenth year, about the time that he was completing high school. He has not seen his father since and has never forgiven him. He feels differently about his mother whom he regards as another unwilling victim of his father's viciousness and he sees her from time to time.

The patient married for the first time at 19. Neither he nor his wife was ready for marriage. Both were unfaithful and the marriage ended in divorce. Several years later, the patient married a devout Catholic. He partially accepted her faith and consented to a religious upbringing for their two sons, now seven and nine years old. He credits his wife with having transformed him from the wild, unsettled ways of his earlier years, into stable, self-respecting citizen. He and his wife get along in harmony for the most part. He does have an explosive temper which is most likely to be aroused when he feels his wife is dominating him. He is frightened of his violent feelings at such times and wonders if after all he is not a good deal like his father whom he has hated so intensely over the years. Such thoughts have a mollifying effect upon him.

About a year before his admission to the hospital, Mr. V. B. decided to fulfill an old desire to move to California. He never really understood his motives for uprooting himself at a time when his home life and job were going so well. The move proved to be a calamity. Shortly after arriving in Los Angeles, the first symptoms of cancer (melanoma) appeared, leading to a radical dissection of his neck. By unlucky coincidence, his wife required a thyroidectomy, and one of the children an appendectomy during the same period. Their savings dwindled rapidly. When the outlook was most dismal, a letter from his present employer arrived offering him a job, and a very good one, in his leather works. The family returned with feelings of relief to Detroit. The employer lent Mr. V. B. funds for a down payment on another house and everything appeared to be going remarkably well.

The return to Detroit was the occasion for the first serious marital strife between Mr. and Mrs. V. B. Mr. V. B. began to spend Friday evenings at a neighbor's home watching TV and drinking coffee until well past midnight. His wife sometimes joined him, but she objected to the late hour and finally refused to go along. At the same time she resented her husband's visiting alone. In this she was somewhat justified since her friend's husband frequently was not home. Mr. V. B. denied that an actual affair was in progress, but the overtones were rather obvious. The struggle between the two of them became quite bitter. There were threats of separation and divorce. Mr. V. B. was determined that his wife would not dominate him in his pursuit of innocent pleasure. Mrs. V. B. was equally determined to break up this quasi-affair. It was in this emotional environment that the chronic vomiting and other digestive symptoms made their first appearance.

Thus it seemed reasonable to assume, without concluding that vomiting was altogether of psychogenic origin, that there was something in his psychological situation that Mr. V. B. could not "stomach." To yield to his wife's domination was something he could not tolerate; nor could he allow himself to react to the situation as his father might have. His history shows that his digestive tract had already been highly sensitized as an organ of stress. As a boy, he would vomit after being unfairly beaten by his father, or at times of extreme anxiety. Whenever his stomach was upset, vomiting was his common response (and this was true in later years when he would induce vomiting to head off an anticipated "hangover"). He was also unusually bowel conscious. When he was a boy, his father, regarding regularity as the keystone to health, ritualistically administered to the entire family a sturdy draught of pluto water on the first day of each month. Furthermore, Mr. V. B. had always been a fussy eater, confining himself to a rather narrow range of foods. He was capable, however, of gorging himself. In his preadolescence he was obese, weighing over 170 pounds at the age of eleven.

Not all of his anxieties could be somatically channeled, and his history shows other neurotic mechanisms at work, such as the nightmares from which he suffered for many years. He had and still has many fears: of falling, of being pierced by needles, of pain, of snakes, and so on. He has an intense fear of having his arms pinioned (as in a straitjacket), and associated with this, of being confined in a small space. He cannot, for example, tolerate being in a phone booth with the door closed.

His personal history, phobic tendencies, inability to handle powerful emotions, his casual acceptance of his illness (which at times approximated the classical "belle indifference" of the hysteric), a tendency to use his illness to exact concessions from his family and from the hospital staff were all factors supporting a psychogenic origin of his illness. Psychological tests also favored this viewpoint. The MMPI showed marked elevations on the Hypochondria and Hysteric scales. The Rorschach indicated difficulties in controlling intense feelings of hostility with dependence upon repressive mechanisms to prevent an intense and dramatic acting out of impulses.

Certainly, it appeared sound to conclude that if there was not a psychological basis for the vomiting there was at least an impressive psychological overlay or exaggeration involved. Nevertheless, because of the background of organic illness, it was decided to use hypnotism to refine further the diagnostic picture. Mr. V. B. proved to be an excellent subject, going into a deep trance upon the first induction. In subsequent sessions he was able to go into a deep trance upon the signal of a touch on the shoulder accompanied by the suggestion "Now you will go into a deep sleep." Interview in the hypnotic state did not disclose fresh dynamic factors, but it did reveal a depth of despair about his domestic situation and about the current illness which was not apparent in the waking state. While Mr. V. B. was under deep hypnosis, reassuring suggestions were made and he was encouraged to eat and retain his food. The results of this suggestive therapy were impressive, even if they were not all that was hoped for. Mr. V. B. continued to vomit bile upon awakening, and occasionally lost his breakfast, but was able to retain his other meals. He became more optimistic and began to think again about his future outside of the hospital. Our discussions in and out of the hypnotic state helped him to appreciate his wife's point of view, and they were fully reconciled during his hospital stay.

With all the evidence for the psychogenesis of his illness, it was most tempting to explain it on this basis, but at no time were we satisfied that this in itself was an adequate explanation. In spite of his hysterical proclivities, there was no precedent for this particular pattern of food intolerance. Furthermore, vomiting almost always followed exertion (shaving and showering) in which there was no psychological stress, and this appeared to be more characteristic of an organic disorder. But the most convincing indication that psychological factors were only partially involved was his limited response to hypnotic suggestion. This was in itself diagnostic. His ability to respond to hypnotism at a somnambulistic level in the context of an excellent relationship with his psychologist would lead one to expect a complete rather than partial remission of a psychogenic symptom. Psychological treatment had the effect of reassuring him and diminishing the hysterical overlay. In accomplishing this much, it left a residue of symptoms that were almost certainly of organic origin, and this was the diagnostic opinion conveyed to the referring physician.

Following our diagnostic study and our series of therapeutic contacts, Mr. V. B. became well enough to go home. He gained significantly in weight, expressed feelings of well-being, and spoke about his desire to return to work. Sad to say, he did not remain out of the hospital for long. At home he began to experience a blurring of vision and spells of dizziness. A number of neurological findings suggested organic brain lesions of metastatic origin. His downhill course was rapid and he expired several weeks after his return to the hospital. During this period he was unable to retain food. The vomiting, which had at first been regarded as a psychogenic symptom, was now clearly related to the spread of malignancy. His qualified response to hypnotism was the first clear indication that his remission had come to an end. Were it not for this clue to an emergent organic disease, we would have been fully content to accept the overwhelming evidence in favor of a psychogenic hypothesis.

Hypnosis Used to Explore Psychodynamics. Among the many uses of hypnotism in the field of psychodiagnosis, undoubtedly most attractive to the clinician is its power in elucidating psychodynamics. It provides the means for an "instant analysis" in the literal sense. This is the way it was used by Breuer and Freud in their *Studies of Hysteria* (1955), and no matter what Freud's later criticism of hypnotism as a curative agent there is no gainsaying its efficacy as a method of exploring and comprehending personality and psychopathology. The literature illustrating this application of hypnotism is too extensive to cite. All clinical workers using hypnotism in this way have their own favorite cases. A case in the recent literature of particular fascination is that reported by Ehrenreich (1960), which describes his investigation under hypnosis of the dynamics of necrophilia in a man convicted of a shockingly heinous murder.

The following case, reported by the writer's colleague, Dr. Herbert

Malos, is more typical. It demonstrates the use of hypnotism in discovering the meaning of a conversion symptom by way of abreaction. The fact that this abreaction had a curative effect is gratifying in iteslf, but it is incidental to the diagnostic objective. As the history will show, the case presented a tangle of complexities involving situational, organic, traumatic, psychosomatic, and, finally, hysterical factors.

The tentative diagnosis for the admission to the hospital under discussion was: CONVERSION HYSTERIA AND MIGRAINE HEADACHES. At the time of his most recent admission, in 1962, the patient, whom we shall call Mr. N. P., was 31 years of age, married, with three children, and successfully employed in his own plumbing business. He first came to the attention of the Psychology Service in 1952 at the age of 21. At that time it was noted that he had recently been discharged from military service with a diagnosis of "Headaches secondary to traumatic concussion." His father, to whom he was very closely attached, had within the year died of a heart attack. The patient completed high school at the age of 17, and almost immediately thereafter entered the service. He worked his way up to Platoon Sergeant, and considered his service career as generally successful.

During his first admission he reported two incidents of head injury which he felt contributed significantly to his headaches. The first incident occurred when he was struck with a baseball bat during a softball game. The second incident took place in Korea when he volunteered for a special patrol to rescue wounded GI's from a mine field. He was struck on the helmet by a piece of shrapnel and became quite confused. The important similarity between these two incidents is that in neither case did he lose consciousness until the activity at hand had been completed and all realistic danger had passed. The patient further indicated an extremely passive approach to authority figures with complete denial of any other personal, or interpersonal psychological problems. Testing at that time revealed a man of superior intelligence (a Fullscale IQ of 128), who presented a personality picture of excessive control and a strong impression of deep emotional conflicts. His position as head of the household following the death of his father provided him with excessive responsibilities, which interfered with his own efforts to attain personal independence and recreated long-buried guilt feelings over his oedipal conflicts. He was unable to acknowledge this material or to cope with his feelings of self-hatred.

The patient was briefly re-evaluated in 1960. Since his first examination he had married, had fathered two children, and had begun work as a plumber's apprentice. He continued to deny any significant personal problems, professing concern only about his migraine headaches. He did not at all consider that his problem might have psychological aspects.

The patient returned to the hospital in August 1962, with radically altered symptoms. It was reported that following a "blackout" while he was at work, his wife had taken him to their family physician whose office was on the second floor of a building. While climbing the stairs, the patient became dizzy and upon reaching the doctor's office, again blacked out. When he recovered, he noted a paralysis of the left arm, an alteration of speech that produced a high-pitched, squeaky tone of voice, visual images of intense and multicolored flashes of light, and extreme dryness of the throat. Because the patient was well known to the psychologist with whom he had always been in good rapport, the advisability of investigation of the symptoms under hypnosis was discussed with him at the first interview. The patient was quite fearful of this suggestion, but promised to discuss it with his wife and consider it overnight. That very night, he had a "blackout" following which all of his hysterical symptoms miraculously disappeared. However, with the encouragement of his wife and his physician, he agreed to cooperate with the hypnotic investigation. He proved to be an excellent subject, easily responding to a wide variety of test suggestions and capable of spontaneous amnesia for the hypnotic trance. During the first two hypnotic sessions, he was quite unproductive verbally, but was able to discuss various aspects of his present symptom development following the hypnotic session. During the third session, while the patient was under deep hypnosis, his left shoulder began to twitch. When this was brought to his attention, the patient began to abreact the war experience that accounted for his second service injury. The reconstruction of this experience follows:

The patient, despite his youthfulness (age 19 at that time), had become a Platoon Sergeant of a front-line company in the Korean conflict. He had been within two days of receiving a battlefield commission, when a replacement officer was assigned to his unit. Although this officer was injured in the second day, the patient's commission was suspended. Approximately one month later, a second officer was assigned to the patient's platoon, and it was on the first night of this officer's duty that the critical incident occurred. The patient, despite an imminent regular discharge from the service, volunteered for a night time patrol in which several GI's injured on previous patrol were to be located and returned through a dangerous mine field. The new Lieutenant accompanied them. Early in the patrol, the patient was hit on the shoulder with a rock from an exploding mine, which numbed his arm for a few minutes. This seemed to have accounted for the muscular twitch observed under hypnosis, which precipitated the subsequent abreaction. The injured men were located, but in the process the Lieutenant was wounded by a piece of shrapnel that struck his throat. The Lieutenant was unable to talk and when he was given a drink, the water poured out of the hole in his throat. The patient, despite his numb and semi-paralyzed arm, carried the Lieutenant up the hill, through the mine field, back to friendly lines. His glasses had been lost, his helmet had been knocked off by a piece of shrapnel, which left him headachy and confused; but despite all these afflictions he did not lose consciousness until his patrol had returned and his mission accomplished. The Lieutenant died the same night.

The patient was advised that he would now be able to remember the whole incident if he so desired, and was awakened from hypnosis. For the first time in our contacts, he experienced a great emotional release with much crying, and the expression of great anxiety and guilt. He insisted that many things he had never understood about himself had now become clear. With no difficulty at all, he related the paralysis of his arm to the blow he received from the mine field explosion, related his speech difficulty and excessive thirst to his feelings toward the injured Lieutenant, and related the multicolored flashes of light to the flares and explosions seen on the Korean front. Incidentally, the onset of his present symptoms occurred almost to the day on the tenth anniversary of that long-repressed event.

After much reassurance, the patient seemed to feel much better and was allowed to go home on a weekend pass. Discussions with his wife and friends helped to clarify certain other aspects of the mystery. He was now able to view war movies, which he had always avoided in the past. He was able to understand why he had been awarded the Bronze Star. He was also able to understand many other minor symptoms, which he had never discussed before. Subsequent sessions revealed many hostile feelings to the "intruding" officers who had kept him from getting a battlefield commission. At a deeper level, this material related to hostile feelings toward his father who died shortly after the patient's return from service.

Two weeks after this abreactive experience, the patient reported renewed feelings of self-confidence and an expansive sense of the possibilities for a successful and happy life, an attitude that was altogether new to him. Subsequent follow-ups two and six months later revealed that he had kept his gains. He complained only of an occasional abortive migraine episode, which he was able to relate to the vicissitudes of his vocational and domestic life.

The hypnotic intervention did not answer all questions in this case. We do not know why Mr. N. P. waited for ten years to express his neurotic conflict in the language of hysteria, but we know a good deal more about his psychodynamics than could be inferred from conventional psychological study via projective tests and clinical interview. The previous psychodiagnostic study had outlined the structure of the neurosis, whereas the hypnodiagnostic study gave us a vital view of its contents. Interestingly enough, the mere suggestion of intervention by hypnotism appeared to accomplish a remission of his symptoms. Fortunately, it was possible for the patient to overcome his anxiety so that hypnotism could be used successfully in this diagnostic way and as it turned out also in this therapeutic way.

Hypnosis Used to Assess Motivation for Psychological Treatment. In many instances a patient presents symptoms that require a quick and active therapeutic intervention if it requires any at all. In such cases there is not time for the leisurely reconnaisance that answers many diagnostic questions and serves so well the function of a trial psychotherapy. The case of Mrs. P. R. illustrates how hypnosis might be used in arriving at a decision about the suitability of psychotherapy, and, indeed, about the suitability of hypnotism as an adjunct to psychotherapy.

Mrs. P. R. is a woman of 40, married, with two children, who consulted the writer about a most unusual symptom. The middle finger of her right hand would on occasion and without provocation fly up and assume a rigid form, which naturally interfered with many of her manual activities. The symptom had first appeared four years before, and she had during this period consulted several neurologists and other medical doctors without success. She reluctantly accepted a referral to a psychologist when it was suggested that hypnotic intervention might prove of value in relieving her of the symptom only because she was faced with an emergency that made her quite desperate. She was scheduled the following week to take a typing test for a new job, and she was sure that the unfortunate tendency of this finger to produce an unwanted erection would seriously penalize her on the test. Nevertheless, it was not possible to discover her resistance in her surface behavior. She expressed a sincere desire for help as one would expect of an individual with such an affliction. There was time for just two appointments before the typing examination.

In the first interview, the patient revealed enough about her personality and circumstances to provide at least a good working hypothesis concerning the meaning of her symptom. In the second interview, a moderately deep hypnotic state was induced without difficulty, and she was instructed to respond "Yes" or "No" to questions by signaling with her finger. To put this more correctly, it was suggested that her finger would respond for her and would not require deliberate thought on her part. In response to the question, "Do you want to understand the meaning of your symptom?" her finger slowly rose signifying "No." This was quite interesting and rather surprising. The writer then asked, "I want to know if you really want help with this problem, whether you really want to be relieved of the troublesome symptom which limits the use of your finger." Again she responded according to the prearranged signal with an unequivocal "No." Upon her return to the normal waking state she had full recall for her response under hypnosis and expressed bewilderment. She had come for help, but it was plain that at a deeper level she did not want it. At this point she began to sob and confided a part of her history that she had concealed in the first interview. Four years before she had experienced a psychotic episode whose most obvious feature was a depressive-paranoid coloring. She was hospitalized and treated with electric shock. She returned home after several weeks, apparently recovered, but terrified and ashamed of her experience. It was now her constant anxiety that she might experience another such episode and have to endure the shattering effect of both the illness and its treatment. It was at the time of her recovery that the peculiar finger symptom made its first appearance. It was now easily possible to understand the meaning of her refusal to surrender her symptom. She had lived with it for a long time. It satisfied certain psychological needs she could not fathom. In electing to keep her symptom, she was saying, "I suffer but I do not suffer too much, and I have achieved an equilibrium for myself. Please don't upset it."

Of course her equilibrium was not upset. She was reassured and glady agreed that further appointments were not indicated. She was grateful that her need to keep her symptom was understood and supported and she called back several weeks later as a way of saying so. In spite of her finger's capricious behavior on the typing test, she did well enough to get the job and she felt she could keep it. She thought that someday her symptom would go back where it came from, and perhaps it will.

This technique of investigation is a variant of ideomotor signaling described by LeCron (1954). It serves especially well as a cautionary device in the probing of sensitive regions of conflict. It makes the patient an active participant in the uncovering task and gives him the opportunity to say in the first place whether or not it shall take place. In the case reported, it might well be asked if Mrs. P. R.'s response was consciously or unconsciously determined. There is no way of knowing this. It is enough to say that the hypnotic state provided her with a way to express what she already deeply knew about herself and yet was not prepared to admit for good defensive reasons in the conventional clinical interview.

The case of Mr. L. T. illustrates the value of hypnodiagnosis as an ongoing aspect of hypnotherapy.

Mr. L. T. first consulted the writer because he hoped that hypnosis would cure him of lifelong nailbiting. He was about to enter a professional field in which this conspicuous evidence of neuroticism was altogether inappropriate. In reviewing his history, it did not appear that the nailbiting habit served any significant psychodynamic purpose. It was simply a habit he could very well do without. Mr. L. T. was an excellent hypnotic subject, achieving a somnambulistic trance, and in a series of six sessions was entirely relieved of nailbiting.

Several weeks later he consulted the writer concerning his smoking addiction. He had often been advised to give up smoking because of a mild bronchial irritation and now, encouraged by his conquest of nailbiting, he decided the time was right. There seemed to be no contraindication, because by this time the writer was well acquainted with his history and favorably impressed by the easy success in eliminating nailbiting. Accordingly, suggestions were given in the hypnotic trance of the usual kind to reinforce his aversion to cigarettes. In a short period, it became apparent from his unaccustomed feelings of depression and irritability, and an altogether unanticipated outbreak of rage directed against his wife, that smoking was by no means a peripheral issue in his life as his nailbiting apparently was. In the hypnotic state he was asked why he did not wish to give up smoking, and he responded with the words, "I want to die." For many years he had entertained a fantasy about dying and in this way punishing his adoptive parents for their rejection of him. These forgotten fantasies had been succeeded by an indulgence in smoking which he secretly hoped would one day produce a lung cancer that would kill him. He had decided in favor of a slow suicide, a decision which gratified his masochistic needs, and one which he was able to deny with a smiling depression. Smoking was not simply a habit, it was a symptom.

Superficially, smoking seemed no less peripheral than nailbiting, but it touched the core of his neurosis, and required altogether a different kind of resolution. A neurosis of this depth and severity would undoubtedly have expressed itself in symptom formation requiring therapeutic intervention at some time in his life, but it was a great advantage to be able to expose it so quickly, directly, and clearly via hypnosis and then to modify psychotherapy accordingly.

Confession in Hypnosis. Just as there are individuals like Mrs. P. R. who do not wish to be confronted with a knowledge of the significance of their symptoms, there are those who, on the other hand, have a need to confess, but this need can be expressed only under the special conditions of the hypnotic trance.

Mr. G. S., a young veteran of 24, was referred to the Psychology Service because of a peculiar conversion symptom which he described as a "contorting of the left side," along with a spastic turning of the head in the manner of an incipient tortocollis. His history presented in a guarded and laconic way was not revealing. Mr. G. S. welcomed the suggestion of continuing the interview under hypnosis. He responded to induction with a writhing of his body. His mouth was agape with the tongue thrusting out spasmodically as though trying to eject an object. This fuguelike behavior lasted no longer than ten seconds, and it culminated in a deep sigh. The patient had presented his confession in this charade of fellatio, and experienced enormous relief. In the moderately deep trance that followed, he was assured that all would be well, and that it might help his recovery to discuss his homosexual problems, but that he would do this only if he wished to. In the waking state that followed, he was able to discuss his long-standing homosexual conflict, which only recently had been expressed under rather traumatic circumstances in an overt act. The hysterical symptoms had succeeded the overt act and were altogether abreacted in his confession without words. In this case we might reasonably assume that Mr. G. S. was aware of his homosexual conflict, but nevertheless, that he was not able or willing to acknowledge it fully either to himself or to others. Perhaps one might say that hypnosis made it possible for the patient not so much to egotize as to humanize his conflict by allowing him to act out in primitive language what he was not yet ready to express in words.

SOME CAUTIONS

The diagnostician ordinarily is not faced with the decision of whether to remove symptoms, substitute symptoms, and the like as is the hypnotherapist. It is true that in such cases as Mr. G. S., the decision may be made spontaneously by the patient who has an urgent communication to make, which he cannot express in a state of conscious responsibility but which he can release under the special conditions of the hypnotic state. However, in no instance can the clinician be oblivious of the effects of his hypnodiagnostic venture. How the clinician will evaluate the possible dangers of hypnotic intervention, which are no less present in diagnosis than in therapy, will depend upon his theoretical outlook, which in turn will influence the setting where he works and the patients he will select. Thus, psychologists who follow the behavioral school of Eysenck (1957) and Wolpe (1958) will not hesitate to treat or to investigate symptoms for fear that their removal or scrutiny will expose still other symptoms. For the behavior psychologist the symptom is the neurosis, not merely an expression of it. On the other hand, psychologists following psychoanalytic precepts will be concerned about a decompensation process following symptom removal or investigation, which could ultimately expose a fulminating psychosis. The writer is in favor of a middle position. Some symptoms appear to be peripheral to inner conflict, and their existence seems to be determined by reinforcement learning principles. Such symptoms can safely be removed by desensitization processes and simple suggestion without disturbance to a psychodynamic structure, and can also be safely studied by various hypnodiagnostic methods that we have discussed. Other symptoms are central to the economy of the neurosis and, consequently, serve a necessary homeostatic function. Unfortunately, there is no simple way to decide whether a symptom is central or peripheral. Lists of symptoms cannot be substituted for clinical acumen. In the case of Mr. L. T. it was natural to consider his cigarette smoking a peripheral issue, yet this apparently innocuous habit concealed a dynamic of central importance in understanding his personality.

Fortunately, there are ways of making the patient an active participant in the diagnostic exploration so that he himself will know what secrets he is ready to reveal and what symptoms he is ready to part with. The use of ideomotor signaling is one such way, but often it is enough to assure the patient that he need not express any more than he can deal with comfortably. The respect for his needs implied by such assurance in itself encourages him to confront and share a greater part of his hidden private world.

The caveats in applications of hypnodiagnosis are not different in kind from those which are part of all psychodiagnostic explorations except that they are somewhat dramatized by the novelty and vividness of hypnotic events and by their accelerated tempo. The sensitive clinician who respects the integrity and needs of his patient will not fail to be cognizant of the priority of therapeutic requirements over the purely diagnostic ones in all aspects of his clinical work. He is wise enough to know that the patient needs always to keep certain secrets to himself. In taking this attitude he finds a ready ally in his patient, for, contrary to popular conceptions, the ego of the hypnotized patient is not in limbo. Its critical and integrative powers are available to the patient when he needs them. He becomes the willing collaborator of the hypnotist in the exploration of his personality, in the lifting of repressions, in the elucidation of conflict just so long as it is in his interest to do so. Even if the clinician makes an occasional inevitable mistake in judgment, the patient's ego is not so fragile as to be unduly endangered. Of course, it is the task of the clinician to convince the patient from the very beginning of the clinical interaction that he is safe and secure in embarking upon this enterprise of self-discovery and sharing, that hypnosis is simply one other benign agent of psychological exploration and of therapy.

We have seen that one advantage of hypnosis over conventional diagnostic methods is that the patient is enabled to regard events under hypnosis as the responsibility of the hypnotist. Thus, an inhibitory force is removed, which can be enough to tip the scales in favor of conflict expression through fantasy, verbalizations, and so on, and to provide enriched material for diagnostic study. The special character of hypnosis in its meaning to the patient and in the close hypnotic relationship provides some variables not always present in the conventional diagnostic situation, and these variables often significantly enhance the diagnostic yield. Perhaps one may summarize the advantages of hypnosis by saying that it provides new conditions for experiencing the self and its history. To paraphrase Szasz (1961), hypnosis provides the individual with a new definition of rules of the game by which he may determine what he will know and reveal of himself. It is the function of the clinician to anticipate and to educate the expectancies of his patient in developing the rules of the game and in utilizing its outcome in a clinically fruitful way. Against the many advantages of hypnodiagnosis, its limitations and possible dangers loom small indeed.

Finally, a cautionary word is in order about the interpretation of material derived from hypnodiagnosis. In evaluating the "truth" of verbal and behavioral responses secured under hypnosis, one must be satisfied to apply pragmatic tests. Even so-called objective facts of a life history are constantly undergoing refinement and redefinition in the context of growth and experience. To some extent the individual is always rewriting his history to serve the adjustment needs of the present and of the future. Whether the data derived from hypnodiagnosis are unique, whether they confirm, contradict, or confuse, it is the task of the clinician to create a new synthesis of meaning that will take them into account at least as currently operative fantasies, along with all the other information derived from the clinical interaction.

SUMMARY

In this survey hypnodiagnosis is defined as the use of hypnotism for the purpose of exploring personality and investigating psychopathology in the practical clinical situation. The clinical interview with the hypnotized patient, the adminstering of psychological tests to the hypnotized patient, the evaluation of the patient's response to hypnotic induction and his idiosyncratic concept of hypnotism, are all aspects of hypnodiagnosis. Indeed, whatever psychodiagnosis is, it becomes hypnodiagnosis when it is accomplished in association with the procedures of hypnotism. Thus hypnodiagnosis is a suitable term to describe a number of techniques that make use of hypnotism to extend, to supplement, and to facilitate the process and objectives of psychodiagnosis. To the psychologist who knows when and how to use it, hypnotism becomes a potent ally in the investigation of psychopathology and in the exploration of personality. Because hypnodiagnosis makes use of an experiential state, which is in its essense psychological, it has a natural place in the repertory of the well-qualified clinical psychologist who is informed about its advantages and limitations, and who knows how to use it to serve at once his clinical objectives and his patient's well-being.

REFERENCES

Beck, L. (1949). *Unconscious Motivation.* New York: Association Films.

Biddle, W. (1957). "Investigation of the Oedipus phantasy by hypnosis," *Amer. J. Psychiatry*, **114**, 75.

Breuer, J. and Freud, S. (1955). *Studies in Hysteria* (1895). Translated by J. Strachey. Standard Edition, *The Complete Psychological Works of Sigmund Freud*, 2 vols. London: Hogarth.

Dorcus, R. M. (1956). "The use of hypnosis as a diagnostic tool." In Dorcus, R. M., *Hypnosis and Its Therapeutic Application.* New York: McGraw-Hill.

Ehrenreich, G. A. (1960). "Headache, necrophilia, and murder: A brief hypnotherapeutic investigation of a single case," *Bull. Menninger Clinic*, **24**, 273–287.

Erickson, M. H. (1939). "Experimental demonstrations of the psychopathology of everyday life," *Psychoanal. Quart.* **8**, 338–353.

EYSENCK, H. J. (1957). *The Dynamics of Anxiety and Hysteria.* London: Routledge and Kegan Paul.

GILES, E. (1962). "A cross-validation study of the Pascal technique of hypnotic induction," *Int. J. of clin. and exper. Hyp.* **10**, 101–108.

GILL, M. and BRENMAN, M. (1959), *Hypnosis and Related States.* New York: International Universities Press.

HAMMER, E. (1954). "Post-hypnotic suggestion and test performance," *J. clin. exper. Hyp.*, **2**, 178–185.

HARRIMAN, L. (1942). "The experimental induction of a multiple personality," *Psychiatry*, **5**, 181.

ISRAELI, N. (1953.) "Experimental study of projection in time: 1. Outlook upon the remote future—extending through the quintillionth year," *J. clin. exp. Hyp.*, **1** (2), 49–60.

JENNESS, A., (1944). In Hunt, J. McV. *Personality and the Behavior Disorders*, Vol. I, New York: Ronald Press.

KELSEY, D. E. R. (1953). "Phantasies of birth and prenatal experiences recovered from patients undergoing hypnoanalysis," *J. ment. Sci.*, **99**, 216–223.

KIERSCH, T. A. (1962). "Amnesia: A clinical study of ninety-eight cases," *Amer. J. Psychiat.*, **119**, 57–60.

KLINE, M. V. (1963). "Hypnosis in clinical psychology." In Schneck, J. M. (ed.) *Hypnosis in Modern Medicine.* Springfield, Ill.: Charles C. Thomas.

——— and SCHNECK, J. M. (1951). "Hypnosis in relation to the word association test," *J. gen. Psychol.*, **44**, 129–137.

——— and SCHNECK, J. M. (1952). "An hypnotic experimental approach to the genesis of occupational interests and choice. 1. Theoretical orientation and hypnotic scene visualization," *Brit. J. Med. Hyp.*, Winter, 168–179.

KODMAN, F. and PATTIE, F. A. (1958). "Hypnotherapy of psychogenic hearing loss in children." *Amer. J. clin. Hyp.*, **1**, 9–14.

LECRON, L. M. (1954). "A hypnotic technique for uncovering unconscious material," *J. clin. exp. Hyp.*, **2**, 76–79.

LEVITT, E. E., DEN BREEIJEN, A., and PERSKY, H. (1960). "The induction of clinical anxiety by means of a standardized hypnotic technique," *Amer. J. clin. Hyp.*, **4**, 206–214.

LURIA, A. R. (1932). *The Nature of Human Conflicts.* New York: Liveright.

MEARES, A. (1954). "Hypnography—A technique in hypnoanalysis," *J. ment. Sci.*, **100**, 965–974.

PASCAL, G. R. and SALZBERG, H. C. (1959). "A systematic approach to inducing hypnotic behavior," *Int. J. of clin. exp. Hyp.*, **7**, 161–168.

REYHER, J. (1961). "Posthypnotic stimulation of hypnotically induced conflict in relation to psychosomatic reactions and psychopathology," *Psychosom. Med.*, **23**, 384–391.

ROSEN, H. (1952). "The hypnotic and hypnotherapeutic unmasking, intensification, and recognition of an emotion," *Amer. J. Psychiat.*, **109**, 120–127.

——— (1953). *Hypnotherapy in Clinical Psychiatry.* New York: Julian Press.

RUBENSTEIN, R. and NEWMAN, R. (1954). "The living out of 'future' experiences under hypnosis," *Science*, **119**, 472–473.

Sarason, S. and Rosenzweig, S. (1942). "An experimental study of the triadic hypnothesis: reaction to frustration, ego-defense and hypnotizability. II. Thematic apperception approach," *Character & Person.* **3**, 150–165.

Schneck, J. M. and Kline, M. V. (1952). "Hypnotic scene visualization and the word association test," *J. Gen. Psychol.*, **46**, 29–42.

Secter, I. I. (1961). "TAT card 12M as a predictor of hypnotizability," *Amer. J. clin. Hyp.*, **3**, 179–184.

Seitz, P. F. D. (1953), "Experiments in the substitution of symptoms by hypnosis: II," *Psychosom. Med.* **15**, 405–424.

Shor, R. E. (1960). "The frequency of naturally occurring 'hypnotic-like' experiences in the normal college population," *Int. J. clin. exp. Hyp.*, **8**, 151–164.

Spiegel, H., Shor, J., and Fishman, S. (1945). "An hypnotic ablation technique for the study of personality development," *Psychosom. Med.*, **7**, 273–278.

Sumner, J. W., Jr., Cameron, R., and Peterson, D. B. (1952). "Hypnosis in differentiation of epileptic from convulsive-like seizures," *Neurology*, **2**, 395–402.

Szasz, S. (1961). *The Myth of Mental Illness.* New York: Hoeber-Harper.

Ventur, P., Kransdorf, N., and Kline, M. V. (1946). "A differential study of emotional attitudes toward hypnosis with card 12M of the Thematic Apperception Test," *Brit. J. med. Hyp.*, **8**, 5–16.

Wagner, F. F. (1959). "A clinical study of attitudes towards hypnotic induction," *Int. J. clin. exp. Hyp.* **1**, 3–8.

Weitzenhoffer, A. M. and Hilgard, E. R. (1958). *Stanford hypnotic susceptibility scale.* Palo Alto, Calif.: Consulting Psychologists Press.

White, R. W. (1937). "Prediction of hypnotic susceptibility from a knowledge of subjects' attitude," *J. Psychol.*, **3**, 265–277.

Wilkins, W. L. and Adams, A. J. (1947). "The use of the Rorschach test under hypnosis and under sodium amytal in military psychiatry," *J. Gen. Psychol.*, **36**, 131–138.

Wolberg, L. R. (1947). "Hypnotic experiments in psychosomatic medicine," *Psychosom. Med.*, **9**, 337–342.

Wolpe, J. (1958). *Psychotherapy by Reciprocal Inhibition.* Stanford, Calif.: Stanford Univ. Press,

Zolik, E. (1958). "An experimental investigation of the psychodynamic implications of the hypnotic 'previous existence' fantasy," *J. clin. Psychol.*, **14**, 179–183.

8

Brief Crisis-Oriented Hypnotherapy

C. SCOTT MOSS[1]

THE use of hypnosis in psychotherapy this past century has generated a curious, fluctuating ambivalence, resulting in a waxing and waning of enthusiasm and frequent, sometimes vitriolic, differences of opinion. The present high level of interest, which began during World War II, has persisted without visible diminution for two decades. However, there is no assurance that hypnotherapy will not again fall into disrepute, notwithstanding the best efforts of interested professional persons to safeguard against the exaggeration and sensationalism that contributed to its demise in the past. Despite recent evidence of increased acceptance by the major professional societies in medicine, psychiatry, and psychology, treatment with hypnosis remains highly controversial; and practitioners are still confronted with a degree of career risk occasioned by the suspicious attitudes of their professional colleagues.

[1] National Institute of Mental Health, United States Public Health Service Department of Health, Education and Welfare, San Francisco. This article was written in the author's private capacity, and it does not reflect the opinions or policies of the National Institute of Mental Health.

This chapter will focus specifically on the employment of hypnosis in relatively brief, crisis-oriented psychotherapy. It is predicated on the assumption that resolution of even one immediate, major conflict situation may enable the patient to mobilize his resources and resume a reasonably adequate problem-solving mode of adjustment. In this approach the therapist trains the patient in hypnosis in the early sessions, and then conducts treatment in conventional fashion until severe resistances are encountered, whereupon hypnosis is rapidly induced, the resistance evaluated; and the knowledge acquired is then used in whatever manner seems expeditious in the attainment of usually fairly immediate and circumscribed therapeutic goals. The most frequently adopted pattern involves a restricted number of sessions, say, once or twice a week for several months, followed by an interruption to test the results of treatment, and with one or two terminal interviews.

Advocates of hypnotherapy report success in the treatment of the full spectrum of psychopathology from the neuroses and psychoses, to alcoholism and addiction, psychosomatic disorders and even organic conditions.[2] Obviously, success or failure will be determined to considerable extent by the particular proficiency of a therapist in dealing with specific disorders, and the more objective studies report inexplicable successes and failures with the same category of patient even when treated by the same therapist. Nevertheless, the tantalizing possibility that hypnosis may yet provide an avenue for appreciably reducing the oft-extended duration of psychotherapy has always been a main attraction to members of the clinical community.

The wide variety of specialized techniques available to the hypnotherapist are generally familiar to professional persons today, and no effort will be made at an exhaustive listing and description. This chapter will present a number of illustrative techniques allowing for evaluation in the context of three case vignettes: free and directed associations; scene visualization involving time-distortion; a method of relaxation in stress periods through autohypnosis; age regression for uncovering the meaning behind symptoms and resistances; the employment of a visually hallucinated symbol as a method of deconditioning to a phobic object; the use of hypnosis to mobilize motivation and encourage active "homework" between therapy sessions; visual imagery in association with automatic drawing; hypno(electro)shock as a means of temporarily reinstituting repressive defenses, a variety of methods of dream elicitation and analysis, and so forth. Needless to say, permutations in hypnotic

[2] Readers are apprised of the following recent articles representative of relatively brief hypnotherapy with various types of behavior disorders: Hodge (1959), management of dissociative reactions; Magonet (1960), hypnosis in asthma; Mason (1961), motivation of aphasics; Spankus and Freedman (1962), hypnosis in cerebral palsy; Taylor (1962), hypnoanalysis of a fetishism; Abrams (1963), brief hypnotherapy in schizophrenia; Richardson (1963), treatment in frigidity; Slater and Flores (1963), organic symptom removal.

technique are almost infinite, being limited only by the ingenuity and creativity of the clinician. The cases that follow were reported elsewhere in substantially greater detail.

THREE CASE VIGNETTES

Case One (Moss, 1958)

The patient, aged 32, hospitalized for a service-connected chronic anxiety reaction, reported a consistent pattern of neurotic behavior since the torpedoing of his ship, in which only two out of 101 men in his compartment survived. Since that time, any stimuli faintly reminiscent of combat, such as violence on television or even a thunderstorm, stimulated a nocturnal re-experiencing of that traumatic episode, leaving him tense, highly irritable, withdrawn, and unable to work.

The patient had received professional assistance periodically for 12 years without appreciable relief. The treatment problem was further complicated by a residual claustrophobia, which generalized to an intense fear of hospital confinement. He promised to remain only three weeks and the problem was to develop a brief, effective treatment program. Hypnosis seemed the method of choice, and the patient proved an excellent somnambulist.

A basic question concerned the reason for the ego's failure to either assimilate or repress the traumatic experience. To seek an answer to this question, hypnosis was used to revivify the original trauma. As a precaution, emotional involvement was attenuated by having the patient view the event on an imagined movie screen. Another important technique involved time-distortion; the scenes were played and replayed in "slow motion," allowing minute examination of an action originally occurring in approximately 90 seconds. Although memory for the event was sharpened, no important dynamic elements were disclosed; and it was concluded that this trauma had been a catastrophic experience for an already inadequate ego and had exaggerated a basically passive-dependent adjustment.

Thereafter several supportive hypnotic techniques were employed, designed to control and alleviate the disruptive effect of the patient's nightmares. These dreams seemed to occur with greatest frequency when the patient slept on his back, so it was hypnotically suggested that he sleep on his side or stomach and that his "unconscious" prevent him from rolling over. A second hypnotic suggestion was that whenever such a dream began, he would immediately awaken. At the same time the possibility existed that these dreams served some important function, such as a continuing attempt to master the experience, and desensitization was attempted through periodic employment of the aforementioned scene-visualization technique.

An immediate, dramatic improvement in the patient's condition was attributed by the therapist to the gratification of the patient's intense dependency needs, and to control this element of the relationship, the patient was trained in autohypnosis. He was taught, for instance, to relax himself whenever he felt particularly tense or irritable. As he gained in self-comfort, he was encouraged to examine the basis for current interpersonal difficulties with his wife, children, employer, and fellow workmen, and to attempt a more satisfactory mode of relatedness.

The patient was seen for 12 sessions prior to discharge, and thereafter appointments were at the patient's discretion. He returned once a week for two months, and averaged one "maintenance" visit per month for the next year. Sessions typically resulted in temporary, marked improvement. Although the patient's basic personality pattern remained unaltered, his symptoms were less troublesome and his general adjustment relatively improved; for example, his loss of work time was reduced 35 per cent in comparison with the preceding three years. However, the relationship had to be terminated due to the therapist's departure from the vicinity and it seemed predictable that the patient would regress without this supportive relationship.

It is anticipated that this case presentation will restimulate the old allegation that hypnotherapy is after all only a palliative form of treatment and any remedial effects are necessarily short-lived. It is not the author's intent to advocate a general practice of symptom removal without prior inquiry into its possible significance to the patient. Nevertheless it should be remembered that the "protective function" of psychological symptoms is a working assumption inherited from psychoanalysis, and not a proven fact. At this stage in our knowledge of psychopathology, subscription to this concept may be a wise precaution; however, this tenet should not act to circumscribe and inhibit the creative operations of the psychotherapist.

A variety of therapies that focus directly on symptom relief are seemingly efficacious, and there is little or no evidence of a higher rate of recidivism, formation of substitute symptoms, or even the development of undue anxiety, when compared with results obtained by so-called psychodynamic or reeducative therapies (see Dorcus, 1960 for a provocative discussion of the treatment and removal of symptoms by hypnosis). There is ample evidence on the other hand that new modes of behavior can be acquired without an uncovering of psychodynamics, and conversely, that "insight" is often unaccompanied by appropriate modifications in behavior.

In the reported case, measures were employed to provide the patient temporary respite from his symptoms and to intervene in the vicious pyramiding of distressing emotional reactions of fear, anger, and anxiety. Upon occasion the effort was made to encourage him to examine actively the "meaning" of certain aspects of his past or present behavior, but there was never any satisfying evidence that he benefited appreciably by such confrontations. It has long been suspected that many classes of patient may be unresponsive to dynamically oriented psychotherapy and clinicians court failure by their persistent efforts to impose such an indiscriminate demand.

Suggestion has been a basic medical tool for thousands of years and it is an inevitable component of all treatment, whether the physician welcomes it or not. Perhaps the key to effective treatment in certain cases is simply the direct employment of suggestion uncontaminated by the doubt, reservations, or guilt of the therapist. The current conflict in medical circles concerning the employment of placebos is indicative of a marked division of opinion surrounding this issue. Shapiro (1960) reports striking differences between psychiatric and nonpsychiatric physicians on the use of placebos; the former tend to advocate and sanction their use, whereas the latter oppose and condemn this device. In the field of psychotherapy, Frank (1961) is only the most recent to document convincingly the lack of evidence for the effectiveness of one method of treatment over another, or for that matter whether any contemporary approach is demonstrably more effective than faith healing.

Case Two (Moss *et al.*, 1962)

The patient, aged 31, a divorcée and mother of three daughters, voluntarily had herself hospitalized, and was diagnosed "Psychoneurotic Reaction, Conversion type." Her main complaints were of periodic feelings of unreality and "seizures," the onset dating about six months earlier. She was also distraught concerning her interpersonal relationships; for example, while admitting a fear of adult obligations, she expressed resentment at being treated by people as an irresponsible child; she identified sex as a problem, stating that she couldn't stand physical contact with her former husband; and she designated her eldest daughter's rebelliousness as a particularly aggravating problem.

A co-therapist relationship was structured in which a primary therapist conducted conventional therapy on a three-times-per-week basis, and once per week an ancillary therapist employed hypnosis in the rapid analysis of resistances. Intensive, long-term psychotherapy designed to effect a degree of personality reconstruction that would allow independent self-management, seemed unrealistic in view of the patient's lifelong history of excessive dependency, and thus a more modest goal was agreed upon. For a year the patient had been caught in a triangle composed of her ex-husband and a paramour. The former was a competent provider but she abhorred sexual relations with him; she was not physically repulsed by the latter, but he could not assure material security to the patient and her children. It was decided initially to focus on the psychological barriers that prevented the patient from re-establishing herself in a comfortable dependency in a marital relationship, though as it turned out, this involved her central neurotic conflict and the problem could not be circumscribed in this manner.

The dynamics of this case are somewhat involved; however, five major highlights will be sketched to convey a flavor of the sequential development of treatment and the techniques employed at each stage. A possible obstacle to remarriage was the patient's Catholicism. She attributed her conversion five years earlier to a lifelong fear of death, and volunteered a recurrent, terrifying childhood dream in which she slammed shut the door on a small, furry white dog as somehow, inexplicably, related to this fear. Hypnosis elicited a terrifying re-experiencing of this dream. While still hypnotized, the patient was handed a paper and pencil and told that upon opening her eyes, she would "see" the little dog clearly etched on the paper and she was to carefully trace over its outline. After successful compliance with these instructions, she was told that when she opened her eyes again she would see a second image representing the central meaning of the little dog, and she was to again "trace these lines exactly as they appear there on the paper." She responded with a body in a coffin. In this manner the patient was suddenly confronted with the full significance of her dream—the traumatic death of her beloved grandfather, when she was six—and she abreacted violently.[3]

The patient's "feeling of unreality" antedated hospitalization by several months

[3] Klemperer (1961) describes a similar technique of symbol analysis in which the hypnotized subject is induced to allow a visualization to change to what it means or represents via a series of images. She claims that this method is more direct and effective than verbal free association.

and was vaguely related to her seizures, which began about the same time. An investigation of these complaints led to the next major therapeutic development. She began the session with a reference to a recent seizure experienced during ward rounds. "I got terribly upset, though I don't know why. I had told Dr. A. that I was ready to go home to my sister's and go to work, and he told me he had written to get her. I got awfully afraid and just went to pieces. And afterwards, for one whole day, I thought I was a Joan Whitmier. The thought scared me, 'cause I thought, supposing I wouldn't know my mother when she came, or the members of my family? It scared me so I pushed it out of my mind. I kept telling myself, 'No, I'm Alice M.' I was afraid if I didn't convince myself that I would become this Joan Whitmier and maybe stay her." Thus Alice revealed for the first time the presence of an embryonic second personality. Through hypnosis direct communication with Joan was readily established, allowing a detailed comparison with the conscious, dominant personality. In essence Joan represented the "little girl" aspect of the patient who wanted only to enjoy herself and to escape all obligations. She explained that she came into existence as a consequence of the patient's ambivalence over resumption of responsibility for herself and the children. The therapists thought it strategic to avoid encouraging this dissociative process through further exploration, and "Joan" did not spontaneously manifest herself again.[4]

A third significant therapeutic advance was achieved when the patient recalled her unhappy childhood and her intense jealousy of a younger sister whom she felt had deprived her of her mother's attention and love. Through a process of hypnotic age regression, the patient was confronted with a direct comparison between the early feelings toward her younger sister and her present attitudes toward her older daughter. For the first time she recognized the parallel and acknowledged her hostile, jealous, competitive parataxic distortion.

P: "She's been the sister that I hated, the sister I was jealous of, the sister that I didn't like. She even looked like her, talked like her, she was just like her in every way, that's why I didn't like her. . . . It seemed like everybody I ever loved has been taken away from me . . . my grandfather, then my (older) sister left home—she ran off and got married, and then I didn't have her anymore, and then I was all alone again. So I ran off, just like she did, and got married, too. Frankie loved me. Then I had Connie, and after that I had to share Frankie with her. And she took Frankie away, and I didn't have anyone."

Another critical insight into her relationships with her parents occurred while again reminiscing about her childhood. She suddenly recalled her fear of an older man, a friend of her father's, "who always carried a little snake in his pocket." Age regression was employed and almost immediately she reexperienced in detail a very traumatic incident at age four when this man had taken her into a barn and used her as a stimulant for masturbation. The patient reacted to recall of this experience with a sizable cathartic release. A synopsis of her verbalizations is quite revealing:

"It seems strange now that I never remembered that. I guess it scared me so much that I didn't want to remember it. It was better not to remember it. . . . It looks like my mother should have taken better care of me when I was a little girl. Any mother that loves her daughter will protect her and take care of her, so that these things don't happen to her. I always protected my girls. If a mother doesn't care enough to protect you, then there just isn't anyone you can depend on." (She went on to express her resentment of her husband for the times he had forced sex relations on her.)

The day following, the patient, in a state of considerable agitation, requested another meeting. She reported a vague awareness of another, related episode but

[4] See a critical review of the literature on multiple personalities, with special reference to hypnosis, by Sutcliffe and Jones (1962); the article includes a 76-item bibliography.

that it had proven elusive to recall. Hypnosis allowed her immediately to recapture in convincing detail an experience from age five. She vividly recalled being forcibly fondled and then finally ejaculated upon by her alcoholic father. The patient again connected this episode with her hatred of her husband, her hostility toward her mother for not having protected her, and the attraction felt for her lover—like her grandfather, he had loved her for herself, not sex. The next few sessions brought increasing expression of hostile feelings toward her husband and an exploration of the following event, which had precipitated her hospitalization.

One night, when she and her husband were sleeping apart (as usual), the eldest daughter came to her room crying and saying that she was afraid of her father. Instantly the patient *knew* that her husband had molested the girl and went into the living room to accuse him. At this moment, without any awareness of its source, she had blurted out, "I know just how she feels because my father tried that on me once." Her husband vehemently denied the accusation but she remained adamant, felt physically ill, and possessed of an intense hatred for him. "I told him I wanted to kill him, that a man who does that to his daughter isn't fit to live!" In the next couple of weeks the effort was made to work through this insight; and although recall of the childhood experience raised some doubt in her mind regarding the validity of her interpretation, she remained highly undecided.

The last major therapeutic progress was made in an exploration of the meaning of her seizure pattern. Hypnosis was used to regress her to the time of each of a half-dozen seizures, and a detailed analysis was made of the circumstances surrounding each event. The recurrent theme was a conflictual situation associated with overwhelming feelings of hopelessness and an appeal for help. The first seizure occurred two days after the situation in which she accused her husband of molesting their daughter. She had continued to press the issue and in a fit of rage he picked her up and threw her on the floor.

"I remember thinking, 'Oh, my God, I can't move, my back's broken!' I couldn't move and I couldn't get up. I couldn't get up! And I crawled across the floor, got to the phone and called the police. And he just stood there and looked at me!"

Questioning at this juncture elicited for the first time that an older sister had always been subject to "spells" and as a young girl the patient had the assignment of sitting on this sister's feet until the tremors passed.

Unfortunately, this promising therapeutic beginning over a four month period did not bring lasting improvement. The patient had never relinquished her wish for a reconciliation with her ex-husband; it was truly a situation in which she couldn't live with or without him. She prevailed upon the therapists to effect a meeting with him, but Mr. M., while expressing interest in the patient's welfare, refused to even consider the possibility of remarriage. The patient interpreted his action as one more in a long succession of rejections and reacted accordingly. She became dispirited and depressed, lost her motivation for therapy, and her mood fluctuated widely and rapidly.

The final episode occurred about one month later. The patient demanded electroshock treatment, and after some hesitation it was decided to administer a course of hypnoshock. One actual full electroshock was administered, and thereafter a series of seven simulated shocks were instituted through hypnotic regression back to the original treatment. After the first three "shocks" the patient felt well enough to go on an extended leave to her parents' home; the remainder were administered on an out-patient maintenance basis over a period of two months. A few months later she married her paramour, but unfortunately a modern "miracle cure" (*sic*) was contaminated when she and her new husband received actual electroshock treatment at another institution in an effort to resolve marital discord. A follow-up inquiry a year later revealed that the patient had resumed a pattern of vacillation between home and hospital.

Psychotherapy is a highly reflective exercise requiring that a patient assume progressively increased responsibility for his own thoughts and actions, and this is the antithesis of well-established behavior patterns in the neurotic. This patient made a marginal marital adjustment for almost 20 years, until circumstances forced a penetration of her repressive defenses. In experiential terms, the hysteric has forsaken the world of reflection for impulsive action; personal responsibility is discounted so that things "just happen," seemingly at the instigation of others or of impersonal events. For instance, this patient's seizures represent a prostration in the face of danger, which annihilated the threatening perceptual image by temporarily rejecting consciousness itself, a maneuver consistent with the device of slamming an imaginary door in a childhood dream.

Resistance to psychotherapy was therefore to be anticipated in this case, and the patient's willingness to relinquish her repressive controls initially was quite possibly an expression of her readiness again to pay the price demanded to attain satisfaction of her gross dependency needs by an omnipotent but sexually safe male therapist. The eventual demand for mechanical reinstitution of "forgetfulness" through electroshock was also completely consistent and predictable.[5]

There is seemingly no more convincing demonstration of the psychological genetics and dynamics of neurotic symptomatology than such a hypnotic exploration of hysteria. Even this brief account of a treatment failure exhibits the operation of unconscious motivation with startling clarity. The elicited dynamics bear a remarkable resemblance to those advanced by Freud early in his career, though later, of course, he concluded that these recitals of childhood sexual seduction were wish-fulfilling fantasies.

Although the author tended to accept the veridicality of the patient's memories, he is well aware that such accounts in psychotherapy characteristically have a convincing logic and consistency. Alternate possibilities are certainly tenable. Reports of this nature could be unwittingly solicited by a therapist's implicit or covert expectations, though in this case the author would be more willing to consider such a proposition if either of the therapists had been psychoanalytically oriented, and if the conformity of these "memories" to Freud's observations had not come as such a distinct surprise.

It is true that the patient had a tendency to sexualize her relationships and this leads to the suspicion that the reported "memories" could constitute defensive fantasies in which she obtains oedipal grati-

[5] The employment of simulated electroshock through hypnotic suggestion has been reported by others: Schafer (1960), Guido and Jones (1961), Backus (1962), and Stratas (1962).

fications while blaming her mother for not protecting her against her own wishes. It has been suggested that she must have been quite a "Lolita" to evoke as many sexual attacks as she "remembers."

In the last analysis, the question of validity is largely irrelevant to the treatment, because the current function of this content is the important consideration. The psychological reality that these "memories" possessed for the patient has an infectious quality, however, reflected in this instance in the therapist's lingering feeling that it is unfortunate in cases like these that objective evidence is unavailable.

Case Three (Moss, 1960)

The third case to be described represents perhaps a paradigm of the brief successful employment of hypnotherapy in the treatment of a chronic neurotic condition.

The patient, aged 45, an art instructor, sought treatment for a lifelong, intense fear of dogs. She was motivated by the desire to present her adopted daughter with a puppy on the occasion of her ninth birthday, two weeks hence. The patient made a favorable initial prognostic impression; that is, she seemed intelligent and sensitive, the problem appeared circumscribed, and her current environmental adjustment adequate. Her response to induction procedures was favorable, and it was agreed that treatment would be undertaken for a maximum of seven or eight sessions over a three-week period. The remainder of the session was spent in training her in rapid entry into hypnosis. At the conclusion of the hour, she asked that the attempt be made first to recapture the memory of "something important" associated with the birth of a child ten years earlier.

In the second session the patient revealed that her baby had died during delivery (as had two earlier children), and she believed that she had forgotten some vital fact concerning its death. She was regressed to the delivery scene, and although she recalled many long-forgotten details, she was unable to recapture the specific memory at the end of the hour. She was given the posthypnotic suggestion that between sessions the sought-after memory would gradually enter awareness and that she would probably be prepared to recall it at the next session.

The patient reported at the third session that the intervening period had been fraught with anxiety because she found herself preoccupied with memories from the unhappy era in question. Hypnosis was induced and the delivery scene revivified. She immediately "heard" the physician remark, "Its neck is broken." She identified this statement as the elusive verbalization. The full significance of this episode did not become apparent until the next session, though the patient expressed relief and also remarked that one benefit of these sessions was that for the first time she and her husband had been able to talk freely about this painful period in their lives. At the conclusion of the session, she was given the posthypnotic suggestion that the meaning of her lifelong fear of dogs would begin to manifest itself between sessions; but to protect her from a possibly traumatic revelation, it was further suggested that if these memories were too disturbing, they would be communicated to her in night-dreams.

In the fourth session the patient reported having experienced "a horrible dream." It concerned two little girls, "One child was playing with the other as if she were a doll. . . but the one that was being carried around was dead." The patient volunteered that this disturbing dream resulted in recall of the death of a younger sister 41 years ago. Other waking associations were not immediately forthcoming, so hypnosis was induced, resulting shortly thereafter in a flood of memories that she had apparently repressed since childhood. The essence of the recovered content was that at age four, she had been playing in the backyard of their home with the younger sister when the family dog inadvertently knocked the little girl down and she suffered a splinter wound in her cheek. Several days later the child died, apparently of an infection; and the mother openly blamed the patient, accusing her of knocking her sister down. The patient had never consciously recalled this episode as an adult. At the conclusion of the session, a posthypnotic suggestion was given that the full meaning of this experience and its total effect upon her life, past and present, would begin to make itself evident.

In the three days between sessions, the patient experienced a compulsive recall of a series of memories beginning in the recent past and extending back to early childhood. These memories were explored in detail in the waking state and under hypnosis. Through them ran a theme of feeling misunderstood and mistreated by her parents, particularly her mother, with an accompanying strong resentment and associated guilt, and a continuous struggle for independence and self-realization. Also in this session the patient was regressed to successive age levels back to the time of the early trauma, and no evidence whatsoever could be found to indicate that she had ever sustained an attack by a dog that would account for her fear—indirect testimony to the validity of her recall of the early experience.

In the sixth hour the patient appeared more relaxed, and verbalized a number of new insights; for instance, she now understood her deep-seated fear of offending others and a childhood tendency to volunteer her guilt and to seek punishment in situations where actually she was innocent. Another insight pertained to her revulsion at touching dogs: the lively or frisky feeling of the dog brought back, through contrast, the limpness of her little sister at the time of her funeral, at which the family dog had torn the sister's shroud, for which the patient was again blamed. During the session the technique of age regression was again employed, and the period between her early traumatic experience and age eight was carefully explored. Conscious memory of the disturbing event apparently ceased to exist even prior to age five.

A major therapeutic tactic designed to facilitate the relearning process was introduced near the end of the session. The patient was given the posthypnotic suggestion that between sessions, whenever she was alone and desired to re-establish her acquaintance with the dog of her early childhood, she could experience a vivid visual hallucination of him. It was emphasized that the dog *symbolized* her disturbed history, and this fantasy relationship provided her with the opportunity to make peace with the past. It was further emphasized that she had complete control of the relationship and could "allow the dog as close as she desired or keep him, as distant as her fear dictated."

In the seventh session the patient reported increased feelings of comfort with dogs. She had been able to experience the hallucinated presence of the dog quite vividly and also had succeeded to some extent in making friends with him. She laughingly referred to him as "my little black Harvey." At this juncture, the patient agreed that sufficient progress had occurred to warrant a month's vacation from therapy; however, she requested that she be allowed to keep Rover to renew further their acquaintance.

A relatively brief session was held one month later. The patient reported that five days after the previous session she had gone skating with her daughter and met several dogs. "It seemed very natural to reach down and pet them. There was no fear of doing it. They did not feel like dogs used to feel. I heard Jane yell, 'Oh, look,

Mommy used to be afraid of dogs and isn't anymore,' and then it dawned on me that I really wasn't. It seemed that right after that I lost Rover." Laughingly she inquired, "You don't have him around here anymore, do you?" Three weeks later, the patient phoned to report that she had purchased a black cocker spaniel puppy and had named it Happy Siesta (a synonym for "hypnosis," and note that the last name phonetically represents the therapist's initials)

Almost one year to the day later, a follow-up interview was held with the patient. Discussion revealed evidence of some residual resistance against a complete emotional acceptance of her childhood trauma; for instance, some elements of the experience were now incompletely remembered, and she described the memory as "not quite real." She also reported that although her mother continued to deny that the event had ever happened, a brother had confirmed the existence of such a family dog and also the fact that she and her sister had been left momentarily alone at the time of the fatal accident because the two brothers, who had been carrying in wood, had gone to witness a fire at a neighbor's. Another younger sister also recalled that as long as she could remember, the patient had anxiously protected her in the presence of any and all dogs.

It was explained to the patient that it was relatively unimportant whether the memory of her childhood experience was correct in every detail, that the important factor was the effect of the therapeutic experience on her present adjustment. She reaffirmed that therapy had somewhat altered her relationship with her mother, daughter, and husband. The most evident effect of psychotherapy, however, continued to be a marked change in the patient's attitude toward dogs. "All my life the touch of one gave me a feeling of something horrible. I'm still surprised that I feel so differently now."

This case provides a clear demonstration of the use of a psychotherapeutic procedure in modification of a long-standing learning process. Adjunctive hypnotic techniques were of especial value in rapidly uncovering and revivifying the childhood pathogenic experience, allowing the adult ego to grapple with it in a new attempt at mastery. Relearning was further facilitated by reinstatement on a symbolic fantasy level of the patient's relationship with the original object of her phobia and with sufficient vividness to make it a realistic and immediate emotional experience. Hypnosis was also of value in reinforcing the patient's motivational level and at times in providing an almost compulsive reexperiencing of long-forgotten memories. In this manner, substantial progress was facilitated between sessions and following the termination of formal sessions, apparently significantly shortening the period of actual treatment. Success in this direct relearning procedure was naturally dependent on the assessed capacity of the patient's ego to assimilate repressed infantile experiences into conscious awareness.

The approach employed encouraged the patient to re-evaluate the influence of her childhood experiences in terms of present-day understanding and to effect a fuller readjustment, not only to the original conflict, but to its ramifications in her past and present life. No claim is made for achievement of a complete cure in the sense that the patient achieved full readjustment to all aspects of the widely generalized effect of the original conflict. Neither should the impression be conveyed that hypnotherapeutic techniques afforded a panacea per se. The patient described her youth as characterized by "a fear of people, new situations, many things," and her marriage as having had a highly therapeutic effect. The death of a beloved older sister when the patient was aged 27 helped the patient partially to work through her fear of death. Factors such as these contributed to a substantial degree of "spontaneous recovery" and established a "readiness" to circumvent the repressive defense upon which the hypnotherapeutic procedure then capitalized.

THE HYPNOTIC RELATIONSHIP

These cases were deliberately chosen to represent contrasting problems, strategies, tactics, and goals, and they are also intended to demonstrate the limitations as well as virtues of brief crisis-oriented hypnotherapy. Obviously, this approach is not restricted to palliative suggestion; at the same time it should be equally evident that it is not a panacea. The dramatically successful case report in the literature is no more representative of the general practice of the hypnotherapist than are similar accounts by the adherents of other methods of psychological treatment.

Patients who improve with hypnotherapy appear to possess characteristics essentially similar to those of patients responsive to other forms of psychotherapy, but in addition, they must be susceptible to hypnotic suggestion. This requirement is not as restrictive as once thought because most persons demonstrate at least moderate hypnotizability and clinicians seem agreed that a deep-level hypnosis is not a prerequisite for successful treatment. In fact, hypnotherapists rarely bother to make accurate estimates of depth because they see no apparent relationship between depth and success. A recent, notable exception is Weitzenhoffer (1962) who maintains that depth is a relevant variable in hypnotherapy. At the same time he concludes that "Perhaps in the end what is far more important than the depth attained is the therapist's ability to use hypnosis to establish the kind of interpersonal relationship which will allow him and the patient to work successfully toward relief and cure" (p. 77).

Now, judged by any standard, the traditional hypnotic relationship appears to the casual observer as bizarre and unnatural, and hardly conducive to improved mental health. The dominance-submission aspect, for example, seems blatantly apparent and quite incompatible with the encouragement of emotional growth and enhanced self-management. Dreikurs (1963) states that incompatibility with democratic ideals has led hypnotherapists to pose as "benevolent autocrats," but he still perceives a clear and present danger in the patient's abdication of individual responsibility in the hypnotic relationship. Many experienced psychotherapists would express similar sentiments.

In refutation of this and other general misconceptions concerning the nature of the hypnotic relationship, many illustrations can be cited that prove conclusively that the hypnotized patient need not be and in point of fact is not an automaton. The hypnotic subject's passivity is primarily a result of his own expectations in combination with the operator's attitude; given the freedom to act spontaneously, he will do so. Even in the traditional relationship the passivity of the subject is much more apparent than real. This can be seen in the following discussion of the initial induction or training phase of the relationship.

In brief hypnotherapy time is naturally at a premium and not too many sessions can be expended in training a patient in the appropriate role. Unfortunately the personality correlates of hypnotic susceptibility remain elusive, and even the experienced hypnotherapist has no alternative to actual induction in the selection of those patients possessed of the necessary aptitude. However, the neophyte hypnotherapist rapidly learns that it is best to avoid being too descriptive, and to allow the patient to structure the situation in terms of his own needs. This lesson was sharply etched early in the author's experience in the use of an induction technique involving a fantasy scene in which the patient was asked to imagine that she was strolling along a beach, when a wave rolled in over her, sweeping her into peaceful ocean depths (presumably symbolic of the "unconscious"). At a much later date, when the patient felt more comfortable in the relationship, she spontaneously confessed to a fear of water and revealed that from the beginning she had simply ignored the instructions and substituted her own. She volunteered, "Remember 'Alice in Wonderland?' Well, I always imagined that like Alice I was falling into sort of a deep hole where I tumbled slowly down through space. I found this a most effective means of helping me to relax and *it got me where I wanted to go*." Thus in the induction phase, the hypnotherapist learns that it is usually best not to do or say too much to interfere with the subject's rapid entry into hypnosis. This is not to say that induction techniques are without importance; hypnosis is the use of suggestion to increase the susceptibility of basically suggestible people, and, as with placebos, a red pill may be more effective than a white one (Weitzenhoffer and Sjoberg, 1961). But the point remains that there is no inherent need for the hypnotic relationship to be strictly organized around dominance and submission, any more than need any doctor-patient relationship.

Hypnosis can be conceptualized as a contractual relationship in which subjects volunteer with a readiness to respond. The behavior a subject manifests initially is a function of his expectations as to how a hypnotized subject should behave, as continuously modified by direct and implicit cues from the psychotherapist. Orne has stated the point succinctly:

> Probably most, if not all, of the behavioral characteristics of hypnosis can be understood in terms of the subject's previous knowledge and the cues transmitted during the process of induction. It is entirely possible to conceive of the typical hypnotic trance for the most part as an historically developed artifact, occurring along with a process, the actual behavioral manifestations of which are little known (1962, p. 1096).

In the same article, Orne advances another cogent point concerning the *mutual* role expectations inherent in the hypnotic relationship:

> Many aspects of hypnosis can best be conceptualized as folie a deux (a set of complementary role expectations about an unreal definition of the situation). Thus, the subject acts as though he were unable to resist the suggestions of the hypnotist and the hypnotist acts as though he were all-powerful. . . . Perhaps one of the major problems in the psychiatric use of hypnosis is the great difficulty of employing a technique which demands that the therapist enter into a folie a deux with the patient. One requirement of successful hypnosis is that the patient should be able to ascribe magical powers to the therapist. It is necessary for the therapist employing hypnosis to enter into this relationship, act out and participate in the folie a deux, while maintaining sufficient objectivity to recognize that he does not acquire the power the patient ascribes to him (p. 1101).

Successful hypnotherapists do not advocate the "use of magic in lieu of logic." On the other hand many would agree with Bromberg (1959) that "the healing arts have never lost their overtones of magic and supernaturality in the inner experience of the patient," and they would accept that faith in the therapist is an essential element in the treatment process. Treatment undertakes to utilize these reactions productively.

The frequent charge that the prospect of hypnosis stimulates the patient's expectations for a "magical cure" has considerable validity; however, this is, of course, an anticipatory attitude shared by most patients who seek psychological treatment. A high level of anxiety and attendant feelings of "copelessness" lead to a regressive state, which generates the hope that the therapist will do all of the work and guarantee a cure. It is an early objective in psychological treatment to substitute adroitly a cooperative working relationship wherein the patient can be helped to help himself. There is no reason why this cannot be done in hypnotherapy; the following nocturnal dream (Moss, 1958) illustrates this crucial and inevitable choice point in psychotherapy:

> The patient is invited to play cards, but his unidentified acquaintance states that he knows a better place and exits. The patient follows and finds himself alone at the head of a long flight of stairs. Arriving at the bottom, he is confronted with two hallways. In the entrance to one lies a bitch nursing puppies. He chooses the opposite

hallway and enroute squeezes by workmen who are energetically erecting a wooden construction. He finally emerges into a large empty room in whose center is a small Dodge truck. His friend reappears, but is now dressed in overalls. The friend says, "We'd better hurry or we'll be late!" The patient feels irritated and thinks, "Why the hell did he bring me here to work?"

The patient's waking associations were limited, but his hypnotic associations (paraphrased) quickly revealed the meaning of the dream:

The two levels represent the conscious and unconscious, and the connecting stairway is the method of hypnotic induction (the patient had been trained to enter hypnosis step by step as he walked down an imaginary staircase). The two hallways depict a choice point or decision; that is, the patient can effect a reconciliation with his wife or continue in therapy. A current conflict between them is her desire to become pregnant, much against his wishes. He related that the evening before, she persuaded him to have intercourse without a contraceptive. The patient chooses therapy and is confronted with the busy workmen, representing a hastily erected barrier, or his defensive attitude to treatment. The room represents his empty life, and the truck alludes to a desire to escape by reversion to the old "dodge" of established neurotic behavior patterns. He is then confronted by the acquaintance, who is now identified as the therapist, and who demands his active cooperation. The dream thema is clearly seen as representing the patient's feeling of negativism toward therapy; that is, at first he thought it would be fun (a game of cards—an exciting gamble), but now finds that the sessions are hard work, and he awakens feeling resentful.

Only the predisposition to view hypnosis in terms of the well-engrained historical stereotype, including the widespread tendency to conceive of it as a physiologically determined state, prevents recognition that the hypnotic relationship is as malleable as any other therapeutic transaction. The nature of the relationship, including the specific hypnotic techniques used, will vary with the therapist's personality, training, and clinical competence, and most importantly, the special needs of the patient. The successful hypnotherapist knows that the hypnotized patient remains an individual with full rights and privileges whose wishes and needs must be constantly consulted and consistently respected.[6] If the situation requires it, hypnotherapy can be a highly nondirective venture, at least in the sense that it is possible to provide patients with illuminating and convincing insight-producing experiences that largely obviate the need for direct interpretation. Witness this crucial event in treatment:

[6] Kuhner (1962) is among the many recent advocates of striking modifications in induction methods. He refers to Milton Kline's prediction that the need to hypnotize will diminish as therapists learn to reduce the distance between the doctor and the patient. "This is in accord with a fundamental concept in today's thinking that the hypnotic state is not an anomaly of human behavior that results from some technical manipulation or suggestion per se, but that it develops in a naturalistic way out of an interpersonal relationship in which the patient has a need to enter this state and the doctor provides the stimulation for entering it." (pp. 93–95)

The patient, aged 30, employed as an embalmer in a funeral home, was diagnosed "conversion hysteric"; he complained of blackouts or "seizures," dating back five years to combat experiences in the South Pacific. His attacks were always preceded by a feeling of extreme heat, the sensation of "millions of hot needles," and sometimes a violent headache. He claimed loss of consciousness for periods from a couple of hours to several days and amnesia for these periods. Among his numerous minor complaints was a repetitive anxiety dream in which he remarried his former wife in a funeral home "though the stained glass window also reminds me of the church I attended as a child." A bizarre feature was that behind the minister stood an open coffin; "someone is getting married, and someone buried at the same time." The dream always ended before the patient could see who was in that casket. It became opportune in the twentieth session to analyze this dream. The dream was reinstituted twice through hypnotic revivification and each time it terminated spontaneously as the service ended and the patient started toward the coffin. It was then stimulated a third time, and as it progressed toward the point of interruption, the therapist intruded:

"Now this time something different will happen. Instead of the dream ending, it will continue on. You hear the minister pronounce you 'man and wife'? Now step forward and look into the casket! Who do you see?"

"Why, it's my father! He always stopped me from anything I wanted to do, and mother, too. He tried to stop my marriage but he couldn't do it. Now he won't be in the road any more. I feel glad! How I hated him!"

This episode constituted the patient's first direct undeniable confrontation with the full intensity of his hostile feelings toward his father and was a springboard into an exploration of several crucial parataxic distortions, including a direct transference reaction to his company commander in service.

What is the especial virtue of hypnotherapy that compensates for the undoubted complications engendered by the technique? Contrary to popular misconception, the technique neither eliminates nor reduces resistances; defenses in various forms appear during all phases of hypnosis. Whatever insights take place are determined by the patient's readiness to assimilate the knowledge without undue anxiety; the therapist must let him determine the pace. The possibility does exist that hypnosis actually strengthens the patient's ego through a process of identification with the therapist (Baron, 1960). That is, hypnosis precipitates an almost immediate state of intimate rapport and in the security of this relationship the patient is infused with an increased capacity to tolerate anxiety. Specialized hypnotic techniques then provide the means whereby distorted perceptions and conceptions can be rapidly uncovered, ramifications traced, implications explored, and a re-evaluation effected in terms of present reality. Most authorities agree that to be effective, psychotherapy must be more than an intellectual exercise—it must be an "emotionally corrective experience." Brief hypnotherapy allows for a decisive, convincing confrontation with troublesome memories, attitudes and feelings, and even one such experience can have a healthy catalytic effect on treatment, leading to an acceleration of the whole process.

Can hypnosis appreciably reduce the duration of treatment in the majority of cases? Experience imbues most psychotherapists, including the practitioners of hypnotherapy, with a sense of sincere humility. The dawning realization of the limitations of hypnotic techniques contributes to a phemonenon described by Wolberg (1959, pp. 1466–1467) as the *meta-morphosis* of the hypnotist. He identifies three distinct stages: an initial overconfidence in hypnosis, a growing skepticism and disappointment, and if he persists, a sophisticated integration of hypnosis into his armamentarium of therapeutic techniques. Schneck probably expresses the consensus of experienced hypnotherapists in the following statement: "Much is said about hypnoanalysis reducing sharply the total length of treatment, but one must be careful not to exaggerate or generalize broadly. Circumscribed problems and individual symptoms can be investigated rapidly at times with achievment of significant understanding by the patient. This is more likely to occur if the patient is functioning well in areas other than the presenting difficulty. Basic ego strength and reorganizational aptitude would permit patients to tolerate incisive probing," (1962, p. 2). Conn (1960) makes much the same point when he writes: "The value of suggestion and abreaction lies not in themselves but in the fact that the patient is ready (set), able (mature enough) and willing (unconsciously wishes) to get well and to remain well (self-sufficient and realistic). Only then can he endow the therapist of his choice (the transference-object) with the power to cure him" (p. 12). In short, the ability of hypnotic techniques to reduce the duration of treatment depends, like any other technique, on the characteristics of the patient as well as on the skill of the therapist, and technique alone cannot make up for deficiencies in these two areas.

CHARACTERISTICS OF HYPNOTHERAPISTS

This chapter has been intentionally autobiographical, a reflection of the author's conviction that the conduct of psychotherapy remains a highly personal venture, and the worth or limitations of any technique are best evaluated in the context of detailed case and treatment information.[7] That is, each psychotherapist will choose those techniques

[7] The following articles, selected from the recent literature, provide a broad perspective of developments and current practices in the field of hypnotherapy: Bowers (1961), use of hypnosis in the treatment of schizophrenia; Fox (1960), employment of hypnosis in individual and group psychotherapy; Freidman (1961), dynamics in hypnosis failures; Freytag (1959, 1961), two books describing techniques of hypnoanalysis, replete with illustrative case material; GAP symposium on hypnosis (1962); Haley (1961), brief hypnotherapy; Kaufman (1961), status of hypnotherapy; Kline (1960), age regression and psychotherapy; LeBaron

that he finds personally compatible and he will tend to employ them in an idiosyncratic manner; the choice of hypnotic techniques is an expression of such personal preference.

It is indeed a curious fact that although numerous studies have attempted to establish the personality correlates of the "good" hypnotic subject, with negative, contradictory, and inconclusive results, investigators have largely ignored the objective identification of the hypnotherapist, though this has not inhibited speculation, much of it rather derogatory in character (Pardell, 1950; Gill and Brenman, 1961; Lindner, 1960). Obviously, who makes use of hypnosis will determine how such techniques are utilized, and quite possibly the success or failure of the entire operation.

In a recently published study, Moss *et al.* (1965) undertook to identify some of the personality and behavioral correlates of experienced psychologist-therapists who use hypnosis in psychotherapy. A lengthy questionnaire was completed by 147 doctoral-level psychologists, nationally dispersed, and selected on the basis of a highly visible interest in psychotherapy. The experience level of the respondents ranged from two to over twenty years of practice, with a median in excess of seven years. Eight schools or theoretical orientations were represented within this population. An intriguing consistency to the pattern of intercorrelations between items lends itself to the following speculative characterization of the two extreme attitudinal groups. Psychologist-therapists who have an unfavorable attitude toward hypnosis tend to choose psychology as a career on the basis of a desire to increase their own self-understanding, and follow through with an intensive, usually psychoanalytic, personal therapy. The typical member of this group was highly influenced during his formulative years by members of the medical profession, usually a psychoanalyst or psychiatrist, and after graduation he elected the practice of psychotherapy as his major activity. In contrast, the typical member of the favorable attitude group chose psychology because of reasons such as "the wish to understand others," and financial and status considerations. Personal therapy, if any, was relatively short-term, often nonpsychoanalytic in nature, and he was more highly influenced by clinical and other psychologists during and immediately following his academic training. After graduation he tended to become a teacher or administrator, and was likely to claim an eclectic orientation.

(1962), ideomotor signalling in brief hypnotherapy; Luthe (1962), method and research of autogenic training; Maher-Loughnan (1961), treatment by autohypnosis; McCartney (1961), short-term hypnotherapy; Raginsky (1961, 1962), use of sensory plasticine in hypnoanalysis; Spiegal (1963), rapid clinical relief through hypnosis; Stachowiak and Moss (1963), hypnotic alteration of social attitudes; Wolpe (1961), systematic desensitization of neuroses.

In the actual conduct of psychotherapy, there were more similarities than differences in techniques, other than the use or nonuse of hypnosis. Therapists who favor hypnosis did manifest a proclivity towards a relatively more active, supportive, environmental-manipulative and versatile approach to treatment. For example, psychologists in this group displayed a significant tendency to make more active use of a wider variety of techniques.

Perhaps the most interesting results were obtained on the Intuitive (versus) Objective Orientation Scale originally developed by Shaffer (1953). This scale measures the psychologist's clinical as opposed to experimental frame of reference in psychological activities. It relates to such fundamental questions as the psychologist's conception of his professional role and the type of evidence he will accept in the establishment of the facts and principles upon which he operates. Analysis revealed a very significant difference between the two groups: those favoring use of hypnosis were much more objective or experimentally oriented, a difference significant beyond the 0.001 level of confidence.

Whatever the deeper personality factors involved in the decision to employ hypnosis in psychotherapy, the data from this study suggest that hypnotherapy—probably as a dramatic, seemingly effective facilitant to brief psychotherapy—has particular appeal to psychologists who have not specialized in psychotherapy, but who retain, among a diversity of interests an active desire to "help people." This group appears to possess an adaptive, pragmatic approach to treatment, and a receptivity to a variety of methods, including the environmental-manipulative, in contrast to a more sacrosanct attitude toward psychotherapy. It is a temptation to conjecture further that hypnosis has especial attraction for psychologists with a basic interest in the acquisition of knowledge about the etiology and dynamics of psychopathology, and that in turn, the enthusiasm generated in the therapist by the elicited revelations may have a catalytic effect upon the therapeutic process.

A most positive aspect of this investigation, if verified by future studies, is the relative research orientation of psychologist-hypnotherapists (results cannot of course be generalized to medical practitioners of hypnosis). Despite years of widespread and often intensive interest, the horizon of established fact concerning hypnosis remains decidedly limited. Hypnotherapy today has an inevitably exciting, experimental quality, and therapists who use these techniques are obligated to cultivate a fact-finding attitude that will contribute not only to a more objective understanding of the many questions relative to this elusive phenomenon but to those extant in the surrounding general areas of behavior pathology and personality change.

In summary crisis-oriented hypnotherapy is a prompt, focused, and reality-oriented form of psychotherapy. It is made available to individuals during periods of acute psychological disequilibrium and vulnerability occasioned by inordinate stress. It certainly possesses an emergency character, but should not be demeaned as "psychiatric first aid" only. Serious attention is paid to the clients' presenting symptoms and to precipitating factors, such as birth, injury or illness, separation or death, marital discord and unemployment, and so forth. It is recognized that current problem situations may reactivate past unresolved conflict areas; however, treatment does not involve extended psycho-archeological explorations, nor is it concerned with intrapsychic manifestations to the exclusion of immediate, meaningful, real life problems.

Correctly viewed, hypnotherapy is only one highly specialized treatment technique in the armamentarium of the mental-health professional, who can no longer afford conformity to the rigid, traditional clinic procedure. He must be prepared to intervene via a wide variety of therapeutic strategies: direct advice, medication, psychotherapy, consultation to allied helping professions, and community education aimed at prevention. In short, the mental health professional person must have the knowledge, skill, imagination and audacity to energize and mobilize whatever community resources will benefit his client. It is within this broad context that the contribution of hypnotherapy must eventually be evaluated.

REFERENCES

Abrams, S. (1963). "Short-term psychotherapy of a schizophrenic patient," *Amer. J. clin. Hyp.*, **5**, 237–247.

Backus, P. S. (1962). "The use of hypnotically induced seizures to replace electroschock treatments," *Amer. J. clin. Hyp.*, **4**, 272–273.

Baron, S. (1960). "Levels of insight and ego functioning in relation to hypnosis," *Int. J. clin. exp. Hyp.*, **8**, 141–146.

Bowers, M. K. (1961). "Theoretical considerations in the use of hypnosis in the treatment of schizophrenia," *Int. J. clin. exp. Hyp.*, **9**, 39–46.

Bromberg, W. (1959). *The Mind of Man: A History of Psychotherapy and Psychoanalysis.* New York: Harper.

Conn, J. H. (1960). "The psychodynamics of recovery under hypnosis," *Int. J. clin. exp. Hyp.*, **8**, 3–15.

Dorcus, R. M. (1960). "The treatment of symptoms with special reference to removal by hypnosis," *VII Annual U. Kansas Institute for Research in Clinical Psychology*, Lawrence, Kansas.

Dreikurs, R. (1962). "The interpersonal relationship in hypnosis," *Psychiatry*, **25**, 219–226.

Fox, J. (1960). "The systematic use of hypnosis in individual and group psychotherapy," *Int. J. clin. exp. Hyp.*, **8**, 109–119.

FRANK, J. D. (1961). *Persuasion and Healing: A Comparative Study of Psychotherapy*. Baltimore: Johns Hopkins.

FREIDMAN, J. J. (1961). "Psychodynamics in hypnosis failures," *Psychosomatics*, **2**, 346–348.

FREYTAG, F. F. (1959). *The Hypnoanalysis of an Anxiety Hysteric*. New York: Julian Press.

——— (1961). *Hypnosis and the Body Image*. New York: Julian

GILL, M. and BRENMAM, M. (1961). *Hypnosis and Related States*. New York: International Universities Press.

GROUP FOR THE ADVANCEMENT OF PSYCHIATRY (1962). "Medical uses of hypnosis," *GAP Rep.*, **8**, 641–708.

GUIDO, J. A. and JONES, J. (1961). "'Placebo' (simulation) electroconvulsive therapy," *Amer. J. Psychiat.*, **117**, 838–839.

HALEY, J. (1961). "Control in brief psychotherapy," *Arch. gen. Psychiat.*, **4** 139–153.

HODGE, J. R. (1959). "The management of dissociative reactions with hypnosis," *Int. J. clin. exp. Hyp.*, **7**, 217–221.

KAUFMAN, M. R. (1961). "Hypnosis in psychotherapy today," *Arch. gen. Psychiat.*, **4**, 30–39.

KLEMPERER, E. (1961). "'Shortest distance' therapy in hypnoanalysis," *Int. J. clin. exp. Hyp.*, **9**, 63–77.

KLINE, M. V. (1960). "Hypnotic age regression and psychotherapy: clinical and theoretical observations," *Int. J. clin. exp. Hyp.*, **8**, 17–35.

KUHNER, A. (1962). "Hypnosis without hypnosis," *Int. J. clin. exp. Hypn.*, **10**, 93–99.

LEBARON, G. I., Jr. (1962). "Ideomotor signalling in brief psychotherapy," *Amer. J. clin. Hyp.*, **5**, 81–91.

LINDNER, H. (1960). "The shared neurosis: hypnotist and subject," *Int. J. clin. exp. Hyp.*, **8**, 61–70.

LUTHE, W. (1962). "Method, research and application of autogenic training," *Amer. J. clin. Hypn.*, **5**, 17–29.

MAGONET, A. P. (1960). "Hypnosis in asthma," *Int. J. clin. exp. Hyp.*, **8**, 109–119.

MAHER-LOUGHNAN, G. P. (1961). "'Day by day in every way...' Treatment by autohypnosis following preliminary hypnosis," *Medical Press*, **246**, 170–173.

MASON, C. F. (1961). "Hypnotic motivation of aphasics," *Int. J. clin. exp. Hyp.*, **9**, 297–301.

MCCARTNEY, J. L. (1961). "Short term psychotherapy," *Psychosomatics*, **2**, 351–355.

MOSS, C. S. (1958), "Dream symbols as disguises," *Etc.*, **14**, 267–273.

——— (1958a). "Therapeutic suggestion and autosuggestion," *J. clin. exp. Hyp.*, **6**, 109–115.

——— (1960). "Brief successful psychotherapy of a chronic phobic reaction," *J. abnorm. soc. Psychol.*, **60**, 266–270.

MOSS, C. S. THOMPSON, M. M. and NOLTE, J. (1962). "An additional study in hysteria: the case of Alice M.," *Int. J. clin. exp. Hyp.*, **10**, 59–74.

Moss, C. S. Riggen, G., Coyne, L., and Bishop, W. (1965). "Some correlates of the use (or disuse) of hypnosis by experienced psychologist-therapists," *Int. J. clin. exp. Hyp.*, **13**, 39–50.
Orne, M. T. (1962). "Implications for psychotherapy derived from current research on the nature of hypnosis," *Amer. J. Psychiat.*, **118**, 1097–1103.
Pardell, S. S. (1950). "Psychology of the hypnotist," *Psychiat. Quart.*, **24**, 483–491.
Raginsky, B. B. (1961). "The sensory use of platiscine in hypnoanalysis (sensory hypnoplasty)," *Int. J. clin. exp. Hyp.*, **9**, 233–247.
——— (1962). "Sensory hypnoplasty with case illustrations," *Int. J. clin. exp. Hyp.*, **10**, 205–219.
Richardson, T. A. (1963). "Hypnotherapy in frigidity," *Amer. J. clin. Hyp.*, **5**, 194–199.
Schafer, D. W. (1960). "As-if electroshock therapy by hypnosis," *Amer. J. clin. Hyp.*, **2**, 225–227.
Schneck, J. M. (1962). "Hypnoanalysis," *Int. J. clin. exp. Hyp.*, **10**, 1–12.
Shaffer, L. F. (1953), "Of whose reality I cannot doubt," *Amer. Psychologist*, **8**, 608–623.
Shapiro, A. K. (1960). "Attitudes toward the use of placebos in treatment," *J. nerv. ment. Dis.*, **130**, 200–211.
Slater, R. C. and Flores, L. S. (1963). "Hypnosis in organic symptom removal: a temporary removal of an organic paralysis by hypnosis," *Amer. J. clin. Hyp.*, **5**, 248–255.
Spankus, W. H. and Freedman, L. G. (1962). "Hypnosis in cerebral palsy," *Int. J. clin. Hyp.*, **10**, 135–139.
Spiegal, H. (1963). "Hypnotic intervention as an adjunct for rapid clinical relief," *Int. J. clin. exp. Hyp.*, **10**, 23–29.
Stachowiak, J. G. and Moss, C. S. (1963), "The hypnotic alteration of social attitudes," Unpubl. manuscript.
Stratas, N. E. (1962). "Pseudo-electroconvulsive therapy using hypnosis: a controlled pilot study," *Amer. J. clin. Hyp.*, **5**, 62–64.
Sutcliffe, J. P. and Jones, J. (1962). "Personal identity, multiple personality and hypnosis," *Int. J. clin. exp. Hyp.*, **10**, 231–269.
Taylor, W. S. (1962). "Hypnoanalysis of a fetishism," *Psychiat. Quart.*, **36**, 1–13.
Weitzenhoffer, A. M. (1962). "The significance of hypnotic depth in therapy," *Int. J. clin. exp. Hyp.*, **10**, 75–78.
Weitzenhoffer, A. M., and Sjoberg, B. M. (1961). "Suggestibility with and without 'induction of hypnosis'," *J. nerv. ment. Dis.*, **132**, 204–220.
Wolberg, L. R. (1959). "Hypnotherapy." In *The American Handbook of Psychiatry*. Vol. II, New York: Basic Books. 1466–1481.
Wolpe, J. (1961). "The systematic desensitization treatment of neuroses," *J. nerv. ment. Dis.*, **132**, 180–203.

9

Hypnosis in Psychoanalytic Psychotherapy

LEWIS R. WOLBERG, M.D.

It is one of the ironies of history that the man who made perhaps the most striking contribution to hypnosis in his time was responsible for its eventual discreditment. Exploiting Breuer's innovation of encouraging the hypnotized patient to explore and ventilate past traumatic incidents, Sigmund Freud (1953a) attempted to widen zones of consciousness through hypnosis "by making the patient revert to the psychic state in which the symptom had appeared for the first time." Through this means he hoped that memories, thoughts and impulses, which had dropped out of consciousness, would return, releasing baneful emotions that had been converted into symptoms. Once released, the symptom would forever disappear.

Because his efforts were largely unrewarded, Freud postulated that symptom formation was sponsored not by isolated traumatic incidents in the past, but by a series of impressions that could not be easily grasped, except perhaps in the most profound trance. Few patients, he insisted, could be inducted into the proper hypnotic depth. For this reason Freud experimented with other ways of penetrating the unconscious.

Enjoining his patients to speak freely in the waking state, uttering whatever random thoughts and fantasies flitted before their minds, Freud was satisfied that this mode of "free association" was able to release memories and images with their attendant strangulated affects. Coordinately he became more and more convinced that the beneficial effects of hypnosis were suggestive in nature, being entirely dependent upon the maintenance of a positive relationship with the hypnotist. If this relationship was disturbed, the symptoms reappeared (Freud, 1956, p. 110).

But the technique of "free association" aimed at penetrating the inner recesses of the psyche was not in itself sufficient. Freud began to realize that there were dynamic forces working against the release of emotionally charged and repudiated memories and impulses. Gaps in the patient's memory, forgotten occurrences, confusion in chronological order, broken causal connections in events, pointed to the phenomenon of purposeful forgetting. This he insisted, was brought about by a process of repression energized by a need to avoid pain (*Unlust*). The psychical forces responsible for *repression* were traceable to *resistance* against the reintegration of painful memories. Many psychic distortions resulted from these defensive operations.

To render the unconscious in mental life accessible to consciousness without hypnosis, it was necessary to deal with the resistances by proper confrontations and interpretations. The "art of interpretation" consisted of a number of rules, reached empirically, which reconstructed unconscious material from free associations, dreams, and seemingly purposeless actions and blunders.

Freud believed that hypnosis had proven itself to be unsuccessful because it did not deal definitively with resistances. Rather it by-passed them, divulging the nascent content of the unconscious briefly, with restoration of the status quo after the hypnotic state had been terminated. "Hypnosis" he wrote, "does not do away with resistance but only avoids it and therefore yields only incomplete information and transitory therapeutic success" (Freud, 1953a, p. 269). Because hypnosis concealed resistance "the history of psycho-analysis proper, therefore, begins with the new technique that dispenses with hypnosis" (Freud, 1953a, p. 298).

These arguments against hypnosis, formulated by Freud in 1904, are still being promulgated by some persons who have accepted them at face value without analyzing their underlying meaning. In utilizing hypnosis as a penetrating weapon to uproot traumatic conflicts and experiences, in employing it to reinforce authoritative suggestions so as to coax away symptoms, the capriciousness and impermanence of its effects are as notable today as they were in the early observations by Freud. Helping an individual to overcome an emotional problem permanently necessitates an alteration of his defenses. Freud's injunction that a working through of resistance was a mandatory ingredient of any rational therapeutic process has, throughout the years, been amply substantiated. In the early uses of hypnosis, the emphasis was placed upon either a surgical exposure of repressed material through a circumvention of resistance or the implantation of powerful suggestions to neutralize or banish symptoms. In either instance, the effects of hypnosis were bound to be temporary and disappointing, not because hypnosis was an ineffective procedure, but rather because the uses to which hypnosis was put could not possibly have yielded substantial therapeutic results.

Freud was inveighing not so much against hypnosis as against its improper usage. That he was not antagonistic toward the hypnotic method is apparent from his writings. "We have developed the technique of hypnotic suggestion, and psychotherapy by diversion of attention, by exercise, and by eliciting suitable affects. I despise none of these methods and would use them all under proper conditions. If I have actually come to confine myself to one form of treatment, to the method that Breuer called *cathartic*, which I myself prefer to call 'analytic,' it is because I have allowed myself to be influenced by purely subjective motives. Because of the part I have played in founding this therapy, I feel a personal obligation to devote myself to closer investigation of it and the development of its technique" (Freud, 1953a, p. 252). Freud readily acknowledged his debt to hypnosis in bringing him to an awareness of the dynamic forces operating in neurosis. He never discarded hypnosis as a potentially useful method, even though he had been accused of this. Long after he had evolved the technique of psychoanalysis, he spoke of the need for blending "the pure gold of analysis with the copper of other therapies." He avowed that in "the application of our therapy to numbers. . . . hypnotic influence might find a place in it again, as it has in the treatment of war neuroses" (Freud, 1953b, p. 402). Had Freud continued utilizing hypnosis as he evolved his theoretic and methodological systems, he undoubtedly would have extended the uses of hypnosis beyond its original designs.

But prejudice has deep roots, and in their attitudes toward hypnosis, psychoanalysts have tended to revive the most obstinate of Freud's old arguments. Particularly rampant has been feeling that hypnosis obliterates the ego during the period of its employment, and that the ego revolts against the element of the id that is forced on it with vitiation of therapeutic success (Freud, A., 1939, pp. 11–12). That this is not the case may easily be demonstrated by utilizing hypnosis properly as an adjunct in psychoanalysis. *Not only is hypnosis incapable of circumventing all resistance, or of eliminating the ego, but it may, with proper suggestions, be employed to increase resistance and repression, and more important, to help analyze and work through resistances that stubbornly refuse to yield with the traditional techniques.*

Unfortunately, some therapists constantly rediscover Breuer's and Freud's old applications of hypnosis. Whenever the patient presents a symptom, a frantic search into the past is initiated, with revivification of early experiences dynamically linked to the present complaint. In certain susceptible subjects, dramatic outpourings occur, which temporarily alleviate symptoms, but the initial impressive reports when published are rarely followed up with subsequent studies. One may suspect the authenticity of such "cures," which generally indicate the naïveté of the authors.

This does not mean that probing procedures may not be facilitated by the use of hypnosis. Hypnosis permits of entry into zones of unawareness that may help the psychoanalytic process in persons who are immobilized by anxiety or paralyzed by resistance. However, the therapeutic process is much more complex than a mere exposure of unconscious content.

Of particular importance is the relationship that develops between patient and therapist. No matter how well trained the therapist, or how eager the patient may be to get well, little progress may be expected unless the therapeutic climate is appropriate. The relationship is a two-way feedback system, anxieties between the participants flowing back and forth, influencing the patient's responses and the therapist's technique. The patient will bring into the hypnotic situation his customary reactions to authority as well as those that are related to the unique meanings that the trance state may have for him. These may be helpful or antagonistic to the therapeutic objective. For example, the immediate impact on the patient of a proper hypnotic induction is generally a feeling of confidence and faith in the helping authority. This is actually an exaggerated "placebo" effect, which may reduce inner tension, relax resistances, and enhance cooperation with the exploratory techniques utilized by the therapist. Sooner or later, however, less favorable responses ensue, such as unreasonable dependencies, fears of attack, intense sexual yearnings, and destructive impulses, which may interfere with the therapist's efforts. The proper handling of these reactions constitutes the prime work in the analysis, and is responsible for the principal reconstructive changes that develop in the personality structure itself. The reactions of the patient in the trance are only quantitatively different from those that occur in waking analysis. Being more intense, they call for skillful handling; hence sophistication in analytic method is a requirement in employing hypnosis in an analytic program. Fears that the expedited revival of memories, the accelerated release of repressed emotions, and the intensified transference reactions may produce psychotic reactions in weak ego structures need not deter the experienced therapist from employing hypnosis even in borderline cases or with schizophrenics. In my experience, no more untoward reactions occur with hypnosis in such cases than with ordinary psychoanalysis. Indeed, hypnosis may be employed in a supportive way at times when the coping powers of the ego appear overburdened. In this way one may regulate the tension level to a point where analytic productiveness continues almost without interruption, refuge being taken temporarily in supportive measures, where too intense anxiety has been released.

The chief deterrent to the employment of hypnosis in psychoanalysis is countertransference. Where the analyst is intrepid enough to experiment with hypnosis in spite of the traditional criticism of his more orthodox colleagues, he will soon discover whether his own personality can adjust itself to the altered relationship that develops with his hypnotized patients.

Hypnosis may release powerful strivings in the therapist of a sadistic nature. These strivings may interfere with the proper therapeutic relationship, destroying the therapist's perceptivity, objectivity, sensitivity, and empathy. His verbal behavior may influence the productions of the patient who will relay to the therapist personal reactions promoted by the therapist's neurotic designs. There are analytically oriented therapists who are capable of relating quite adequately and constructively to their patients in the waking state, but who, in response to the patient's trance behavior, completely lose their analytic acumen. Reports of murderous and sexually perverse behavior exhibited by patients during hypnosis may be products of the patient's personal problems, or they may be projections of the therapist's own unconscious. Where his patients constantly exhibit disturbed behavior in the trance, it is essential that the therapist examine himself courageously. It may be that he is unable to work with hypnosis because of its effect on him.

Because hypnosis imposes new variables on the psychoanalytic process, it is essential that eventually he experiment with hypnosis in various patients and under different circumstances. The special utilities of hypnosis for him will soon become apparent. No book can teach a therapist how to adapt hypnosis to his work; the therapist will undoubtedly develop modifications of hypnotic method, as well as unique modes of employing the various hypnoanalytic procedures.

Elsewhere I have described a number of technical innovations (Wolberg, 1945), which are interesting, but not universally applicable. Most therapists find free association and dream induction the only techniques of any value to them. Others are able to utilize automatic writing, the induction of experimental conflicts, mirror gazing, and hypnodramatics with facility in their more deeply hypnotized subjects. My personal inclinations have diverted me from dramatic maneuverings during hypnosis except in very rare instances where repression is extremely intense.

Conditions under which hypnosis may be advantageously employed in the course of psychoanalytic psychotherapy have been outlined in a paper the repetition of aspects of which may be pertinent to the present chapter (Wolberg, 1957).

1. *Where the patient lacks motivation for psychoanalytic therapy.* Many patients seek an immediate interruption of their problem through some sort of magical means. They are generally not motivated to accept the conditions of analytic therapy. Hypnotic techniques may be helpful in convincing a nonmotivated patient that he can derive something meaningful from treatment. Resentment toward the referring agencies, fear of revealing secret or disgusting aspects of one's life, distrust of the therapist, refusal to recognize an emotional basis for one's complaints, and other obstructions that contribute to the lack of incentive for therapy can usually be handled by a skilled therapist in the initial interviews without recourse to hypnosis. But occasionally even adroit management does not resolve the patient's resistance to the acceptance of help. Here hypnosis, if the patient permits the induction, may provide him with a positive experience that significantly alters his attitudes.

For example, a patient was referred to me by an internist with the symptom of urinary frequency, which had defied all medical intervention and which had become so urgent that it threatened the patient's livelihood. He resented being sent to a psychiatrist, and he announced that he could see no sense in starting what might prove to be a long and costly process when he was not fully convinced that he needed it. I accepted the patient's negative feelings, but I speculated that his tension might be responsible for at least some of his symptoms. I then offered to show him how to relax himself so that he might derive something beneficial out of the present session. He agreed, and I induced a light trance in the course of which he achieved a generalized state of relaxation. After the trance was terminated, the patient spontaneously announced that he had never felt more relaxed in his life, and he asked if he could have several more sessions of hypnosis. In the course of hypnorelaxation, I casually suggested to him that there might be emotional reasons why his bladder had become tense and upset, and I inquired whether he would be interested in finding out whether this was so. He agreed and I gave him a posthypnotic suggestion to remember any dreams that might occur in the next few days.

He responded with a series of dreams in which he saw himself as a mutilated and frightened person escaping from situations of danger and being blocked in his efforts toward freedom. His associations concerned themselves with the democratic rights of oppressed people throughout the world, and with the futility of expressing these rights in the face of cruel and uncompromising dictatorship that seemed to be the order of the day. When asked how this affected him personally, living as he was in a democratic regime, he sarcastically replied that one could be a prisoner even in a democracy. Since his father had died, he had been obliged to take over the responsibility of looking after his mother. Not only did she insist on his staying in her home, but she demanded an account of all of his movements. He realized that she was a sick, frightened woman, and therefore he believed that duty demanded that he devote himself to her comfort for the few of her remaining years. It was possible to utilize these revelations as a fulcrum to convert our sessions from palliative relaxation to active exploration of his needs and conflicts. As he recognized his repressed hostility, and his powerful demands for personal freedom, he realized that he was largely responsible for the trap that was virtually mutilating him. It was possible then for him to help his mother find new friends and make plans for an independent life. With resolution of his dependency and his deep resentments, his bladder symptoms disappeared completely. More significant was a growth in assertiveness and selfesteem that promoted a much more constructive adaptation to life.

2. *Where the patient refuses to begin therapy unless he is assured of immediate symptomatic relief.* Symptoms may be so upsetting to the patient that he refuses to engage in a therapeutic exploratory process unless there is first a reduction or removal of his symptoms. Where the patient's complaints are of a conversion nature and actually constitute an emergency, such as severe vomiting, hiccoughing, aphonia, or paralysis, the therapist may be able to restore function through hypnosuggestion, following which he may proceed with the usual analytic techniques. In less severe cases, the patient's insistence on relief is often a cover for demands that the therapist demonstrate himself as a sympathetic person concerned with the suffering of the patient. The latter resistance is sometimes resolvable by simple interpretation. Where interpretation fails, hypnosis with suggestions aimed at relaxation, tension control, and symptom reduction may create an atmosphere conducive to a therapeutic working relationship.

A patient with an obsessional neurosis complained that belching and hiccoughing following meals caused her great embarrassment and frequently forced her to skip meals. She was so preoccupied with whether or not her symptoms would overwhelm her that she could scarcely enjoy food when she did dine. Inanition forced her to seek medical help in the course of which she was referred to me. At the initial interview, she testily protested starting psychiatric treatments in view of a past unsuccessful psychotherapeutic experience. What she wanted, she insisted, was sufficient relief from physical distress to enable her to function at work and in her relationship with her family.

Recognizing her disappointment with her former therapist, I suggested hypnosis as a possible way of helping her stabilize herself. She agreed to give it a trial. The next five sessions were spent in teaching her how to relax and how to control her symptoms. Her response was dramatic, and her attitude toward me changed from suspicion and hostility to friendly cooperativeness. She readily entered into a therapeutic relationship, and, once therapy had started, recourse to further hypnosis was unnecessary.

3. *Where the patient has a negative transference or a defensive characterologic detachment that obstruct the development of a working relationship.* Mandatory for any kind of psychotherapy is a good working relationship between patient and therapist. This is particularly essential in reconstructive therapy where considerable anxiety may be released in the course of probing for conflicts, challenging habitual defenses, mobilizing transference, resolving resistance, and laboriously completing the working-through process. In some sick patients, such as borderline cases, the proper working relationship may never develop or may take many months to appear due to such factors as fear of closeness or intense hostility toward authority. Hypnorelaxation may resolve fears, reduce hostility, and cut down the time required for the development of rapport. The patient often feels, even after only one or two hypnotic sessions, an extraordinary warmth and closeness toward the therapist. His dreams may indicate that he projects into the hypnotic relationship hopes for an idealised parental image. A therapeutic relationship may crystallize under these circumstances so that it is possible thereafter to proceed with psychotherapy without hypnosis.

One of the most difficult patients I have ever treated was a paranoidal man who upbraided me severely during the first session for my delay in arranging a consultation. He was upset, he said, because he was involved in litigations against his business partners for presumably deceiving him about the prospects of their business when they first induced him to buy a share. Another legal case was pending against a neighbor who had built a garage which the patient considered an eyesore. But what he most desired from the consultation with me was to determine the feasibility of hypnotizing his wife to extract from her the truth of her exact whereabouts during an evening when he was out of town on business. He had carefully examined her tube of contraceptive jelly prior to his departure, and again upon his return. At first he could see no difference; but he compulsively returned to it, ruminating about whether he had made a mistake in his original estimate of his wife's innocence. For weeks he had been subjecting his wife to a cross-examination, carefully tabulating contradictory remarks until he had convinced himself she was concealing the truth about a rendevous with her lover. The poor woman, protesting her innocence from the start, had become so confused by his confrontations that she desperately tried to make up stories to cover tiny discrepancies in her minute-by-minute account of activities on the fatal evening. With acuity, the patient had seized on her flounderings to trap her into an admission of lying, which then convinced him all the more of her infidelity. A firm believer in the powers of hypnosis, he challenged her to submit herself to a hypnotic reliving of the evening in question.

Upon presenting this complaint and request, the patient inquired about the methods I employed of trance induction. I volunteered to demonstrate the hand-levitation technique to him, and he cautiously agreed to be a subject. In not too long a time he entered into a deep trance, during which I suggested that he would soon begin to feel more relaxed, secure, and self-confident. If he visualized a happy scene or had a dream about the most wonderful thing that could happen to a person, he would probably feel freedom from tension as well as a general state of pleasure that would make him happier than he had ever been in his life. After an interval of ten minutes he was brought out of the trance. Upon opening his eyes, he revealed with humor having had a dream of lying on a hammock while lovely slave girls circled around him with baskets of fruit. I suggested that he return in two days and bring his wife if she desired to accompany him.

During the second session, his wife tearfully proclaimed her innocence, whereupon the patient petulantly asked her to leave my office if she was going to "act like a baby." When she promised to control herself, he requested that she wait for him in the reception room. He then confided having felt so well since his first visit that he had decided that several more sessions of hypnosis would be valuable for his insomnia. His wife's problem could wait, he claimed, until he had "healed his own nerves." After this initiation into therapy, he received 90 sessions of psychotherapy with and without hypnosis, during which he worked out several important aspects of his personality problem. He terminated therapy when he had achieved a marked reduction of his symptoms, an easing of his tensions with his partners, and the re-establishing of a satisfactory relationship with his wife.

Another patient spent the first three months of his treatment with me in empty associational explorations. He protested that "nothing was happening" in regard to his symptoms or "anything else." He felt neither good nor bad about me; indeed, he avowed, I was "neither his friend nor his enemy." He resented any continued questioning about his feelings about me, insisting that I was being paid to do a job and that it was not necessary for him to get personally involved. There was constant negation of my interpretations. Inducing him to try hypnosis, he was able to achieve a medium trance. From the very first session, his enthusiasm and energy increased, resulting in a cessation of broken appointments. His activity and productivity improved remarkably and we were able to achieve a good therapeutic result. Without hypnosis, I am convinced his detachment could not have been penetrated.

4. *Where the patient is unable to verbalize freely.* Where communication is blocked, there can be no therapy; however, the usual unblocking techniques may fail to restore verbalization and hypnosis may sometimes be effective here. The manner of its employment will depend on the causes of the difficulty. The mere induction of a trance may uncork explosive emotions against which the patient has defended himself by not talking in the waking state. Cathartic release in the trance may restore normal verbalization. If the patient's silence is due to some resistance, it may be possible to explore and resolve this by encouraging the patient to talk during hypnosis. In hysterical aphonia these techniques may not suffice and direct suggestion may be indicated toward reduction or removal of the symptom. Speech disorders may respond to the lessening of tension in the trance, and there may then be a carryover into the waking state. Where the speech difficulty is caused by needs to prevent oneself from expressing painful sounds or ideas, an explosive outburst during hypnosis may not only release the capacity to talk freely, but also will open up pockets of conflict that may be beneficially explored.

A young woman, a severe stammerer, came to therapy because of incapacitating phobias. Once she had established contact with me, she verbalized satisfactorily, but as we began to examine her fantasies and dreams, she experienced so pronounced a relapse in her speech disturbance that she was practically inarticulate. She complained that although she could verbalize better with her friends than ever before, she could scarcely talk with me. Because progress had come to a halt, I suggested hypnosis as a way of helping her relax. She responded with anxiety, but agreed to try nevertheless. During the process of deepening the trance, she suddenly broke down and cried fitfully. Encouraged to discuss what she felt, she clenched her fists and shrieked, "No, no!" She then exploded with a coughing spell and could hardly catch her breath as she gasped over and over that she was choking. To my suggestion that she "bring it up," she broke into a torrent of foul language, pronouncing the word "shit" repeatedly, spitting with angry excitement. A few minutes of this frenzied behavior were followed by complaints of exhaustion. A restoration of normal speech followed, which persisted for the remainder of the session even after she had been aroused. This performance was repeated in subsequent sessions, but she responded with diminished fury. The analytic process gained great momentum, being concerned with a working through of the anal material, which she was resisting articulation by her speech symptom.

5. *Where the patient is unable to engage in free association.* Fears of penetrating conflictual areas may force the patient to maintain rigid control over his verbalizations. He is thus unable to permit his ideas to bounce around in an unrestrained way while exploring unguarded aspects of his psyche. Where free association is the preferred kind of communication and the patient is unable to engage in it due to resistance, hypnosis may not only cut through resistance immediately bringing the patient into contact with the repudiated material, but it may also help the patient to analyze his blocks.

A patient relapsed from free association to highly structured and rigidly directed content. Attempts made to analyze his loss of spontaneity brought little response. After a week of floundering, with repetition of insignificant items, hypnosis was induced and the patient was encouraged to talk in the trance about what really was bothering him. He responded by revealing how guilty he felt in the past weeks for having masturbated after one of our sessions in my office bathroom. He had not wanted to tell me about this incident because he knew it was not an adult act. He then associated having been caught as a child masturbating in his aunt's bathroom. Not only had he been reprimanded and warned by his aunt, but his parents had promptly been notified. The physician who had referred the patient to me had also frowned on his masturbatory practices, classifying masturbation as "idiot's delight which was never indulged in by a mature person." Reassured by my handling of these revelations, the patient was able to continue with his free associations in the waking state.

Hypnosis facilitates free association by making available to the individual subconscious zones ordinarily beyond the scope of conscious awareness. Often, as has been indicated, the mere induction of hypnosis releases emotionally laden verbalizations. Fantasy material is richer and less restrained by reality considerations.

Resistance to some unconscious material continues in force, nevertheless, and where anxiety invests repudiated elements, the threat of a breakthrough may awaken the patient or enforce on him a stubborn silence. Sometimes the injunction to think of a word or picture at the count of five and then to talk about what had flashed in his mind at the end of the count opens the door to productive areas.

Where the resistance is still too strong, certain techniques for the circumvention of resistance may be employed. For instance, the patient may be told that at the count of five a number will appear before him in any way he would like, written on a blackboard, spelled out in the sky by a skywriting airplane, or in any other convenient form. This number will be the key to a significant word, since it contains the number of letters in this word.

What is the value of free association during hypnosis? Are the usual resistances restored to the individual when he comes out of the trance? Actually the person is better able to cope with his anxiety after undergoing a release in hypnosis. He may dream more clearly about his conflicts and associate more easily in the waking state. It is as if a corrosive process has been started that continues to enable him to break up his resistances until he is able to deal with his inner fears without retreating from them. It may be helpful to ask the patient to associate freely to anxiety material on progressively lighter and lighter hypnotic levels, until he deals with the same material in the waking state. The working-through process may be helped in this way.

6. *Where the patient is unable to dream or to remember his dreams.* In cases where there is a dearth of dream material, it may be possible to train the patient to dream in the trance or to stimulate spontaneous dreaming by posthypnotic suggestions. Once this process is started, it may be possible for the patient to continue dreaming without hypnosis. Hypnosis can also be used to restore forgotten elements of dreams, to clarify secondary elaborations, and to help the patient explore by means of dreams his attitudes toward selected suggested topics.

Hypnotic dreams resemble in their symbolism and structure both daydreams and dreams in deep slumber. In light and medium hypnotic states the kinds of symbolization, condensation, displacement, distortion, and secondary elaboration are not too elaborate. They are similar to those in daydreams. In deep hypnosis, dreams take on the more profound elaborations of night dreams.

Dreams in hypnosis may be spontaneous, reflecting releases of unconscious attitudes, memories, emotions, and conflicts, along with the ideational manifestations indicative of the meaning to the patient of the immediate hypnotic experience, the relationship to the therapist, and transference distortions, which may be particularly vivid in the trance.

General topics or specific topics may be suggested as the dream content during hypnosis or posthypnotically. In patients who are unable to remember their dreams, hypnosis may be remarkably effective. In dreams that have been forgotten, hypnosis may activate the same dreams spontaneously.

When resistance develops during psychoanalytic therapy, hypnotic suggestions that the patient dream about his feelings may release dreams and affiliated associations revelatory of the operative resistance.

Dreams may help restore memories of an actual single experience, the symbolization of a group of significant experiences or a cover memory that conceals a more significant memory.

Whether to interfere with the memory of the hypnotic dream upon awakening will depend on the depth of hypnosis and the extent of anxiety investing the dream. In most cases the patient will remember his dream whether or not the therapist asks him to forget it. In somnambulistic states injunctions to forget the dream may be successful, although listening to free associations upon awakening usually reveals a filtering through of the content into awareness. Some therapists attempt to protect the patient by giving them free choice of remembering or forgetting his dream. One technique that I have found successful in somnambules is to ask them to forget their dreams, but, if they wish to remember and can absorb their significance, the dreams will suddenly come into awareness when I rap three times on the table near my armchair. This maneuver may have the effect of demonstrating to the patient how the unconscious operates.

An example of how valuable hypnotic dream induction may be is illustrated by a patient with severe rectal itching who came to psychotherapy after experiencing no relief with medicinal and injection treatments. Although a good working relationship was soon established, his productions were minimal; there were no dreams. In the trance it was suggested that he would have a dream that would explain his rectal itching. He responded with an anxiety dream of a man with a huge penis approaching him from the rear. He was told to forget the dream or recall any part of it that he wished to remember after he had awakened. Upon opening his eyes he complained of tension, but he recalled no dream. He admitted some relief in his rectal itching. The same evening he had a dream of riding a roller coaster with a male friend. In later dreams, he was able to countenance homosexual impulses and to discuss them during the session. Hypnosis served here to open up a repressed and repudiated pocket of guilt and conflict.

7. *Where the patient seems blocked in bringing up transference material.* In cases in which the development and exploration of transference is essential and where the patient cannot seem to experience transference, hypnosis may facilitate its appearance.

A female patient, who suffered from periodic attacks of nausea, vomiting, and gastrointestinal crises, was referred to me for hypnoanalysis after two years of traditional psychoanalysis had failed to relieve her symptoms. Because of the hysterical nature of her complaints and the intense repression, I felt that transference, which had not developed significantly during her previous therapy, might be important in activating processes of insight. After she had been trained to enter a medium trance, I suggested that she would dream of her feelings about me. She failed to produce a dream, but instead she developed a gustatory hallucination, a peculiar taste in her mouth that she described as "bittersweet." This taste persisted for several hours after her session. That evening she had a nightmarish dream in which a woman with the initials B.S. on her handbag took a small boy into the bathroom to help him to urinate and to wash up. She was unable to associate to the dream. A trance was induced in which she recalled forgotten elements of the dream, namely that the sexes of the two participants had changed as they had entered the bathroom; the adult had been a man, the child a girl. The next few sessions were spent discussing a "reaction" to me that the patient had developed that made her want to stop treatment. She was positive that I resented her, and she recounted several minor incidents which indicated to her that I had not had her best interests at heart. She was positive that I preferred a young man whose sessions had preceded hers because I once had kept him late overlapping her time.

In the trance that followed, she broke into hysterical crying, identifying me as her father, whose nickname was Bing Steward (initials B.S. in the dream), who had both fathered and mothered her (changed from a male to female in the dream), had preferred her brother to her (her reaction to the male patient whose hour preceded hers), and had always reminded her that he regretted that she had not been born a boy (her being brought into the bathroom as a boy in the dream possibly indicated that she had finally succeeded in achieving a masculine status). Thereafter she experienced strong sexual feelings toward me and demanded that I express a preference for her among all my other patients. It was possible then to analyze the origins of these feelings in her relations with her father and to see that her gastric symptoms were associated with fantasies of incorporation of a penis. Hypnosis here succeeded rapidly in precipitating transference.

8. *Where the patient has repressed certain traumatic mermoies, elucidation of which may help the therapeutic process.* In certain conditions, particularly hysteria and traumatic neurosis, painful past experiences and memories may be repressed, initiating, by their constantly threatening exposure, anxiety and defensive symptoms to bolster repression. Sometimes the elucidation in the trance of the repressed experience and the working through of the associated emotions helps to eliminate offensive symptoms.

A patient with periodic attacks of dyspnea resembling asthma was given a suggestion in hypnosis that he would regress to the first attack of shortness of breath. He described a scene in which he saw himself as a child of three standing in a snow suit on a back porch, slipping and falling into a huge snow drift and gasping for breath as the snow filled his nose and throat. With great panic, choking as he talked, he described his rescue by his mother and father. It was possible to validate this fantasy as a true experience by checking with his parents, who were amazed that the patient had remembered the exact details of the accident. They recalled that "asthmatic" attacks had followed the accident. It was established in therapy that interpersonal situations where the patient felt trapped caused him to respond with the symptom of choking for breath, which had developed originally under circumstances when he actually had been physically trapped. A complete eradication of the symptom was soon accomplished.

9. *Where the patient seems to "dry up" productively and is unable to produce any more significant material.* Periods of resistance, characterized by an almost complete cessation of activity, may develop during the course of therapy. The patient will spend many sessions in fruitless attempts at free association; he seems up against a barrier that he cannot surmount. Attitudes of disappointment and hopelessness contribute to his inertia until he resigns himself to making no further efforts. He may even decide to abandon therapy. Where such circumstances threaten, hypnosis may be tried to stimulate productivity. A variety of techniques may be utilized, including free association in the trance, dream and fantasy stimulations, mirror gazing, automatic writing, play therapy, dramatic acting, regression and revivification, and the production of experimental conflicts. The specific method employed is usually determined by the therapist's experience and preference as well as by the patient's aptitudes in working with one or another technique. The therapist may advantageously acquaint himself with different hypnoanalytic procedures to coordinate those with the specific needs and aptitudes of his patients (Wolberg, 1946).

10. *Where the patient is unable to deal with forces that block a translation of insight into action.* The mere development of insight is not enough to ensure correction of neurotic attitudes and patterns; it is essential that insight be employed toward constructive action. Unfortunately, many anxieties and resistances obstruct this aim and may bring therapy to an incomplete end. Hypnosis is sometimes useful here, and it may achieve this goal in a number of ways. First, one may attempt by various hypnoanalytic techniques to explore resistances to change, the patient associating in his fantasies, dreams, or dramatic acting out certain healthy courses of action. Second, posthypnotic suggestions may be made to the effect that the patient will want more and more to expose himself to the actions that are necessary and that are being resisted. Third, role-playing may be used, the patient projecting himself into various situations in the present or future and play acting his insights or fears. Fourth, in somnambulistic subjects, experimental conflicts may be set up to test the patient's readiness to execute necessary acts and to investigate his reactions to their positive completion.

A patient with a passive personality makeup had during therapy gained insight into the roots of his character problem and into the destructive consequences of his failures in self-assertion. He expressed a wish to change, but he was paralyzed in initiating change. The most he could do was to fantasize himself walking into his employer's office boldly asking for a promotion and being rewarded with a higher post and a handsome raise in salary. But he could not muster the courage actually to face his employer. In the trance, he voiced fears of being turned down. In hypnotic role-playing, he took the part of himself and his employer and discussed with vehemence pros and cons of his position. However, he could still not get himself to act. Because he was able to develop posthypnotic amnesia, I decided to try to set up an experimental conflict. I suggested that he fantasy asking for a promotion, forget having been given the suggestion, yet feel, upon emerging from the trance, as if he had actually gone through with the act. The first two attempts were followed by tension, headaches, and discouragement that indicated that the patient was not yet prepared to take the necessary step forward. With continued discussion and role-playing, a third experimental situation resulted in a feeling of elation and accomplishment. The next day the patient spontaneously approached the employer and his effort fortunately was rewarded with success. This was the beginning of a series of positive actions, which were coordinated with continued therapeutic improvements.

11. *Where the patient has problems in terminating therapy.* Difficulties in termination are sometimes encountered in patients who, having found freedom from symptoms in therapy, are fearful of giving up their gains and suffering a relapse. Patients with weak ego structures, especially borderline cases and extreme characterologic dependencies, may resist ending treatment with a confounding determination. Contrary to what may be anticipated, the adroit application of hypnosis may help some of these patients toward self-reliance by relaxing their tensions at points where they are obliged to exercise independent actions. The patient may also be taught to induce self-hypnosis for purposes of relaxation, and to investigate spontaneously, through dreams, fantasies and associations, problems as they arise in his daily adjustment demands. In this way responsibility is transferred to the patient, and he may become more and more capable of depending on himself. Intervals between visits with the therapist are gradually prolonged. At the start, the patient may, because of anxiety, resort to daily sessions of self-hypnosis; but as he develops more and more confidence in his ability to survive, he usually forgets to invoke regular self-hypnosis, finally employing it only when his tensions cause him to seek relief. Eventually, as his thrusts into the world are rewarded, he becomes capable of functioning without the need for any props. In very sick patients, however, regular relaxation exercises constitute an important adjustment measure and may be indulged indefinitely with beneficial effect.

The above outlined indications for hypnosis in psychoanalytic therapy are merely suggestions of how the trance may be employed as an adjunctive procedure. Again, it is wise to re-emphasize the fact that individual therapists may best utilize hypnosis after experimenting with the effects of the trance on their own ways of functioning. Because all psychotherapy is a blend of the personality structure of the therapist and his techniques, no two therapists will be able to operate identically. There are a number of books that may teach the induction of hypnosis and the implementation of various hypnoanalytic procedures. However, it is essential that each therapist do original research on how hypnosis influences, positively or negatively, his specific modes of working. There are some therapists who, for personality reasons or because of unresolvable prejudices, will be unable to use hypnosis with any measure of success. This does not invalidate hypnosis as a procedure; it merely proves that a particular therapist is unable to amalgamate hypnosis with his personality and technical training.

Even though a therapist may become skilled in executing hypnotic procedures, it does not necessarily follow that he will be able positively to influence all patients with hypnosis. Hypnosis will give him one more tool in dealing with resistance. However, resistance may be so strong that it may negate all of his hypnotherapeutic attempts as it has frustrated all of his conventional psychoanalytic efforts. Nor will hypnosis compensate for technical inefficiency nor for destructive countertransference. Didactic courses, personal psychoanalysis, and intensive supervision are mandatory for the fullest development of the therapist's potential.

A word about the presumed dangers of hypnosis. Any therapist who employs hypnosis will be convinced that these have been greatly exaggerated. Indeed, they are nonexistent if the therapist is well trained and has a good idea of what he is doing. Hypnotic rape fantasies, sexual acting out, and unfortunate dependencies resulting from hypnosis are no more common than in psychotherapy without hypnosis.

Hypnosis possesses values not only in exposing preconscious and unconscious material, but even more important, of precipitating in the process defensive-coping maneuvers. This allows for a controlled situation under which we may study basic responses. It is as if a biopsy is being performed in a live setting that can identify both conflict and defense in a direct and dramatic manner.

The patient will respond to the hypnotic induction and to the modes of trance utilization with his customary defenses, the resolution of which, like the resolution of transference in psychoanalysis, is helpful in producing constructive psychological change. Hypnotic intervention in a sense may be regarded as an instrument similar to that of the transference neurosis, which also will precipitate conflicts and defenses, the working through of which is the core of the psychoanalytic process.

It goes without saying that hypnosis must be intelligently used within the context of a comprehensive treatment plan and with due regard for its indications and limitations. Applied indiscriminately, hypnosis not only serves no therapeutic purpose, but also its failures tend to discredit it as a scientific procedure and to relegate it to a position of undeserved oblivion. Utilized at strategic points in analysis, hypnosis may facilitate the exploratory process, help resolve resistance, and expedite the working-through process. In this way it may add an important dimension to the technical skills of the psychotherapist.

REFERENCES

Freud, Anna (1939). *The Ego and the Mechanisms of Defense*. London: Hogarth.

Freud, S. (1953a). "Freud's psycho-analytic method." In *Collected Papers*, Vol. I. London: Hogarth.

——— (1953b). "Turnings in the ways of psycho-analytic therapy." In *Collected Papers*, Vol. II, London: Hogarth.

——— (1956). "Psychoanalysis." In *Collected Papers*. Vol. V, London: Hogarth.

Wolberg, L. R. (1964). *Hypnoanalysis*. New York: Grune & Stratton.

——— (1957). "Hypnosis in psychoanalytic psychotherapy." In Masserman, J. H. and Moreno, J. L. (eds.), *Progress in Psychotherapy*, New York: Grune & Stratton.

IV

THEORIES OF HYPNOSIS

10

The Metapsychology of Regression and Hypnosis[1]

MERTON M. GILL and MARGARET BRENMAN[2]

In this chapter we will attempt to formulate a metapsychological theory of hypnosis as a regression. If there existed an integrated account of the metapsychology of regression itself, we would have only to relate the special theory of hypnosis as a regression to the general theory of regression. There is no such general theory and we shall not attempt to offer one here, though in our presentation of the metapsychology of hypnosis we will occasionally remark on a more general metapsychological theory of regression.

A general theory of regression would have to distinguish between regression proper and regression in the service of the ego. Since we regard hypnosis as a regression in the service of the ego, we shall

[1] This chapter is reprinted by permission from Merton M. Gill, and Margaret Brenman, *Hypnosis and Related States* (New York, 1961). International Universities Press. This chapter is preceded by four chapters, which move from concrete description of the data and observational base through increasing levels of abstraction, culminating in this generalized and abstract statement of theory. The reader is encouraged to study the original work in its entirety for a more thorough understanding of the empirical referents of the theory and of the theoretical considerations that led to the position described in this chapter.

[2] We wish to thank Dr. George Klein for his thoughtful criticism of and helpful suggestions concerning this chapter.

occasionally have to distinguish the metapsychology of regression proper from regression in the service of the ego.

Our metapsychological treatment of hypnosis as a regression rests on the familiar concept of relative autonomy of the ego from the id, the much less familiar concept of relative autonomy of the ego from the environment (Rapaport, 1958), and the relationship between these two autonomies. Before we can specifically discuss hypnosis, therefore, we shall have to make a wide detour for a general treatment of autonomy.

THE CONCEPT OF AUTONOMY

The central advance in the theory of psychoanalytic psychology in the last two decades has been the concept of relative autonomy (Hartmann, Rapaport) which has begun to free psychoanalytic theory from its unduly tight motivational, i.e., instinct, lacing. Formerly all motivations, conflict solutions, and defenses were seen as not only arising from, but also as functionally still completely directed by, primitive id strivings. The concept of relative autonomy argues that though strivings, conflict solutions, and defenses may actually derive from primitive id impulses, these constellations develop a relative autonomy and can operate without direct dependence on id strivings. The derived constellations become structuralized in the personality, and indeed the structural point of view is the foundation of the concept of relative autonomy. Two kinds of autonomy have been distinguished. The one we have just sketched is usually referred to as secondary autonomy, the adjective "secondary" denoting that these relatively autonomous functions and structures were originally derived from id strivings. The concept of primarily autonomous structures designates those elements of the psychic apparatus which are not derived from id strivings. The main examples of such primarily autonomous functions are the ego apparatuses, such as memory, perception, and motility. It is now recognized that these ego apparatuses are primary givens in the same sense in which id impulses are, and enter into the development and functioning of the psychic apparatus as independent variables.[3]

We have been describing autonomy as autonomy of the ego from the id, but the concept of relative autonomy must be systematically broadened so that it includes other relative autonomies. One can conceptualize relative autonomy intrasystemically, for example, that a particular form of ego activity pursues a path relatively independent of other ego activities. One can conceive of intersystemic autonomy of the ego not only from the id but from the superego as well, and of

[3] The concept "conflict-free" cuts across primary and secondary autonomy, since both primarily and secondarily autonomous functions and structures may be conflict-free.

autonomy between one of the psychic institutions and external reality. To say this is only to state familiar considerations more systematically. A certain balance between any particular relative autonomy and its opposite—we might call it dependency or influenceability—is apparently necessary for adaptive functioning, but varies in degree for various relative autonomies. The relative autonomy of id[4] and superego from external reality is normally much greater than that of the ego from external reality. As between the ego and the external world, if the ego were blown aside by every gust of change, it could hardly be a stable functioning apparatus, but if it were rigidly resistant to influence by external changes, however powerful, its adaptability would likewise be seriously impaired.

Despite the fact that relative autonomy of ego from id[5] has received much more attention in the psychoanalytic literature than any other, we believe that relative autonomy of the ego from external environment is equally important.

Relative Autonomy from the Environment

Relative autonomy of the ego from the external environment has been systematically discussed only by Rapaport (1958). The concept was described—though not so named—by Hartmann in his *Ego Psychology and the Problem of Adaptation* (1939) in terms of "internalization" and the creation of an "inner world." This inner world he calls "one of the ego's regulating factors" (p. 57). He regards the human intellect as the high point in the evolution of this process of internalization, and then expresses what we will call relative autonomy from the environment in the following way: "Causal thinking (in relation to perception of space and time), the creation and use of means-end relations, and particularly the turning of thinking back upon the self, liberate the individual from being compelled to react to the immediate stimulus" (p. 60). Thus, just as the ego is not enslaved to the immediate drive demand, so is it not enslaved to the immediate external conditions.

The ego is therefore not simply a mediator between id and environment and the slave of both; it is a structure with energies at its disposal

[4] For a correction of this terminology, see p.176 of Gill and Brenman (1961).

[5] We follow Rapaport (1958) in speaking here and throughout this chapter of relative autonomy of the ego from the "id." The ego comprises various kinds of structures and functions. Certainly two major classes are means structures and motivations. Employing the concept "id" in the sense of the congeries of basic drives, we mean by relative autonomy of the ego that both means structures and motivations are relatively autonomous from basic drive. It is also true that means structures are relatively autonomous from derived motivations as well as from basic drive. But we retain the designation "relative autonomy from id" rather than "from motivation" because we wish to include the idea of relative autonomy of ego motivations from basic drive. There are clearly many complex questions here, but a further discussion would carry us away from our present purpose. We want to indicate that we are not unaware of the sloppiness in thinking which the concept "id" often seems to invite.

and as such it has autonomy from—that is to say, can pit forces against—the id on the one hand and the environment on the other.

Any fruitful application of the concept of relative autonomy from the environment would require an analysis and systematization of the concept "environment" (1959). Here we can touch on only a few main points. We must distinguish between the space-time environment and the social environment, that is, between the world of objects in the usual sense of physical objects and the world of objects in the psychoanalytic sense of other human beings. It seems clear that of the two, the space-time environment is the "simpler"; an environment that is differentiated in social terms is necessarily also differentiated in space-time terms, whereas an environment may be differentiated in space-time terms but not in social terms. We will later ask whether one can distinguish two kinds of relative autonomy from the environment, one from the space-time and the other from the social.

Besides this differentiation into two kinds of environment, we must also distinguish between the environment as an external system of forces and the environment as it is intrapsychically represented. Relative autonomy from the environment is possible only when external reality and its internal representation are more or less congruent. These two environments usually are congruent, since the normal human being does come to know reality more or less "as it really is," though in saying this, we do not intend to minimize the actively selective role the organism plays in perception. In extreme situations, however, this veridical framework can be overthrown in favor of a restructuring of reality in conformity with drive, and relative autonomy from the environment will be impossible, since the ego must have a fairly good representation of reality if it is to deal with it. When the ego does not have a good representation of reality, it may be said to be ignoring reality, a situation of reality obliviousness rather than autonomy. In fact it may be that such a state of obliviousness comes about as the result of a sharp decrement in relative autonomy. As the ego loses its ability to pit forces against the environment it may resort to a psychotic denial of reality.

An immediate response to a noxious stimulus does not necessarily mean loss of autonomy from the environment; such a response may be the most adaptive one. Immediate response would have the significance of loss of autonomy only if it could be demonstrated that the ego had lost its capacity to choose not to respond immediately.

There are limits set to relative autonomy from the environment by the nature of the environment. The organism can ignore external reality—whether it knows the reality or is oblivious to it—only up to a point, beyond which reality will make itself felt. A man on a hunger strike will eventually die. Psychotic denial of the death of a loved one does not undo the reality of the death. Needless to say, it is also not possible for the environment to force an individual to do what "it is not in him to do." If a child does not have the capacity to read, no amount of urging will make him read. And if a man cannot love or fight or surrender, exhortation will not make him do so.

A concept which is corollary to relative autonomy from the environment, and one which will bulk large in our future considerations, is automatization. This concept was first given a clear and detailed statement by Hartmann in *Ego Psychology and the Problem of Adaptation* (1939):

> The ego uses somatic apparatuses to execute actions. I will discuss first the motor apparatuses. In adults they are organized for certain achievements. In well-established achievements they function automatically: the integration of the somatic systems involved in the action is automatized, and so is the integration of the individual psychological acts involved in it. With increasing exercise of the action its intermediate steps disappear from consciousness. To explain this Kretschmer proposed a law of "formular abbreviation."[6]. . . Not only motor behavior, but perception and thinking, too, show *automatization.* Exercise automatizes methods of problem-solving just as much as it does walking, speaking, or writing . . . Observations of automatized functions, and of some other phenomena as well, warn us that the conception of a thoroughly flexible ego is an illusion; yet normally even well-established actions and methods of thinking are not completely rigid. Besides the adaptedness implicit in their use, automatized activities have a certain leeway (of varying latitude) for adaptation to the momentary situation. (pp. 87–88)

Later he makes the point which we wish to stress especially:

> Actually both flexibility and automatization are necessary to and characteristic of the ego; purposive achievements depend on some functions taking a flexible, others an automatized form, and still others combining these two forms in various proportions. The ego must also be able to encompass automatized functions in its adaptation processes. (p. 92)

Hartmann's automatizations are those of the apparatuses: perception, motility, and thinking. Automatized apparatuses execute impulses from all levels of the impulse hierarchy; in other words, automatizations are closely related to autonomy. The automatized apparatuses are not only the means by which relatively autonomous motivations are expressed; their formation is a safeguard for the maintenance of the relative autonomy. On the other hand, as Hartmann points out, both flexibility and automatization are necessary for normal functioning. Automatization can interfere with relative autonomy if it means the loss of the capacity to adapt to changing conditions. Thus de-automatization of automatized functions is a part of normal functioning. In what follows we shall show how de-automatization plays a role in the induction of hypnosis.

[6] We will return to this concept in our discussion of the disappearance of the phenomena of the induction stage.

The Decrease of Relative Autonomy

Though there are many important and interesting problems in how the ego develops its relative autonomy, our principal concern here is with hypnosis, and for hypnosis the issue is that of how relative autonomy can be decreased. In this section we will discuss this issue in general terms preparatory to our later, more specific discussion of hypnosis.

In order to discuss this problem we shall have to distinguish between relative autonomy, obliviousness, and loss of information or input.

The condition of loss of information or of input is not relative autonomy, even though under such circumstances the influence of id or environment on the ego may appear to diminish. We speak of relative autonomy only when the ego is getting information from id or environment, but is not enslaved in the sense that it does not have to respond immediately and in terms of the stimulus, whether from outside or inside.

As we mentioned earlier, relative autonomy must also be distinguished from obliviousness. Relative autonomy from the environment does not mean that the environment is disregarded, but that the environment does not determine in detail the course of events regarding action upon, or perception of, the environment. The normally functioning ego, as described above, must be able to abandon an automatization if environmental circumstances make a more specific and flexible adjustment desirable. Analogously, relative autonomy from the id does not mean obliviousness to motivational urges, but the capacity to assess them and, if necessary, to abandon habitual inhibition or facilitation of discharge. If the ego is oblivious to the id or environmental situation, even though the input is "available," we do not speak of relative autonomy.

Interpersonal perception—that is, the evaluation and understanding of the meaning of interpersonal actions—is probably much more subject to falsification by drive than is the impersonal space-time environment. The primarily autonomous apparatuses of the ego are concerned in the perception of the latter, but there is no similar primarily autonomous apparatus for the former. (This is not to deny that the newborn has an apparatus for socialization [Erikson's concept of mutuality]; but this apparatus is not autonomous from drive in the sense in which are the apparatuses of memory, perception, motility, and the thresholds.)

We make these distinctions because we feel that theoretical discussion would be much obscured if loss of input or obliviousness to id or environment were called increased autonomy. It is true that disregard of id or environment by the ego may appear to be an increase in autonomy, but it is not an increase of *relative* autonomy; it is rather a movement toward total isolation, quite a different thing. In fact, as we shall soon show, when id or environment is disregarded, the id dominates the ego if the environment is disregarded, while the ego comes to be dominated by the environment if the id is disregarded. To forestall confusion, then, we shall speak of increased autonomy only when we mean increased autonomy in an ego which both has access to input and is not oblivious to this input.

A further distinction must be made between decrease of autonomy from id or environment and domination of ego by id or environment. That agency from which autonomy is decreased is not necessarily the agency which dominates; and again autonomy may be decreased from both id and environment, leaving one still to ask which of the two comes to dominate the ego. We shall exemplify various possibilities in discussing the relationship between the two autonomies.

It will be noted that we speak only of the ego as having autonomy. We do not say of either id or environment that it becomes autonomous when it dominates the ego. Autonomy is the name for that relative independence which the growing and maturing ego attains from the id on the one hand and the environment on the other. It is not properly applicable to the id even though the id, like the ego, is an intrapsychic system, because the independence of the id can be only an early normal stage of development or the result of a regression, and not the result of growth and maturation. Nor is it properly applicable to the environment, not only because the environment is an extraorganismic set of forces, but also because domination by the environment can also come about only either as an early normal stage of development or as the result of a regression, and not as a result of the individual's progressive growth and maturation.

It will be useful to have general terms to describe the environmental or motivational situation, since it may or may not be exerting strong pressure on the ego. We will refer to the internal situation as "urge" and to the environmental situation by Murray's term "press" (1938).

There are two major ways in which a decrease of relative autonomy may be brought about. These are limitation of input and strong press or urge.

Limitation of input is that situation in which the influx of stimuli to the ego from id or environment is decreased. The decrease may be absolute, as for example in the experiments by Lilly (1956) in which the subject is immersed in water, or those by Bexton *et al.* (1954), in which touch, sound, and hearing are significantly reduced. The decrease may be a result of monotony, because the mechanism of sensory adaptation makes monotony equivalent to diminution. This may be called "blocking the channels of intake"; on a level higher than that of purely sensory input, blocking the channels is exemplified by stimuli which give little information. The decreased input may result from decreased motor activity toward the environment, since this cuts down the feedback from activity and thus reduces information or input.

Diminished input from the id is possible only when internal barriers to the reception of stimuli from within are erected, in short, when there exists some form of repression, or more generally, countercathexis. This is likely to be a more or less static condition and is less subject to experimental manipulation than is input from the environment.

We will defer our description of what happens when there is diminution of input until we come to the relationship of the two autonomies, because a change in autonomy from either id or environment is often so closely followed by a change in the other.

The other general way in which autonomy may be diminished is by urge or press becoming strong, since it becomes more difficult for the ego to take distance from and not be compelled to make an immediate response to such a force. A strong social press may range all the way from "keeping up with the Joneses" to brain-washing. A strong nonsocial press may be pressures to attend carefully and for a prolonged period to a space-time stimulus, for instance, driving along a superhighway, flying a plane in close formation, or attending vigilantly to a radar screen while watching for an incoming signal.

A relatively lesser diminution of stimuli from the nonsocial environment can coincide with a relatively greater diminution of social stimuli, as, for example, in solitary confinement.

A strong urge means an increased impulse, however brought about, whether by a process of maturation, as for example puberty, or as a result of the presentation of a particular external object.

Now that we have proposed that diminished input and increased press or urge are two conditions which lead to decreased autonomy, we further suggest that de-automatization is a condition which opens the way for a change in relative autonomy, either an increase or a decrease. De-automatization is an undoing of the automatizations of apparatuses —both means and goal structures—directed toward the environment. De-automatization is, as it were, a shake-up which can be followed by an advance or a retreat in the level of organization.

De-automatization of the apparatuses requires interference with their functioning but is probably not brought about directly by diminished input or increased urge or press. Some manipulation of the attention directed toward the functioning of an apparatus is necessary if it is to be de-automatized, and while such a manipulation of attention may result from diminished input or increased urge or press, these two conditions need not lead to changes in the distribution of attention; and, on the other hand, manipulations of attention with resulting de-automatization may be brought about by means other than these two conditions.

If de-automatization has been brought about as a secondary result of diminished input or increased press or urge and these latter two conditions persist, there will be a decrease of relative autonomy, but if these two conditions either were not originally present or do not persist, an increase in relative autonomy may result, though it need not. For example, strong environmental pressure may forcibly direct attention to a habitual value pattern which then becomes de-automatized. If the pressure continues there may result the substitution of a new value pattern, perhaps even less relatively autonomous than was the old. But if the pressure relaxes, there may result a generally broadened perspective on the issue involved, with an increase in relative autonomy.

THE RELATIONSHIP BETWEEN THE TWO AUTONOMIES

We must ask whether the autonomies of the ego from the id and from the environment are symmetrical, and whether decrease in one is necessarily followed by decrease in the other.

There are reasons to believe that the relationship is not symmetrical, despite the fact that organism and environment must not be viewed as sharply separable, but rather as an organism-environmental matrix. The assumption of asymmetry follows from consideration of the well-established psychoanalytic proposition which differentiates drive from external stimulus: while drive is constant and inescapable, external stimulus is discontinuous and can be avoided by flight (Freud, 1915a). Both autonomies are relative, but the range of relative autonomy from the id is generally more circumscribed than the range of relative autonomy from the environment. Related to this asymmetry is the relative inflexibility of the aim of an instinct as compared with its object.

We must also ask whether decreases of relative autonomy from id and environment always take place together: does one inevitably lead to the other or may they vary independently? The asymmetry of which we have spoken seems to provide a partial answer. The proposition suggests itself that since relative autonomy from the id is the more vulnerable and must be decreased first, the environment will, under circumstances of decrease of autonomy from both sufficient to "dethrone" the ego, be recast in the image of the id forces which gained ascendancy first. But to attribute this leading role to the id without reservation would be to fall into the old fallacy of underestimating external reality. The autonomy of the ego relative to id and external environment is dependent not only on the strength of the ego, not only on the strength of the instincts, but on the "strength" of the environment too. Certain environmental conditions are far more insistent than others. Relative autonomy from the environment is a function of the environment as well as of the ego.

A complexity thus appears in the relationship of the two relative autonomies. In a situation of overwhelming environmental "press," relative autonomy from the environment may be decreased even though there has been no decrease of autonomy from the id. But if the decrease from the environment goes so far that the environment comes to dominate the ego, there will necessarily be a decrease of relative autonomy from the id too, and the motivational pattern will be structured according to the environmental situation (keeping up with the Joneses), and not the environmental pattern according to the motivational press ("wishful thinking").

We will now review what happens when loss of information occurs alone and when it occurs in combination with strong press or urge. If information from the outside world is lost and there is no external press, the result is a restructuring of the external world by idiosyncratic id motivations. The sensory deprivation experiments reported by Bexton *et al.* are an excellent demonstration of this situation. When the loss of information is from within and there is no strong urge, the result will be behavior determined by the motivation arising from the countercathexis which led to the loss of information from within. This motivation may be primarily derived either from drive or from environmental conditions. The loss of information from outside with a strong environmental press is likely to lead to conformity with this press—a conformity which finally structures the motivational pattern. The famous confessions of the Russian trials seem to be an example of such a situation (Bonnard, 1954; Koestler, 1941; Moloney, 1955). If there is loss of information from inside, but a strong internal urge, the result may be a condition such as the first stage of fugue, with the environment restructured according to the dominant motivational urge. (It will be noted that loss of information of both environment and the internal state means a loss of all information except as there exists press from outside or imperious urge from inside. In such circumstances it is no longer possible to compare various environmental configurations with one another, or to weigh and balance various and even conflicting motivations.)

Let us review these last considerations in the light of the question of the relationship of the two autonomies. We suggested that when with the loss of autonomy the id comes to dominate the ego, whether because of loss of information from the outside or because of strong urge, the environment is restructured by motivation; when the environment comes to dominate the ego, whether because of loss of information from within or because of strong press, the motivations are restructured by the environment. But a restructuring of either environment or motivation by the other means that there is a decrease of autonomy from the one which is restructured too. In other words, when the ego is dominated by the id, autonomy is also decreased from the environment, and when the ego is dominated by the environment, autonomy is also decreased from the id. In both cases then, the loss of one relative autonomy leads to the decrease of the other. The schizophrenic, for example, who is essentially dominated by the id, may show such a phenomenon as command automatism while the thoroughly brain-washed prisoner who is essentially dominated by the environment may nevertheless show general evidences of an increased emotional lability, albeit in the service of the goals instilled from without. If there is loss of input but no press or urge, the dominating agency becomes the one from which input is coming. But when there is great press or urge, the dominating agency is likely to be the one from which the press or urge comes.

It should also be noted that when as a result of great urge or press either id or environment restructures the other, this also leads to a relative obliviousness to the other, with of course a resulting blocking off of input or information from the other. Furthermore, a great press or urge also leads to a loss of any other input from the same side from which it comes, because the press or urge utilizes all available attention. In other words, great urge or press leads to diminished input from both id and environment except for the urge or press itself.

To summarize: in the normal functioning of the ego, the environmental input is the ultimate safeguard of autonomy from the id, while the id input is the ultimate safeguard of autonomy from the environment.

We must make clear, however, that neither the loss of environmental information nor great environmental press will necessarily lead to decreased autonomy from the environment. Though Bexton *et al.* say that "the maintenance of normal intelligent adaptive behavior probably requires a continually varied sensory input" (Bexton *et al.*, 1954), this is true only within limits. To disregard these limits is to value too cheaply the structure of the ego. Only some of their subjects showed regressive phenomena; those who resisted the effects of loss of information from the environment did not show evidences of decreased autonomy from the id. If we believe that constant input is necessary to maintain ego-functioning, then we are viewing the ego merely as a mediator between id and environment instead of as a cohesive structure in its own right, and approach the "seething cauldron" concept (Rapaport, 1951a) of psychic functioning. But if we take seriously the ego as a structure, with genuine relative autonomy, we will recognize that it is not so immediately at the mercy of the environment (or the id).

But the examples we have so far offered of what happens when loss of information occurs alone or when it occurs in combination with strong press or urge could all be covered by the hypothesis that relative autonomy from the id and from the environment are parallel and reciprocal phenomena. We have yet to demonstrate the asymmetry which it seemed to us we would expect on theoretical grounds.

We believe that two phenomena demonstrate that this asymmetry exists and has very real consequences.

The first is that when there is a loss of input from the environment, evidences of decreased autonomy from the id appear much more quickly than do evidences of decreased autonomy from the environment when there is a loss of input from the id. In the experiments of Bexton *et al.* (1954), for example, evidences of decreased autonomy from the id appear quickly. But in repression, unless there is some strong external press, the environment is likely to be seen in id terms rather than impulse in environmental terms. Only in obsessive-compulsive extremes, when action initiated from within is paralyzed, may the environment appear to dominate behavior.

Related to this evidence of asymmetry is another. There can be domination by the id with obliviousness to the environment to the point of hallucination (restructuring of the environment in id terms); but asymmetrically, domination by the environment will not be with obliviousness to the id, but will harmonize with id demands. (When we come to the transference aspect of hypnosis we will be able to show how hypnosis exemplifies this proposition.) In other words, if the ego surrenders to the id, its mode of surrender will be much less dictated by the nature of the environment than will its mode of surrender be dictated by the nature of the id if it surrenders to the environment.

Our last major consideration on the relationship between the two autonomies—one which is intimately related to the asymmetry of id and environment—is that an interpersonal relationship constitutes an environmental force which at the same time is an expression of an id urge. In fact, it is just because of this that surrender to the environment can come to harmonize with an id demand. Our point here is a corollary of the whole series of concepts expressed in various forms by both Hartmann and Erikson as the preadaptedness of drive to environment by way of the object of the drive. These concepts have recently been analyzed and compared by Rapaport (1959).[7]

[7] Before leaving the problem of the relationship between the two autonomies, we would like to make a brief comment on the question of choice and freedom. We are referring to choice as a concept, not as a subjective belief. People acting under extreme compulsion may believe they are freely choosing, and people acting freely may insist they are compelled. As far as the philosophical doctrine of free will is concerned, we simply affirm the postulate of psychic determinism, rule out any *deus ex machina*, and define choice as a psychological concept. Choice is possible when the ego is relatively autonomous, both from id and environment. The ego can select both from a number of potential motivational urges and from a number of environmental possibilities. A shift in either id demand or environmental press is rapidly and flexibly responded to. The ego takes both the potential motivational urges and the existing environmental configurations into account in determining on a particular behavior. When a motivational urge becomes so strong that the ego has to seek its discharge no matter how unpropitious the environmental circumstances, or when an environmental press becomes so demanding that the ego has to conform to it no matter how undesirable it is from the point of view of the motivational patterns, choice is lost. The fluid interplay in which both organismic demands and environmental press are rapidly and flexibly attuned to each other with feedback on each other yields the familiar synthesis referred to as the organismic-environmental matrix. The function of choosing itself becomes an apparatus which we call the will. This apparatus shows differing degrees and types of development from person to person (Wheelis, 1956). As we will note later, a structure or apparatus itself gives rise to motivations and serves the function of a saving of energy.

REGRESSION AND THE LOSS OF AUTONOMY

We now turn to the metapsychology of regression proper and regression in the service of the ego. Our considerations in the previous section seem to us to be a basis for renaming the phenomenon of regression; we would like to call it loss of autonomy, since it seems to us that this is just what regression is, and because the new name would enable us to distinguish more readily between decreased autonomy from the id and decreased autonomy from the environment.[8]

We believe that instances of regression proper can be divided into those in which the loss of autonomy is followed by domination by the id and those in which it is followed by domination by the environment. Schizophrenia is an example of domination by the id, while the results of brain-washing and the confessions at the Russian trials are examples of domination by the environment.

We believe that regression in the service of the ego can be divided into decrease of autonomy from the id and from the environment. Examples of decrease of autonomy from the id are dream, artistic creativity, scientific creativity in which the investigator is led by a "hunch," and humor; examples of decrease of autonomy from the environment are scientific creativity in which the investigator is led by the "material," and the established hypnotic state (we hope later to show that in the induction phase of hypnosis the regression in the service of the ego has not yet been established).

We suggested earlier that the so-called "highway hypnosis" (Campbell, 1955), or effects seen in observers intently watching a radar screen on which for long periods of time nothing happens but where attention must remain vigilant, are examples of a de-differentiated external environment with a strong press of an impersonal type resulting in a loss of autonomy with domination of the ego by the external impersonal press. It will, of course, have to be demonstrated that these are not simply drowsy states.

We have called a regression in the service of the ego a decrease of autonomy. Yet from another point of view the capacity for regression in the service of the ego may clearly be seen as a regressive adaptation which increases the relative autonomy of the ego. As we will later show, this paradox is resolved by recognizing that the loss of autonomy is by a subsystem of the ego whereas the increase of autonomy is by the overall ego.

THE METAPSYCHOLOGY OF HYPNOTIC INDUCTION

A discussion of the metapsychology of the loss of autonomy must first deal with the dynamics of the initiation of such loss. We must distin-

[8] Regressed states then have varying degrees of autonomy. States of fixation or arrest could be thought of as conditions of incompletely developed or retarded autonomy.

guish sharply the dynamics involved in the movement toward regression from the dynamics of a regressed state itself.

A regressive movement can be initiated in any one of a number of ways. We shall not discuss the general ways in which regression can be initiated except to state that we see them as divided into three main classes: (1) an increase in strength of instinctual impulse; (2) a change in the apparatuses available to the ego for adaptive functioning; and (3) an alteration in the external situation.

It will be recalled that earlier we listed the two major ways in which a decrease of relative autonomy could be initiated as loss of input and strong press or urge. Loss of external input and strong press would be classified under "an alteration in the external situation;" strong urge would fall into the class of "an increase in strength of instinctual impulse;" a change in intake from either id or environment could result from "a change in the apparatuses available to the ego for adaptive functioning." The most general classification, then, would be into changes in id, ego, or environment. The first move in the initiation of hypnotic induction is a change in the environment—the behavior of the hypnotist—but changes in id and ego soon follow.

We will now draw together the implications of the preceding general discussions for a theory of the induction phase of hypnosis. We must emphasize that here we are dealing only with the initiation of regression by attack on the ego apparatuses. We will later present our view of how it is initiated by way of the interpersonal relationship.

We believe that the manipulations of the hypnotist can all be looked upon as an attempt to disrupt the ego's control of its apparatuses. This seems reasonably clear as regards the perceptual and motor apparatuses, but not so clear concerning the various apparatuses relating to thought.[9]

We earlier suggested that de-automatization is brought about by manipulations of attention, whether directly or as a secondary result of diminished input or increased press or urge. We believe that during induction the hypnotist, by directing the subject's conscious attention to automatized apparatuses, attempts to de-automatize them. The act of de-automatization expends attention energy formerly available for other uses, and even fresh accessions of attention may be necessary, for with de-automatization an act becomes difficult to perform. In other words, the energy which, as Hartmann has pointed out, is saved by automatization is now once again required as a result of the de-automatization. When attention is absorbed in this way, it is no longer

[9] The apparatuses are usually listed as motor, sensory, and memory, with Rapaport adding thresholds, but these are only the primarily autonomous apparatuses. In speaking of "apparatuses relating to thought" we are considering those which are secondarily autonomous too.

available for sensory or motor exploration of the outside world. A secondary effect of de-automatization, then, will be diminished input. Since we have already seen that diminished input can secondarily lead to de-automatization, we now see that these two conditions reciprocally act to augment each other.

It has been suggested (Rapaport, 1955) that the energy saved through automatization is available for the synthetic function of the ego, since this energy becomes available as hypercathexis, and it is by means of such hypercathexis that the synthetic function takes place. To the extent that the "saved" energy is lost again as a result of de-automatization, the synthetic function will suffer, the result will be a more primitive variety of synthetic function (since some variety of synthetic function is always present), and thus the way has been paved for the re-establishment of a more regressed state of the psyche.

In dissociation, a formerly integrated movement, perceptual act, or mental activity is split up into its component parts, or made to function as an independent unit instead of as a tool in the service of the integrated ego. We have already described one of the hypnotist's activities as directed toward a dissociation in which parts of the body develop an "independent" functioning. It seems to us that the aspect of dissociation which is a decomposition is to be subsumed under de-automatization (and as we shall later show, function as an independent unit results from the establishment of a new automatization). The advantage of the concept of de-automatization is that it carries the rich connotations of the concepts of primary and secondary autonomy (the ontogenesis of automatization).[10] We are suggesting that dissociation, de-automatization, and interference with the synthetic function of the ego are all different ways of conceptualizing the same phenomenon.

We must introduce here the concept of consciousness as an apparatus of the ego. We mean of course consciousness as it operates in the secondary process where it is brought about by attention cathexis and not as in the primary process in which drive cathexis is responsible for the quality of consciousness (Rapaport, 1951b). The concept is not new; it is Freud's, and has been spelled out and clarified by Rapaport (1951c, and unpublished ms.). Freud called consciousness a "superordinate sense organ," which makes it quite clear that he considered it an ego apparatus. The term "consciousness" is used both for the apparatus and for the result of the functioning of this apparatus as it employs attention cathexes. Consciousness seems to be equivalent to attention, since "attention" may likewise be used to designate an

[10] We may incidentally note that here is perhaps the germ of truth in Janet's (1920) conception of dissociation being due to an "enfeeblement" of psychic energy, since there is a relation between dissociation and interference with the synthetic function.

apparatus or the result of the functioning of that apparatus. The conception of attention or consciousness as an apparatus enables us to state that in the induction of hypnosis the ego's control of its apparatuses of motility, perception, and attention is attacked.

To turn now to the other two major factors which can precipitate a decrease of autonomy—loss of information and strong press or urge.

In the induction of hypnosis the hypnotist deprives the subject of information about the environment, and exerts a strong pressure on the subject to behave in the manner in which he directs. We might expect to see a decrease of autonomy from the environment during induction, but what we actually see seem to be derivatives of the id. The spontaneous outbursts of affect, the accessibility of motility to previously repressed urges, the appearance of ideational representations of such urges in consciousness, the evidence of archaic ego states in the alterations of body image and sensation, and the depersonalization phenomena—fragmentary though these manifestations are—appear to be previously repressed material now released, indicative of a weakening of the relative autonomy of the ego from the id. These phenomena are evidences that the synthetic function of the ego is interfered with. We see in these phenomena one of the evidences of the asymmetry of the relative autonomies. Even in this process which will go on to domination by the environment, there first or more obviously appear evidences of decrease of autonomy from the id.

In hypnotic induction, the hypnotist attempts to bring about a dedifferentiation of the space-time environment and exerts a strong environmental press. Since the same kind of phenomena appear as do in the experiments of Bexton *et al.* (1954), we can assume that the environmental press is not responsible. But the press *is* responsible for the fact that the situation moves on to what will become the established hypnotic state with the loss of autonomy resulting in domination by the environment. The phenomena during the induction period are not only those of decreased autonomy from the id, but also those of beginning suggestibility and compliance to the hypnotist which will become more fully developed in the established hypnotic state.

In this induction period, the subject is in a more favorable position than the subjects of Bexton *et al.*, who were perforce deprived of various stimuli. The potential hypnotic subject need only refuse to obey the hypnotist. He can walk around and look around if he decides to do so—and many subjects do just that, however much they may protest their wish to be hypnotized. In short, if hypnosis is to occur, the ego must accede, meaning that it must select from among its potential motivational patterns one which will conform to the external press. Here we encounter the second consideration we advanced in our discussion of the asymmetry of the two autonomies: with domination by the environment there cannot be obliviousness to the id, but a harmonizing motivational pattern must be found. For hypnosis to be possible, a particular kind of motivational pattern must be accessible to the ego in the particular individual.

As we see it, then, the sequence of events is this: when the hypnotist begins his manipulations, several forces are set in motion. There is a strong environmental press; the search for an appropriate motivational pattern begins, and the usual functioning of the autonomous apparatuses begins to be interfered with. Now the usual synthesis of ego-functioning is not in command, nor has the new synthesis, the established hypnotic state, as yet been formed. This interim period—the induction period—is characterized by evidences of a fragmentation of the ego synthesis, or what we might call fragmentary ego syntheses. We have already discussed the similarity of the phenomena during the induction phase to those produced by Bexton *et al.*, in whose experiments there was an absence of information from the outside, no strong environmental press, and no strong internal drive. Since these phenomena indicate decreased autonomy from the id, one would have to conclude that, though during induction the external press is great, it has been only partially accepted by the ego, and indeed this still partial acceptance can be considered indicative of the induction phase rather than of the established hypnotic state.

The fact that the external press has been accepted even though only partially is what would make it oversimple to view the induction phase as simply a loss of autonomy with domination by the id. As we have indicated, the ego must accede, and searches for a motivational pattern which will correspond to the environmental press. But the established state itself we do regard as a loss of autonomy with domination of the ego by the social environment—specifically by the hypnotist.

We have already discussed the stress which we lay on an important phenomenal difference between the induction phase and the established state: the fact that in the established state the subject is potentially capable to varying degrees of apparently regaining control of the use of his apparatuses. As the apparatuses come under the control of the ego in the established state there takes place a reversal of whatever de-automatization has occurred in the induction phase, that is, a re-automatization.

But now the question becomes: under the control of what kind of ego? We introduce here one of our central proposals for a theory of hypnosis: that in hypnosis a subsystem is set up within the ego. This subsystem is a regressed system which is in the service of the overall ego; it has control of some or all of the apparatuses, and to the extent that it has control, those apparatuses which were de-automatized are now re-automatized. It is this subsystem alone which is under the control of the hypnotist, and it is by virtue of this control that the hypnotist can control and direct the apparatuses. The overall ego also maintains a relationship with the hypnotist, the nonhypnotic, reality-oriented relationship. The overall ego relinquishes control of the subsystem to the hypnotist only temporarily and tentatively. It is the fact that this relinquishment of control is only provisional to which we pointed when we earlier described evidences of persisting control of the apparatuses by the ego during the hypnotic state; the overall ego can yield control of the subsystem to the hypnotist but can at any time take it back. We will attempt a more detailed analysis of this subsytem when we discuss the metapsychology of the hypnotic state.

We do not believe that a regression in the service of the ego has already been established in the induction phase. The organization of the subsystem within the ego is an achievement of the synthetic function of the ego; it is an organized structure. During induction, this structure has not yet been built. And now we can also state more concisely the difference between a regression proper and a regression in the service of the ego, though we again emphasize that this difference is a matter of degree and is a function not only of the manifest phenomena but also of the kind of ego in which the phenomena are taking place. In a regression proper it is the overall ego which has changed, has suffered a degree of decreased autonomy from id and environment. In a regression in the service of the ego a subsystem within the ego has been formed and it is this subsystem which shows in varying degrees diminished autonomy from the id and from the environment.[11]

It is this distinction between the two kinds of regression which enables us to describe the differences between certain phenomena characteristic of each, superficially similar but vastly different in their actual dynamics. There are many phenomena in the hypnotic state which look like id manifestations—the capacity for hallucinations, the access to repressed material, for example—yet are very different from what is seen in a regression proper, a schizophrenia, for example. Admitting that we run the risk of taking a too reified and manikinlike view of the subsystem, we would say that these id-like phenomena are produced by way of the subsystem rather than the system, that it is the subsystem which can hallucinate, which can recall previously repressed traumatic material. This would be a formulation analogous to the one we made about the apparatuses; in the established state the subsystem controls both the apparatuses and the gateway to the repressed to varying degrees. That the access to the repressed is integrated with the subsytem but not with the overall system is seen in the phenomenon of

[11] To say that the induction phase is a regression proper and the established state is a regression in the service of the ego would make too sharp a cleavage between induction phase and established state.

posthypnotic amnesia—admittedly relatively infrequent without suggestion, though more common when hypnosis is used in therapy: that the repressed material gained in the hypnotic state is ordinarily not accessible to the ego after the hypnotic state is terminated.

We suggest instead the following formulation: we spoke of the established state as a loss of autonomy with domination of the ego by the environment. We have earlier suggested that when the ego is dominated by either id or environment there is also a diminution of autonomy from the other. The phenomena we have been describing illustrate this principle. With the subsystem's domination by the environment there also occurs a decrease of autonomy from the id, shown by the increased access which the subsystem has to the id.

Throughout our discussion we have described the induction phase as brief and unstable and the established state as more enduring and stable. This difference between instability and stability is related to the fact that in the induction phase there is a regressive movement which necessitates interference with the ego apparatuses, while in the established state there may be a return of control of the apparatuses to a new and different regulation by a subsystem of the ego. We may ask whether this is a difference which can be more widely generalized. Are the unstable states those which do not, the stable those which do have access to the apparatuses? Do we have other criteria to determine whether a state is unstable or stable? Or is the distinction rather that the relationship to the apparatuses must be decisively settled for a state to be stable, whether it is so settled that these are or are not accessible to the ego? Is the dream state a relatively stable one then, which does not have access to the motor or perceptual apparatuses? Or is the sleep state the one we should speak of as stable and is the dream state actually unstable?

Whatever the answers to these questions, there can be no doubt that transitional states of upheaval with disturbance of accessibility to the apparatuses differ in important ways from the stable states with accessibility to the apparatuses. In the chaos of an acute schizophrenia, for example, the disturbance may be so severe that even some of the most ancient, firmly structuralized anticipations and tools of syntax are no longer freely at the disposal of the ego. After the process "settles," even if the disease remains as malignant as before, these structures once again become re-automatized if they have been de-automatized, and come under the dominion of the ego, a reconstituted ego in which the synthetic function has again stabilized, albeit at a new and lower level. It is also well known that a sign of chronicity in schizophrenia is the apparently unaltered functioning of the apparatuses under the hegemony of the ego. Here are seen such phenomena as the thought disorders which are revealed only on psychological testing, after a searching clinical interview has failed to turn them up. With the guideposts of a structured conversation, the apparatuses function with sufficient automaticity, despite the altered ego structure, that the disturbance cannot be seen.

In a somewhat analogous sense the overall ego is more involved in the regressive process during the induction phase of hypnosis than it is during the established state. Chaos and disorganization are characteristic of the induction phase; during the established state, stability has been restored. The regression is of the subsystem which now has hegemony over the apparatuses. The overall ego remains "quietly" in the background, maintaining the reality orientation which it has never really relinquished.

A SYNTHESIS OF THE TWO KINDS OF REGRESSION INITIATION—ALTERED STATE AND TRANSFERENCE

We must now integrate into the preceding description of the development and establishment of the hypnotic state its usual description as a transference phenomenon, by which is meant that the hypnotized subject engages in regressive interpersonal relationships. The external press is toward regression. The hypnotist declares himself possessed of great powers and proposes that the subject submit to these. If the subject can find an available regressive motivational pattern with which to respond to this press toward regression, hypnosis proceeds.

To recapitulate and organize some of our central theses: hypnosis is a condition of loss of autonomy with domination of a subsystem of the ego by a part of the social environment. Hypnosis is characterized by the fact that the subject is in a regressed state and engages in regressive interpersonal relationships. Hypnosis is therefore both an altered state and a transference relationship. The normal ego maintains relative autonomy from drives from within and the environment from without. There are two major ways in which this autonomy can be disrupted. An attack on the apparatuses is an attack on the ego state. An attack by way of offering a regressive interpersonal relationship is simultaneously an attack from the outside—the social environment—and an attack from within through the opportunity to regress offered to the drives, which are always to a greater or lesser extent seeking such an opportunity. With the success of the attack on one of the two fronts there is a repercussion on the other. And, as we have already emphasized, regressed state and transference are inextricably linked.

Early in our work we considered regarding the transference as a regression in the id and the regressed state as a regression in the ego, but came to see that this would be incorrect. Apart from the fact that transference manifestations, like any other behavior, are mediated by way of the ego, we believe, as we shall discuss in our metapsychology of the state of regression, that only in regression proper are id, ego, and superego all altered. In regression in the service of the ego the subsystem is simultaneously the altered state and the agency which engages in altered interpersonal relationships. As we earlier remarked, we also considered at one time regarding the induction as a loss of autonomy followed by domination by the id and the established state as a loss of autonomy followed by domination of the ego by the external environment. There is some truth to this conception, but it is also somewhat in error. During induction there are evidences of decrease of autonomy from both id and environment, though the evidences of decrease from the id may be more spectacular, partly because of the asymmetry of autonomy from id and environment; and in the established state, though the domination of the ego is by the external environment, there is also the concealed decrease of autonomy from the id by way of the regressive motivational pattern which must be activated to make possible the domination by the social environment.

We are perhaps in a better position now to evaluate the relative importance of the two avenues of approach, the manipulation of the apparatuses and the invitation to a regressed interpersonal relationship. We remember the opposing views—Freud's, that the manipulations are mere technical devices, and the view exemplified by Kubie and Margolin (1944), that the hypnotist is a kind of adventitious factor.

There is one phenomenon which at first seems to bespeak the correctness of Freud's view—namely that there are people in whom hypnosis can be brought about quickly and simply by the invitation to regress, without any manipulation of the apparatuses. These are people in whom there must already exist the subsystem in the ego, ready to be triggered into action. Clearly the regressed interpersonal relationship is the *sine qua non*. Once it is established, the regressed state is inevitable. But on the other hand, despite beginning disruption of the functioning of the apparatuses, the process may fail to go on to the development of hypnosis.

If one could be convinced that the skill with which the hypnotist carries out his manipulations could significantly influence the outcome, the view that the manipulations cannot be simply passed off as a smoke screen would be strengthened. It must be admitted that we have given short shrift to any differential introduced by the skill of the hypnotist. There is, however, a strong current of such belief in some present-day practicing hypnotists. There are a number of instances attested to by hypnotists of an especially skilled and experienced hypnotist succeeding where they had failed. We have made a number of attempts to see whether other experienced hypnotists could succeed in subjects with whom we have failed, but we have been unable to persuade ourselves that we have actually seen such successes. But this is clearly an area open to subjective bias, and one which could be illuminated only by careful empirical work. It would be expected that hypnotists would wish to claim a premium by virtue of their skill and experience. It is possible that the master-apprentice relationship which still exists in the realm of the acquisition of hypnotic skills is an evidence of that aspect of the psychology of the hypnotist to which we referred as his identification with his subject.

It is probable that in any particular instance of hypnotizability, the more important is the manipulation of the apparatuses, the less important is the establishment of a transference, and vice versa. Success in inducing hypnosis in refractory instances by the use of the newer and more potent techniques of manipulating the apparatuses will be required before it is possible to establish solidly the view that such manipulation does indeed play an important role in inducing hypnosis in at least some instances. And in such work it will be important to design experiments with controls for the transference effects of these manipulations.

In either case, whether emphasis is placed on transference or on manipulation of the apparatuses, as long as one sees hypnosis as a regression in the ego, one will look for the explanation of hypnotizability in ego factors—something like ego weakness or a susceptibility to regression, however this would be assessed. Regression in the service of the ego, as we have shown, is evidence rather of a "strong," not a "weak" ego, or probably more correctly, it is evidence of an ego which has the capacity to regress in part while the depth and duration of regression are controlled by the ego as a whole. This is an intrasystemic view of the ego, dealing as it does with the manner in which the synthetic force of the ego can build a total unity which includes a regressed subsystem.

With a predominantly transference point of view of hypnosis, the explanation of hypnotizability will naturally be sought in the motivational patterns of the subject. In *Hypnotherapy* (Brenman and Gill, 1947) we suggested that there may be nothing specific about the hypnotic state, but that it represents an altered state only in the sense of an as yet incompletely defined specific constellation of the strivings of the subject. We would now disapprove of our original statement on the grounds of its implications about the transference aspects of hypnosis, because it implies that they are the same from person to person. We do not have enough evidence for such a view, and do not know whether it is true. We believe that the psychodynamics of various hypnotizable people—at least as far as "strivings" are concerned—may be significantly different, and that hypnotizability may rather be the result of the balance which is struck between the various opposing forces. This balance results in the development of a particular structured state and kind of interpersonal relationship. The ease with which this structure can be brought into play will vary widely even among those who possess it.

Here we wish to turn to another statement we have made earlier, and try to restate it in more formal terms more consistent with our present views of the nature of hypnosis. We have previously suggested that in a psychotherapy employing hypnosis there are at least two kinds of transference involved—the transference underlying hypnotizability and then the usual kinds of transference manifestations seen in any psychotherapy. In terms of our description of hypnosis as a regression in the service of the ego, with a regressed subsystem in the persisting over-all ego structure, we would suggest that the transference underlying the hypnosis is the constellation of strivings within the subsystem, while the "usual transferences" are, together with the current reality interaction, the manifestations of the "persisting ego" relationship with the hypnotist.

STRUCTURALIZATION OF THE PROCESS OF LOSS OF AUTONOMY

We turn now to the issue of the disappearance of the phenomena of the induction phase. Whatever question may be raised about whether or not the phenomena of the induction period disappear, there is no question that the induction period shortens in time. The progressive rapidity with which the hypnotic subject learns to go into hypnosis is frequently explained as a conditioned reflex. We cannot here embark on a discussion of conditioning or habit formation, but our point of view is unsympathetic to such an explanation.

Kubie and Margolin (1944) propose a somewhat more dynamic explanation than habit formation for the disappearance of the induction phenomena:

> That in any individual who has been hypnotized repeatedly, the hypnotic state can be induced almost instantly by the mere presence of the hypnotist is not surprising, because the hypnotic reaction becomes a complex conditioned unit in the total ego Gestalt, an organized ego fragment into which the individual can be thrown in a flash, just as the patient with a specific phobia can be thrown into a panic by the appropriate danger signal. (p. 617)

In psychodynamic terms it might be assumed that the subject is ordinarily afraid of hypnosis but that as his fear lessens with increased familiarity, he struggles less against its establishment, and therefore enters it more easily.

But for our explanation, we will take our point of departure from

Rapaport's remarks on the use of the concept of automatization to explain much of what is ordinarily explained as conditioning and habit formation (1951d, 1953). We suggest that it is the automatization of the process of going into hypnosis which is responsible for the disappearance of the induction phenomena.

Various fragmentary ego syntheses are seen in the induction period. We may now view these as indications of the struggle which goes on while the ego searches for a motivational pattern which will conform to the external press. To say that the established state has become automatized means that this previously *ad hoc* correspondence of motivational pattern and external press has become organized into an ego structure. Therefore, the struggle need not be repeated again and again, and the evidence of the struggle—the induction-phase phenomena—fall away. The relative rapidity with which hypnosis can be induced, if the subject is one who will respond successfully, suggests that the elements which will become organized into the subsystem—the intra-ego structure—must be readily available.

We apply the concepts of autonomization and automatization (Hartmann, 1939) to the change in the induction phase as the neophyte becomes experienced. Autonomization and automatization are concepts which have not been distinguished in the psychoanalytic literature and we too believe they are best used synonymously. But the phenomenon we mentioned previously, called by Kretschmer "formular abbreviation," should be distinguished from these. Both autonomization and automatization refer to the same phenomenon—structure formation. Autonomization stresses the relative independence from drive and environment; automatization stresses the triggering of the structure into action by external or internal stimulus. Formular abbreviation, on the other hand, is a process, not a state: it refers to the dropping out of awareness of many details of a process as that process becomes structuralized. With the dropping out of awareness of details, attention cathexes are saved and become available to the ego for other uses. Formular abbreviation is thus a descriptive term referring to a phenomenon accompanying structure formation.

It is the process of going into hypnosis which becomes formularly abbreviated, not the established state. That the phenomena of the induction period may still persist despite their dropping out of consciousness is suggested by the evidence indicating that a certain time must elapse in each separate induction before the established state is actually well established, however experienced the subject may be. An effort to produce certain hypnotic phenomena immediately after the signal has been given for an experienced subject to go into hypnosis *may* fail. We suggest that despite the establishment of an automatization, there may persist in the preconscious or unconscious a potentiality for the revival of the dynamic interaction on deeper levels of the motivational hierarchy which had earlier led to the first and *ad hoc* appearance of this later automatized structure.[12] Such a view would be consistent with the general theory of *relative* autonomy; in fact, without such a view it would be difficult to explain the de-automatization of what has become automatized. A similar view is implied by Isakower (1938) in his discussion of the phenomena which some people occasionally experience while falling asleep. He implies that when these phenomena are not present in consciousness in these people they persist preconsciously or unconsciously, and are presumably preconsciously or unconsciouly present in all people while they are falling asleep.

THE METAPSYCHOLOGY OF THE HYPNOTIC STATE

We proceed now to a more detailed consideration of the metapsychology of the established state of hypnosis. Rapaport and Gill have argued elsewhere (in press) that a metapsychological discussion must include five points of view: structural, dynamic, economic, genetic, and adaptive. Although we shall not review here the arguments they present, we will organize our discussion of the metapsychology of the hypnotic state under these five points of view.

The Structural Point of View

We have already said that our descriptive differentiation of the two kinds of regression suggests that, structurally, in regression in the service of the ego the usual ego structure persists, but that at the same time a subsystem which has regressive characteristics is formed in the ego. It is also possible in a regression proper for a subsystem within the ego to develop subsequently. But in regression proper the ego within which the subsystem forms is itself an ego which shows regressive features, whereas in regression in the service of the ego the usual ego persists, perhaps even strengthened by the development of the subsystem.

In our description of the metapsychology of the established state, we shall have to deal with the overall system and the subsystem and with the relationships between the two. The description of the regressed subsystem as such will in many ways parallel what would be the description of a regression proper, except as the subsystem always operates under the domination, whether actual or potential, of the total ego. Edward Glover's (1943) theory of ego nuclei provides a genetic underpinning for the kind of subsystem in the ego which we postulate.

We must first characterize the structural relationship of this sub-

[12] One has to beware of falling into the "seething cauldron" view with such a hypothesis. Compare Freud on whether when a drive produces derivatives, the drive cathexes are all transferred to the derivatives (1926, footnote pp. 82–83).

system to the psychic organization. Fisher (1953) has suggested that in hypnosis there is regression in all three psychic systems—ego, superego, and id. We would seriously question this; we believe rather that this is a description of the state of affairs in regression proper, and that it describes, as a matter of fact, one of the major differences between regression proper and regression in the service of the ego. We believe that in hypnosis there exists an *intra-ego structure* which has access to regressed id and superego derivatives. There are significant relationships between this problem and the problem of the concept of the self, which is now being discussed more frequently in the literature. The subsystem is like a subsidiary self. Hartmann, followed by Jacobson (1954), employs the concept of the self as a supraordinate one and argues that the opposite of object is self and not ego. He further implies that self-cathexes are found in id, ego, and superego (Hartmann, 1950). Rapaport (1957) believes that this use of the concept self leads to theoretical difficulties, and proposes instead a definition of self as a "function of the ego selectively representing the total personality, and which as such has conscious and unconscious aspects." He suggests further that this "ego subsystem—the self—is 'responsible' for (representative of, reflective of) the ego's intersystemic relationships—among others."

In a similar fashion we are arguing that the subsystem which is established in the ego during hypnosis selectively represents the total personality—and thus has id, ego, and superego aspects. The superego components of the subsystem are derived not only from the subject's superego but also include incorporated aspects of the hypnotist—the so-called parasitic double of the superego (Rado, 1925).

We speak of id and superego derivatives rather than simply id and superego because we are dealing with the same problem with which any consideration of id, ego, and superego relationships must deal. Id and superego never act directly. What we actually know of them we know through the interaction of their derivatives in the ego. The phenomena of the induction phase, for example, which we earlier described as fragments of archaic ego states, are remnants of earlier stable ego syntheses formed as a result of the interaction of id, ego, and superego components.

One of the central structural issues in the relation between the overall ego and the subsystem is one already discussed—the degree to which the structures de-automatized during induction become re-automatized under the hegemony of the subsystem. To the extent to which this occurs they are of course an essential part of its structure and account for the apparently normal functioning during the established state.

We turn then to the metapsychology of regression proper from the structural point of view. First the intersystemic aspects: the id, ego, and superego relationships alter, and earlier structural organizations and relationships are reinstated. Granting that the demarcation of these psychic institutions is only relative, in regression there takes place a partial dissolution of these boundaries and the lines of division become less distinct. Superego and id invade ego, the ego losing some of the territory it has wrested from these two, and withdrawing into earlier ego positions. Clinically this is perceived as the coexistence of savage self-condemnation and frank instinctual urges.

More systematically expressed, in regression proper the relative autonomy of the ego breaks down, but the ego becomes reconstituted and is again relatively autonomous, though now in a regressed and earlier form. In addition to our previous description of the ego as relatively autonomous from id and environment, we must add that it is relatively autonomous from the superego.

In hypnosis the situation is quite different from the one just described for regression proper. The id and superego derivatives which interact with ego structures in the subsystem are regressed, but the id and superego themselves are not regressed as they are in regression proper. Applying our principle of differential regression (which should actually be named differential access, since it refers not to regressed id and superego but to access to id and superego derivatives), there may be different types of intersystemic relationships in various hypnotic subsystems; some subjects may show marked alterations in ego-superego relationships, but little change in id-ego relationships, or the opposite may be true. Some of these differences may account for some of the conflicting results obtained from experiments on the production of antisocial behavior in hypnosis (Brenman, 1942; Young, 1948).

Intrasystemic structural alterations occur in all three systems in regression proper, while in hypnosis they occur only in the ego and in the subsidiary ego, the subsystem. The general concept to be described for the subsystem is a loss of established structure or of yet another kind of relative autonomy—intrasystemic relative autonomy. Structures within the several systems in regression proper, and in the components of the subsytem in regression in the service of the ego, may be differentially affected: for example, ego apparatuses may be variously influenced by the hypnotist, depending, in Fisher's terms, on various fantasy systems, and in ours, on their history as autonomous structures. The same considerations apply to secondarily as to primarily autonomous structures. Secondarily autonomous structures in the ego are likely to lose their autonomy and consequently to function more directly in relationship to instinctual energies. (This last point clearly involves the economic point of view.)

We shall not discuss here intrasystemic structural alterations in superego and id. While these topics would need to be taken up in a metapsychology of regression proper, they are not germane to a discussion of the hypnotic state because id and superego, we argue, are not structurally altered in hypnosis.

The Dynamic Point of View

We have already mentioned that a sharp distinction must be made between the dynamics involved in the movement toward regression and the dynamics of the regressed state itself. To discuss the dynamics of the established state of hypnosis requires a further distinction between the dynamics of the subsystem and the dynamics of the relationship between subsystem and overall ego.

The dynamics of a regressed state can only be described as a more primitive kind of mental functioning in comparison to that of the state before regression. How primitive the functioning will be depends on the degree of regression. The description of the dynamics of the subsystem in hypnosis and of the dynamics of regression proper will differ therefore only in terms of the degree of regression which has occurred. The dynamics of psychic functioning in general can be described as follows: forces bent on discharge interact with inhibiting and channeling forces (in other terminology, defensive and controlling forces). Primitive mental dynamics are characterized by urgency of drive discharge, a relatively direct clash of discharge-bent force and inhibiting force, and relative paucity and inflexibility of channeling forces. More mature mental dynamics are characterized by delay of discharge, and by subtle, complex, and flexible channeling of discharge instead of direct inhibition.

A more global way of dichotomizing mental dynamics is into primary and secondary processes, and in general we may say that the dynamics of a regressed mental state show a movement toward primary-process functioning and away from secondary-process functioning. Freud's view of the relationship between primary- and secondary-process functioning as a central one in regression is seen in the following quotation: "Unconscious [primary] processes only become cognizable by us under the conditions of dreaming and of neurosis—that is to say, when processes of the higher, *Pcs.*, system are set back to an earlier stage by being lowered (by regression)" (Freud, 1915b, p. 187). The characteristics of the primary and secondary processes will not be detailed here. In intersystemic terms the difference in dynamics may be characterized by saying that in more primitive functioning, superego and id forces may join or clash directly without being buffered by higher-level ego organizations, while in more mature functioning many and flexible controlling ego forces bring the id and superego motivations to an adaptive discharge. Evidence of diminished integration of superego and ego is seen in the increased ease with which the superego can be "bribed."

A regressive change massive enough to alter the intersystemic dynamics will surely involve intrasystemic dynamic changes too. Altered ego-functioning is shown by: (1) shift to more primitive defensive mechanisms; (2) greater preponderance of discharge by affect processes as against intellectual processes; (3) movement from action to less adaptive discharge patterns; (4) movement toward dedifferentiation. In general, these changes may be viewed as impairments of various signal functions in favor of uncontrolled defensive and executive functions. We have already described these changes in ego-functioning as characteristic of the functioning of the subsystem in the established state (Brenman, Gill, and Hacker, 1947).

Here again, as under the structural point of view, we shall not discuss changes in intrasystemic dynamics of superego and id, since we do not have propositions to suggest which are peculiar to hypnosis. But the question of intrasystemic dynamic changes does lead us to Freud's only explicit formulation of the metapsychology of regression: "The metapsychological explanation of regression I have thought to find in an instinct defusion, in the segregation of the erotic components, which with the onset of the genital phase were joined to the destructive cathexes of the sadistic phase" (Freud, 1926, p. 46). Of course, instinct fusion and defusion refer not only to conditions within the id, but to derivatives of libidinal and aggressive drives throughout the psychic apparatus (Freud, 1938).

Again, because so far as we can see there are no issues specific to hypnosis involved, we shall not enter the complex issues of defusion, deneutralization, and sublimation, though a systematic treatment of regression would have to deal with them.

The dynamic relationship between the overall ego and the intra-ego subsystem may be one of conflict or cooperation. If the conflict is of any severity, the overall ego re-establishes its hegemony and the hypnosis is interrupted. If the relationship is one of cooperation, the hypnosis persists and the overall ego may progressively "lend" its functions to the subsystem for automatized functioning under the aegis of the subsystem.

The Adaptive Point of View

In our general discussion of autonomy we have described how the ego gains a measure of autonomy from the external environment. The ego can henceforth engage in experimental action in thought by way of small cathectic displacements among intrapsychic representations of the environment, instead of acting on the actual external environment by way of large energy displacements (Freud, 1900).

With the regression in hypnosis the subsystem reverts to earlier forms of relationship with the environment, forms both more magical and more dependent on the environment. We emphasize the subsystem here because, as we have said, the overall ego system remains in its usual adaptive relationship to the hypnotist. In fact, it is this maintenance of the usual adaptive relationship (together with the altered one by way of the subsystem) which constitutes an essential distinguishing feature of the hypnotic state.[13]

It must be pointed out, however, that a regressed state is not simply less adaptive, since each stage of development is an integrated one and constitutes an adaption. In fact, a regression may be looked upon as an effort to increase adaptation: when the organism meets environmental stress with which it cannot cope—to which it cannot adapt—it regresses to an earlier adaptive organization, as though in the hope of magically reinstating the earlier form of organism-environment interrelationship. But since the environment is likely to resist this effort at magical manipulation, the regressed state actually turns out to be maladapted.

In hypnosis, however, the environment (the hypnotist) has encouraged the regression, and the adaptation required is to him. Thus the development of the subsystem, which is the means by which this relationship with the hypnotist and his specific demands is established, is itself an adaptive achievement. It is of the kind which Hartmann (1939, p. 36) has called a regressive adaptation—in contrast to a progressive adaptation—and which he specifically links to Kris's regression in the service of the ego. The spontaneous fluctuations in the hypnotic state which we have described represent shifts in defense and adaptation.

In regression there is a reversal of the normal developmental progression involving the intrapsychic representation of the external world, both personal and impersonal. We may call this reversal reprojection or exteriorization. Insofar as the superego is built up around the incorporation of an external object, a massive reversal of this intrapsychic incorporation may be conceptualized as exteriorization of a whole psychic institution. The description of hypnosis as characterized by the development of a parasitic double of the superego makes use of such a conception (Rado, 1935). Again this must be recognized as the statement of the extreme form of a model, since in normal development the superego never becomes completely autonomous from external objects, nor is its complete exteriorization possible.

But in addition to such massive shifts, there can be exteriorization on a broad continuum, ranging from larger to smaller "segments" of psychic structure. Such exteriorization may be not only of superego components but of ego functions too. We have already discussed examples of the exteriorization of such smaller "segments" of ego-functioning in describing the varying degrees to which the apparatuses come under

[13] For purposes of clarity we are here and elsewhere making the distinction between subsystem and "overall" ego somewhat too sharp.

the hegemony of the subsystem. Here we are proposing that the extent to which they do is a measure of the extent to which they are exteriorized, of the extent to which they have become drawn into the altered adaptive relationship between subject (via the subsystem) and outside world (here the hypnotist). We have also commented on the differing ease or exteriorization of various structures, depending upon the fantasies with which they are linked or on the history of their development of autonomy. Another important factor determining the ease of exteriorization is the closeness of the function or structure to the "central core" of personality.[14]

We have described the adaptive point of view as involving for hypnosis the assumption of both ego and superego functions by the hypnotist and in this sense the relative and partial exteriorization of these functions. A parallel process occurs for the id, giving rise to the realm of phenomena ordinarily called "projection." This may take place with massive segments of instinctual urges, such as the whole range of aggressive impulses, or with the more delimited and specific impulses, such as homosexual urges.

In addition to the reversal of internalization by exteriorization, we must discuss the relation between the psychic institutions and the environment in terms of the sharpness of definition between the internal and external worlds. Just as before we have spoken of a blurring of the boundaries between the id, ego, and superego, so must we speak now of blurring of boundaries between self and not-self. Earlier in psychoanalytic theory this was usually discussed as the problem of ego boundaries (Federn, 1952). But, in accord with our earlier remarks on the concept of self, we would speak instead of the boundaries between one intra-ego structure—the self—and another—the representation of the outside world. Clarification of the meaning of regressive alterations of self-outside boundaries would follow from a clearer knowledge of the genesis of these boundaries. The accepted psychoanalytic view is that originally all is self and that the self progessively detaches the external world from itself. "The ego feeling we are aware of now is thus only a shrunken vestige of a far more extensive feeling—a feeling which embraced the universe and expressed an inseparable connection of the ego with the external world" (Freud, 1930, p. 13). This description seems to be in terms of exteriorization (that is to say, that the self progressively detaches *from itself* the external world) and forces us to ask whether it is contradictory to our view of development as a progressive internalization. Actually, these two points of view can be reconciled by the hypothesis that from the beginning, just as id and ego

[14] Schilder discussed a related problem in describing two kinds of depth of hypnosis—the usual phenomenal one and one dependent on "genuine" involvement in the hypnosis (Schilder and Kauders, 1956).

are undifferentiated, so are self and outside representations undifferentiated. From the point of view of the self, progressive differentiation results in a loss of what becomes outside world. From the point of view of the outside world, progressive differentiation results in a loss of what becomes self. Freud's statement that object loss is a precondition for the development of reality testing is actually a statement of an aspect of this differentiation, since the object has to be not immediately available for the self-object unity to begin to break up (Freud, 1925, p. 184; also Freud, 1923).

We have already discussed the importance which Kubie and Margolin ascribe to contraction and expansion of ego boundaries in their differentation between the induction phase and the established state. Freud described an "oceanic feeling" as related to a dedifferentiation of the self-object demarcation and suggested that this oceanic feeling may have "connection. . . with many obscure modifications of mental life, such as trance and ecstasy." (Freud, 1925, p. 22)

The Genetic Point of View

The most widespread genetic theory of the hypnotic state is of course that it is a regressive revival of earlier child-parent relationships.

The genetic point of view is especially important in a discussion of regression, since a regression is a reversion to earlier states. A central question is: to what degree can an earlier state of the psyche be reinstated? Discussions of "revivification" as against "regression" in hypnosis deal with a related issue, though, as we pointed out earlier, the concept "regression" in such discussions is somewhat different from that which we use.[15]

Freud discussed the revival of earlier states of mind in *Civilization and Its Discontents* (1930), where he concludes, "We can only be sure that it is more the rule than the exception for the past to survive in the mind" (p. 20), though by this he certainly does not imply that it can be revived in its old form.

In *The Problem of Anxiety* (1926) he discusses this problem specifically for the id, and, as we have already mentioned, suggests that there may be the complete transfer of the cathexis of the original wish to its lineal descendants. But even this would leave the "third possibility that in the course of the neurosis the wish was reactivated through regression, so out of accord with the present may it be" (p. 83).

From the metapsychological point of view a regressed state cannot be considered equivalent to an earlier stage of developmental organiza-

[15] We believe that a hypnotic "regression" approaches "revivification" to the extent to which there has been an adequate development of the subsystem with thoroughgoing synthesis of its various elements, but that revivification in the sense of the complete restoration of an earlier state is a fiction.

tion: despite the fact that there are important similarities, there are also important differences, resulting from the development subsequent to the stage to which there is regression. It would seem obvious that no stage of psychic development could ever be reinstated point for point. The ego apparatuses to which the stabilized regressed state has access differ in both structure and function from those to which it originally had access. The subsystem in hypnosis may in some respects resemble early parent-child relationships, but the automatized apparatuses which it may come to control are very different from what they were during childhood. Earlier psychoanalytic thinking was inclined to view regression too schematically as a reinstatement of earlier developmental stages, but, as Hartmann (1939) said,

> Differentation progresses not only by the creation of new apparatuses to master new demands and new tasks, but also and mainly by new apparatuses taking over, on a higher level, functions which were originally performed by more primitive means . . . when superordinate apparatuses are blocked or disordered, no pure form of a previous developmental stage emerges. (p. 50)

We have alluded to the fact that later stages of mental development cannot be looked upon as more adapted than earlier stages, since every stage is an adaptation. In a similar sense, the synthetic function of the ego is not something which simply synthesizes more and more elements of psychic structure in the course of development, but functions in every stage of development and achieves some kind of a total unity or integration at each stage. Hypnosis, once the established state has been stabilized, is not less of a unity but rather a different kind of unity.

The Economic Point of View

Kris (1951) has given the most complete description of the metapsychology of the economics of regression in the service of the ego. He suggests that in the inspirational phase of creativity (regression in the service of the ego), countercathexes are withdrawn from their use in repression and added to the speed, force, or intensity with which preconscious thoughts are formed. He contrasts this to the elaborational phase of creativity in which the countercathectic barrier may be reinforced and cathexis directed to other ego functions such as reality testing, formulation, communication, etc. In further discussing shifts of cathexis in ego-functioning he points to a shift between perception and preconscious thought, suggesting that the one operates at the expense of the other. In effect, he proposes three kinds of ego function —repression, preconscious thinking, and reality testing, including perception. In regression in the service of the ego, cathexes are withdrawn both from repression and reality testing and used for preconscious thinking. In the elaborational phase repression and reality testing are the preferred functions and preconscious thinking suffers.

In all of these considerations we speak in relative terms; cathexes do not totally shift from one function to another.

Using Kris's formulation as our point of departure, we would like to suggest several additions to clarify and sharpen the differences between regression proper and regression in the service of the ego, and between several kinds of regression in the service of the ego. First, we have proposed the subsystem as a structural concept. Whether or not a subsystem is established in all forms of regression in the service of the ego, we do not doubt its existence in hypnosis. Not only the apparatuses (and this would include much which for Kris would be preconscious thinking), but also the "higher" ego functions of reality testing, formulation, communication, etc., can, to a greater or lesser degree, as we have pointed out, come under the dominion of the subsystem. Second, as regards the cathexis of the higher functions, Kris speaks only of the withdrawal of cathexes from these functions. It may be true that in a regression in the service of the ego characterized by inspiration, cathexis may be withdrawn from these functions; still, they can remain cathected in hypnosis. Third, because the overall system remains in effect, it must to some extent retain cathexis. To maintain itself and to prevent the "recapture" of the apparatuses and higher functions by the overall ego, the subsystem will have to expend some energy in the countercathexis of these remaining cathexes in the overall system.

Actually, the retention of cathexis by the overall ego in the hypnotic regression (and the consequent necessity for countercathexis) is a central feature in what makes hypnosis possible. The organism is assured, as it were, that the overall ego is in only temporary abeyance. To speak anthropomorphically, the overall ego must be sufficiently secure in its ultimate mastery to permit an apparent loss of control.

Fourth, we suggest that in regression *proper*, not only are cathexes withdrawn from "higher functions," but that some structures are "dissolved" so that the defensive and controlling functions which they exercise with relatively small quantities of hypercathexes must now be carried out in a fluid struggle employing greater quantities of cathexes at a lower "potential." In regression in the service of the ego, cathexes are only partially withdrawn, and partially they remain, so that countercathexes must be erected against them by the subsystem, and structure is not dissolved. (We are again speaking of the poles of processes which exist on a continuum.)

We may speculate about the way in which the cathexes are deployed in the two main kinds of regression. In regression proper, the cathexes withdrawn from higher functions are employed to guard against even deeper regression. A new overall ego comes into being, not a subsystem within the usual ego integration. (Again, this distinction is a matter of degree.) In regression in the service of the ego, the countercathexes withdrawn from their use in withholding the repressed material, now permitted to emerge, may be employed as countercathexes against higher functions, or against the overall ego.

To summarize, in regression proper, cathexes are withdrawn from higher functions and distributed among ego functions, a larger share than before going to defense. In regression in the service of the ego, cathexes are withdrawn from defense and employed in the building of a subsystem whose maintenance requires a countercathexis of some of the cathexes retained in the overall ego.

It is probable that in the functioning of the subsystem, synthetic achievements on this "lower" level require greater quantities of energy, though on a lower potential. We may further suggest that unconscious energies no longer countercathected by defensive energies likewise contribute to the enhancement of preconscious thinking in the manner in which, to quote Freud, "the unconscious becomes ego-syntonic" and the result is that "they make specially perfect functioning possible, and they manifest a resistance in the face of opposition" (Freud, 1915, p. 195)—in other words, are strongly cathected.

We turn again to Freud in *The Interpretation of Dreams* (1900): his remarks on the state of mind required for dream interpretation—which he regards as akin to the hypnotic state of mind—describe the withdrawal of energy from one function (defense?) and its use for another.

> In the state used for the analysis of dreams and pathological ideas, the patient purposely and deliberately abandons this activity ["a certain deliberate (and no doubt also critical) activity which we allow to influence the course of our ideas while we are awake"], and employs the psychical energy thus saved (or a portion of it) in attentively following the involuntary thoughts which now emerge, and which—and here the situation differs from that of falling asleep—retain the character of ideas. *In this way the "involuntary" ideas are transformed into "voluntary" ones.* (p. 102)

It becomes clear now why the capacity for regression in the service of the ego is the mark of a "strong" ego. Only the "strong" ego can allow the emergence of the repressed without having to erect a countercathexis against an upsurge of even more deeply repressed contents, and have available countercathexes to employ against higher functions. One more consideration, following Kris, suggests itself. The transiency, reversibility, and employment of countercathexes against higher functions in regression in the service of the ego suggest that the cathexes employed in these operations are largely neutralized, whereas those employed against even deeper regression in regression proper are rather deneutralized cathexes, whether libidinized or aggressivized. These cathexes are the ones which come from "dissolved" structure. Just as structure formation involves neutralization and the availability of hypercathexes, so does structure dissolution involve deneutralization and the loss of available hypercathexes.

This economic description makes more understandable the clinical fact of the higher incidence of hypnotizability in the normal as against the neurotic. In the neurotic with precarious defenses, the countercathectic energies holding down the primitive instinctual impulses cannot be spared to be used as countercathexis against the overall ego or for the building of the subsystem. However, as we have mentioned, there are instances in which hypnosis is possible despite severe psychiatric illness. These pose crucial problems for the theory just stated, but we offer these suggestions: First, it may be that these are instances in which countercathexis against primitive instinctual drives is loosely held and easily yielded. Second, it may be that in such instances the amount of countercathectic energies necessary to hold the overall ego in abeyance is less.

This economic view likewise enables us to advance a hypothesis for the metapsychological description of the greater hypnotizability of hysterics as against obsessional neurotics. Granted that we are schematizing, we follow Freud (1925) in finding repression the major mechanism of defense in hysterics, and isolation and undoing the major mechanisms in obsessional neurosis. It is probable that the forms of countercathectic energy distribution in hysteria are different from the forms in obsessional neurosis. To speak in terms of an analogy, in hysteria the energy distributions are ranged along a front, with a well-defined no-man's land between ego and id. In the obsessional neurosis the warfare is more of the guerrilla type, with deep invasions of each force into the other's territory and islands of the enemy within each country. We are only stating here in another form the phenomena described as the manifestations of the synthetic function of the ego, the erotization of thinking, and the conversion of a defense into a gratification as, in a general way, they characterize the obsessional neurosis in contradistinction to hysteria. We speculate that these different ways of deploying countercathexis make massive cathectic shifts more possible in hysteria than in the obsessional neurosis, and thus account for the greater ease of hypnotizability in hysteria.

These economic explanations of problems of hypnotizability are not intended to minimize the role of transference factors in explaining hypnotizability. Again we stress that both altered state and transference factors must be considered.

It should be pointed out once again that regression proper and regression in the service of the ego are not as sharply dichotomous as is implied in some of this discussion. Not only are there transitional and complex mixed states, but also what began as a regression in the service of the ego may get out of hand, as it were, and become much closer to a regression proper. We have already discussed such changes as clinical phenomena observed in hypnosis.

REFERENCES

Bexton, W. H., Heron, W., and Scott, T. H. (1954). "Effects of decreased variation in the sensory environment," *Canad. J. Psychol.*, **8**, 70–76.

Bonnard, A. (1954). "The metapsychology of the Russian trials confessions," *Int. J. Psa.*, **35**, 208–213.

Brenman, M. (1942). "Experiments in the hypnotic production of anti-social and self-injurious behavior," *Psychiatry*, **5**, 49–61.

Brenman, M. and Gill, M. (1947). *Hypnotherapy*. New York: International Universities Press.

——— (1961). *Hypnosis and Related States*. New York: International Universities Press.

Brenman, M., Gill, M. and Hacker, F. (1947). "Alterations in the state of the ego in hypnosis," *Bull. Menninger Clin.*, **11**, 60–66.

Campbell, J. W., Jr. (1955). "Design flaw," *Astounding Science Fiction*, October, 85–94.

Federn, P. (1952). *Ego Psychology and the Psychoses*. New York: Basic Books.

Fisher, C. (1953). "Studies on the nature of suggestion. Part II: The transference meaning of giving suggestions," *J. Amer. Psa. Assoc.*, **1**, 406–437.

Freud, S. (1900). *The Interpretation of Dreams*. Standard Edition, Vol. 4 and 5. London: Hogarth, 1953.

——— (1915a). *Instincts and Their Vicissitudes*. Standard Edition, Vol. 14, London: Hogarth, 1957.

——— (1915b). *The Unconscious*. Standard Edition, Vol. 14, London: Hogarth, 1957.

——— (1923). *The Ego and the Id*. London: Hogarth, 1927.

——— (1925). "Negation," *Collected Papers*, Vol. 5, London: Hogarth, 1950, 181–185.

——— (1926). *The Problem of Anxiety*. New York: Norton, 1936.

——— (1930). *Civilization and Its Discontents*. London: Hogarth, 1946.

——— (1938). *An Outline of Psychoanalysis*. New York: Norton, 1949.

Glover, E. (1943). "The concept of dissociation," *Int. J. Psa.*, **24**, 7–13.

Hartmann, H. (1939). *Ego Psychology and the Problem of Adaptation*. New York: International Universities Press, 1958.

——— (1950). "Comments on the psychoanalytic theory of the ego," *The Psychoanalytic Study of the Child*, **5**, New York: International Universities Press, 74–96.

——— (1956). "Notes on the reality principle," *The Psychoanalytic Study of the Child*, **11**, New York: International Universities Press, 31–53.

Isakower, O. (1938). "A contribution to the patho-psychology of phenomena associated with falling asleep," *Int. J. Psa.*, **19**, 331–345.

Jacobson, E. (1954). "The self and the object world: Vicissitudes of their infantile cathexes and their influence on ideational and affective development," *The Psychoanalytic Study of the Child*, **9**, New York: International Universities Press, 75–127.

Janet, P. (1920). *The Major Symptoms of Hysteria*, 2nd ed. New York: Macmillan.

KOESTLER, A. (1941). *Darkness at Noon*, New York: Macmillan.

KRIS, E. (1951). "On preconscious mental mechanisms," in Rapaport, D., (ed.), *Organization and Pathology of Thought*. New York: Columbia University Press.

KUBIE, L. and MARGOLIN, S. (1944). "The process of hypnotism and the nature of the hypnotic state," *Amer. J. Psychiat.* **100**, 611–622.

LILLY, J. (1956). "Mental effects of reduction of ordinary levels of physical stimuli on intact, healthy persons," *Psychiat. Res. Reports*, **5**, 1–9.

MOLONEY, J. (1955). "Psychic self-abandon and extortion of confessions," *Int. J. Psa.*, **36**, 53–60.

MURRAY, H. (1938). *Explorations in Personality*. London: Oxford University Press.

RADO, S. (1925). "The economic principle in psycho-analytic technique," *Int. J. Psa.*, **6**, 35–44.

RAPAPORT, D. (1951a). "The autonomy of the ego," *Bull. Menninger Clin.*, **15**, 113–123.

——— (1951b). "The conceptual model of psychoanalysis," *J. Pers.*, **20**, 56–81.

——— (1951c). "Consciousness: A psychopathological and psychodynamic view," in *Problems of Consciousness*, Transactions of the Second Conference. New York: Josiah Macy, Jr., Foundation, 18–57.

——— ed. (1951d). *Organization and Pathology of Thought*. New York: Columbia University Press.

——— (1953). Review of Dollard, J. and Miller, N. (1950) *Personality and Psychotherapy*. *Amer. J. Orthopsychiat.*, **23**, 204–208.

——— (1955). "The development and the concepts of psychoanalytic ego-psychology," *Western New England Institute for Psychoanalysis*, Mimeographed ms.

——— (1957). "Seminars on advanced metapsychology," *Western New England Institute for Psychoanalysis*, Mimeographed ms.

——— (1958). "The theory of ego-autonomy: A generalization," *Bull. Menninger Clin.*, **22**, 13–35.

——— (1959). "The structure of psychoanalytic theory: A systematizing attempt," in Koch, S. (ed.), *Psychology: A Study of a Science*, Vol. III, New York: McGraw-Hill, 55–183.

——— (unpublished ms.). "The psychoanalytic theory of consciousness and a study of dreams."

RAPAPORT, D., and GILL, M. (in press). "The points of view and assumptions of metapsychology," *Int. J. Psa.*

SCHILDER, P. and KAUDERS, O. (1956). "A textbook of hypnosis," in Schilder, P. (ed.), *The Nature of Hypnosis*. New York: International Universities Press, 43–184.

WHEELIS, A. (1956). "Will and psychoanalysis," *J. Amer. Psa. Assoc.*, **4**, 285–303.

YOUNG, P. (1948). "Antisocial use of hypnosis," in LeCron, L. (ed.), *Experimental Hypnosis*. New York: Macmillan, 376–415.

They seemed to utilize very efficiently cues contained in the manners, looks, voice or physical manipulations of the operator and to be affected in accordance with what they believed to be the will and intention of the operator, even when the latter wanted just the opposite.

All these phenomena, as wonderful as they may be, are only increases in physical or psychological functions which we all possess to a large extent in a waking condition.

James Braid, 1860

11

Role-Theoretical Analysis of Hypnotic Behavior

THEODORE R. SARBIN and MILTON L. ANDERSEN[1]

University of California, Berkeley

THEORIES of hypnosis have been classified as "skeptical" and "credulous" (Sutcliffe, 1960). Role theory is unmistakably a skeptical theory. The "trance," and "hypnotic induction" are seen as *not necessary* to bring about the behaviors and experiences usually regarded as "hypnotic phenomena." As a corollary, role theory skeptically questions the use of such terms as "trance" or "hypnotic state" to explain hypnotic phenomena. The skeptical attitude does not deny that the hypnotic experience may be intensely meaningful and dramatic to the subject. The person with a skeptical attitude simply does not regard hypnosis as a special state, or hypnotic behavior as unique and isolated from other forms of social psychological behavior.

[1] This author was supported by NIMH grant number: 1-T1 MH 8104-01, while this chapter was being written.

THE SKEPTICAL ATTITUDE AND ITS NEGLECT

Several contemporary investigators (Barber, Sutcliffe, Fisher) and a number of eminent writers in the history of hypnosis (Bertholet, Bailly, Bertrand, Braid in his third theory, and Bernheim in his 1903 work) have expressed this skeptical attitude. Today, the skeptics have achieved a hearing, and represent an important bloc within the field of contemporary hypnosis research. That the research and opinions of the earlier skeptics were neglected is easily documented. Why? What were the social and intellectual conditions that, in the continual advocacy of the skeptical view, fostered this consistent neglect? As we shall attempt to demonstrate, this neglect, coupled with acceptance of credulous theories, was a by-product of inadequately formed social psychological concepts. Intimately connected to the impoverished conditions of early social psychology was the utilization of inappropriate metaphors.

To set the stage for our presentation of role theory, an excursion into historical materials is necessary. We shall try to make clear that the skeptical attitude appeared early in the history of hypnosis, and that various metaphors—appearing from time to time to "explain" the phenomena—were found wanting for lack of empirical support. We begin, then, with a brief look at some historical materials that demonstrate that the skeptical attitude was expressed in the very first attempts to understand hypnotic behavior.[2]

The Early Skeptics

The study of hypnotic phenomena begins with the Marquis de Puységur, who is usually and properly given credit for being the first to record behavior regarded as artificial somnambulism, and now called "hypnosis." (The "crisis" behavior observed by Mesmer is *not* the behavior we now regard as hypnotic.) The historical discussion usually skips from de Puységur to James Braid. This skipping ignores an important investigator who lived before Braid, Alexandre Bertrand, the founder of the theory of suggestion and hypnosis (Janet, 1925, Vol. I, pp. 156–157; Weitzenhoffer, 1963, p. 296–297). Strikingly similar to modern research trends, and to the basic role-theory approach, Bertrand's view is indicated in the following statement:

> . . . The psychological phenomena observed during the magnetic state are not exceptional phenomena, but are normal, or are at least phenomena which can be observed under various other conditions. Artificial somnambulism . . . serves merely to render conspicuous and to amplify phenomena dependent upon the working of the

[2] The section of this chapter concerned with historical matters is taken freely from Andersen (1963) and Sarbin (1962).

general laws of imagination, expectant attention, and desire. If normal psychology could give a satisfactory explanation of these phenomena, the same explanation would be applicable to all that was witnessed in somnambulist patients, however strange it might appear at first sight. (Bertrand, 1823, In Janet, Vol. I, 1925, p. 157)

Although our terminology is not the same as that employed by Bertrand, the content and the theoretical approach bear a striking resemblance.

Twenty years after Bertrand's work appeared, in 1843, Braid's book *Neurohypnology* was published. Braid was not the discoverer of a set of phenomena that we categorize as "hypnotic phenomena." His fame rests on the fact that he hit upon a simple technique of hypnotic induction, the well-known technique of ocular fixation upon a single object. Prior to Braid, hypnotic phenomena or "artificial somnambulism" had been elicited and reported by de Puységur, Bertrand, and many others. In fact, all the phenomena had been observed and catalogued before Braid's time (Janet, 1925, p. 156; Weitzenhoffer, 1963, p. 297).

Braid, however, gave us the terms "neurohypnology," "neurohypnotism," and so on. Later, dropping the prefix "neuro," he provided the terms "hypnotize," "hypnotism," and so forth (Bramwell, 1903, pp. 23–24). We should not, however, regard Braid as having simply renamed a set of previously known phenomena. His new terms were metaphors embodying a new theory about these phenomena. The new concepts introduced by Braid enabled investigators to think of hypnosis as sleeplike or trancelike states, instead of in the old concepts of "magnetic states" and "artificial somnambulism."

Braid held *three* different theories about hypnosis during his lifetime. He advocated the first theory, a physiological explanation, for a very short time. His second theory, emphasizing the concentration of attention upon a single object, is best known. The third theory of Braid's is virtually unknown to students of hypnosis, for it appeared mainly in his last manuscript, as yet unpublished in English. From Bramwell, we can see what these three theories of Braid's involved:

In the first theory, he explained hypnosis from an almost purely physical standpoint; in his second, he considered it to be a condition of involuntary monoideism and concentration of the attention. His third theory differed from both of these. In it he recognized that reason and volition were unimpaired, and that the attention could be simultaneously directed to more points than one. The condition, therefore, was not one of involuntary monoideism. Further, he recognized more and more clearly that the state was essentially a conscious one. . . . (Bramwell, 1903, p. 293)

The third theory was strikingly similar to modern skeptical theories and included the following propositions:

1. It is not necessary to have a subject stare at a bright object. Hypnosis can be done in the dark, and with the blind. The subject is simply instructed to close his eyes without prolonged fixation.

2. Hypnosis occurs only if the subject knows what is expected of him and voluntarily conforms to the demands of the operator.
3. Volition is unimpaired, the concern for morals increased, and suggested crime is impossible.
4. The mentally healthy are the easiest, and the hysterical the most difficult to influence.
5. Important differences exist between hypnosis and normal sleep.
6. Suggestion is the device used for exciting the phenomena, and is not sufficient to explain them. (from Bramwell, 1903, p. 41, and pp. 293–294)

It is interesting that Braid, who was the first to elaborate the theory of suggestion, rejected it as a concept explanatory of hypnosis almost a century ago. Nevertheless, hypnosis is still sometimes regarded as a form of suggestibility or "hypersuggestibility." It is instructive to notice that Braid's third theory emphasized that hypnotic enactment occurs *only if* the subject knows what he is to do, and voluntarily strives to perform well. The views held by James Braid in his third theory and the views held by role theorists stem from the same skeptical attitude.[3]

Interest in hypnosis has gone through several cycles in the past two hundred years. After Mesmer, after Braid, and after Charcot, there were abrupt declines in the amount of work and experimentation devoted to hypnosis. We will find, as already mentioned, that adequate social psychological concepts were lacking, and that as various physical or physiological metaphors were seen to be inappropriate, interest in hypnosis declined. Another way of looking at the waxing and waning of interest in hypnosis is in terms of the utility of the metaphors that were employed. But first, a short digression on the use of metaphors in science.

The Use of Metaphors in Science

A metaphor is a term that has denotative "concrete" meaning in one idiom and is applied to a phenomenon from another idiom. For example, metallurgists talk about "metal fatigue," borrowing the term "fatigue" from muscle physiology. Many other examples can be found

[3] It is most unfortunate that Braid's third theory is so little known. Bramwell said this of the matter: "Few seem to be acquainted with any of his works except *Neurohypnology*, or with the fact that this was only one of the first of a long series on the subject of hypnotism, and that later his views completely changed" (Bramwell, 1903, p. 22). "He not only invented the terminology we still use, but even, at a later date, rejected it as misleading" (p. 434). Braid's third, and last, theory was apparently contained in a manuscript sent three days before his sudden death on March 25, 1860, to Dr. Azam in France. From Azam the pamphlet went to the American hypnotist Dr. G. M. Beard, and from Beard to W. Preyer in Germany, who published it in his *Die Entdeckung des Hypnotismus*. Even such a person as Braid's major editor, Arthur E. Waite, failed to recognize that Braid's last writings comprised a new theory of hypnosis. In the Waite edition on Braid (Braid, 1960) this last manuscript is not published. There is only the statement that "passages of importance" from the last manuscript were added by Waite to the appendix (Braid, ,1960 p. ix). However, an inspection of the appendix does not reveal any passages which are indicative of a new theoretical viewpoint by Braid. A retranslation of Braid's last manuscript is being prepared by Andersen and Kroger (in preparation). The quote from Braid in the chapter opening is taken from this manuscript.

in psychology, a field which has produced a great variety of metaphors. Some of these are: psyche, persona, the machine, various marking metaphors (traces, neurograms, imprinting, stamping in and stamping out, and, of course, the *tabula rasa*), hierarchical metaphors (levels, depth, and so on), fluid flow metaphors (McDougall's hydrologic system of streams, currents, and channels, and Freud's hydraulic system, the libido and its tributaries) (Nash, 1963).

All that is intended in the borrowing is that certain effects can be colorfully described by likening them to effects with which we are familiar. The use of the fatigue metaphor does not carry with it the meaning that metals and muscles are alike. It is frequently the case, however, that the original metaphorical meaning drops out and we then regard the metaphor as having literal, denotative meaning. For example, in the proper use of metaphor we act *as if* the human body is like a machine. But we may forget the *as if*, and assert that the human body *is* a machine. This is the reification of a metaphor. Many long-term arguments in the hypnosis literature can be traced to such reification. Mesmer and Elliotson argued that the behavior they elicited *was* a form of animal magnetism, whereas their opponents argued that it was not. Similarly, Charcot asserted that hypnotic behavior *is* a form of neurological disorder. Regrettably, neither side in these arguments recognized the *as if* aspect of metaphors, and argued for or against the reified form of the metaphor.

The Use of Metaphors in the History of Hypnosis

In the history of hypnosis, as in the history of any other field, various metaphors have been introduced that carry different implications for research, for therapy, and for explanatory efforts. The metaphor that Mesmer used 200 years ago to account for the observed crisis behaviors was "magnetism." He referred to the process that produced remarkable, dramatic changes in his patients as a form of animal magnetism. Until that time no concept of animal magnetism had been systematically used, although the concept of mineral magnetism was well known. By borrowing the term "magnetism," Mesmer also borrowed the set of concepts associated with it, including induction (the transference of magnetism), which was utilized in his invention, the *baquet*. Through this device, a large number of people could be treated simultaneously by grasping iron rods that had been placed in a large, oval-shaped vessel and that presumably contained animal magnetism induced by Mesmer. Galdston (1948) indicates both the advantages and disadvantages created by the use of Mesmer's magnetism metaphor:

In his animal magnetism he blended in an unholy alliance the metaphysics of Paracelsus with the physics of Franklin. It is this very admixture of the unmixables that has assured Mesmer an enduring place in the history of medicine and of psychiatry.

> Mesmer so ravelled matters that it took many good men close to a hundred and fifty years to untangle them. Simpler or wiser men would have dealt with the phenomena Mesmer observed in simpler and wiser ways (as indeed many have done), and the world no doubt would have paid little attention to them. . . . It can thus be said that Mesmer was fruitful because of his errors. This in turn suggests a theme worthy of the medical historians, namely, to establish by the witness of the real events *the creative* function of the erroneous idea [metaphor]. (pp. 832–833)

Bailly, on the Committee of the French Royal Academy of Sciences which investigated Mesmer, entitled one section of its report: "Imagination is Everything, Magnetism is Nothing" (Galdston, 1940, p. 214). Bailly and the Committee apparently felt that the claims of Mesmer could be dismissed, because the Mesmeric phenomena were not due to magnetism.

> By this report Mesmer was in effect branded a quack and a charlatan. The Medical Faculty of the University of Paris forbade the practice of Mesmerism to all its members, threatening with expulsion those who violated this order. (Galdston, 1948, p. 835)

The Committee, unfortunately, was not interested in the dramatic behavior exhibited by Mesmer's patients, but was interested instead in the proposed explanation. The concept of magnetism seemed palpable and real when applied to the attraction of one metallic object to another but was rejected as an appropriate metaphor for psychological influence. The concept of Imagination had no scientific status and could not be justified as a metaphor for the phenomena under scrutiny. Hence, scientific investigations of hypnoticlike phenomena went into decline for a few decades until Braid introduced the metaphor of sleep through the employment of the word "hypnosis."

Viewing influence phenomena as sleeplike had certain implications for scientific theorizing and for psychological treatment. The theorizing led to studies of hypnosis based on the physiology of sleep. Many hypnotists at that time, painfully aware of the outcome of the overambitious claims of the Mesmerists, wrote very cautiously, and mainly about the practical uses of hypnosis, especially as a means of anesthesia for surgical operations. Soon after the discovery of ether in 1846 and chloroform in 1847, the study of hypnosis again declined sharply. Attacks upon various explanations of hypnosis became more devastating. The concept of "suggestion," developed by Braid, was too slender a reed to carry the burden as an explanatory concept for hypnotic phenomena. And, as in Mesmer's time, the critics of hypnosis were not so much concerned with the phenomena produced as they were with the metaphors employed to account for these phenomena.

For a time, hypnosis was studied and used only by practitioners of questionable scientific status. Then, with Charcot, and his use of the neuropathological metaphor, hypnosis again became a respectable field of inquiry. Charcot propounded a clear and simple doctrine, which aroused widespread interest, although the doctrine had a very short life. This doctrine asserted that the hypnotic state is an artificial hysteria, a form of neurological disorder. Thus, if hypnosis was a form of neuropathology, scientists could then study hypnosis with the aid of the reflex hammer and with a checklist of reflexes, signs, and symptoms such as were employed at that time by trained neurologists. Articles, journals, and books poured forth. But, Charcot's neuropathological doctrine died with him in 1892. Without this medically respectable neurological metaphor, hypnotic phenomena no longer seemed sufficiently real. The decline in interest was so abrupt that many of the neurologically oriented students of hypnosis were left with journals entitled "hypnological reviews," which they quickly retitled "neurological reviews."

Each of these metaphors, and others as well, has declined and died when displaced by metaphors more in keeping with concurrent scientific vocabularies. Also, as we know from the history of science, inventions and discoveries in other areas provided a cognitive framework for establishing a new metaphor.

THE ROLE METAPHOR

The present century has witnessed the development of the discipline of social psychology. This discipline has coined new terms, borrowed concepts from other disciplines, and—most significant—developed research methods. One could have predicted from the nineteenth-century theories of Bertrand and Braid that when a social psychological vocabulary was constructed, the description of hypnosis would be based on social psychological concepts. The particular social psychological concept that has been widely used in connection with hypnosis has been that of role. Drawn from the theater and from everyday life, this metaphor regards the actions of the hypnotist and of the subject as determined in a large part by the situation in which both participants are trying to enact reciprocal roles. When one looks at hypnosis in this way, of course, the implications are quite different from that which follows when one looks at hypnosis as a physiological event or as an event mediated by animal magnetism. The implications for theory and practice are drawn from the study of persons working in the theater or enacting roles in everyday life, and emphasize, among other things, reciprocal conduct, acting skill, and the function of the audience. (In the idiom of the role metaphor, the hypnotist-subject relationship is parallel to the director-actor relationship during rehearsals.)

The referent object of our dramaturgical metaphor is the Stanislavski actor, and not the Jacobean actor, or the actor in a Japanese Nō play. The Jacobean acting style, dominant in the late eighteenth century, utilized a set of fixed gestures to indicate various moods, emotions, and so forth. In contrast, the Stanislavski actor attempts to become genuinely and intensely involved in his particular dramatic role. In his classic work, *An Actor Prepares*, Stanislavski presents a detailed account of the procedures by which an actor can achieve this degree of involvement, and thereby create an effective role performance. These procedures are indicated by a listing of some of the chapter headings: "Concentration of Attention," "Relaxation of Muscles," "Imagination," and "Faith and a Sense of Truth." Perhaps the simplest way to indicate what Stanislavski meant by "complete absorption in the role" is to present a Hindu tale he used.

> ... A Maharajah who, about to choose a minister, announced that he would take only the man who could walk around on top of the city walls, holding a dish full to the brim with milk, without spilling a drop. A number of candidates, yelled at, frightened, or in other ways distracted, spilled the milk. "Those," said the Maharajah, "are no ministers."
>
> Then came another, whom no scream, no threat, and no form of distraction could cause to take his eyes from the rim of the bowl.
>
> "Fire," said the commander of the troops.
>
> They fired, but with no result.
>
> "There is a real Minister," said the Maharajah.
>
> "Didn't you hear the cries?" he was asked.
>
> "No."
>
> "Didn't you see the attempts to frighten you?"
>
> "No."
>
> "Did you hear the shots?"
>
> "No. I was watching the milk." (Stanislavski, 1961, p. 81)

This tale, and the discussions throughout Stanislavski's book of what is required of the good dramatic actor, describe the dramaturgical metaphor which is utilized in our role-theoretical interpretation of hypnotic behavior.

In brief, the adoption of the dramaturgical metaphor leads to conceptualizing hypnosis as the enactment of a role. The analysis of the role of hypnotic subject proceeds in the same manner as the analysis of any other role, be it an assigned dramatic role such as Hamlet, an occupational role such as a nurse, a family role such as a mother, or a group role such as a leader. Sarbin (1964) has already illustrated how a set of constructs may be used to analyze any role. The role of the hypnotic subject is no exception. It is unnecessary to invoke additional constructs to analyze the role that has been labeled—since Braid's time—hypnotic.

To recapitulate: When we try to describe any behavior, particularly complex behavior, we find ourselves using metaphors. The choice of metaphors directs our search for facts and our practical applications of these facts. A number of different metaphors have been used during the history of hypnosis. Scientific interest in hypnotic phenomena was linked to the acceptability of these metaphors. As is usually the case, these metaphors were employed in their reified form, instead of in their *as if* form; hence the abrupt decline of hypnotic research with the "undressing" of each metaphor. The skeptical attitude was ever present during these times, but did not take hold for lack of an adequate social psychological metaphor. This lack no longer exists, and the implications of the skeptical attitude are presently being tested by several investigators. The role-theoretical position incorporates this skeptical attitude, and utilizes a basic role metaphor, supplemented by secondary variables drawn from present-day social psychological conceptual systems. Our use of the role metaphor is predicated on the belief that it is productive of propositions that can be empirically tested.

Role Enactment and Simulation

Some will criticize the use of the role metaphor because acting (role enactment) is often regarded as sham behavior, that is, as simulation. Although it is true that some types of professional acting may be so described, acting in the general social sense does not require this qualification. The confusion created by the use of the term "role playing" has been so pervasive, that we now employ the term "role enactment." That the term "role playing" should connote commitment, involvement, and even dead seriousness in carrying out one's role has been discussed in a series of articles (Sarbin, 1943, 1950, 1956, 1964). However, many persons still interpret the term "role playing" to mean "playing at" such as in children's playing at being adults, whereas "playing" should be interpreted as it is in "playing the violin." The term "role enactment" is now used to avoid these semantic difficulties, and to indicate that role behavior is best characterized by the adjective "earnest." For example, a physician may enact his role before a variety of audiences each day over a span of years. He may strive to create certain impressions and to achieve certain purposes. But there is nothing that is necessarily sham about his role behavior. Likewise, the hypnotic subject strives to perform his role in accordance with the expectations and wishes of the hypnotist. The subject will attempt to create impressions through gestures and postural behavior. This behavior, too, is not necessarily sham behavior. The subject's arm may or may not feel rigid when he communicates that he cannot bend it, or that it would take a great effort to bend it. In any event, it is an empirical matter concerning the degree to which any particular episode of role behavior is sham. We cannot simply accept the statement that all role enactment is bogus. Orne (1959) has shown empirically for hypnosis, and Sadow and Suslick (1961) have shown for the Ganser syndrome, that simulation of role behavior is difficult to detect.

> In simulation of previous psychotic states, and in the behavior pattern known to psychiatrists as the Ganser syndrome, it is apparently almost impossible for the observer to separate feigning of symptoms from involuntary acts with any degree of certainty. (from Sadow and Suslick, 1961)
>
> The difficulty is probably that the patient is just as confused by his own behavior as is the observer. (Scheff, 1963)

Ryle (1949) has shown logically for the general case, that any particular bit of behavior does not carry its own credentials.

> In judging that someone's performance is or is not intelligent [or hypnotic], we have, as has been said, in a certain manner to look beyond the performance itself. For there is no particular overt or inner performance which could not have been accidentally or "mechanically" executed by an idiot, a sleepwalker, a man in panic, absence of mind or delirium . . . [or a simulator]. But in looking beyond the performance itself, we are not trying to pry into some hidden counterpart performance enacted on the supposed secret stage of the agent's inner life. (Ryle, 1949, p. 45) [Words in brackets added.]

It is necessary to observe *other* behavior (questioning of the subject after the session, his responsiveness to other tasks, and so on) to determine the degree to which the subject's intrapersonal experiences and observable behavior were "congruent." The term "congruent" has no inherent meaning, of course, but refers to the *inference* made by the observer concerning the relationship between subjective experiences and observable behaviors. Those who employ the trance metaphor are forced into a difficult position on this issue. This difficulty is highlighted when the hypnotic subject's behavior is described as congruent with his "inner state" (that is, not sham) only when this state is regarded as the trance state. But when the "inner state" is not appraised as a true trance state, any "hypnotic" behavior of the subject is by definition sham. Further, the inability of trained observers to differentiate between "genuine trance subjects" and simulators places great strain on the trance metaphor.

The Trance Concept and Mediational Processes

The role-theoretical approach does not deny that hypnotic and other behavior is accompanied by an experiential state (subjective state). But this experiential state is part and parcel of the hypnotic performance, and, therefore, cannot be used to explain itself. The traditional belief is that there are two processes occurring within the hypnotized person. The trance is regarded as one process—the mental, subjective, or experiential aspect. The overt behavior of the hypnotized person is regarded as another, and separate, aspect. But this is the commission of the "category-mistake" as discussed by Ryle (1949). Our view is that hypnotic behavior can be described as observable processes, or as psychological experience, but *not* as two processes.

Another set of logical problems arise when the trance is regarded as a mediating process, that is, the mental process that mediates between the utterances that the hypnotist makes and the subject's overt behavior. Characteristically, the word "trance" is not defined. Rather, it is treated as a primitive word that presumably everyone understands with the same denotation. It has been fashionable to employ concepts of mediating processes to account for human behavior. To conceptualize problems in terms of chain-processes, such as stimulus-organism-response, has been traditional in psychology. The difficulties and frustrations encountered with the utilization of purely ecological (stimulus) and purely behavior (response) terms often leads to an escape into the use of inferred internal mediational processes.

Gibson (1960) has mentioned the danger of psychology "sinking in a swamp of intervening variables," and Koch (1959) has discussed the confusions engendered by a focus on mediational processes during the "Age of Theory." The use of mediational processes, however, involves an inference. The inference is from observed events to an inferred inner process (such as the trance) and back to observable events. The use of the concept "trance" usually includes the implicit premise that the hypnotic induction produced mental changes within the person which, in turn, were responsible for changes in physiological condition or overt behavior. But the precise nature of these internal changes has never been spelled out. Some authors have tried to write a neurophysiological view of how the hypnotist's message gets into the auditory channels, is processed through the cerebrum, and results in behavior. Others have mixed physiological and psychological metaphors to account for hypnotic behavior. These metaphor mixtures usually link together a number of inferred internal processes. The problem with the use of all inferred internal processes concerns the necessary and sufficient behavioral events that must occur before we can invoke the inferred process. Secondly, we must specify what is denoted by the inferred process. That is, the various denotations of such a term as "trance" must be specified in objective terms. When the theorist who employs the trance metaphor is pushed into defining a trance, he often asserts that it is a change in mental state. But this is not helpful for we need an empirical test for the mental state. The theorist is required to specify some observable events as consequents of the trance state. In a definition of the trance, these consequents must always be present when the trance is "activated," and must not be present when there is no trance. Recent research has shown that many so-called hypnotic behaviors can be elicited without the hypnotic induction procedure (Andersen and Sarbin, 1963; Barber and Calverly, 1962, and Barber's chapter in this volume). If behaviors can be elicited *without* the trance that are thought to be accounted for by the trance process within the individual, what is the status of the trance concept? We suggest that its status as a respectable scientific concept is dubious. We propose that we can better describe hypnotic conduct by eliminating the word from our professional vocabulary.

The Trance Concept and " Spontaneous Amnesia "

An interesting example of the problems one encounters with the trance concept is Braid's difficulty in deciding what behaviors to call hypnotic.

> On the one hand, he [Braid] had those instances in which presumably spontaneous amnesia followed the disappearance of hypnosis. However, there were also a great many instances in which no amnesia was present, but in which, nevertheless, some of the characteristics accompanying hypnosis were seen; and there were even cases of patients who, in spite of showing none of the characteristic symptoms of hypnosis, nevertheless showed improvement and even cures after submitting to his procedures. (Weitzenhoffer, 1963, p. 298)

Braid decided that hypnotism should be defined only by the presence of spontaneous amnesia.

> Hypnotism shall designate only those cases in which sleep is produced artificially and is accompanied by loss of memory such that the patient, after awakening, has no memory of the events which occured during the sleep but recaptures these memories completely upon being put into the hypnotic state later (Translated from Preyer, 1881, pp. 80–81).

Braid's definition of hypnotism is overly restrictive, and leaves out many phenomena discussed in the hypnosis literature. But he provided an unequivocal criterion for the concept of hypnotism to be invoked. Many present-day investigators have not provided such a criterion. With an unequivocal criterion, tests can be made to determine if certain behaviors are elicited only from those persons who also demonstrate spontaneous amnesia.

In addition, the concept of spontaneous amnesia is being exploded through the use of several recent experimental techniques. Hypnosis subjects are now tested more intensively for their memory of events during hypnosis, rather than with just a bland inquiry such as : " What do you remember from the trance? " We would expect that experiments into the problem of "spontaneous amnesia," utilizing the postexperimental inquiry techniques described by Orne (1962), would indicate that spontaneous amnesia is very rare, and is probably related to variables such as the subject's perception of the hypothesis held by the hypnotist. We would also expect that pre-experimental inquiry of both subjects and hypnotists would indicate that many of them operate prior to any hypnotic interaction with the belief that tests of amnesia will prove loss of memory. A shared belief such as this will effectively prevent the pursuing of procedures likely to elicit recall of events during the so-called "trance."

The Problem of Individual Differences

We shall begin our role-theoretical formulation with the problem of individual differences.[4] The earlier hypnotists were not concerned with the fact that although some people responded to the hypnotic induction and performed the motions expected of them, others did not. In Mesmer's time, individual differences were attributed to inauspicious astrological conditions or to failures in technique. Later, nonperformances were regarded almost entirely as failures in technique. Such nonperformances were considered as not important enough for mention in a scientific report. Thus, the early reports all contain accounts of persons who were successfully hypnotized, and hardly any of those who did not perform according to expectations. In contemporary psychology the notion of individual differences is profound and inescapable. Any attempt to explain hypnotic behavior must take into account the fact that not all persons respond in the same way to standard induction procedures. One must raise the question: What are the conditions under which persons respond according to expectations when assigned the hypnotic role? Or, because individual differences are demonstrable, we would raise the further question: What accounts for observed differences in hypnotic role enactment?

The referent for the expression, "hypnotic role enactment," requires some elucidation. Today we employ a standard set of signs that we regard as characteristic of the hypnotic role. This standard set of signs has been codified in various kinds of scales. Friedlander and Sarbin (1938) prepared such a scale 25 years ago. More recently Hilgard and his associates (Weitzenhoffer and Hilgard, 1959) prepared a similar scale, which contains the behaviors presumably descriptive of all associated with the phenomena of hypnosis. These signs, as it turns out, are quite arbitrary and are modified from time to time. For example, in Mesmer's time the "crisis," something similar to an hysteroepileptic convulsion, was regarded as one of the signs of a trance. If he had had the knowledge and skill to construct a scale such as the Stanford Scale, he would have included the crisis as one of several items. When Braid began to work with influence phenomena some 50 to 60 years later,

[4] See Chapter 13 by Hilgard for a more detailed discussion of the problem of individual differences.

none of the subjects he encountered exhibited the crisis, so this sign was not incorporated into his descriptions of hypnosis. The standard signs that currently are grouped together in hypnotic scales are (a) catalepsy and other motoric behaviors; (b) posthypnotic behavior, that is, the subject receives an instruction during the treatment period which is carried out at some later time; (c) amnesias, that is, the person "forgets" certain events that occurred during the hypnotic performance, and (d) the modification of perceptual behavior, such as forming hallucinations. This set of signs provides the hypnotist with a list of expectations of how the subject is supposed to perform. If one performs according to this scale, then he is considered a good hypnotic subject; he is enacting the role according to the experimenter's expectations. If the subject responds to about half the items in the scale, then he is called moderately hypnotizable. If he can respond to none, then he is considered to be unhypnotizable. If he is hypnotizable by this standard, and some change in behavior occurs after the induction of hypnosis, it is assumed that the hypnotic induction, or the effects of the induction, was the responsible agent for the behavior change. We must now ask: what are the characteristics of the person or of the interaction situation that account for differences in hypnotic performance, that account for the fact that some people and not others enact this special role?

When we observe two people interacting in a hypnosis setting, we can describe their conduct from our present knowledge in terms of six social psychological variables, each of which has a contribution to make to the total performance. These six variables are: (1) the validity of the subject's role expectations, (2) accuracy of role perception, (3) role-relevant skills, (4) self-role congruence, (5) sensitivity to role demands, and (6) responsiveness to reinforcement provided by the audience. These will be discussed one at a time.

1. *The validity of the subject's role expectations.* Role expectations are acquired from the mass media and from communications in face-to-face settings. The hypnotist will generally not depend entirely on the fact that the subject has been exposed to mass media but will also include in the beginning of his induction a statement outlining his expectations. He expects the subject to cooperate, to listen carefully to everything he has to say, and so on. A personalized set of expectations are built upon those brought to the laboratory by the subject. If the subject is resistant to the expectancy statements made by the hypnotist, such as might occur when the subject is a member of a religious group that has prescribed the use of hypnosis, then he probably would not perform according to the hypnotist's expectations. However, the subject might have these expectations for the behavior of another person who was asked to play this role.

An experiment of Orne's (1959) illustrates the way expectations function. He used two classes of undergraduates for his experiment. In one class he demonstrated hypnotic phenomena in which he used a subject who had previously been hypnotized and given the instruction that when he accepted the hypnotic role there would appear a catalepsy of the dominant hand. For the second class of undergraduates, he omitted this instruction. In the course of the demonstration, Orne casually remarked that in hypnosis there is usually a spontaneous catalepsy of the dominant hand. Then he went on to other facts. To repeat, there were two undergraduate classes, one witnessed a standard hypnotic demonstration, and one a standard demonstration *plus* spontaneous pathology of the dominant hand of the subject. Subsequently he called for volunteers from both classes. These volunteers were tested one at a time by one of Orne's associates who was uninformed in regard to the antecedent conditions. As expected, those students who had witnessed the demonstration where the catalepsy-of-the-dominant-hand expectation had been built in, exhibited this behavior when they accepted the hypnotic role. In the second sample, where this expectation had not been incorporated into the role expectation, the phenomenon was absent.

Another approach is to determine the expectations that potential subjects hold prior to any direct experience with hypnosis. Most people who have been exposed to the mass media of communication, such as radio, television, newspapers, books, comic magazines, and so on, exhibit a fairly standard set of beliefs and expectations about hypnosis. From time to time in our classes at the university we have distributed questionnaires to undergraduates and asked them to indicate the kinds of behavior that are characteristic of hypnosis. We find a surprising consensus among our subjects, many of whom have never witnessed a hypnotic performance but know about it only vicariously through the mass media (Andersen, 1963). Thus, if a person who has been exposed to the mass media volunteers for an experiment in hypnosis, he is not naïve and uninformed. He comes to the experiment with a set of expectations in regard to his own conduct and that of the hypnotist. A number of other experiments have been reported that show unmistakably that the expectations one brings to a situation function in the outcome. This, of course, applies to any social psychological situation, not only to the hypnotic one.

2. *Accuracy of role perception.* A second variable that contributes to the effectiveness of role enactment is accuracy of role perception. This variable is not to be confused with the variable of role expectations, which refers to beliefs the subject holds before he enters the hypnosis situation, whereas role perception refers to the perceiving process *within* the hypnosis situation itself. Accuracy of role perception is not so important in hypnosis experiments where the hypnotic induction

procedure provides statements repetitively of what is expected and demanded of the subject. The variable of role perception is thereby swamped by providing all subjects with a plethora of information concerning their proper role behavior.

In the standard hypnosis experiment the subject knows or is told that he is to enact the role of the hypnotic subject when he perceives himself in a situation with a hypnotist. His knowledge is such, that when he comes into the waiting room and sees a young woman at a typewriter, he perceives her as the secretary and not as the experimenter. Consequently, he does not enact the hypnotic role or "go into a trance" but waits until a person identifies himself as the experimenter or clinician and emits behaviors that are perceived as cues to initiate his role performance. The opportunity to perform according to his beliefs and expectations occurs after the subject has perceived the other as enacting the role of hypnotist. Also, during the hypnosis session the hypnotist will continually emit cues that the subject will perceive, and these will provide further specification of the subject's role.

Although the variable of role perception may not be too important when college students are used as subjects, the variable may have significance in a clinical setting. In a university setting, a person behaves hypnotically in very few and very specific situations. In a clinical setting, a patient may be required to enact a submissive role in various situations, which are not clearly delineated from other situations. Also, certain behaviors demanded of the patient in these situations may be similar to what is demanded of him in the hypnosis situation. Under such conditions where both situational demands and behavioral requirements are not clearly distinguished, the patient may not know which cues are supposed to trigger off a full-blown enactment of the hypnotic role, and which cues are to trigger off behaviors that are only similar to some aspects of the hypnotic role. Of course, it is always possible to render a situation ambiguous so that a person's perception of the situation plays a crucial role. In a study by Fisher (1954) posthypnotic behaviors were elicited only when the subjects perceived the hypnotist-subject relationship as still existent. Furthermore, if the relationship had been broken, the reinstatement of the relationship would again permit the elicitation of posthypnotic responses.

3. *Role-relevant skills.* A third variable has to do with the skills that a person brings to the hypnotic situation. When we consider hypnosis with the aid of the dramatic role metaphor, we concurrently think of actors and directors, and of individual differences in histrionic skill in dramatic performing. Anyone with the least experience in amateur or professional dramatics recognizes that some persons respond readily to a role assignment and others are awkward and unconvincing. When we examine the items that comprise the usual scale of hypnotizability,

we find that many of these items have to do with motoric and gestural behavior. Sarbin and Lim (1963) performed an experiment to test whether, in fact, it was true that persons who responded well to the hypnotic induction were particularly skillful in role enactment in a nonhypnotic setting. A number of volunteers were hypnotized one at a time according to a standard method (Friedlander and Sarbin, 1938). From one to two weeks later each of these students appeared at the Department of Dramatic Arts where they individually engaged in pantomime improvisations. Members of the staff of Dramatic Arts rated the subjects on acting ability, not knowing what the subjects' scores were on the hypnotic scale. In general, those subjects who were particularly adept at taking the hypnotic role (which demanded certain kinds of gestural and other motoric behavior) were also rated high on the basis of the pantomime improvisations.

Another experiment was designed to illustrate a widespread misunderstanding in hypnosis and to meet a methodological problem. The problem is that most assessments of hypnotic skills have first tested subjects under nonhypnotic conditions in which they were told that only tests of imagination were being given under normal conditions, and that later they would be tested under hypnotic conditions (see Weitzenhoffer and Sjoberg, 1961). This procedure is likely to activate greater expectations and motivations to perform well in the hypnotic situation. An adequate design would require two independent groups of subjects, each adequately motivated to perform well. One group would be tested under hypnotic conditions, the other under nonhypnotic conditions. We carried out in Berkeley an experiment that fulfilled these requirements and that was designed to determine the base rates for motoric skills often involved in hypnosis research. Eight tasks from the Stanford Hypnotic Susceptibility Scale, Form A, were utilized, and presented to a group of 120 nonvolunteers as "imagination tasks." No hypnosis was utilized. The degree of responsiveness in this group was comparable to that of the group of 124 hypnotized subjects, the original Stanford standardization sample. We interpret our results as indicating that ability of subjects to present motoric phenomena without hypnosis is comparable to that obtained with hypnosis (Andersen and Sarbin, 1964).

In addition to the motoric skills, the hypnotic performance may call for perceptual skills, such as in the production of hallucinations. An experiment was designed to test for base rates in the production of visual hallucinations. The experiment that served as the stimulus for ours was reported by Underwood (1960) in which the induction of hypnosis was antecedent to producing perceptual changes tested by a little-known illusion. Underwood started with a pool of about 200 volunteer student subjects and hypnotized each of them individually. He selected six subjects who met all his criteria for being "deeply hypnotized." Included in his criteria of selection were not only the usual items drawn from standard scales but also the ability to produce vivid hallucinations with ease. In fact, he mentions that these subjects were selected mainly because they were able to create hallucinations. Then he proceeded to test the hypothesis that hypnotic induction produces changes in perceptual processes, by comparing these six subjects with the rest on a perceptual illusion test.

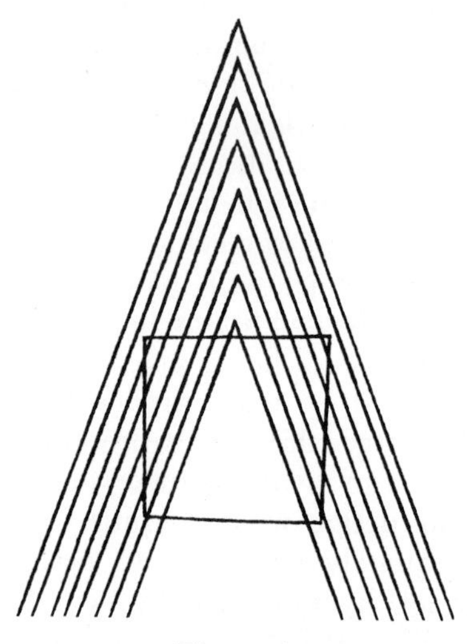

Figure 1.

In the standard illusion, the presence of a set of inverted *V*'s distorts a superimposed quadrangle. When a perfect square is superimposed, the top of the square appears to be wider than the bottom of the square (see Figure 1). By superimposing, one at a time, a number of quadrangles that vary in their degree of "squareness," the experimenter can determine the amount of distortion produced by the set of inverted *V*'s. In this experiment, the quadrangles were first presented in the absence of the inverted *V*'s, the field or ground. Underwood instructed his six subjects to hallucinate the absent field. If they could hallucinate the field, then their perception of the quadrangle would be distorted in the same way as when the actual inverted *V*'s were presented later. Underwood reported that the hypnotic hallucination of a nonpresent field (the set of inverted *V*'s) produced a degree of distortion in the perception of the quadrangles similar to that produced by the actual presence of the inverted *V*'s. Thus the conclusion was drawn, although cautiously, that being hypnotized changed the perceptual apparatus in such a way that the visual functions were modified.

We repeated this experiment without using hypnotic inductions. We used 120 subjects in three classes in undergraduate psychology. We presented the same material except that we instructed the subjects to imagine vividly the presence of the background (the inverted *V*'s), to throw themselves into the task, and so on. There was no mention of hypnosis, no hypnotic induction, only instructions to the subjects to use their "powers of imagination." Of these 120 subjects, 11 (9 per cent) were able to report the distortion of the quadrangles in the absence of the background. In Underwood's experiment, five of his six hypnotic subjects were able to report hallucinations out of a total of almost 200 subjects; that is, 3 per cent. The conclusion to be drawn from this (and other studies not reported here, see Chapter 14 by Barber) is that hypnotic induction is unnecessary to obtain changes in behavior either of a motoric kind or of a perceptual kind. Rather, behavioral changes may follow, among other things, from unwitting preselection of subjects on the variables under study (Sarbin and Andersen, 1963).

4. *Self-role congruence.* Another variable that is readily applicable to everyday behavior as well as to hypnotic behavior is the congruence of the role requirements with characteristics of the self. Andersen has recently completed a study (1963) in which he called this variable "role comfort" in connection with the acceptance of a role that is considerably dissimilar to one's usual roles, that demands a considerable degree of commitment, and that is potentially embarrassing. The role of the hypnosis subject is this kind of role. All of us feel more comfortable in some roles than in others. Presumably we can do a more convincing job of enacting a role if we are comfortable in it. How do we test whether a person is comfortable in the role that he is asked to perform? A number of recent studies are leading us to an understanding of this variable. Ås (1963), Shor, Orne, and O'Connell (1962) and Andersen and Sarbin (1964) have approached this problem by designing several questionnaires that tap self characteristics that presumably make the hypnotic role a comfortable one. One of these, for example, is *absorption in the role.* Most of the roles in which we engage in everyday life require only a minimum of concentration or absorption. However, a person engaged in his daily occupations may be called upon to become deeply absorbed in some aspect of his work, and as a result pays no attention to an incidental stimulus.

In our questionnaires we have found that the self-descriptive items that correlated with effectiveness of hypnotic performance fell into three categories: (1) items referring directly to the hypnotic role, such as: "There are things that would worry me about being hypnotized;" (2) items denoting the ability to become deeply absorbed in a role or some event, for example: "I sometimes find that when I'm studying hard I don't notice the passage of time;" (3) items denoting the ability to resist distraction; an example is: "I find it difficult to read or study in a noisy or busy place." We have obtained correlations with these three types of items using both hypnotic performance and performance on hypnoticlike tasks ("imagination tasks") as criterion measures. With hypnotic performance as the criterion measure, the role-absorption items tend to produce higher correlations than do the ability-to-resist-distraction items. This finding is similar to that reported by Ås (1962). The questions that inquire *directly* about the role behavior of the hypnosis subject, however, tend to produce the highest correlations with criterion performance on hypnotic or hypnotic-like tasks.[5]

5. *Sensitivity to role demands.* This is the fifth in the set of variables that presumably accounts for individual differences in role enactment. When a therapist and patient or an experimenter and subject interact, there must be considered not only the expectations that each brings to the situation, not only the accuracy of the perceptions of each other, not only the skills that each possesses, but also the demands of the situation. The demands of the situation are overriding and have been described in other contexts as the recognition of mores. To illustrate, we can point to the studies carried out to demonstrate the operation of a cognitive-effective variable: perceptual defense. To describe these experiments briefly, subjects were shown a list of words flashed on a screen, some taboo, others, neutral. In general, the subjects had difficulty in reporting taboo words. The premature inference that was drawn at that time was that the inability to recognize the taboo words was due to the operation of a process called perceptual defense. Later experiments showed that subjects, when they perceive themselves in the roles of proper ladies and gentlemen, are not likely, in the presence of an experimenter, to employ such taboo words, even though the instructions to report are clear. There was an overriding demand not to utter the taboo words; the subjects were not only acting in the role of experimental subjects, they were also enacting their proper social roles taking into account the mores or role demands. These studies are somewhat oversimplified here, but our description is close to the facts. The role demands were not taken into account (Sarbin and Chun, unpublished ms.).

Orne (1962) showed unmistakably the operation of role demands. He designed an experiment in which a sample of subjects had been hypnotized. That is to say, they had been tested on their ability to perform the hypnotic role. A second set of subjects had been motivated

[5] In the study by Andersen (1963), three scales were constructed several months prior to the experiment proper. Each scale was simply a set of items that seemed to be rationally related. The scales and their correlation with hypnotic performance (Stanford Hypnotic Susceptibility Scale, Form C) are as follows: (1) items referring directly to the hypnotic role (Role Comfort Scale), $r = .47$; (2) ability to become absorbed in a role (Role Involvement Scale), $r = .40$; (3) ability to resist distraction (Attention-focusing Scale), $r = .10$.

to *simulate* the hypnotic role. Experienced hypnotists were unable to distinguish whether a subject was hypnotized or simulating. Earlier experiments had demonstrated only that waking behavior was somehow a little different from hypnotic behavior, but this was because of a failure to recognize differential role demands. In Orne's study the situation was so constructed that the simulating subjects were strongly motivated to perform and to convince the experimenter that they were genuinely enacting a role. Another method of assessing the explicit demands in the hypnosis situation is to analyze the content of the hypnotic induction protocol.

An analysis of the eye-closure instructions of Stanford Scale, Form A (Weitzenhoffer and Hilgard, 1959, pp. 13–16) produces 158 identifiable statements. Of these, 101 statements refer to relaxation directly, or to the supposed concomitants of relaxation. The use of this scale would certainly communicate to the subject that relaxation is a central aspect of his role. The remaining statements fall almost entirely into two broad categories: (1) general instructions, and requests to listen, to cooperate, to concentrate, to let things happen, and to pay attention; (2) descriptions of what hypnosis is like, such as, "Hypnosis is not fearful," "It's not mysterious," "It's not embarrassing," and so forth. These instructions can be regarded as role demands concerning the proper behavior of the hypnosis subject.

Kroger (1963) utilized still another method of assessing the demands in the experimental situation, although he studied test-taking behavior instead of hypnotic behavior. He designed two test-taking situations that were identical concerning the behavior demanded of the subjects, but differed concerning the available cues in the situation relating to what was being measured by the tests. The cues in one situation suggested a test of "military effectiveness," in the other a test of "artistic ability." Significant differences in test-taking behavior were obtained between the two situations.

Another approach to the problem of role demands is to examine the procedures employed in an entertainment situation to avoid embarrassment. In the entertainment situation where a large number of persons are present, there is an implied contract between the experimenter and the subject, indicating "if you do something for me, I will do something for you in return," a form of the standard contract in any social interaction. In a public setting, the possibility exists that the experimenter may be embarrassed if the subject does not perform according to expectations. To prevent embarrassment is a potent role demand in our polite society. A few years ago a hypnotist received advance publicity for his television act. A volunteer coed had been previously hypnotized; $100,000 in paper currency was placed on the table. The hypnotized subject sat three feet away from the money and was told by the hypnotist that if she reached over and took the money she could have it all. But earlier, before he had given this challenge, he had used an instruction of this nature: "You cannot get out of this chair. No matter what you do, you can't get out of this chair." Of course, to reach the money, she would have to remove herself from the chair. The subject did not budge. A person versed in role theory would not have been surprised by this at all; first, a relationship had been built up between the two interactants on the basis of prior sessions, and second, there may have been 40,000,000 people in the audience and this would have been a great embarrassment to the hypnotist. Anyone reconstructing his own social experiences will recall the lengths to which he will go to prevent oneself or others from meeting an embarrassing situation.

In addition to the variable of potential embarrassment, there is the matter of the subject's belief in the genuineness of the offer of the $100,000. For the subject to perceive the situation as a genuine possibility of getting $100,000, some of the following requirements would have to be met. The provider of the money should be identified. Money always has an owner. This provider should sign a formal contract in the presence of legal counsel and the subject, which commits him to the potential loss of this money. The act which if carried out by the subject would give her the money should be carefully specified. The details of transmittal and depositing of the money should be decided. And, the actual amount the subject would receive, after all tax deductions, should be computed and presented to her. The meeting of these requirements would more adequately test the hypothesis that the effect of "hypnosis" kept the woman from getting $100,000. Also, this approach would also put the embarrassment variable to a more severe test. Then we would be in a better position to know if potential enrichment is stronger than potential embarrassment.

Thus far, we have discussed five variables that individually or in combination account for individual differences in responsiveness to the hypnotic induction. The sixth variable contains the notion of social reinforcement.

6. *Responsiveness to reinforcement provided by the audience.* The audience in most hypnotic experiments is singular, the therapist or experimenter, but audiences may be multiple (and complex) such as when hypnosis is used in an entertainment setting. In considering size of audience, it has frequently been noted by experienced hypnotists that for a larger audience, the number of volunteers who can perform hypnotic behaviors is greater than for a small audience. This suggests that the size and the nature of the audience is a potent factor in determining performance. Before going on with size of audience, let us mention something about the nature of the audience in social psychological settings.

Experiments have been reported in the literature that indicate clearly that the depth of hypnotic response is greater when the hypnotist is a prestigeful person, such as a professor, a doctor, or a therapist, than when the hypnotist is a student (Das, 1960). This occurs even when the same person is enacting the role of hypnotizer, at one time introducing himself as "Doctor so-and-so" and at another time as "Mr. so-and-so." Thus the role of the potentially reinforcing person (the audience) has something to do with the outcome, as we know from other contexts, as well as the number of persons who make up the audience.

In an experiment by Coe (1964), one group of hypnosis subjects were told that four or five clinical psychology students would be observing them through a one-way mirror during the hypnosis session. At the beginning of the hour, an accomplice of the experimenter knocked on the door and reported that "everyone is here now." The only actual observer was this accomplice, but the actual presence of observers could not be determined by the subject through the one-way mirror. The effect of the audience reduced the degree of hypnotic responsiveness in this group as compared to a control group. Coe interprets the reduced responsiveness as due to his "audience subjects" feeling somewhat defensive and uneasy while being observed by a group of clinical psychology students with whom there was no possibility of interaction. The only "audience subject" that scored higher than his matched partner in the control group was, significantly, an actor. Except for this subject, all the subjects in his audience group appeared uneasy about being observed and tended to constrict their hypnotic behavior. Coe's results point to several variables that could be investigated, such as: (1) the effect of possibilities of interaction between actor and audience; (2) the effect upon the subject of the purposes of the observers; (3) the complexity of the audience, that is, the different roles of various members of the audience, (4) the relationship of the audience to the hypnotist, and (5) the relationship of the audience to the subject.

SUMMARY

In this chapter, we have sketched a set of constructs to facilitate the analysis of hypnosis. These constructs are features of role theory, a contemporary social psychological formulation of human interaction. To prepare the way for the employment of the role metaphor, we first laid out the basis for the skeptical-credulous polarity. The assignment of role theory to the skeptical branch of the scientific family follows logically from the nonemployment of mentalistic, superempirical constructs. Then, through selected illustrations, we attempted to show that the various theories of hypnosis, propounded from time to time, were no more than reformulations occasioned by the discovery of a new metaphor. To speak of hypnosis as a role is another in a long line of metaphors. Its virtue lies in its capacity to provide the raw material for forming hypotheses that are subject to empirical examination (Andersen, 1963; Coe, 1964). In using the role metaphor, we are cognizant of the possibility that some readers might equate hypnotic role enactment (role playing) with sham behavior. Sham is not a simple concept. The appraisal of the degree of genuineness, sincerity, and earnestness with which a person enacts *any* role is not easily accomplished. We tried to show that one of the reasons for interpreting role behavior as sham behavior lies in the widespread use of the equivocal term "role playing." In some settings "playing" is opposite to "working," in others, "playing" and "working" are not differentiated (as in playing a violin, playing professional baseball, and so on).

One feature that differentiates role-theoretical and other social psychological formulations of hypnosis from the more credulous theories is the nonemployment of the trance either as a descriptive device or as a mediational process. Role theory attempts to account for hypnotic phenomena by seeking out the antecedent and concurrent events that are associated with individual differences in the convincingness, validity, or propriety with which a person performs the hypnotic role. To account for these individual differences, six variables are proposed: (1) the validity of the subject's role expectations; (2) the accuracy of the subject's role perceptions; (3) the presence of role-relevant skills; (4) the degree of congruence of the requirements of the role with self-characteristics; (5) sensitivity to role demands; and (6) responsiveness to reinforcement provided by audiences. The same variables are claimed to be useful in analyzing individual differences in the effectiveness, validity, or convincingness of any role performance.

REFERENCES

Ås, A. (1962). "A note on distractibility and hypnosis," *Amer. J. clin. Hyp.*, **5**, 135–137.

——— (1963). "Hypnotizability as a function of nonhypnotic experiences," *J. abnorm. soc. Psychol.*, **66**, 142–150.

Andersen, M. (1963). *Correlates of Hypnotic Performance: An Historical and Role-Theoretical Analysis.* Unpublished doctoral dissertation, University of California, Berkeley.

Andersen, M. and Kroger, R. O. (1964). "Braid's last theory and manuscript, a re-translation into English. In preparation.

Andersen, M. and Sarbin, T. R. (1963). "Correlates of responsiveness on hypnotic-like tasks."

Andersen, M. and Sarbin, T. R. (1964). "Base rate expectancies and motoric alterations in hypnosis," *Int. J. clin. exp. Hyp.* **12**, 147–156.

Barber, T. X. and Calverly, D. S. (1962). "'Hypnotic behavior' as a function of task motivation," *J. Psychol.*, **54**, 363–389.
Bernheim, H. (1903). *Hypnotisme, Suggestion, Psychothérapie. Avec considerations nouvelles sur l'hystérie.* Paris: Octave Doin.
Braid, J. (1843). *Neurohypnology: On the Rationale of Nervous Sleep Considered in Relation with Animal Magnetism.* London: John Churchill.
——— (1960). *Braid on Hypnotism.* New York: Julian. Edited by H. E. Waite.
Bramwell, J. M. (1903). *Hypnotism.* London: Grant Richards.
Coe, W. C. (1964). *The Heuristic Value of Role Theory and Hypnosis.* Unpublished doctoral dissertation, University of California, Berkeley.
Das, J. P. (1960). "Prestige effects on body-sway suggestibility," *J. abnorm. soc. Psychol.*, **61**, 487–488.
Fisher, S. (1954). "The role of expectancy in the performance of post-hypnotic behavior," *J. abnorm. soc. Psychol.*, **49**, 503–507.
Friedlander, J. W. and Sarbin, T. R. (1938). "The depth of hypnosis," *J. abnorm. soc. Psychol.*, **33**, 453–475.
Galdston, I. (1940). *Progress in Medicine.* New York: Knopf.
——— (1948). "Mesmer and animal magnetism," *Ciba Symposia*, **9**, 832–837.
Gibson, J. J. (1960). "The concept of the stimulus in psychology," *Amer. Psychologist*, **15**, 694–703.
Janet, P. (1925). *Psychological Healing*, Vols. I and II (translated by E. Paul and C. Paul). New York: Macmillan.
Koch, S. (1959). "Epilogue to study I." In S. Koch (ed.), *Psychology: A Study of a Science*, Vol. III, 729–788. New York: McGraw-Hill.
Kroger, R. (1963). *Role-Theoretical Analysis of Test-Taking Behavior.* Unpublished doctoral dissertation, University of California, Berkeley.
Nash, H. (1963). "The role of metaphor in psychological theory," *Behav. Sci.*, **8**, 336–345.
Orne, M. T. (1959). "The nature of hypnosis: artifact and essence," *J. abnorm. soc. Psychol.*, **58**, 277–299.
——— (1962). "On the social psychology of the psychological experiment: with particular reference to demand characteristics and their implications," *Amer. Psychologist*, **17**, 776–783.
Preyer, W. (1881). *Die Entdeckung des Hypnotismus.* Berlin: Paetel.
Ryle, G. (1949). *The Concept of Mind.* New York: Barnes and Noble.
Sadow, L. and Suslick, A. (1961). "Simulation of a previous psychotic state," *Amer. Med. Assoc. Archives of Gen. Psychiat.*, **4**, 452–458.
Sarbin, T. R. (1943). "The concept of role-taking," *Sociometry*, **6**, 273–284.
——— (1950). "Contribution to role-taking theory. I. Hypnotic behavior," *Psychol. Rev.*, **57**, 255–270.
——— (1954). "Role theory." In Lindzey, G. (ed.), *Handbook of Social Psychology.* Cambridge, Mass.: Addison-Wesley.
——— (1962). "A historical sketch of theories of hypnosis." In L. Postman (ed.), *Psychology in the Making.* New York: Knopf.
——— (1964). "A role-theoretical interpretation of psychological change." In P. Worchel and D. Byrne (eds.) *Psychological Change.* New York: Wiley.
Sarbin, T. R. and Andersen, M. L. (1963). "Base-rate expectancies and perceptual alterations in hypnosis," *Brit. J. soc. clin. Psychol.*, **2**, 112–121.

SARBIN, T. R. and CHUN, K. "Role-demands, stimulus types and perceptual defense." Unpublished manuscript.

SARBIN, T. R. and JONES, D. S. (1956). "An experimental analysis of role behavior," *J. abnorm. soc. Psychol.*, **60**, 236–241.

SARBIN, R. T. and LIM, D. T. (1963). "Some evidence in support of the role-taking hypothesis in hypnosis," *Int. J. clin. exp. Hyp.* **11**, 98–103.

SCHEFF, T. J. (1963). "The role of the mentally ill and the dynamics of mental disorder: a research framework," *Sociometry*, **4**, 436–453.

SHOR, R. E., ORNE, M. T., and O'CONNELL, D. (1962). "Validation and cross-validation of a scale of self-reported personal experiences which predict hypnotizability," *J. Psychol.*, **53**, 55–75.

STANISLAVSKI, C. (1961). *An Actor Prepares*. New York: Theater Arts Books.

SUTCLIFFE, J. P. (1960). "'Credulous' and 'skeptical' view of hypnotic behavior," *Int. J. clin. exp. Hyp.* **8**, 73–102.

TURBAYNE, C. M. (1962). *The Myth of Metaphor*. New Haven and London: Yale University Press.

UNDERWOOD, H. W. (1960). "The validity of hypnotically induced visual hallucinations," *J. abnorm. soc. Psychol.*, **61**, 39–46.

WEITZENHOFFER, A. (1963). "The nature of hypnosis," *Amer. J. clin. Hyp.*, **5**, 295–321.

WEITZENHOFFER, A. and HILGARD, E. R. (1959). *Stanford Hypnotic Susceptibility Scale, Forms A and B*. Palo Alto, Calif.: Consulting Psychologists Press.

WEITZENHOFFER, A. and SJOBERG, B. M. (1961). "Suggestibility with and without 'induction of hypnosis,'" *J. nerv. ment. Dis.*, **132**, 204–220.

12

Stimulus-Response Theory of Hypnosis

WILLIAM E. EDMONSTON, Jr.[1]
Washington University School of Medicine

BECAUSE we learned from our fathers and they from theirs and they from theirs, the perpetuation of error is one of the most reliable of human behaviors. It is one of our most cherished defenses against new ideas and change. Thus, many ideas may be repeated and repeated throughout the history of man before they are finally recognized and drawn together into a formal theory.

If many ideas form a theory, we might then ask: How does one date its beginnings? Unfortunately, the point in time at which a theory has its beginnings in the vast ocean of human thought is about as simple to designate as the point in time at which a wave becomes a wave in an ocean of water. Are we, for example, to say that a stimulus-response learning theory began with Clark L. Hull, or with Pavlov, or Bechterev,

[1] Supported in part by USPHS Undergraduate Training Grant in Psychiatry (MH 5938) and by USPHS Research Training Biological Sciences Grant in Psychiatry (MH 7081). The author is now at Colgate University.

or Carnap, or William James, or Charles Peirce; or do we need go back further in time to Hume, to Locke, to Hobbes, or beyond?

Perhaps the British associationists are the men to choose for dating purposes, or are we on safer ground to *assume* that this theory had a beginning in time and avoid the problem altogether? Although neither choice is welcome, their presence makes us aware that theories grow out of a vast panorama of historical forces. As an example, *modern* stimulus-response learning theory is usually dated by the well-known works of Bechterev and Pavlov in the late 1800's and early 1900's, but it was not until much later (Hull, 1943) that a well-systemized stimulus-response learning theory appeared.

It is also clear that some theories are never theories at all, but merely a loose confederation of statements and hypotheses. This is particularly true with regard to the so-called "stimulus-response (S-R) theory of hypnosis." As we will see, the dating of its precise beginnings is virtually impossible, for we find that throughout the history of modern hypnosis, statements and hypotheses have appeared that are closely akin to statements and hypotheses set forth in more formalized and rigorously determined theories of behavior. Through this apparent kinship, these statements have been loosely and informally grouped together and misnamed a theory.

Our task, then, is to show that hypnosis, like the statements made about it, bears a close enough resemblance to all human behavior that it can be subsumed under the more formalized and rigorous hypotheses of an already established S-R theory of behavior.

S-R LEARNING THEORY

Regardless of to whom we attribute the beginnings of S-R theory and to whose particular set of notions we adhere, S-R, conditioned-reflex, associationistic learning theory is basically a formal, attempted explanation of infrahuman and human behavior. Behavior is considered to be an organization of S-R pairings. Thus, " . . . the whole organismal activity is subsumed in the two words, stimulus and response. The organism, like the cell, does not act; it only reacts" (Smith, 1949, p. 37). Of course, if this is the nature of behavior—and it would seem the only reasonable, scientific approach—then a great many cherished, erroneous beliefs will cease being perpetuated.

Principles of Learning

Throughout this chapter we will concern ourselves—in varying degrees—with the manner in which hypnosis adheres to the basic principles of S-R (conditioned) learning, and thus shows itself to be a special case (verbal) of learning (conditioning). We will not consider here many of the subtle, but quite meaningful, problems of learning theory per se, except as they might more directly relate to hypnosis. Excellent summaries of the various learning theories, both associative and field, are already available (such as Hilgard, 1948; Osgood, 1953). Also, we will not present evidence for the existence of these general principles, for this would be beyond the scope of this work and such evidence can be found in the general body of psychological literature. The principles listed and defined below will form the foundation of our argument that for hypnosis, as for all human behavior, an S-R approach offers the most promise for the future understanding, prediction, and quantification of the behavior. (This list is not inclusive, but is a selection of the main features of learned behavior.)

The acquisition of responses to stimuli is depicted by:

1. *Facilitation by practice.* Within limitations, the probability of the occurrence of a given response is increased by repeated performance of that response. Repetitions of an S-R pairing facilitates the elicitation of the R of that pair to later S presentations.
2. *Practice curve negatively accelerated.* The relationship of the number of response evocations per unit time shows a progressive deceleration.
3. *Decrement with interpolated activity.* Interpolated activity between two performances of a response reduces the probability of its repetition.
4. *Massed-spaced practice.* The decrement occurring with interpolated activity is greater (lower probability of response evocation) when original practice was temporally massed than when original practice was interspersed with rest periods.
5. *Recovery of response.* With resumed practice, the decrement which occurred with interpolated activity will be recovered in a negatively accelerated manner.
6. *Savings.* Less practice is required for the recovery of a response than was necessary to bring it to its original level of facilitation.
7. *Transfer of training.* Under certain specifiable conditions (see Osgood, 1953, for summary) a stimulus other than that used in original practice will elicit the original response, and/or the practice of one S-R sequence will facilitate the evocation of the R of another different S-R pairing.

Notice at this point that in the presentation of these principles we have meticulously avoided the use of the term "learning." Performance is all we can measure. Learning, like "habit," is inferential.

HYPNOSIS AND S-R LEARNING THEORY

In 1890 William James wrote: "The law of habit dominates hypnotic subjects even more than it does waking ones" (James, 1890, p. 601).

Although given credit for encouraging the use of the term "habit" (Hilgard and Marquis, 1940), James was not the first to use it in connection with hypnosis. As early as 1844 hypnosis explained as "a habit of intense abstraction" (Royal Manchester Institution, 1844, p. 138) was attributed to Braid; and in the next year Braid himself used this same descriptive phrase (Braid, 1845). To be sure, some may argue that the meaning placed on "habit" in the 1840's could be considerably different from that more than a century later. Habit, today, is varied in meaning, from the probability of a response induced by a single S-R pairing to a complex, largely automatic, "unconscious" series of behaviors. It would seem, however, that when Braid (1844) stated that hypnosis was "a systematic mode practiced for dethroning these noble attributes [reason and will] and reducing rational man to a state of abject and helpless imbecility" (Braid, 1844, p. 226), he could as well have been alluding to habit as a series of automatic behaviors. (It would also seem that he was quite in error in the latter portion of his statement.)

Braid, of course, was not the only individual to precede James in using the concept of habit with reference to hypnosis. Both Wood (1851) and Bennett (1851) spoke of ideas suggested by words or actions being the prime movers of behavior, and that their ability to call forth behavior was based on the "laws of association." At least as early as 1851 we find the expression "laws of association" being offered as an explanation for the ability of ideas, conveyed through words and action, to call forth the behaviors of hypnosis (Wood, 1851; Bennett, 1851). Not only did these men (and no doubt many others before them) anticipate Bernheim's ideomotor explanation of hypnosis, but Pavlov's notions on the relation of natural sleep to hypnosis as well. Bennett, for example, tells us that the condition of hypnosis "seems analogous to that of sleep or dreaming, in which certain faculties of the mind are active, and may be even stimulated into excessive action, whilst others are suspended" (Bennett, 1851, p. 17); whereas Wood speaks of only certain nervous centers being in a state of rest, others remaining active (Wood, 1851).

Bernheim, of course, was noted for expounding the notion that in hypnosis ideas are transformed into action, and Moll (1894) explicitly brings this together with the "laws of association," through which chains of concepts are elaborated. He was very much aware that ideas are stimuli to action. Thus, from the very early workers to the more modern (Hull, 1933; Young, 1941; Weitzenhoffer, 1953; Das, 1958b, 1959a) an S-R theory of hypnosis is not only feasible, but necessary—"... even though we may seem thus to have gone back to the old ideomotor hypothesis" (Young, 1941, p. 100).

The Stimulus in Hypnosis

Some writers have been greatly concerned with the question of the *apparent* discrepancy between the magnitude of the stimulus, S, and that of the response, R (for example, White, 1941; Sarbin, 1950, 1962). These same authors also ponder what is most likely a meaningless voluntary–involuntary dichotomizing of human behavior in the "problem" of transcendence of "voluntary capacities" under hypnosis.

Both of these points were dealt with by Hudgins in 1933, although he was not explicitly concerned with hypnosis. Basing much of his work on Cason's (1922), who conditioned the pupillary reflex to light stimulation to a bell, shock, and a telephone buzzer, Hudgins (1933) conditioned pupillary contraction and dilation to a bell, hand movements, and words. By pairing a light stimulus with a bell, hand clenching (or relaxing), and the word "contract" (or "relax"), a conditioned pupillary reflex was established to all three. He found also that the reflex could be conditioned to nonsense syllables, to the whispered words and even to the subjects' thought of the words "contract" or "relax." The conditioned responses (CR's) elicited could not be distinguished from the unconditioned by latency, and "in no case during all of these measurements did the response disappear. The responses [to words] were larger, as a rule, than the responses to the bell or the hand movements, and they tended to continue as long as the tests were made" (Hudgins, 1933, p. 33); that is, experimental extinction was inoperative on verbal stimuli. Furthermore, the conditioned pupillary response lasted, without retraining, up to 15 days and longer. Thus, from this one study alone we can see that the "discrepancy" noted by others (White, 1941; Sarbin, 1950, 1962) is only apparent, and that without an explicit definition of "voluntary" or "involuntary," these terms create more problems than they solve.

Actually, Hudgins (1933) was not the first to offer experimental evidence for words as conditioned stimuli. Platonov (1959) points out that as early as 1911, in Bechterev's laboratory, conditioned responses were being elaborated to verbal stimuli. Speaking of the works of others (Pshonik, 1952; Felberbaum *et al.*, 1953) and his own 1926 efforts, he (Platonov, 1959) informs us that not only have gross motor movements been reliably conditioned to verbal stimuli, but various physiological responses as well (respiration rate, pulse rate, and vascular reactions).

What is perhaps even more instructive with regard to the effectiveness of verbal stimuli is the finding that words can be used as conditioned stimuli to instruct the *opposite* of the natural physiological response—to reverse the unconditioned response. For example, in a series of studies from 1928 to 1932, Platonov and his associates found they could obviate the natural respiratory response to cold stimulation by coupling it with the word "heat," reverse the effects of intoxication by verbal stimulation to the contrary, reduce pulmonary ventilation by verbal stimulation of reduced work load, and produce the reversal of many other natural physiological responses. In fact, Platonov offers an excellent summary of the Russian and some of the Scandinavian literature demonstrating the reversal of natural processes through words as conditioned stimuli (Platonov, 1959, pp. 106–119).

It is not difficult to see striking similarities to the evidence noted above in other areas of study. The "placebo effect" is a ready example of the effectiveness of verbal stimulation. Wolf (1950), for example, found that pharmacological drug action could be reduced or reversed, and that sterile water could yield physiological changes usually attributed to pharmacological agents through appropriate verbal stimuli. The literature is replete with such observations. The present interest in verbal conditioning (Krasner, 1958) also reflects the importance of words as stimuli to human action. It is the semantics, not the sonorics (sound image), that dictate human responses to verbal stimuli (Shvarts, 1948, 1949).

Das (1959b), noting findings similar to Hudgins (1933) with regard to the extinction of verbal conditioning, found a nonsignificant relationship between acquisition and extinction, a relationship that is significant in usual classical conditioning. It may well be that verbal conditioning leaves its mark on the organism in a manner quite different from nonverbal conditioning, and might be partially irreversible. At the very least, it appears to be highly resistive to extinction.

This resistance to extinction has been clearly demonstrated in studies actually involving hypnosis (neither Hudgins [1933], nor Das [1959b] used hypnosis). Surveying 25 years of literature, Weitzenhoffer (1950) found that posthypnotic suggestions (verbal conditioning) were reported to have lasted indefinitely. Kellogg (1929) reports an initial (first three weeks) decrement in the strength of the posthypnotic instruction, followed by a persistence lasting, apparently, indefinitely. Patten (1930), repeating Kellogg's work and, controlling for practice effect, found a persistence of at least one month. Wells (1940) reported a duration of a year, and Hull (1933), a month or more. In Weitzenhoffer's own study (1950), a single subject demonstrated an effective duration of posthypnotic instructions ranging from five to 134 days. Although no controlled experimentation has been conducted, rapid induction signals have demonstrated an effectiveness over a period of eight or nine months with no intervening reinforcement (practice) in the experience of this author.

Thus, as early as the beginning of this century experimental evidence that verbal stimuli (words) were extremely important in the evocation of human behavior was appearing. The fact that these types of stimuli seem to be in a class by themselves with respect to their high resistance to extinction, both in the hypnotic and the nonhypnotic literature, draws our attention still further to their importance. We must agree with Salter (1949) that the evidence is not to be ignored, and words as stimuli to action are fully as powerful, if not more so than nonverbal stimuli. Perhaps we should cease wondering why the response is so great in relation to the stimuli, and begin to wonder why, in some cases, the response is not much greater than it is.

In the following sections of this chapter we will explore some of the already stated theories and positions concerning hypnosis as a predictable response to environmental stimuli (primarily verbal). This discussion will point up the large body of experimental evidence in support of the S-R position, which may finally lead us out of the abyss of perpetual error in at least this one area of human behavior.

THE PAVLOVIAN THEORY

After his graduation from the University of St. Petersburg, Ivan Petrovich Pavlov spent a year with Heidenhain, during which he developed the technique of the chronic fistula. This was later applied, not only to the stomach, but to other aspects of the digestive process. From his early interest in gastrointestinal secretions and their neural concomitants came the development of the studies that gave rise to the elaboration and refinement of the concepts of conditioned reflexes. As he observed and considered the various behaviors of his experimental animals (primarily dogs), certain "laws" were hypothesized that offered a general theory of neural functioning. This theory was generalized to the behaviors of human beings, including hypnosis; and at the age of 80, when most men are completing their careers, Pavlov launched into a new phase of his already brilliant career—psychiatry. Just as his work on the gastric fistula led directly to and became a part of his studies on conditioned reflexes, so, now, did he attempt to expand the conditioned reflex hypotheses into a theory of types and an explanation of human neuroses and psychoses. However, "this attempt to erect such general and far-reaching truths on so limited a base was perhaps the greatest fallacy of Pavlov's work," according to Gantt in his introduction to his translation of Pavlov's work (Pavlov, 1941, p. 28).

Only past, present, and future investigations will determine whether Pavlov's theoretical suppositions are fallacious or not. It is enough for us here to familiarize ourselves with his ideas, keeping in mind that Pavlov based his theories on animal experimentation. This is not to obviate their worth by questioning the validity of extrapolation, but to caution the reader against undue enthusiasm.

One of Pavlov's most significant contributions to psychology and hypnosis was his notation of the second-signal system, or the verbal, inferential capabilities of the human organism. The dichotomy of first- and second-signal systems closely follows the dichotomies of subcortical-cortical, concrete-abstract, and nonverbal-verbal. Thus, abstraction—the work of the second-signal system—". . . is achieved because the image of objects and actions expressed in words and ideas replaces their concrete effect on the organism" [via the conditioned reflex bonds] (Platonov, 1959, p. 16). This concrete effect is the response of the first-signal system.

If Pavlov's theory of hypnosis could be characterized by one word, that word would be "inhibition."[2] Inhibition, the antithesis of excitation, is the protector of the organism, protecting it from excessive, damaging stimulation, from stimulation without survival purpose (unreinforced conditioned stimuli), and from monotonous stimulation. Thus, inhibition is a form of exhaustion, dichotomized into external and internal categories. The former relates to passive, unconditioned inhibition, originating outside the original activity; whereas the latter refers to active, conditioned inhibition, developed within the same activity, such as extinction. The relationship between internal inhibition and sleep is most important in placing wakefulness, hypnosis, and sleep in proper theoretical perspective.

Sleep

Sleep is characterized by inhibition, and is subdivided into three categories: total, partial, and "broken-up." For Pavlov, there was no particular sleep center, as others posit (for example, Nauta, 1946), but rather an inhibitory involvement of the major portions of both cerebral hemispheres and other subcortical areas—especially the midbrain. Thus, in the case of total sleep, such spread of inhibitory effect is considered most extensive. Partial sleep, although also depicted by widespread inhibition of the CNS, is marked by the presence of regions of excitation or wakefulness. As we will see, these regions of "rapport" and this particular phase of sleep hold a central position in Pavlov's theory of hypnosis.

Finally, the third type of sleep is the "broken-up" sleep. This most closely approximates wakefulness, in that there is a "complex mobile mosaic" (Platonov, 1959, p. 27) of cells in both the inhibitory and excitory stage of functioning, the advantage being quantitatively to the inhibition side. Wakefulness, however, is an irradiation of excitation

[2] Pavlov's former professor, Heidenhain, concurred as early as 1888 in the view ". . . that the cause of the phenomena of hypnotism lies in the inhibition of the activity of the ganglion-cells of the cerebral cortex . . ." (Heidenhain, 1888, p. 46).

over the cortex. Thus there is an inverse, quantitative relationship between inhibition and excitation leading to the opposite gross characteristics of sleep and wakefulness. Simply:

$$Sl \text{ (sleep)} = fI \text{ (inhibition)} \tag{1}$$

where

$$I = 1/E \text{ (excitation)} \tag{2}$$

As E approaches zero, I approaches infinity and total sleep is realized. Or, as I decreases and approaches zero, E approaches infinity and wakefulness abounds. (Neither Pavlov nor his students dwelled on degrees of wakefulness, as they did on degrees of sleep.)

Although transitions from more or less inhibition to more or less excitation have not been minutely quantified experimentally, Pavlov did note various gross stages of increased inhibition in his experimental animals. The first, that of "equalization," is characterized by the ability of both weak and strong stimuli to elicit responses. This is followed by the "paradoxical phase," which derives its name from the observation that weak stimuli are as effective, if not more so, as strong stimuli, illustrating the point at which Pavlov's law of the relationship between the magnitude of the effect and the strength of the stimulus reverses from its supposed one-to-one relationship (Pavlov, 1941). As inhibition continues to spread, an "ultraparadoxical phase" is reached, in which excitory stimuli lose their effectiveness. Finally, total sleep ("complete inhibition") appears.

Before proceeding to hypnosis proper, a word should be said about "conditioned reflex sleep." It was Pavlov's view that sleep occurs under conditions of cellular fatigue; however, he noted that his dogs would often become lethargic and sleepy merely upon entrance into the experimental room. Because there was no apparent fatigue element operating, it was hypothesized that those behaviors (both external and internal) that have been associated with the onset of sleep develop, through repeated contiguity, not only an association to sleep, but the stimulus power to induce the sleep state—in the face of nonfatigue. Moreover, the sequence of acquisition is dependent upon both the degree of involvement of different muscle groups and ontogenetic development. For example, Pavlov noted that the first responses of his dogs to become diminished during "hypnotization" were those of chewing—those most involved with the consumatory act. "During the repeated act of eating the maxillary muscles and tongue were most exercised, then the neck muscles and lastly the trunk, and inhibition follows in that same sequence" (Pavlov, 1941, p. 81). Platonov (1959), reporting on Y. Povorinsky's 1937 work, concludes that: "The more complex and ontogenetically later conditioned bonds of the speech-motor analyzer are inhibited first as the subject lapses into a state of suggested sleep and are disinhibited last as the subject awakens from this state" (p. 75).

Hypnosis

"Inhibition, ordinary sleep and hypnosis are one and the same process" (Pavlov, 1923, p. 604). Pavlov, of course, was not the first to note the apparent similarities between sleep and hypnosis, the Marquis de Puységur receiving original credit. Braid also felt that his method of suppressed respiration, and thus vascular deoxygenation, created "a disposition to sleep" (Braid, 1845, p. 627). Pavlov's predecessor and contemporary, Bechterev, pointed out in 1906 that "... hypnosis is nothing but a modification of normal sleep" (Bechterev, 1906, p. 24). He further anticipated (and inspired) Pavlov with: "... [Hypnosis is] a special modification of normal sleep which can be induced by physical as well as by psychical means" (p. 23). I. Narbutovich demonstrated this point in 1933 by training subjects to enter hypnosis either to verbal instructions or to a specific metronome rate (58 beats per minute). Arousal from hypnosis was achieved either by a different rate (200 beats per minute) or different words (Platonov, 1959). Das (1958a) demonstrated the development of inhibition with monotonous sound and light stimuli.

For Pavlov, hypnosis is a behavior of partial sleep, in which there is widespread cortical inhibition with certain "rapport centers" in the obverse condition of excitation. "The *rapport zone* produced in the sleeper by verbal suggestions is a more or less confined centre of concentrated excitation isolated from the remaining regions of the cortex ..." (Platonov, 1959, p. 43). Evidence that centers of wakefulness are present even in natural partial sleep is offered in the form of analogies (Platonov, 1959). The sleeping physician who hears the telephone's ring, but not his baby's cry, while his sleeping wife responds to the cry and not the ring are examples of "sentry post" centers of excitation in an otherwise inhibited CNS.

However, it need be pointed out that "rapport zones" are second-signal system phenomena, and, therefore, not equated in detail with the "sentry post." It is through the rapport centers that the hypnotist maintains contact with the subject. As various verbal instructions are given to the subject through the rapport centers, excitation spreads to other centers necessary for compliance with the content of the instructions. Thus, by disinhibition the instructions are given behavioral substance. Here we may note that hypnosis, according to this theory, is a *process of inhibition*; whereas the enactment of the various phenomena of hypnosis is a *process of later disinhibition.*

Two further distinctions are made with regard to the hypnotic state —hypnotic sleep and suggested sleep. The first is applicable to all animals, including the human; whereas the latter applies only to man in that it is initiated through verbal instructions—the second-signal system. Thus, suggested sleep differs from hypnotic sleep in (a) its applicability; (b) its method of induction (hypnotic sleep is nonverbally induced); (c) the presence of rapport centers for the reception of further instructions; and (d) the heightened susceptibility to verbal instructions commensurate with rapport centers. Suggested sleep is also akin to the conditioned reflex sleep mentioned above, with the exception that the latter involves (as does hypnotic sleep) inducement primarily by first-signal system stimuli.

Suggested sleep can be distinguished from natural sleep by: (a) the specific rapport zone that: (1) is isolated from the surrounding inhibitory processes; and (2) offers the mechanism through which hypersuggestibility is achieved; (b) the functional nature of the inhibited and excitory aspects of the cortex; and (c) the possibility of the hypnotist controlling the depth of the suggested sleep by reason of its independence of cortical fatigue.

Not only has there been a conceptual division of partial sleep into hypnotic and suggested sleep, but suggested sleep (hypnosis in man) is further reduced to three stages, each of which is subdivided into three degrees (Platonov, 1959, pp. 425–428). It is within these nine subdivisions of suggested sleep (dependent upon the relative extent of cortical excitation and inhibition) that the phases of inhibition noted above become explicitly related to the Pavlovian theory of hypnosis.

In the first degree of the First Stage, cortical tone begins to weaken and restfulness is felt. As this stage progresses to its second degree, cortical tone decreases, inhibition of the "kinesthetic system" begins, and heaviness is experienced. At the third degree, further irradiation of cortical inhibition occurs with the deepening of kinesthetic and second-signal system inhibition.

The first degree of the Second Stage offers cataleptic symptoms and a clearer inhibition of the second-signal and kinesthetic systems. As this stage enters its second degree, inhibition of the second-signal system continues (the kinesthetic system is now totally inhibited) and the beginnings of cutaneous inhibition are noted. Finally, it is in the third degree that the equalization phase of inhibition is reached (". . . the word and the actual stimulus seem to balance one another when the patient's eyes are closed, but reality prevails as soon as the eyes are opened. . .") (Platonov, 1959, p. 427).

By the time the subject has reached the first degree of the Third Stage, the first-signal system prevails and illusions are effected easily. The second degree marks the total inhibition of the second-signal system, with positive hallucinations being the behavioral manifestation. Finally, the paradoxical phase is reached in the third degree and only "isolated rapport" remains of the second-signal system.[3] Should the subject slip beyond this stage and degree, the ultraparadoxical and complete inhibition phases of total sleep ensue.

Table 1
Schematic Presentation of Pavlov's Theory

STATE OF ORGANISM	PHASE	DEGREE OF INHIBITION
Wakefulness		Minimal ($E \to \infty; I \to 0$)
"Broken-up" sleep		
Partial sleep		
Natural partial sleep		
Hypnotic sleep		
(1st-signal system)-CR sleep		
Suggested sleep		
(2nd-signal system)		
First stage		
First degree		
Second degree		
Third degree		
Second stage		
First degree		
Second degree		
Third degree	Equalization	
Third stage		
First degree		
Second degree		
Third degree	Paradoxical	
	Ultraparadoxical	
Total sleep	Complete inhibition	($E \to 0; I \to \infty$) Maximum

(Arrow from Minimal to Maximum labelled: Decreasing cortical excitation; Increasing cortical inhibition)

Table 1 depicts Pavlov's continuum from wakefulness to sleep. This table does not present hypnosis as orthogonally related to sleep, as Das (1958a) would have it. Das argues that sleep varies on a continuum ". . . of intensity of complete cortical inhibition" (Das, 1958a, p. 85); whereas hypnosis varies with respect to the quantity of the cortex in a state of inhibition.[4] However, it is quite clear that certain phases of sleep noted above ("broken-up" and partial) do not involve the inhibition of the total cortex with their sole differentiation being intensity. Because we shall explore Das' innovations and ideas more

[3] For a detailed outline of the indices of these nine phases of suggested sleep, see Platonov (1959).

[4] Wood (1851) was of the same opinion: "I think one great difference between natural sleep and that produced in magnetism is this—in the former, *all* nervous centres are tired out, and *all* repose; in the latter, those of sensation and volition are chiefly affected—and they being lulled to rest, the others retain their wonted activity" (p. 433).

thoroughly in a later section of this chapter, our present discussion will be confined to evidence associated with the Pavlovian formulation.

Experimental Evidence

As early as 1933, Hull argued against the Pavlovian view from the standpoints of the dissimilarity of human and animal hypnosis with regard to catalepsy, the nonspontaneity of rapport in human hypnosis, and the dissimilarity between sleep and hypnosis. With the present understanding of the Pavlovian viewpoint, Hull's first two points dissolve in the distinctions Platonov (1959) makes between hypnotic and suggested sleep—the latter being especially peculiar to human beings and not necessarily involving the catalepsy noted in Pavlov's animals. Rapport, for Hull, was "... used to designate the general fact that subjects in the trance sometimes will not accept suggestions from anyone except the person who induced the trance" (Hull, 1933, p. 35). (Hull used the term "selective anesthesia" only as an example and not, as Gorton [1949a] erroneously tells us, as a definition.) For Pavlov, however, rapport was the "... retained possibility for speech communication with the hypnotist..." (Platonov, 1959, p. 41)—a far broader, less restrictive definition that could, or could not, include Hull's interpretation. Hull's final point, regarding the dissimilarity of sleep and hypnosis, is based primarily on Bass' study (1931) showing that the knee jerk does not diminish in hypnosis, as it does in natural sleep (Koster [1954] found opposite results), and that voluntary responding continues in hypnosis, whereas it ceases in natural sleep. Interpreting these two responses as representative of lower and higher CNS functioning, Hull (1933) concluded that hypnosis showed little, if any, inhibition in either.

Like so much of the work quoted as disproving the Pavlovian hypotheses, Bass' work (1931) was predicated on the idea that Pavlovian hypnosis was sleep and if in any aspect it appeared more similar to wakefulness than sleep, the theory was disproved. Das has been strongly opposed to this view for "It has never been claimed by Pavlov or Pavlovians that hypnosis is sleep" (Das, 1958a, p. 85). The foregoing summary of the theory also makes it clear that the identity between total sleep and hypnosis assumed by many investigators (behaviors in hypnosis are usually compared with those at the opposite ends of the continuum in Table 1) is erroneous. Russian workers (for example, Platonov, 1959; Korotkin and Suslova, 1959; and Marenina, 1959) have been quick to point out that most authors "... did not study hypnosis dynamically" (Marenina, 1959, p. 647); that is, they have not considered the stages of hypnosis when looking for similarities to sleep.

Conditioned Responses (*CR's*). Not only did Hull (1933) argue against the sleep-hypnosis identity on the basis of Bass' work (1931), but on

Scott's (1930) as well. Scott (1930) demonstrated that finger withdrawal could be conditioned in the trance state more readily than in wakefulness. Hull (1933) and Scott (1930) thought that if hypnosis were sleep, that is, a state of inhibition, CR's would be difficult, if not impossible, to form. Thus, Scott's evidence (1930) was interpreted—despite an acknowledgment by Hull (1933) that human and animal hypnosis may differ—as contradicting the Pavlovian position. Later reviewers (Gorton, 1949b; Dorcus, 1956; and Crasilneck and Hall, 1959) also cite Bass (1931) and Scott (1930); but it has not been until quite recently (Das, 1958a; Crasilneck and Hall, 1959; and Platonov, 1959) that more attention has been given to the Russian literature. These latter reviewers point out that the vast majority of the Russian literature on the formation of CR's during hypnosis (and other areas, as we will see) is commensurate with the Pavlovian view. For example, Korotkin and Suslova, in a long sequence of studies (1951, 1953, 1955a, 1955b, 1955c, 1959), have demonstrated the diminution of unconditioned responses and a decrement in the performance of simple arithmetic reasoning in hypnosis, as well as progressive difficulty in the formation of CR's as the depth of hypnosis increases to the somnambulistic stage (third) where they cannot be formed at all. Platonov, in his monumental review of 45 years of Russian research (1959), also concludes that changes in establishing new CR's and in already established CR's do occur in suggested sleep (human hypnosis), the type and degree being dependent upon the stage of hypnosis and the individual subjects.

Electroencephalogram (*EEG*). The same controversy is evident with regard to EEG findings. Reviewers (Gorton, 1949a; Weitzenhoffer, 1953; Sarbin, 1956; Crasilneck and Hall, 1959; and Barber, 1961) have faithfully cited Loomis *et al.* (1936), Blake and Gerard (1937, 1939), Davis *et al.* (1939), Dynes (1947), and Ford and Yeager (1948), who, according to Das (1958a), made the same erroneous assumption as investigators of CR's, and concluded "... that in the great majority of instances the hypnotized person continues to show his characteristic waking pattern on the EEG" (Barber, 1961, p. 412). However, in fairness to these reviewers, it should be reported that they also mention the works of Barker and Burgwin (1948, 1949), Darrow *et al.* (1950), and Schwarz *et al.* (1955), each of whom has offered some evidence contradictory to the above.

Marenina (1959) reports EEG changes that are commensurate with the three stages of suggested sleep and show a progressive overall "quieting" and the progressive appearance of sleeplike waves. Perhaps even more important is her reported change in the response to an external irritating stimulus (a 100 watt light). As the stage of hypnosis deepened, the light had less and less influence on the EEG. At the second stage, she noted that what little effect the light had ceased upon its removal (there is a delayed recovery of the prestimulus pattern in wakefulness); and in the third stage, "... this same light irritant ceased to have almost any effect at all on the curve of cerebral potentials" (Marenina, 1959, p. 648). Shpil'berg (1959) also reports similar findings to tone as well as light stimulation. Platonov (1959) reports from his review that "... the electric activity of the cerebral cortex coincides both in suggested and natural sleep" (Platonov, 1959, p. 61). However, from a recent study, Diamant *et al.* conclude: "EEG data does not support the concept that the nature of hypnosis and sleep is qualitatively the same" (Diamant *et al.*, 1960, p. 208). Considering the apparent discrepancies among studies, we might suspend judgment on EEG studies and conclude with Chertok and Kramarz (1959) that: "Electroencephalographic investigations, in the present state of this technique, cannot furnish irrefutable proof regarding the question of similarity or dissimilarity between the hypnotic state and sleep" (p. 237).

Other Physiological Systems. Other systems of the human body have yielded controversial results. Reviewers (Gorton, 1949a, 1949b; Crasilneck and Hall, 1959, 1960; Barber, 1961) all seem to concur generally that blood pressure, pulse rate, respiratory rate, and gastric secretions (with the exception of the Luckhardt and Johnston [1924] and Eichorn and Tractir [1955] studies, which showed opposing results) are little affected by hypnosis per se; that is, without further verbal instructions. Platonov (1959), on the other hand, informs us that the Russian studies show a diminished gastric secretion on induction and general and free acid curves approximating natural sleep during suggested sleep. Furthermore, he states that Tsinkin (1930a, 1930b) demonstrated a retardation in pulse and respiratory rates—the latter becoming more rhythmic, too—and a drop in arterial blood pressure. Platonov (1959) concludes that "... the arterial pressure and the depth of respiration are in inverse proportion to the depth of suggested sleep, and the slower the falling asleep, the slower the drop in arterial pressure" (Platonov, 1959, p. 61). In this connection one should not overlook the work of Lovett Doust (1953), who demonstrated a reduction in arterial oxygen saturation on the induction of hypnosis, or that of Strosberg and Vics (1962), who showed reduced vascular supply to the eye during hypnotic induction.

Changes in motor chronaxie are also reported in Platonov's review (1959), again indicating the similarity between suggested and natural sleep, through the increased inhibition of bodily functions as hypnosis is entered and deepened. Electrodermal response (EDR) studies are beginning to demonstrate consistent findings now. Ravitz (1950, 1951a, 1951b, 1962) has shown a consistent smoothing of the EDR when measuring direct current potentials. Platonov (1959) reports that

Y. Povorinsky has recently completed work demonstrating a decrease in variations of the "skin-galvanic reflexes" during hypnosis. Stern *et al.* (1963), studying the physiological concomitants of hypnotic amnesia, have also noted a reduction in the spontaneous fluctuations of the EDR during the trance period. This reduction was significantly greater than that of an equated control group.

Thus we can see even from this rather cursory summary of the physiological literature that the evidence concerning Pavlov's theory is in a state of flux. Of late, we have had access to an increasing amount of the Russian literature. This has aided us in furthering a more thorough understanding of the Pavlovian view and has provided a wealth of experimental evidence in support of that view. Although these studies are at times difficult to evaluate because of their more descriptive, less statistical and methodological presentation, their results cannot be ignored, and the Pavlovian viewpoint must—at present—be taken into account when considering a theory of hypnosis. As we will see later, inhibition as a basic concept in hypnosis can be accounted for without obviating the learning (S-R) aspects of hypnosis, to be illustrated in the following section.

THE HULLIAN POSITION

In 1916 Clark Leonard Hull began teaching Introductory Psychology to a group of premedical students at the University of Wisconsin. It was here that an interest was aroused that culminated seventeen years later in the now classic *Hypnosis and Suggestibility, an Experimental Approach.* Although begun at the University of Wisconsin, it was completed at Yale University after Hull became Research Professor in the Institute of Psychology in 1929. Actually, the move to Yale was almost disastrous to his hypnosis experiments, for the opposition to his work was so strong that he turned over the completion of the experiments to his students and former students in other parts of the nation. He himself put aside the manuscript, and only the industry and urging of his associates salvaged what might otherwise have been a tragic loss for the field of hypnosis.

Hull's approach to hypnosis differed little from his approach to other human behaviors—he relied upon objective, laboratory experimentation to validate his theoretical hypotheses. It was Hull's contention that for hypnosis to be considered a habit learned through repetitious stimulus-response pairings, a conformation to six known characteristics of habit would have to be demonstrated. If behavior usually defining a trance state (such as eyelid closure) could be shown (1) to be facilitated by practice, (2) to have a negatively accelerated practice curve, (3) to incur a partial decrement with disuse,[5] (4) to have a greater decrement from disuse when the original learning was temporally massed rather than spaced, (5) to recover in a negatively accelerated manner from disuse with resumed practice, and (6) to recover with less practice than required for original learning; then hypnosis was a habit, and could be dealt with as other human behavior, rather than being considered some esoteric phenomenon without reasonable rules of order.

In presenting his and his students' work, Hull (1933) first traced the modern history of the notion that trance induction is facilitated through repetition. From Husson's committee, through Braid, Binet and Féré, Bernheim, Moll, Forel, Bramwell, and James, the facilitation of hypnosis by practice was authoritatively affirmed. For Hull, earlier statements confirmed the conformity of hypnosis to the first basic characteristic of habit. However, this and the other characteristics had to be demonstrated in the experimental laboratory situation.

Nonhypnotic Verbal Stimulation

In 1930 two studies (Hull and Huse; Williams) appeared having direct bearing upon the habit characteristics of nonhypnotic verbal stimulation. Hull and Huse gave eight students verbal instructions for falling forward, until two falls each had occurred under counterbalanced hypnotic and nonhypnotic conditions. The average time for the first fall in the nonhypnotic period was 29.75 seconds, whereas the average for the second was 21.84 seconds. (The hypnotic period will be discussed later.) In the words of the authors "... [the] suggested time of the second of two suggested responses is reduced by approximately a fourth" (p. 283). Although Williams (1930) later reworked this data and found the respective figures to be 26.95 seconds and 20.44 seconds, it remained clear that the response to nonhypnotic verbal stimulation is facilitated by practice.

Williams (1930) demonstrated the same fact (as well as others) in his studies comparing verbal stimulation under hypnotic and nonhypnotic conditions. Fourteen hypnotic and eight control subjects were tested on five tasks—postural sway, length of line and weight estimation, and warmth and touch discrimination—each presented four times on four consecutive days in a counterbalanced order. Williams grouped his hypnotic subjects into a main experimental group (Group 1), a special "technique" group (Group 2 tested only once per day), and a group

[5] Hull's work in hypnosis preceded *The Principles of Behavior* by a decade. Interpolated activity has replaced disuse; it is the strengthening of other S-R bonds through practice or the extinction of the original S-R bond by non-reinforcement, not disuse per se, that accounts for the lowered probability of response evocation. For the sake of historical accuracy, we continue to use the term "disuse" in this section as Hull did in 1933. As we will see, the decrement occurred even if the supposed reason for it was later shown to be inaccurate.

that duplicated the work of Hull and Huse (Group 3). Within each group, he then compared the "comparative" data (hypnotic versus nonhypnotic), the cumulative data (practice effect within a single day), the perseverative data (effect of hypnotic on nonhypnotic period and vice versa), and the practice data (practice effect over days).

Because none of the line, weight, warmth, and touch tests yielded significant results in any direction, we will concern ourselves with the postural sway results. The author suggested that the crucial difference between the sway test and the other tests was the fact that the latter

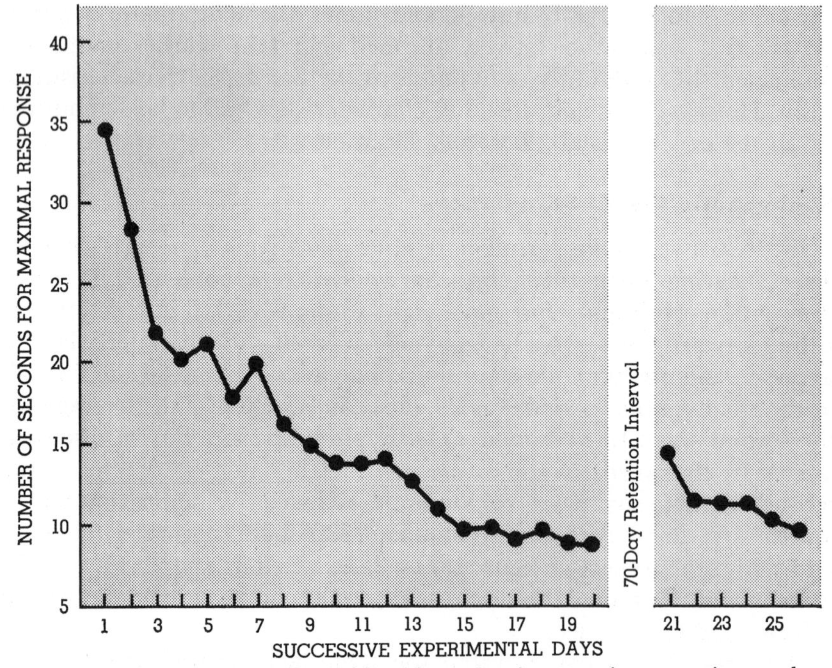

Figure 1. Composite graph from 16 subjects showing practice, retention, and recovery phenomena of waking postural suggestion. From: Patten, E. F., Switzer, S. A., and Hull, C. L. (1932). "Habituation, retention, and perseveration characteristics of direct waking suggestions," *J. exp. Psychol.*, **15**, 541.

required the subjects to read the instructions, whereas in the former, the instructions (verbal stimulation) were spoken—an important distinction. However, with regard to the sway test, Williams' results (1930) are quite comparable to those of Hull and Huse (1930)—the savings of the second nonhypnotic verbal stimulation over that of the first ranged from 4.4 per cent to 28.9 per cent.

Another study (Caster and Baker, 1932), although not directly testing nonhypnotic verbal stimulation, has some information to add. Caster and Baker (1932), using ten students, counterbalanced hypnotic and nonhypnotic conditions over four days, noting the latency of forward arm movement to instructions. The hypnotic period was defined by a positive response to instructions for eyelid closure, and the nonhypnotic by a period of conversation equal in time to that given to eyelid instructions. Subjects served as their own controls. As with the previous studies (Hull and Huse, 1930; Williams, 1930), a practice effect was noted from the first arm response (16.1 seconds) to the second (8.32 seconds) under nonhypnotic conditions.

However, as Hull (1933) pointed out, neither of these studies dealt with the effects of disuse and relearning. This omission was corrected by Patten, Switzer, and Hull (1932), who gave 16 college students nonhypnotic verbal instructions for falling three times at one-minute intervals, on each of 20 consecutive days. Following a 70-day waiting period, the initial procedure was resumed for six more days. From Figure 1 it is clear that (a) a negatively accelerated practice effect is generated; (b) a decrement occurs with disuse; (c) this decrement is recovered through renewed practice; and (d) relearning is more rapid than original learning. Thus, all of the habit characteristics noted above —saved massed versus spaced learning trials—had been experimentally demonstrated in response to nonhypnotic verbal stimulation. Now let us turn to verbal stimulation under hypnotic conditions.

Hypnotic Verbal Stimulation

Not only did the Hull and Huse (1930) study demonstrate practice effects in nonhypnotic verbal stimulation, but in hypnotic as well. The average time for the first fall under hypnotic conditions was 11.97 seconds, whereas the second fall took only 9.12 seconds. In like manner, Williams (1930) found savings from 16.4 per cent to 20.5 per cent when comparing the second hypnotic fall to the first. That the practice effects noted in these two studies were negatively accelerated is demonstrated by Figures 2, 3, 4, and 5. The differing abscissa of Figure 4 reflects procedural differences noted above.

Both of these studies (Hull and Huse, 1930; Williams, 1930) were supported by the later works of Caster and Baker (1932) and Jenness (1933). Caster and Baker (1932) found a 23 per cent savings between the first and fourth test days on all tests, and Figure 6, from their study, again depicts a rather clear negatively accelerated practice curve.

Jenness (1933) used nine subjects to test the facilitation of one response by another, by alternating, over four days, the sequence of presentation of eyelid closure and arm movement instructions, the former being considered a hypnotic procedure. With regard to practice effects, Jenness (1933) also discovered a negatively accelerated phenomenon, which yielded a 51 per cent savings (as measured by latency) from the first to the fourth day of experimentation.

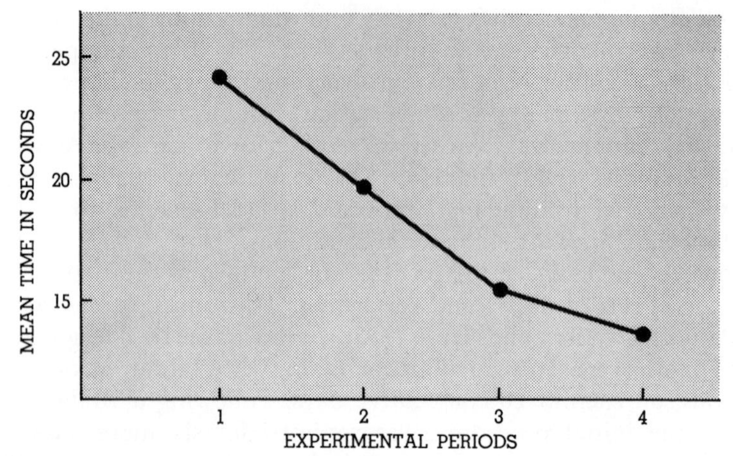

Figure 2. Composite graph showing habituation effects in responding to suggestion. From: Hull, C. L. and Huse, Betty (1930). "Comparative suggestibility in the trance and waking states," *Amer. J. Psychol.*, **42**, 284.

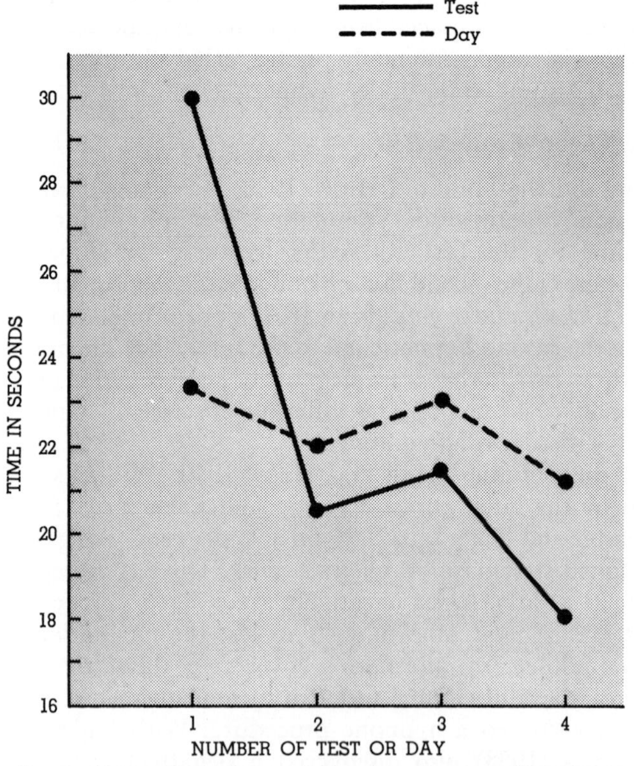

Figure 3. Graph of data from Group 1 showing practice effects in responding to suggestions of postural sway. From: Williams, G. W. (1930). "Suggestibility in the normal and hypnotic states," *Arch. Psychol.*, No. 122, p. 37.

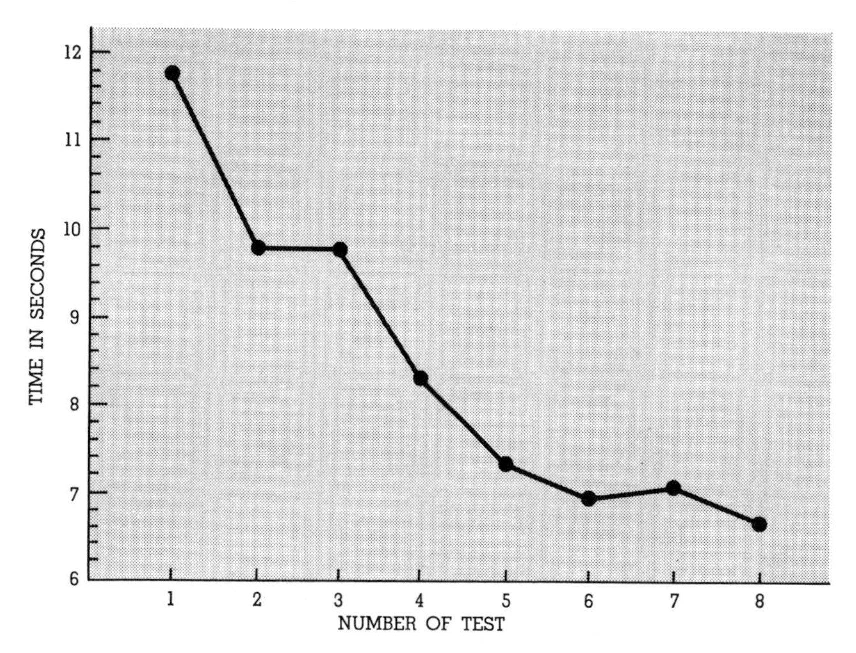

Figure 4. Graph of data from Group 2 showing practice effects in responding to suggestions of postural sway. From: Williams (1930), p. 57.

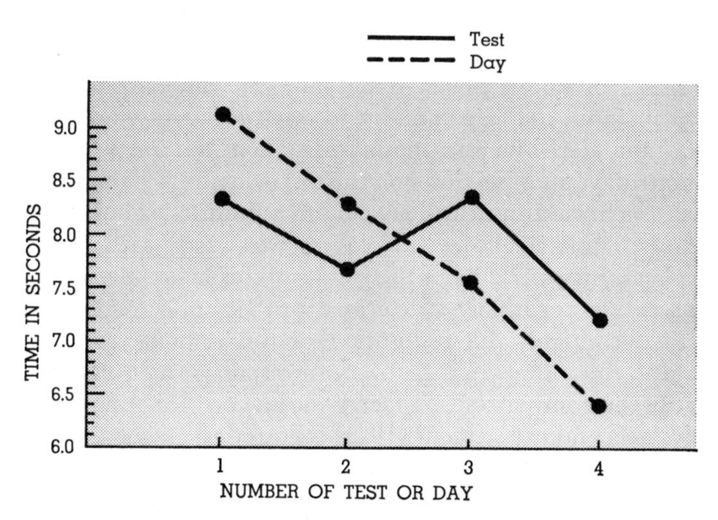

Figure 5. Graph of data from Group 3 showing practice effects in responding to suggestions of postural sway. From: Williams (1930), p. 50.

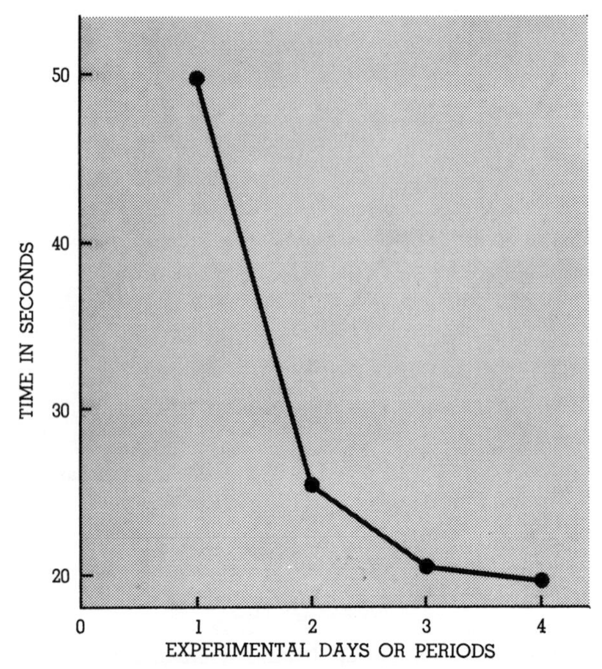

Figure 6. Composite graph showing the influence of repetition on the rate of lid closure at successive trance inductions. From: Caster, J. E. and Baker, C. S., Jr. (1932). "Comparative suggestibility in the trance and waking states—a further study," *J. gen. Psychol.*, **7**, 298.

None of these works touched more than the first two characteristics of habit. However, in 1931, Krueger had published two experiments that brought into clear perspective the fact that hypnosis shares the characteristics of habit. Seven male subjects who had shown eyelid closure to fixation, and an inability to open the eyes when instructed they could not, were given hypnotic instructions ten times (two minutes each) on one day, and five times on the following day. Each two-minute period was separated from the next by five minutes. The time, in seconds, required to achieve eyelid closure was used as the measure of practice effect. Figure 7 depicts the results of this first experiment. From this diagram the negatively accelerated practice effect is evident, as is the disuse decrement, the restoration of the response with resumed practice, and the more rapid recovery of response than original acquisition. Only the comparison of spaced and massed learning was absent.

Krueger's second experiment (1931) followed the same pattern as the first, except that eyelid closure was instructed in his then six subjects every 24 hours for ten days instead of ten times in one day. Following a 13-week disuse period, eyelid closure was again instructed every 24 hours for five days. Between the two experiments Krueger was able to compare massed and spaced learning. Figure 8 contains a much

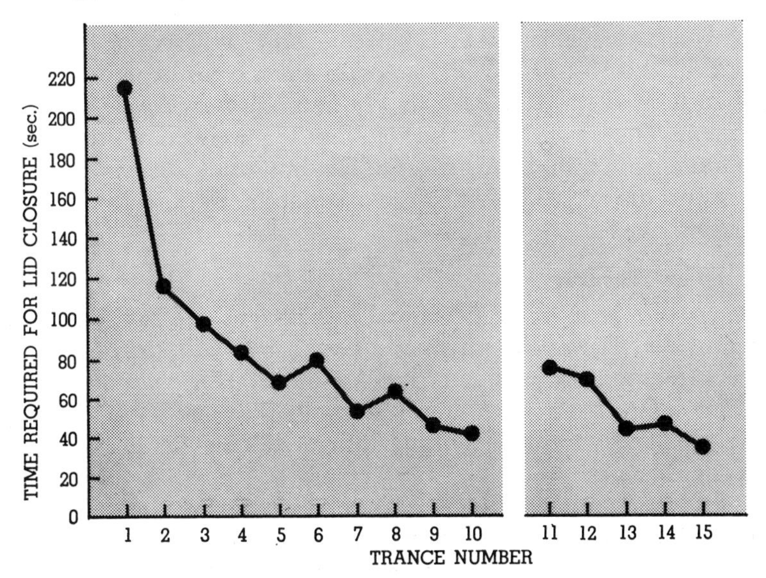

Figure 7. Composite curve from seven subjects showing practice effects resulting from repeated hypnosis. The intervals between trances 1 to 10 and between 11 to 15 were five minutes in each case. That between 10 and 11 was 24 hours. From: Krueger, R. G. (1931). "The influence of repetition and disuse upon rate of hypnotization," *J. exp. Psychol.*, **14**, 266.

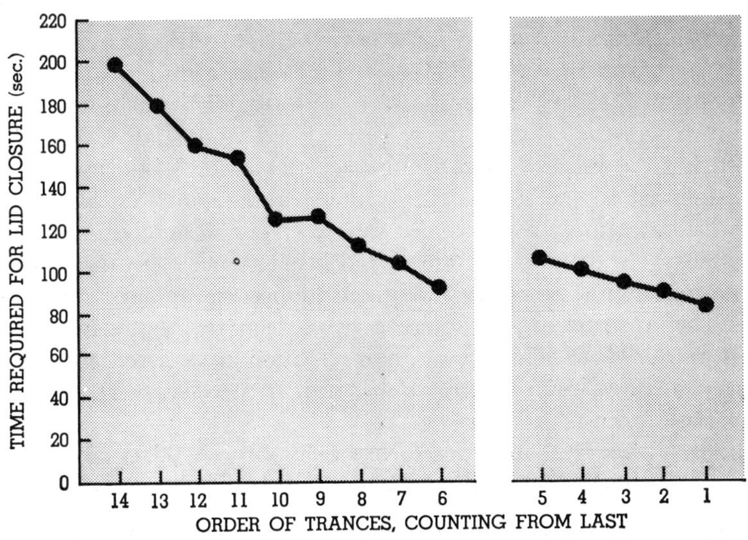

Figure 8. Composite curve from five subjects showing practice effects resulting from repeated hypnosis and the result of a period of no practice. The intervals between trances 14 to 6 and 5 to 1 are at least 24 hours. That between 6 and 5 was approximately 13 weeks. From: Krueger (1931), p. 268.

smoother learning curve than Figure 7, and shows that the loss in facility over the 13-week disuse period of the second experiment is less than one half of the loss over the 24-hour disuse period of the first experiment. Thus it was demonstrated that hypnosis shared the remaining characteristic of habit: the loss of facilitation of a learned response is less over a disuse period when the original learning trials are spaced rather than massed.

Transfer of Training

It may seem that hypnotic verbal instructions are no more or less habit phenomena than nonhypnotic verbal instructions, both having demonstrated the six characteristics of habit. However, it is in the general conformity to transfer of training that hypnotic conditions divorce themselves from the nonhypnotic, and may be clearly labeled habituation.

The first six characteristics of habit cited above have been dealt with through what Hull (1933) termed "homoactive hypersuggestibility" and Weitzenhoffer (1953) has more recently called "homoaction"; that is, the facilitation of a response by practice (simple learning). Now let us turn to Hull's "heteroactive hypersuggestibility" (Weitzenhoffer's "heteroaction") or transfer of training, and consider it from two standpoints: (1) transfer between similar or dissimilar responses,[6] and, (2) transfer of the same or different responses from hypnotic to nonhypnotic periods and vice versa.

Transfer of Responses. As with the other characteristics, Hull (1933) took both a nonhypnotic and a hypnotic verbal instruction approach. Hull, Patten, and Switzer (1933) tested 13 college students four times on 15 consecutive days for responsiveness to two different nonhypnotic verbal instructions: (1) that the subject's head would fall to the chest, and (2) that the subject's arm would sway forward. These instructions were presented to the subjects on phonograph records in alternating order with one minute rest between the two types. If heteroaction could be demonstrated to nonhypnotic verbal instructions, then the response to either instruction should be facilitated by preceding it with responses to the other instruction, as depicted by a decrease in the number of seconds required to elicit the response. Such a positive transfer of training was not shown by this study; in fact the data were consistent with negative transfer of training.

In light of this, and in order to test a hypothesis of social suggestibility set,[7] Patten (1933) did a special study involving the same tech-

[6] The similarity paradox has never been explored in relation to hypnosis.

[7] Hull considered the popular view that once an individual is hypnotized his properties of volition are suspended and he must obey the operator, as a "set" for social suggestibility. If, he thought, this set could be duplicated in nonhypnotized subjects, the negative transfer results might be reversed.

niques and responses as the Hull, Patten, and Switzer (1933) work. However, prior to receiving nonhypnotic verbal instructions, ten subjects read a letter allegedly from another renowned psychologist (Hull) stating that the results Patten hoped to achieve had, in fact, been established. Even this elaborate control of set failed to change the results, and this study too yielded negative results.

Turning, however, to hypnotic verbal instructions, we can observe a different result. Jenness (1933) demonstrated that the mean time required for arm movement was significantly shorter when following hypnotic eyelid closure instructions (70.15 seconds) than when preceding them (83.35 seconds). Although Jenness (1933) also showed the reverse to be true, the major importance of this work is that it further supports previous work in which the times required to obtain the desired response were significantly less under hypnotic than under nonhypnotic conditions. Hull and Huse (1930) found that hypnotic conditions yielded a 59.8 per cent to 58.7 per cent savings (55.6 per cent to 55.4 per cent according to Williams) in response latency over nonhypnotic. Williams (1930) found from 32 per cent to 14.1 per cent, and Caster and Baker (1932) reported 45 per cent savings. Hull (1933) chose to denote this finding as hypersuggestibility: "An example of this form of hypersuggestibility [heteroactive] is seen in the influence of the suggestions [verbal instructions] which lead to hypnosis, manifested objectively by lid-closure, in increasing the subject's susceptibility to suggestion of forward movement of the head or of the horizontally extended arm" (Hull, 1933, p. 287). Nevertheless, it was clear that hypnotic behavior followed closely the principles of transfer of training.

Transfer over Periods. Aside from those studies that directly or indirectly cast doubt on the accuracy of the dissociation hypothesis (Messerschmidt [1927], Mitchell [1932], Patten [1932]), two of the studies already cited offer evidence of transfer from hypnotic to nonhypnotic periods and vice versa. Hull and Huse (1930) compared the average time for the first nonhypnotic fall preceding a hypnotic period (39.94 seconds) with that for the first nonhypnotic fall following a hypnotic period (22.5 seconds), and found a facilitation of nonhypnotic instructions by preceding hypnotic instructions—the second being only 60.9 per cent as great as the first. An almost identical figure (60.3 per cent) is observed when the average time for the second nonhypnotic fall preceding a hypnotic period (27.25 seconds) is compared with the average time for the second nonhypnotic fall following a hypnotic period (16.42 seconds). Although these authors conclude: ". . . the influence of the trance. . . persists very strongly into the following (supposedly) waking state. . ." (Hull and Huse, 1930, p. 284), Williams (1930) showed that the transfer runs in both directions. Whether the hypnotic preceded the nonhypnotic or vice versa, the savings were quite similar, running as high as 20 per cent in one group.

Thus as early as 1933 it had been demonstrated that hypnosis was facilitated by practice; that this facilitation took the form of a negatively accelerated practice curve; that with disuse a partial decrement of the facility occurred, which was greater if original learning was massed rather than spaced; that this decrement was recovered with less practice than needed for original learning; and that transfer of training from one response to another and from one condition to another occurred.

"Such a remarkable and detailed conformity of the phenomena of hypnosis to the known experimental characteristics of ordinary habituation can hardly be accidental and without significance. The indication would seem to be that, whatever else hypnosis may be, it is—to a considerable extent, at least—a habit phenomenon and that quite possibly this hypothesis may furnish the basis for an ultimate understanding and explanation of its hitherto largely inexplicable characteristics" (Hull, 1933, p. 347).

OTHER FORMULATIONS

Pavlov and Hull have not been the only S-R theorists of hypnosis. In this section we will examine two other positions: that of Livingston Welch and that of J. P. Das, only the latter of which is formally presented as a symbolically represented theory.

"Abstract Conditioning"

In 1947 Livingston Welch presented his views on hypnosis, now characterized by the term "abstract conditioning" (Corn-Becker *et al.*, 1949). Basically, he pointed out that in the process of inducing a hypnotic trance most hypnotists make use of associative, verbal conditioning (whether or not they are aware of it). For example, in the use of an eye-fixation, relaxation, induction technique, the experimenter (hypnotist) couples words instructing eye-fatigue with the actual physical event (due to fixation). As the eyes blink, this is verbally noted by the experimenter, until, after repeated associations of words depicting acts and the acts themselves, the subject is conditioned to follow the verbal instructions of the experimenter. There is a positive, higher-order transfer of training: ". . . the generalization in this conditioning is much broader, at a higher level of abstraction than the generalization in the cases of Pavlov's dog. . . ." (Welch, 1947, p. 361).

Armed with this and the notion that words not coupled with physical events must be coupled with the past physical experiences of the subjects, Welch (1947) proceeded to explain hypermnesia, amnesia (recall of experiences of forgetting), hallucinations (generalization of simple, sensory experiences), and anesthesia (recall of numbness of sleeping on one's arm). He, unlike Platonov (1959), did not attempt an explanation of somatic changes, although the study that tested his theory two years later (Corn-Becker *et al.*, 1949) used the EDR.

Corn-Becker and his associates presented words ("breeze," "red," "green," "music," "flicker," "dark," "nothing," "electric shock") on a screen for ten seconds to six groups of subjects (three experimental and three control). The content of each of the projected words was reinforced for the experimental groups by the appearance of the depicted physical characteristic—except for "electric shock." No words were so reinforced for the control groups. EDR's were measured during the series of presentations in both groups, and it was discovered that between 40 per cent and 73 per cent of the individuals in the experimental groups gave their greatest ($p < .01$) EDR deflection to "electric shock," whereas between 75 per cent and 87 per cent of the control group subjects yielded EDR's to "electric shock" that were not different from those to other presented words. The authors concluded that abstract conditioning had been demonstrated, and, when coupled with the principles of generalization, may be extremely valuable in understanding human behavior. Curiously enough, although Welch (1947) had begun his theorizing with hypnosis, Corn-Becker *et al.* (1949) used no hypnotized subjects and did not test the susceptibility of their subjects. One replication of this work has appeared recently (Gladfelter and Hall, 1962) in which no correlation between hypnotizability and physiological responses to "electric shock" could be obtained. If future studies present similar findings, a reevaluation of "abstract conditioning" may be needed. However, the lack of data presentation and mention of specific statistical procedures in this one study forces us to await future developments before passing final judgment on Welch's notions.

The actual demonstration of higher-order (abstract) conditioning in relation to hypnosis was presented by Leuba and Dunlap (1951). More than ten years earlier, Leuba (1940) advocated the use of hypnosis for the control of extraneous stimuli during conditioning experiments. To demonstrate the plausibility of this control technique he had conducted 17 experiments from 1929 to 1939, with and without associates, in which an auditory or tactile stimulus was paired with a visual, olfactory, motoric, or painful tactile stimulus while the subjects were hypnotized. After hypnosis (and with amnesia for the hypnotic period) the auditory or tactile stimulus elicited the sensations previously only temporally associated with them, much to the puzzlement of the subjects. After Leuba's 1941 report of four more similar studies, Leuba and Dunlap (1951) found that it was not necessary for their four subjects to experience the actual auditory or tactile stimuli; they merely had to *imagine* the stimuli for the associated sensations to be experienced. Here was a demonstration of second-signal system, abstract conditioning (Leuba did not use these terms). And so what started out as a hypothesis concerning the nature of hypnosis (abstract conditioning), and has never been fully tested in relation to hypnosis, received some degree of verification through a line of thought not originally intended to explain hypnosis, but to advocate an experimental control for conditioning studies (Leuba, 1940, 1941; Leuba and Dunlap, 1951). Strange are the developments in science.

A Partial Resolution of Pavlov and Hull

We have already seen that J. P. Das (1958a) supported the Pavlovian position both in word and experimental deed. Also, in that year he published a study, based on his 1957 University of London dissertation, in which he offered evidence for a conditioning-hypnosis similarity (Das, 1958b). Fifty-nine subjects yielded a correlation of .509 ($p < .001$) between a seven-point depth of hypnosis scale score and conditioned eye-blink acquisition. The correlation between the same hypnosis scale and extinction was .415 ($p < .001$). Das (1958b), however, points out that these two behaviors (hypnosis and conditioning) could be mutually facilitating and even a counterbalanced design (he did not use one) would not eliminate this possibility. Weiss *et al.* (1960) have dealt with this problem by using an indirect measure of hypnotic ability, the California Psychological Inventory, and verbal operant conditioning in a TAT situation. Thirty-one subjects yielded a correlation of .35 ($p < .05$) between these two measures.

Earlier, Pascal and Salzberg (1959) using a 100 per cent reinforcement schedule to teach 56 subjects behavior progressively similar to that considered indicative of hypnosis (such as anesthesia, posthypnotic amnesia) found 52 per cent went into a "somnambulistic trance." This figure greatly exceeds the usual 10 to 20 per cent and seems to imply that the application of learning principles to the hypnotic situation can greatly enhance otherwise meager results. Giles (1962) confirmed Pascal and Salzberg's finding (1959) with 46 subjects, showing 55.2 per cent of his subjects achieving "deep hypnosis" as measured by a scale combining Weitzenhoffer's (1953) and Pascal and Salzberg's measures (1959).

Later, Webb (1962) also found a positive correlation between verbal operant conditioning and suggestibility level as noted by distance (mm) of body sway. Following body-sway instructions, each subject participated in a verbal operant conditioning period in which plural nouns spoken by the subject were followed by "good" from the experimenter. Of his four experimental groups, the one demonstrating the greatest degree of suggestibility, as measured, also showed the greatest degree of conditioning. The group that was the least suggestible, as measured, yielded behavior indicating counter-conditioning. Thus, both classical (Hull, 1933; Leuba, 1940, 1941; Leuba and Dunlap, 1951; Das, 1958b) and verbal operant (Pascal and Salzberg, 1959; Weiss *et al.*, 1960; Giles, 1962; Webb, 1962) conditioning appear significantly related to hypnotic behavior.

In 1959 Das (1959a), basing his notions on Hullian and Pavlovian work, presented his theory of hypnosis. From two basic assumptions: "... (a) Hypnosis is a form of conditioning or in a broad sense, habit-formation; [and] (b) Hypnosis is a form of inhibition" (p. 69), he defines hypnotizability as: "... an ability to learn to develop a state of partial cortical inhibition" (p. 71). In this manner, he combines his assumptions into a formula for the ideal hypnotic situation:

$$H = f(L \times I) \tag{3}$$

where H = hypnosis; L = learning; and I = partial cortical inhibition.

Learning has a lower threshold, L_t, and I has a lower threshold, I_t, and an upper limit, I_u. Even though I_u, I_t, and L_t must be determined for each subject, the manipulations of I and L within their limits will dictate the value of H. For example, no hypnosis will occur if L is less than its lower threshold, or if I is less than its lower threshold (excited wakefulness) or greater than its upper limit (total sleep). So long as L is greater than L_t and I ranges between I_t and I_u, hypnosis will occur. The degree or amount (perhaps depth) of hypnosis will depend upon changes in $L(\Delta L)$ and $I(\Delta I)$ within the limits just noted.

Thus, within those limits:

$$H'_L = f[(L + \Delta L)I] > H = f(L \times I) \tag{4}$$

and/or:

$$H'_I = f[L(I + \Delta I)] > H = f(L \times I) \tag{5}$$

Speculation on the relationship between H'_L and H'_I is absent, although Das (1959a) did comment on the relation of L to I. It is his view that when I is either less than its lower threshold (excitation) or equal to or greater than (a meaningless concept) its upper limit, L will not occur. Though not considering L and I independent of one another, Das (1959a) does consider the effect of I, within the limits of I_t and I_u, on L to be negligible. Examples of these hypotheses are based on predicting the degree of L and H under increasingly inhibiting doses of drugs.

Das (1959a) recognizes that certain aspects of the theory are only tentative. Because his orientation is more Pavlovian than Hullian, we might expect that he sees I as a more accurate and better demonstrated explanation of hypnosis. For him, L holds an unclear position in the theory, and, as he points out, the relation of L to Hull's ${}_SH_R$ remains to be clarified. So, too, does the relation of I to I_R.

In its present form Das' theory (1959a) appears to be little more than a symbolic representation of what has been stated or implied by earlier writers, particularly Pavlov and Hull. It has symbolized the obvious limits under which overt behavior can operate. So far as it goes, it would seem to be a step toward the prediction and quantification of hypnotic behavior, but it needs more refinement itself before we will know. Perhaps it may, as its author hopes, ". . . serve as a guide to the direction in which a true explanation of hypnosis may be discovered" (p. 75). This only future experimentation will determine.

CRITICISMS

Having presented the various views of S-R theory that have been expressed to date, we will now turn to some of the criticisms of this theory. Most of the criticisms noted below will be of statements other than those regarding the Pavlovian view, for we dealt with the major criticisms of that conception earlier.

Major Criticisms

Although an S-R theory of hypnosis has not been more formally presented than Das' work (1959a), the general viewpoint has been under criticism for many years. Three major criticisms have been voiced: (1) that S-R theory leads to the consideration of the subject as an automaton (White, 1941; Brenman and Gill, 1944; Pattie, 1956); (2) that it gives precedence to external over internal stimuli (White, 1941; Arnold, 1946; Pattie, 1956); and (3) that while the theory may account for hypnotic behavior in general, it falters in accounting for specific and detailed hypnotic behavior (Weitzenhoffer, 1953; Fisher, 1955).

The first of these points makes it quite clear that it is not just the S-R theory of hypnosis that is under criticism, but the underlying assumption that human beings are, after all, nothing more than highly complex stimulus-response organisms; that, like the laboratory dog or cat or rat, our behavior is dictated by stimuli; and that S-R pairings, no matter how complexly arranged, are the atoms of our behavioral essence. It is this concept that the critics have found objectionable.

White (1941), for example, makes this statement in his discussion of theory in hypnosis: "The central difficulty. . . is the stubborn persistence of mechanical ideas and mechanical figures of speech to describe what is essentially a human situation involving a delicate interplay of human strivings" (p. 478). In an apparently similar vein, Pattie (1956) offered as a "very serious" criticism of Hull, that there is ". . . too much intelligent, motivated, and discriminative behavior by the subject. . ." (p. 1/11) to support the idea that subjects are "complete automatons" during hypnosis.

That psychologists (such as White, 1941) find the persistence of S-R ideas a difficulty may only point up how well conditioned we are to the nonacceptance of this view as a plausible and tenable explanation of hypnosis and other human behaviors. Theorists are like any other human beings in that they spend a great deal of their life (usually before reaching graduate training) being conditioned to certain beliefs and attitudes. By and large this early training runs counter to, if not in direct opposition to, some form of S-R explanation of human behavior. For twenty years or more an individual is rewarded for actions, ideas, attitudes, and statements indicating that he believes himself to be *more* than a complexly organized animal, that he believes himself to be endowed with a special quality that sets him apart from the rest of the animal world. To call this quality mere complexity, to suggest that basically we differ little from other animals, and to suggest further that human behavior has rules that may lend themselves to mathematical expression are base heresies to our early conditioning. To be able to consider, at least as tenable, that human behavior is understandable and predictable through an S-R approach is at best a bootstrap operation—even for the theorist who must apply such thinking to his own behavior in creating the theory.

White's argument (1941) is the same as Pattie's (1956) in that he deplores automatism on the ground of improvisations by the subjects, but a vital point seems to have been missed. The behavior will be the same whether it is understood by a teleological, goal-directed, striving hypothesis or by an S-R theory. An S-R theory of explanation does not *make* the behavior mechanical. The theory does not require the behavior; the behavior simply exists. What any theory does is offer a set of rules by which the behavior can be understood and future, similar behavior predicted. The behavior remains unchanged regardless of the manner in which we have been conditioned to understand it. Entertain for a moment the conjecture that even the "improvisations" of the subjects are themselves the result of complex S-R interactions. The improvisations will remain unchanged, but the potential for understanding *and predicting* the behavior will be greatly enhanced.

Pattie (1956) and Arnold (1941) raised the second of these points, the question of stimulus precedence, when considering Hull's view that the symbolic processes of the subjects were replaced by that of the experimenter. As is apparent from the Hullian section of this chapter, we have not concerned ourselves with this theoretical statement. Rather, we have illustrated the work of Hull and his students that later led directly into his more formally structured theory of human behavior. Although Das (1959a) advocates a separate theory for hypnosis, Arnold agreed with our approach: "[A change in our assumptions]. . . will make it possible not only to formulate a consistent theory of hypnosis but to integrate it within our general psychological framework" (Arnold, 1941, p. 109).

Nevertheless, both Arnold and Pattie wondered why the experimenter's stimuli were better able to evoke responses than the subjects' own "symbolic stimuli." Although it does not offer a solution, Hudgins' study (1933) certainly demonstrated the extent of facilitation that can be expected of external verbal stimuli. Another mark of the strength of verbal conditioning has already been seen in his (Hudgins, 1933) and Das' work (1959b) demonstrating the high resistance to extinction of verbal conditioned stimuli. Also, it will be recalled that for Hull the "hypersuggestibility" was due to the fact that the hypnotized subjects had had a practice period involving response to verbal instructions prior to the elicitation of further responses—this practice period is ordinarily called "trance induction."

Pavlov's theory, involving primarily cortical inhibition, offers the most cogent answer to this criticism; for if one considers the cortex as the structure of symbolism, its inhibition will not enhance internally stimulated, second-signal system activity. Only through the rapport zone, dominated by the experimenter through conditioning, can deconditioning be initiated. Finally, except for the first few months of life, our conditioning has been to respond primarily to external stimuli—we eat at mealtime, not when we are hungry—and mainly those emanating from other human beings. Thus the prestige aspect of hypnosis noted by some (such as Hull, 1933), is, in reality, a conditioning to respond more readily or more effectively to individuals defined as authorities. (How we identify authorities is, by the way, a long, painful —for some—conditioning process.) Simply, children are rewarded for positive responses to adults.

The S-R position on these first two points has been summarized earlier (Edmonston, 1961) in a discussion of hypnotic age-regression:

> The verbal conditioning hypothesis implies that the stronger stimuli-to-action are external to the subject, so that the subject's responses to the verbal stimuli from the experimenter are little altered by subject-variables. Just as. . . [other theories do]. . . not totally ignore the influence of the experimenter, verbal conditioning cannot deny the importance of subject-variables. . . . However, it is the relative prominence of these two variables which is important. To state that conditioned responses are the basic units of human behavior does not reduce us to automata. It merely yields a hypothesis for studying the organizational powers of the human being.
>
> . . . In verbal conditioning we assume. . . that something occurs within the organism between the reception of the stimulus (word) and the eliciting of the response. . . . However, a verbal conditioning explanation assumes that this something affects relatively little our prediction of the range of responses elicited by a known stimulus or set of stimuli. (Edmonston, 1961, p. 137)[8]

[8] Corn-Becker *et al.* (1949) pointed this out also: "Obviously, in a conditioning situation we are not working in vacuo. New conditioning processes are being set up, new conditioned responses are being established, which are either directly or indirectly affected by conditioned responses of past association" (p. 220).

Regarding the third point under discussion, Weitzenhoffer (1953) and Fisher (1955) felt that S-R theory needed a great deal more refinement. A decade later we must still agree, but we would take issue with the complaint that hypnotic behavior is infinitely more complex than the experimental situation. We do not disagree with this statement per se, but with its implication that an experimentally based S-R theory is thereby weakened. It is the very nature of experimental investigation (as well as psychotherapy) to study small bits of behavior that occur in larger and more complex amounts in nature in the hope that the findings will account for much of the variance in the natural behavior which our model emulates. This is not a weakness of any theory or investigation. Only when we do not take adequate precautions to allow generalization from model to nature do we falter, and the studies cited throughout this chapter have not, by and large, abused this rule of experimentation.

Actually, the absence of precise detail in the S-R theory may not be a failure on the part of the theory, but on the part of writers supporting this view who have seemed content with more general and less detailed and precise appraisals. This is why, in this chapter, we have suggested that there is enough experimental evidence already present to warrant subsuming hypnosis under an established behavior theory, which would offer the potential for more detailed and precise statements and predictions concerning hypnotic behavior.

Such a move might satisfy Weitzenhoffer (1953), because he uses Hull's "homoaction" and "heteroaction" in his own theory, concludes that Welch's ideas could be counted on for at least a partial explanation of hypnosis, and has shown that Hull's concept of gradient of stimulus generalization can be used to resolve discrepant experimental results (Weitzenhoffer, 1954). However, it would not satisfy Fisher (1955), for he maintains the lack of maturity of general S-R theory and claims, from his own work, that Leuba's conditioning work (1940, 1941, 1951) merely represented posthypnotic suggestions through subject expectations as unwittingly conveyed by the experimenter. Leuba, however, points out that "... post-hypnotic suggestions are themselves examples of conditioning, rather than vice-versa!" (Leuba, 1955, p. 257), and calls for better experimental designs to resolve differences. We concur.

Other Criticisms

In addition to the three criticisms discussed above, two points made by Pattie (1956) necessitate brief comment. Once more the apparent discrepancy between the stimulus and the response is raised in a discussion of Welch's position: "Also, if the whole process depends upon conditioning, how is it possible to make a person who has proved on several occasions to be a good subject, unhypnotizable in the future by merely telling him that all efforts in the future will be unsuccessful?" (pp. 1/13–1/14). As indicated in the introduction, this discrepancy is only apparent, and it is not unreasonable to admit that a response can be conditioned even though its opposite has previously been established.

Finally, Pattie (1956) states that Hull cannot account for remembering, because if the subject's symbolic responses are withdrawn by hypnosis, he does not have any way to symbolize and thus retain what has transpired in the trance. This is an interesting point, but Pattie (1956) may be attributing to Hull more than Hull intended, for it was not that "... the subject's verbal responses are absent..." (Pattie, 1956, p. 1/10), but that the ability of the subjects' own symbolic (verbal) *stimuli* to elicit responses was diminished, relative to the experimenter's verbal stimuli. Thus, there seems to be a confusion between stimuli and responses and a misunderstanding of "absent" and "withdrawn," the former being absolute, the latter relative.

EPILOGUE

At the outset we stated that we would attempt to show that hypnosis could be subsumed under an already established theory of human behavior. Laboratory experimentation has demonstrated that hypnosis adheres quite closely to the general principles of learning outlined in the first section of this chapter; and, although we recognize that similarity does not necessarily imply identity, it at least allows direction for our thesis. On the basis of the foregoing, it would appear that we are indeed justified in including hypnosis under a general S-R theory of human behavior. The choice of Hull's behavior system is obvious.

We would agree with Hilgard (1948) that Hull's system (1943, 1951, 1952) is not the perfect panacea for all of our confusion, and that it rests on a cornerstone of reinforcement[9] with, perhaps, premature quantification; but it remains the most systematically formulated design for understanding and predicting behavior. We also suspect that through this formulation much of the apparently complex hypnotic behavior could be predicted. It remains for some future work to bring together, in detail, Hull's postulates (1951, 1952) and the hypnosis literature.

There also remains the need to resolve the Hullian and Pavlovian conceptions, for it has also been demonstrated that the Pavlovian notion of conditioned inhibition followed by selective disinhibition cannot be omitted from our formulations. Although Welch (1947), Corn-Becker *et al.* (1949), and Leuba (1940, 1941, 1951, 1955) extended the learning model, only Das (1959a) has attempted to resolve theoretically Hull and

[9] A dual theoretical approach (contiguity and reinforcement) in hypnosis may be more advantageous at present.

Pavlov. A comparative study of inductive instructions might offer an experimental resolution. If the increased compliance with verbal (or motoric) instructions following induction procedures is but a cumulative practice effect reinforcing the experimenter's stimulus value, then compliance with *any* experimenter instructions should yield later hyperfacilitation, and the necessity of a partial inhibitory state may be in some doubt. If, however, it is such that the inhibitory content in the instructions is basic to later hypnotic behavior, then conditioned inhibition could not be readily ignored.[10]

According to previously noted work (Shvarts, 1948, 1949) and the use of a brain-wave synchronizer (BWS) to induce hypnosis (Kroger and Schneider, 1959), the Pavlovian position may well be supported by such a study. If so, then hypnosis is a special learning case in which the effective reactive potential, ${}_S\bar{E}_R$ (Hull, 1951, 1952), is enhanced, rather than reduced by conditioned inhibition, ${}_SI_R$, within the limits of inhibition noted by Das (1959a). Thus, the overall S-R statement of hypnosis would be a two-step representation:

$$\text{(a)}\quad {}_SH_{iR} \times D_i \rightarrow {}_SE_{iR} - {}_SH_{eR} \pm I_{iR} \rightarrow {}_S\bar{E}_{iR} \rightarrow {}_SI_{hR}\ \text{(Hypnosis)} \qquad (6)$$

and

$$\text{(b)}\quad {}_SI_{hR} \times {}_SH_{phR} \times D_{ph} \rightarrow {}_SE_{phR} - ({}_SI_{phR} + I_{phR}) \rightarrow {}_S\bar{E}_{phR} \rightarrow \text{Phenomena of Hypnosis} \qquad (7)$$

In step (a) hypnosis is established as conditioned inhibition. The habit of inhibition, ${}_SH_{iR}$, and a drive for inhibition, D_i, lead to a reactive potential for inhibition, ${}_SE_{iR}$, which becomes a reduced effective reactive potential of inhibition, ${}_S\bar{E}_{iR}$, by the opposing action of already established excitory habits, ${}_SH_{eR}$. The positive or negative effect of I_R would be minimal, at best. The effective reactive potential becomes the measurable behavior of conditioned inhibition or hypnosis.

In step (b), the conditioned inhibition of hypnosis enhances the production of further hypnotic behaviors (${}_SH_{phR}$). The multiplication sign between ${}_SI_{hR}$ and ${}_SH_{phR}$ depicts an interaction and not necessarily the mathematical function involved. Drive, of course, is difficult to specify in hypnosis, and for the time being we must assume that the drive or need for the performance of the hypnotic habit is a learned secondary drive. This does not necessarily weaken an S-R theory because even secondary drives are considered originally based on S-R behavior, whether or not we can specify the original stimuli.

In short, step (b) states that the conditioned inhibition of hypnosis (${}_SI_{hR}$), the habit for a given phenomenon under hypnosis (${}_SH_{phR}$), and

[10] This is not the question so often raised as criticism, of whether or not there is an inhibitory state in hypnosis, but whether or not it is necessary. Also, we are not necessarily comparing contiguity and reinforcement.

a drive to perform this habit (D_{ph}), lead to a reactive potential for the act (${}_SE_{phR}$), which becomes a reduced reactive potential (${}_S\bar{E}_{phR}$) by the opposing actions of a conditioned inhibition (${}_SI_{phR}$) and a reactive inhibition (I_{phR}), both specific to the act in question.

Should the Pavlovian position be weakened by the proposed resolution, then hypnosis would readily fit the Hullian habit formulation, in which each expression may be anchored in measurable behavior and thereby reduce our predictive error:

$$ {}_SH_R \times D \rightarrow {}_SE_R - ({}_SI_R + I_R) \rightarrow {}_SE_R \rightarrow \text{Behavior} \qquad (8) $$

We would suspect that ${}_SI_R$ would be quite minimal in this formulation, because it might be considered rare that subjects would practice hypnotic behavior without the reinforcing agent (experimenter) being present. I_R, or the fatigue of repeated, rapidly succeeding inductions has not been determined. In the ordinary course of events it, too, would be minimal.

This brings us to a dual definition of hypnosis by either of the above formulations. First, whether conditioned inhibition must precede the performance of other hypnotic behavior (through disinhibition or practice effect) or not, hypnosis is an intervening variable; and must be anchored both in measurable antecedent and consequential behavior. Thus, when a specified set of stimuli are offered, a predictable range of response occurs. Verbal stimuli, from our introductory discussion, seem to be the primary antecedents of hypnosis, although motoric stimuli may, in special cases, be equally effective. Responses to the content of these stimuli, measured by amplitude, latency, frequency of occurrence, and resistance to extinction, are the consequents.

Second, hypnosis is a relative behavior or set of behaviors, quantitatively relative to the individual performance of the same act(s) without prior induction instructions. Whether hyperfacilitation is achieved by a cumulative practice effect or by preceding conditioned inhibition, any investigation purporting to use hypnotized subjects must show that their performance is individually hyperfacilitated before proceeding further. Thus, hypnosis is simply an S-R defined intervening variable, the observable behavior of which is quantitatively greater than, and relative to, the same or similar behavior under different antecedent conditions.

In conclusion, we submit that considering hypnosis from an S-R theory viewpoint offers us at least three advantages: prediction, self-correction, and parsimony.

Elsewhere (Edmonston, 1962), the need—in any scientific endeavor—to offer a priori predictions of behavior has been discussed. It seems to this author that other theories of hypnosis (such as psychoanalytic, motivational, role-taking) lend themselves too easily to the latter, so that what potential they may have for a priori statements is obscured if not discarded.

Self-correction is a basic requirement for a theory. Here, an S-R theory stands alone. S-R theory is dynamic; it does not claim to have *the* explanation of hypnosis, but it does claim to have cornered enough of the market of evidence in its support to continue to absorb, and *change with* new evidence as it arrives. None of the other so-called dynamic theories can clearly offer the dynamism of self-correction. In this sense, they are static.

Finally, an S-R theory offers the most parsimonious understanding of hypnotic behavior, and therefore all of the other theories of hypnosis can be reduced and subsumed under S-R theory. Thus, if we are to rise above perpetuated error in our considerations of hypnosis, we must hold as tenable and continue to test an operationally defined S-R theory of hypnotic behavior.

REFERENCES

Arnold, Magda (1946). "On the mechanism of suggestion and hypnosis," *J. abnorm. soc. Psychol.*, **41**, 107–128.

Barber, T. X. (1961). "Physiological effects of 'hypnosis'," *Psychol. Bull.*, **58**, 390–419.

Barker, W., and Burgwin, Susan (1948). "Brain wave patterns accompanying changes in sleep and wakefulness during hypnosis," *Psychosom. Med.*, **10**, 317–326.

——— (1949). "Brain wave patterns during hypnosis, hypnotic sleep, and normal sleep," *Arch. Neurol. Psychiat.*, **62**, 412–420.

Bass, M. J. (1931). "Differentiation of the hypnotic trance from normal sleep," *J. exp. Psychol.*, **14**, 382–399.

Beach, F. A. (1959). "Clark Leonard Hull (May 24, 1884–May 10, 1952)." In *National Academy of Sciences' Biographical Memoirs*. Vol. 33, pp. 125–141. New York: Columbia Univer. Press.

Bechterev, W. V. (1906). "What is hypnosis?", *J. abnorm. soc. Psychol.*, **1**, 18–25.

Bennett, J. H. (1851). *The Mesmeric Mania of 1851, with a Physiological Explanation of the Phenomena Produced*. Edinburgh: Sutherland & Knox.

Blake, H., and Gerard, R. W. (1937). "Brain potentials during sleep," *Amer. J. Physiol.*, **119**, 692–703.

Blake, H., Gerard, R. W., and Kleitman, N. (1939). "Factors influencing brain potentials during sleep," *J. Neurophysiol.*, **2**, 48–60.

Braid, J. (1844). "Magic, mesmerism, hypnotism, etc., etc., historically and physiologically considered," *Med. Times*, **11** (273), 224–227.

——— (1845). "Mr. Braid on hypnotism," *The Lancet*, **1**, 627–628.

Brenman, Margaret, and Gill, M. M. (1944). "Hypnotherapy," *Review Series, Josiah Macy Jr. Foundation*, **2**, 80–81.

CASON, H. (1922). "The conditioned pupillary reaction," *J. exp. Psychol.*, **5**, 108–146.

CASTER, J. E., and BAKER, C. S., Jr. (1932). "Comparative suggestibility in the trance and waking states—a further study," *J. gen. Psychol.*, **7**, 287–301.

CHERTOK, L., and KRAMARZ, P. (1959). "Hypnosis, sleep and electroencephalography," *J. nerv. ment. Dis.*, **128**, 227–238.

CORN-BECKER, F., WELCH, L., and FISICHELLI, V. (1949). "Conditioning factors underlying hypnosis," *J. abnorm. soc. Psychol.*, **44**, 212–222.

CRASILNECK, H. B., and HALL, J. A. (1959). "Physiological changes associated with hypnosis: a review of the literature since 1948," *Int. J. clin. exp. Hyp.*, **7**, 9–50.

——— (1960). "Blood pressure and pulse rates in neutral hypnosis," *Int. J. clin. exp. Hyp.*, **8**, 137–139.

DARROW, C. W., HENRY, E. C., GILL, M., and BRENMAN, M. (1950). "Interarea electroencephalographic relationships affected by hypnosis: preliminary report," *EEG clin. Neurophysiol.*, **2**, 231.

DAS, J. P. (1958a). "The Pavlovian theory of hypnosis: an evaluation," *J. ment. Sci.*, **104**, 82–90.

——— (1958b). "Conditioning and hypnosis," *J. exp. Psychol.*, **56**, 110–113.

——— (1959a). "A theory of hypnosis," *Int. J. clin. exp. Hyp.*, **7**, 69–77.

——— (1959b). "Some correlates of verbal conditioning," *Psychol. Studies*, **6**, 30–35.

DAVIS, H., DAVIS, P. A., LOOMIS, A. L., HARVEY, E. N., and HOBART, G. (1938). "Human brain potentials during the onset of sleep," *J. Neurophysiol.*, **1**, 24–38.

——— (1939). "A search for changes in direct current potentials of the head during sleep," *J. Neurophysiol.*, **2**, 129–135.

DIAMANT, J., DUFEK, M., HOSKOVEC, J., KRIŠTOF, M., PEKÁREK, V., ROTH, B., and VELEK, M. (1960). "An electroencephalographic study of the waking state and hypnosis with particular reference to subclinical manifestations of sleep activity," *Int. J. clin. exp. Hypnosis*, **8**, 199–212.

DORCUS, R. M. (1956). "The influence of hypnosis on learning and habit modifying," in Dorcus, R. M. (Ed.), *Hypnosis and Its Therapeutic Applications*. New York: McGraw-Hill, pp. 5/1–5/15.

DYNES, J. B. (1947). "Objective method for distinguishing sleep from the head hypnotic trance," *Arch. Neurol. Psychiat.*, **57**, 84–93.

EDMONSTON, W. E., Jr. (1961). "An experimental investigation of hypnotic age-regression," *Amer. J. clin. Hypnosis*, **3**, 127–138.

——— (1962). "Hypnotic age-regression: An evaluation of role-taking theory," *Amer. J. clin. Hypnosis*, **5**, 3–7.

EICHHORN, R., and TRACTIR, J. (1955). "The relationship between anxiety, hypnotically induced emotions and gastric secretion," *Gastroenterology*, **29**, 417–421.

FELBERBAUM, R., LEVITUS, Y., and SOKOLOVA, K. (1953). "The character of the central nervous system in rheumatic children," *J. Pediat. Ob. Gyn.*, *1*. Cited by Platonov (1959).

FISHER, S. (1955). "An investigation of alleged conditioning phenomena under hypnosis," *J. clin. exp. Hyp.*, **3**, 71–103.

FORD, L. F., and YEAGER, C. L. (1948). "Changes in electroencephalogram in subjects under hypnosis," *Dis. Nerv. Syst.*, **9**, 190–192.

GANTT, W. H. (1962). "Ivan Petrovich Pavlov—Presidential address." In Wortis, J. (Ed.), *Recent Advances in Biological Psychiatry*. Vol. 4, pp. 3–12. New York: Plenum Press.

GILES, E. (1962). "A cross-validation study of the Pascal technique of hypnotic induction," *Int. J. clin. exp. Hyp.*, **10**, 101–108.

GLADFELTER, J. H., and HALL, J. A. (1962). "The relationship of hypnotic phenomena to conditioning," *Texas Rep. Biol. Med.*, **20**, 53–59.

GORTON, B. E. (1949a). "The physiology of hypnosis. I. A review of the literature," *Psychiat. Quart.*, **23**, 317–343.

——— (1949b). "The physiology of hypnosis. II. A review of the literature," *Psychiat. Quart.*, **23**, 457–485.

HEIDENHAIN, R. (1888). *Hypnotism or Animal Magnetism, Physiological Observations*. Trans. by L. C. Woolridge. London: Kegan Paul, Trench & Co.

HILGARD, E. R. (1948). *Theories of Learning*. New York: Appleton-Century-Crofts.

HILGARD, E. R., and MARQUIS, D. G. (1940). *Conditioning and Learning*. New York: Appleton-Century-Crofts.

HUDGINS, C. V. (1933). "Conditioning and the voluntary control of the pupillary light reflex," *J. gen. Psychol.*, **8**, 3–51.

HULL, C. L. (1933). *Hypnosis and Suggestibility, an Experimental Approach.* New York: Appleton-Century-Crofts.

——— (1943). *Principles of Behavior*. New York: Appleton-Century-Crofts.

——— (1951). *Essentials of Behavior*. New Haven: Yale Univer. Press.

——— (1952a). *A Behavior System*. New Haven: Yale Univer. Press, pp. 1–14.

——— (1952b). "Autobiography." In Boring, E. G. (Ed.), *A History of Psychology in Autobiography*. Vol. 4, pp. 143–162. Worchester, Mass.: Clark Univer. Press.

HULL, C. L., and HUSE, BETTY (1930). "Comparative suggestibility in the trance and waking states," *Amer. J. Psychol.*, **42**, 279–286.

HULL, C. L., PATTEN, E. F., and SWITZER, S. A. (1933). "Does positive response to direct suggestion as such evoke a generalized hypersuggestibility?" *J. gen. Psychol.*, **8**, 52–64.

JAMES, W. (1890). *The Principles of Psychology*, New York: Holt, p. 601.

JENNESS, A. F. (1933). "Facilitation of response to suggestion by response to previous suggestion of a different type," *J. exp. Psychol.*, **16**, 55–82.

KELLOGG, E. R. (1929). "Duration and effects of post-hypnotic suggestion," *J. exp. Psychol.*, **12**, 502–514.

KOROTKIN, I. I., and SUSLOVA, M. M. (1951). "Investigation into higher nervous activity in subjects in the somnambulistic phase of hypnosis," *Zh. Vyssh. Nervn. Deiatel.*, **1**, 617–622. Cited by Das (1958a).

———, and SUSLOVA, M. M. (1953). "Investigation into the higher nervous activity in some somnambulistic phase of hypnosis during different depths of hypnotic sleep," *Fiziol. Zhurnal.*, **39**, 423–431. Cited by Das (1958a).

KOROTKIN, I. I., and SUSLOVA, M. M. (1955a). "About some characteristics of the reciprocal influence of signal systems in hypnotic and post-hypnotic states," *Zh. Vyssh. Nervn. Deiatel.*, **5**, 511–519. Cited by Das (1958a).

——— (1955b). "Materials for the investigation into the nervous mechanism of post-hypnotic suggestion with hysterics," *Zh. Vyssh. Nervn. Deiatel.*, **5**, 697–707. Cited by Das (1958a).

——— (1955c). "On the physiological mechanism of inhibitory action on stimuli inhibited by hypnotic suggestions," *Dokl. Akad. Nauk, SSSR*, **102** (1), 189–192. Cited by Das (1958a).

——— (1959). "Changes in conditioned and unconditioned reflexes during suggested states in hypnosis." In *The Central Nervous System and Human Behavior—Translations from the Russian Medical Literature*, pp. 653–670. Bethesda, Md.: U.S. Dept. Health, Education, and Welfare.

KOSTER, S. (1954). "Experimental investigation of the character of hypnosis," *J. clin. exp. Hyp.*, **2**, 42–55.

KRASNER, L. (1958). "Studies of the conditioning of verbal behavior," *Psychol. Bull.*, **55**, 148–170.

KROGER, W. S., and SCHNEIDER, S. A. (1959). "An electronic aid for hypnotic induction: a preliminary report," *Int. J. clin. exp. Hyp.*, **7**, 93–98.

KRUEGER, R. G. (1931). "The influence of repetition and disuse upon rate of hypnotization," *J. exp. Psychol.*, **14**, 260–269.

LEUBA, C. (1940). "Images as conditioned sensations," *J. exp. Psychol.*, **26**, 345–351.

——— (1941). "The use of hypnosis for controlling variables in psychological experiments," *J. abnorm. soc. Psychol.*, **36**, 271–274.

——— (1955). "Conditioning during hypnosis," *J. clin. exp. Hyp.*, **3**, 256–259.

——— (1960). "Theories of hypnosis: a critique and a proposal," *Amer. J. clin. Hyp.*, **3**, 43–48.

LEUBA, C., and DUNLAP, R. (1951). "Conditioning imagery." *J. exp. Psychol.* **41**, 352–355.

LOOMIS, A. L., HARVEY, E. N., and HOBART, G. (1936). "Brain potentials during hypnosis," *Science*, **83**, 239–241.

LOVETT DOUST, J. W. (1953). "Studies on the physiology of awareness: Oximetric analysis of emotion and the differential planes of consciousness seen in hypnosis," *J. clin. exp. Psychopathol.*, **14**, 113–126.

LUCKHARDT, A. B., and JOHNSTON, R. L. (1924). "Studies in gastric secretion: I. The psychic secretion of gastric juice under hypnosis," *Amer. J. Physiol.*, **70**, 174–182.

MARENINA, A. I. (1959). "Further investigations on the dynamics of cerebral potentials in various phases of hypnosis in man." In *The Central Nervous System and Human Behavior—Translations from the Russian Medical Literature*, pp. 645–649. Bethesda, Md.: U.S. Dept. Health, Education, and Welfare.

MESSERSCHMIDT, R. (1927–1928). "A quantitative investigation of the alleged independent operation of conscious and subconscious processes," *J. abnorm. soc. Psychol.*, **22**, 325–340.

MITCHELL, M. B. (1932). "Retroactive inhibition and hypnosis," *J. gen. Psychol.*, **7**, 343–358.

MOLL, A. (1894). *Hypnotism.* London: Walter Scott.

NARBUTOVICH, I. (1933). "The possibility of the production of hypnotic sleep and dehypnosis in man by the indifferent stimulation of conditioned reflexes," *Arch. Biol. Sci.*, **34**. Cited by Platonov (1959).

NAUTA, W. J. H. (1946). "Hypothalamic regulation of sleep in rats: an experimental study," *J. Neurophysiol.*, **9**, 285–316.

OSGOOD, C. E. (1953). *Method and Theory in Experimental Psychology.* New York: Oxford Univer. Press.

PASCAL, G. R., and SALZBERG, H. C. (1959). "A systematic approach to inducing hypnotic behavior," *Int. J. clin. exp. Hyp.*, **7**, 161–167.

PATTEN, E. F. (1930). "The duration of post-hypnotic suggestion," *J. abnorm. soc. Psychol.*, **25**, 319–334.

——— (1932). "Does post-hypnotic amnesia apply to practice effects?" *J. gen. Psychol.*, **7**, 196–201.

——— (1933). *An Attempt to Induce Hypersuggestibility in Waking Suggestion by Means of a Specific Supplementary Suggestion to that Effect.* Unpublished manuscript, Yale Univer. and Miami Univer. (Ohio).

PATTEN, E. F., SWITZER, S. A., and HULL, C. L. (1932). "Habituation, retention, and perseveration characteristics of direct waking suggestions," *J. exp. Psychol.*, **15**, 539–549.

PATTIE, F. A. (1956). "Theories of hypnosis." In Dorcus, R. M. (Ed.), *Hypnosis and its Therapeutic Applications*, pp. 1/1–1/30. New York: McGraw-Hill.

PAVLOV, I. P. (1923). "The identity of inhibition with sleep and hypnosis," *Sci. Mon.*, **17**, 603–608.

——— (1927). *Conditioned Reflexes.* London: Oxford Univer. Press.

——— (1941). *Lectures on Conditioned Reflexes.* Vol. 2. *Conditioned Reflexes and Psychiatry.* Trans. W. H. Gantt. New York: International Pub.

PLATONOV, K. I. (1959). *The Word as a Physiological and Therapeutic Factor.* Moscow: Foreign Languages Pub. House.

POVORINSKY, Y. (1937). "Experiments of blood dynamic changes during hypnosis," *DECC. J.* Cited by Platonov (1959).

PSHONIK, A. (1952). *Cerebral Cortex and the Reception Functions of the Organism.* Moscow. Cited by Platonov (1959).

RAVITZ, L. J. (1950). "Electrometric correlates of the hypnotic state," *Science*, **112**, 341–342.

——— (1951a). "The use of DC measurements in psychiatry," *Neuropsychiatry*, **1** (3), 3–12.

——— (1951b). "Standing potential correlates of hypnosis and narcosis," *AMA Arch. Neurol. Psychiat.* (Chicago), **65**, 413–436.

——— (1959). "Application of the electrodynamic field in biology, psychiatry, medicine, and hypnosis. I. General survey," *Amer. J. clin. Hyp.*, **1**, 135–150.

——— (1962). "History, measurement, and applicability of periodic changes in the electromagnetic field in health and disease." In Wolf, W. (Ed.), "Rhythmic functions in the living system," *Ann. N.Y. Acad. Sci.*, **98**, 1144–1201.

ROYAL MANCHESTER INSTITUTION (1844). "Conversazione on 'Hypnotism'," *Med. Times*, **10** (243), 137–139.

SALTER, A. (1949). *Conditioned Reflex Therapy*. New York: Creative Age Press.

SARBIN, T. R. (1950). "Contributions to role-taking theory. I. Hypnotic behavior," *Psychol. Rev.*, **57**, 227–270.

——— (1956). "Physiological effects of hypnotic stimulation." In Dorcus, R. M. (Ed.), *Hypnosis and its Therapeutic Applications*, pp. 4/1–4/57. New York: McGraw-Hill.

——— (1962). "Attempts to understand hypnotic phenomena." In Postman, L. (Ed.), *Psychology in the Making*, pp. 745–785. New York: Knopf.

SCHWARZ, B. E., BICKFORD, R. G., and RASMUSSEN, W. C. (1955). "Hypnotic phenomena, including hypnotically activated seizures, studied with the electroencephalogram," *J. nerv. ment. Dis.*, **122**, 564–574.

SCOTT, H. D. (1930). "Hypnosis and the conditioned reflex," *J. gen. Psychol.*, **4**, 113–130.

SHPIL'BERG, P. I. (1959). "Human electroencephalography during sleep and hypnosis." In *The Central Nervous System and Human Behavior—Translations from the Russian Medical Literature*, pp. 671–684. Bethesda, Md.: U.S. Dept. Health, Educ., and Welfare.

SHVARTS, A. (1948). "Semantics and sonorics as a result of conditioned stimulation," *Bull. exp. Biol. Med.*, **4**. Cited by Platonov (1959).

——— (1949). "Semantics and sonorics as a result of conditioned stimulation," *Bull. exp. Biol. Med.*, **6** (27). Cited by Platonov (1959).

SMITH, H. W. (1949). "Organism and environment: dynamic oppositions." In Romano, J. (Ed.), *Adaptation*, pp. 25–52. Ithica: Cornell Univer. Press.

STERN, J. A., EDMONSTON, W. E., Jr., ULETT, G. A., and LEVITSKY, A. (1963). "Electrodermal measures in experimental amnesia," *J. abnorm. soc. Psychol., 67,* 397–401.

STROSBERG, I. M., and VICS, I. I. (1962). "Physiologic changes in the eye during hypnosis," *Amer. J. clin. Hyp.*, **4**, 264–267.

TSINKIN, A. (1930a). "Blood pressure in hypnosis (experimental investigation)," *Psychoneurol. Inst., Ukraine*, **14**. Cited by Platonov (1959).

——— (1930b). "Pulse and respiration during normal waking and hypnosis (experimental investigation)," *Psychoneurol. Inst., Ukraine*, **14**. Cited by Platonov (1959).

WEBB, R. A. (1962). "Suggestibility and verbal conditioning," *Int. J. clin. exp. Hyp.*, **10**, 275–279.

WEISS, R. L., ULLMAN, L. P., and KRASNER, L. (1960). "On the relationship between hypnotizability and response to verbal operant conditioning," *Psychol. Reports*, **6**, 59–60.

WEITZENHOFFER, A. M. (1950). "A note on the persistence of hypnotic suggestion," *J. abnorm. soc. Psychol.*, **45**, 160–162.

——— (1952). "The present status of hypnosis and suggestibility. 1. The nature and variety of suggestion," *Brit. J. Med. Hyp.*, **3** (4), 11–15.

——— (1953). *Hypnotism*. New York: Wiley.

——— (1954). "The influence of hypnosis on the learning processes. Some theoretical considerations: I. Retroactive inhibition," *J. clin. exp. Hyp.*, **2**, 191–200.

WELCH, L. (1947). "A behavioristic explanation of the mechanism of suggestion and hypnosis," *J. abnorm. soc. Psychol.*, **42**, 359–364.

WELLS, W. R. (1940). "The extent and duration of post-hypnotic amnesia," *J. Psychol.*, **9**, 137–151.

WHITE, R. A. (1941). "A preface to the theory of hypnotism," *J. abnorm. soc. Psychol.*, **36**, 477–505.

WILLIAMS, G. W. (1930). "Suggestibility in the normal and hypnotic states," *Arch. Psychol.*, No. 122.

WOLF, S. (1950). "Effects of suggestion and conditioning on the action of chemical agents in human subjects—the pharmacology of placebos," *J. clin. Invest.*, **29**, 100–109.

WOOD, A. (1851). "Contributions towards the study of certain phenomena, which have recently dominated experiments in electro-biology," *Mon. J. Med. Sci.*, **12**, 407–435.

WORTIS, J. (1962). "Pavlovianism and clinical psychiatry." In Wortis, J. (Ed.), *Recent Advances in Biological Psychiatry*. Vol. 4, pp. 13–23. New York: Plenum Press.

YAKOVLEV, P. I. (1962). "The traditional and the new in Pavlov's theory of 'higher nervous activity'." In Wortis, J. (Ed.), *Recent Advances in Biological Psychiatry*. Vol. 4, pp. 24–28. New York: Plenum Press.

YOUNG, P. C. (1941). "Experimental hypnotism: a review," *Psychol. Bull.*, **38**, 92–101.

V

CURRENT RESEARCH ON THE NATURE OF HYPNOSIS

13

Individual Differences in Hypnotizability

ERNEST R. HILGARD[1]
Stanford University

It has long been recognized that some people are readily hypnotized and others can be hypnotized only with great difficulty, if indeed at all. This fact poses interesting questions for theory. Is susceptibility some sort of innate ability? Is it a consequence of life experiences, particularly those of early childhood? Is it more a matter of present attitude toward hypnosis and the hypnotist? Opinions can be found supporting many different views; until evidence is firmer, there is much room for speculation. Even those who insist that everyone can be hypnotized admit that some are indeed resistant; the extreme case is that of Vogt, who reported a subject who became hypnotized only after 700 attempts! (Bramwell, 1903.)

[1] Preparation of this chapter, including the investigations within the Laboratory of Hypnosis Research, Stanford University, on which some of its reported data depend, has been aided by grants from the Ford Foundation, the Robert C. Wheeler Foundation, and the National Institute of Mental Health, Public Health Service (Grant MH-3859).

NINETEENTH-CENTURY STUDIES[2]

All investigators have been led to the conclusion that hypnosis occurs in degrees. By analogy with sleep, some people can become more "deeply" hypnotized than others, and any one subject may go through several stages of hypnosis as he reaches the "depth" possible for him. Although the notion of "depth" has been criticized, it causes little confusion so long as its metaphorical meaning is recognized. Perhaps a better expression would be "degree of involvement in hypnosis" but, as we shall see later, there are qualitative differences in this involvement as well as quantitative ones.

Braid (1843) characterized the true state of hypnotic sleep according to complete spontaneous amnesia for all events occurring during the trance, but he was troubled by finding that many of his patients were helped by his procedures even though they failed to meet his criterion. Charcot (1882) and his co-workers Richer (1885) and Gilles de la Tourette (1889) specified three kinds of hypnotic state (catalepsy, lethargy, and somnambulism). These were thought of as discrete, with sharp transitions between them. It was an easy further step, however, for writers such as Pitres (1891), influenced by Charcot, to add other borderline, mixed, and incomplete states (*états frustes*). The implication is still that there is a mixture of states, rather than a true continuum; but once there are enough borderline conditions, there is little distinction between a mixture and a continuum.

The analogy with sleep makes plausible the notion of degrees of hypnosis, expressed as degrees of depth. This idea seems to have been first proposed by Richet (1884). He recognized that the induced somnambulism of the Mesmerists was the same as that produced by other methods, and he rejected the animal magnetism explanation. Three degrees that he recognized were: (1) *torpor*, in which the eyes close spontaneously and can be opened only with great difficulty, if at all; (2) *excitation*, with total inability to open the eyes, unresponsiveness except to the hypnotist, some "automatism" and "double-consciousness"; (3) *stupor*, with previous phenomena in greater degree, spontaneity totally lacking, subject a complete automaton, easily produced "contractures" and "catalepsies." There is usually amnesia in the second state, more complete amnesia in the third. Here we have the beginning of a depth scale.

Not long afterwards, Liébeault (1889) proposed a six-point scale, and Bernheim (1891) a nine-point scale. These are summarized in Tables 1 and 2.

Liébeault felt that his scale was unidimensional in the sense used much later in Guttman-type scales, that is, that an individual who showed the

[2] This section is adapted from the summary of early studies by Hilgard, Weitzenhoffer, Landes, and Moore (1961), and portions are quoted by permission.

Table 1
Depth of Hypnosis According to Liébeault (1889)*

I. Light Sleep	
1. Drowsiness	Torpor, drowsiness, heaviness of the head, difficulty in opening the eyes.
2. Light sleep	Above signs plus catalepsy, but with ability to modify the position of members if challenged.
3. Light sleep: deeper	Numbness, catalepsy, automatism. The subject is no longer able to interfere with rotary automatism†.
4. Light sleep: intermediate	In addition to catalepsy and rotary automatism, the subject can no longer attend to anything else but the hypnotist and has memory only for the interchange between them.
II. Deep or Somnambulistic Sleep	
5. Ordinary somnambulistic sleep	Total amnesia on waking. Can have hallucinations during sleep. Hallucinations vanish with waking. Subject submits to the will of the hypnotist.
6. Profound somnambulistic sleep	Total amnesia on waking. Hypnotic and posthypnotic hallucinations possible. Complete submission to the hypnotist.

* From: Hilgard, E. R., Weitzenhoffer, A. M., Landes, J., and Moore, Rosemarie K. (1961). "The distribution of susceptibility to hypnosis in a student population: A study using the Stanford Hypnotic Susceptibility Scale," *Psychol. Monogr.*, **75** (8, Whole No. 512).

† Catalepsy refers to waxy flexibility, in which the arms remain where they are placed. Rotary automatism refers to the persistence of rotary movement of the hand and forearm, once set into motion by the hypnotist.

Table 2
Depth of Hypnosis According to Bernheim (1891)*

I. Memory Retained on Waking	
1st degree	Torpor, drowsiness, or various suggested sensations such as warmth, numbness.
2nd degree	Inability to open the eyes if challenged to do so.
3rd degree	Catalepsy suggested by the hypnotist and bound up with the passive condition of the subject, but may be counteracted by the subject.
4th degree	Catalepsy and rotary automatism, which cannot be counteracted by the subject.
5th degree	Involuntary contractures and analgesia as suggested by the hypnotist.
6th degree	Automatic obedience; subject behaves like an automaton.
II. Amnesia on Waking	
7th degree	Amnesia on waking. No hallucinations.
8th degree	Able to experience hallucinations during sleep.
9th degree	Able to experience hallucinations during sleep and posthypnotically.

* From: Hilgard, Weitzenhoffer, Landes, and Moore (1961).

symptom characteristic of one of his degrees of depth would always show all of the symptoms of lesser degree. Both scales emphasize spontaneous amnesia as a characteristic of the deeper stages. This is equally true for Bernheim, despite his theoretical position that all phenomena of hypnosis are the result of suggestion. Perhaps he interpreted amnesia as a natural accompaniment of other suggestions, although it was not itself suggested. The appearance of such scales made it meaningful to speak of the distribution of susceptibility according to the depth of hypnosis that could be reached.

Many of those who worked with hypnosis were satisfied with simpler classifications of hypnotic states. A common three-point scale distinguished between "somnolence," "light sleep," or "hypotaxy," and "deep sleep" or "somnambulism." This classification was used by Forel, Loewenfeld, Fontan, Ségard, and Ringier. Others preferred a twofold classification, whereby individuals fell in Group I if only their motor behavior was affected, and in Group II if in addition they yielded also perceptual and ideational changes. Gurney, Delboeuf, Hirschlaft, and Dessoir preferred this scheme.

These nineteenth-century scales have enough in common that it is possible to make some comparisons among the findings of the various authorities. All, for example, give a good deal of weight to spontaneous ("nonsuggested") posthypnotic amnesia as a criterion of deep hypnosis. Other stages are usually described according to classes of events, rather than according to specific tests, so that there is an element of uncertainty about borderline states. Induction procedures were not standardized, except within master-disciple groups, and there was always a certain amount of accepted folklore. For example, it was assumed by many hypnotists that hallucinations were produced by a simple posturing of the subject, without verbal suggestions of hallucination. The word "suggestion" to one hypnotist might mean a verbal command, but to another it might mean a nonverbal suggestion produced by some sort of manipulation. Thus in comparing the distributions of susceptibility as reported by these early writers, one naturally must recognize large elements of uncertainty in making quantitative comparisons.

It comes as something of a surprise to find the very large numbers of subjects for whom records were kept and reported in the latter part of the nineteenth century. In Table 3 are digested the results from two major reviews (Loewenfeld, 1901; Schmidkunz, 1894) adding some cases reported a little later by Bramwell (1903). The 14 summarized distributions in this table are based on records from 19,534 patients—a very substantial number, even with allowance for some duplications in the reports. Included are only those reports that permitted classification (always with a margin of uncertainty) into refractory or nonsusceptible subjects and three degrees of susceptibility: drowsy-light,

Table 3
Distribution of Susceptibility to Hypnosis: Nineteenth-Century Studies*

INVESTIGATOR	SOURCE†	DATE	AGE RANGE	NUMBER OF SESSIONS	NUMBER OF CASES	DISTRIBUTION OF SUSCEPTIBILITY (IN PER CENT) REFRACTORY: NON-SUSCEPTIBLE	DROWSY-LIGHT	HYPOTAXY-MODERATE	SOMNAMBULISTIC-DEEP
1. Peronnet	a	ante-1900			467	25	10	20	45
2. Forel	a	ante-1898			275	17	23	37	23
3. Lloyd-Tuckey	a	ante-1900			220	14	49	28	9
4. Bramwell	b	ante-1900	4–76	Mean: 23	200	11	24	26	39
5. Von Schrenck-Notzing	a	ante-1900			240	12	17	42	29
6. Mosing	c	1889–93	a few children	Mean: 20–30	594	12	42	17	29
7. Hilger	a	ante-1900			351	6	20	42	32
8. Von Schrenck-Notzing (pooling of 15 reports)	a	1892			8,705	6	29	50	15
9. Liébeault	a	1884–89	7–63		2,654	5	22	62	11
10. Von Eeden and von Renterghem	a	1887–93			1,089	5	43	41	11
11. von Renterghem	a	ante-1900			414	4	52	33	11
12. Wetterstrand	a	1890		Failures, 1 or 2 trials	3,209	3	36	48	13
13. Velander	a	ante-1900			1,000	2	32	54	12
14. Vogt	a	ante-1900			116	0	2	13	85
Total cases					$N = 19{,}534$				
Range of per cents						0–25	2–52	13–62	9–85
Mean of per cents						9	29	36	26

* After Hilgard, Weitzenhoffer, Landes, and Moore (1961).
† a. Loewenfeld (1901); b. Bramwell (1903); c. Schmidkunz (1894).

hypotaxy-moderate, and somnambulistic-deep. Because the conditions of each investigation differ, the means of the investigations have been reported without respect to the variation in numbers of cases, thus using each report as one case in computing the means at the bottom of Table 3.

Recognizing the great variability in these figures, a rough summary would be that about a fourth of the subjects enter into only very light states; half are moderately susceptible; and perhaps a fourth can reach a somnambulistic state under favorable circumstances, although very highly susceptible subjects are more likely to number about 10 per cent. As we shall see, these nineteenth-century figures are not greatly out of line with the results of more careful recent attempts at measuring hypnotic susceptibility.

EARLY QUANTITATIVE SUSCEPTIBILITY SCALES

A distinction is sometimes made between aptitude tests and achievement tests, an aptitude test predicting what can be done prior to the training in doing it (as in predicting typing ability before learning to type), an achievement test studying what has been accomplished (as words per minute typed by a trained typist). One might therefore predict hypnosis before a person has been hypnotized, on the basis, say, of answers to some sort of questionnaire; this would qualify as an aptitude test. Or, one can actually hypnotize a person and see what he can do. Such a sample of hypnotic performance is an achievement test. Because hypnosis can be fairly quickly induced in susceptible subjects, the latter form of test has been much the more common, so that a hypnotic susceptibility test or a depth scale turns out to be a work sample of hypnotic-like behaviors yielded under standard conditions. The distinction between aptitude and achievement is not sharp; it may be that a short sample of hypnotic behavior will predict kinds of behavior under hypnosis that have not yet been attempted. In that case early achievement is used as an aptitude indicator of later achievement.

The twentieth-century interest in hypnotic susceptibility scales began with the publication in 1930 of a scale by M. M. White. He made use of specific responses to suggestions given in hypnosis as a means of arriving at scores, and thus began a practice adopted by most of the later scales. Shortly thereafter the Davis and Husband (1931) scale appeared, which, although more detailed and covering a wider range of depth, assigned scores on the basis of responses to classes of suggestions rather than to specific responses. At about the same time Barry, MacKinnon, and Murray (1931) proposed a scale based on a short list of specific suggestions. They placed much weight upon the subject's ability to have some suggested posthypnotic amnesia, and upon suggested inhibition of response, that is, loss of ability to control certain types of movement, such as separating interlocked fingers. Although

Hull (1933) did not develop a scale of susceptibility, he often used speed of eye closure to suggestion as a measure of susceptibility. The well-known scale of Friedlander and Sarbin (1938) combines this emphasis upon eye closure with the kinds of items used in the Barry, MacKinnon, and Murray scale. The scale developed by Eysenck and Furneaux (1945) was similar in many respects to that of Friedlander and Sarbin; but the scales of LeCron and Bordeaux (1947) and of Watkins (1949) were more nearly variations of the Davis-Husband type of scale. Of these, the scale of LeCron and Bordeaux is of great length, and covers a very large variety of hypnotic phenomena. The most widely used of these scales have been those of Davis and Husband and of Friedlander and Sarbin.

Table 4
Davis and Husband Susceptibility Scoring System*

DEPTH	SCORE	OBJECTIVE SYMPTOMS	NUMBER OF CASES	PER CENT OF CASES
Insusceptible	0		5	9
Hypnoidal	2	Relaxation	16	29
	3	Fluttering of lids		
	4	Closing of eyes		
	5	Complete physical relaxation		
Light trance	6	Catalepsy of eyes	10	18
	7	Limb catalepsies		
	10	Rigid catalepsy		
	11	Anesthesia (glove)		
Medium trance	13	Partial amnesia	8	15
	15	Posthypnotic anesthesia		
	17	Personality changes		
	18	Simple posthypnotic suggestions		
	20	Kinesthetic delusions; complete amnesia		
Somnambulistic trance	21	Ability to open eyes without affecting trance	16	29
	23	Bizarre posthypnotic suggestions		
	25	Complete somnambulism		
	26	Positive visual hallucinations, posthypnotic		
	27	Positive auditory hallucinations, posthypnotic		
	28	Systematized posthypnotic amnesias		
	29	Negative auditory hallucinations		
	30	Negative visual hallucinations; hyperesthesias		
		Total	55	100

* After Davis, L. W., and Husband, R. W. (1931). "A study of hypnotic susceptibility in relation to personality traits," *J. abnorm. soc. Psychol.*, **26**, 175–182.

The scoring system of Davis and Husband is outlined in Table 4, along with their report of the distribution of susceptibility among 55 university students. Although this scale has been fairly widely used as a kind of reference standard, the lack of specificity with respect to induction techniques and quantification of response make it unsatisfactory as a psychometric research instrument.

The Friedlander-Sarbin scale is presented in Table 5, along with their normative data.

Table 5
Friedlander-Sarbin Scale with Normative Data*

ITEM	SCORING CRITERIA	SCORE
1. Final lid closure	Depends on period of instructions during which eyes close.	0–5
2. Negative suggestion tests: (eye catalepsy, arm immobilization, arm rigidity, finger lock, verbal inhibition)	Resistance time for each item totalled, maximum of 10 sec. per item. Score is multiple of 10 sec.	0–5
3. Posthypnotic voice hallucination	No prodding needed, 5; prodding needed, 3; no hallucination, 0.	0, 3, 5
4. Amnesia	No items recalled 5 One item recalled 4 Two items recalled 3 Three items recalled 2 Four or five recalled 1 More than five recalled 0	0–5
	POSSIBLE SCORES	0–20

Obtained scores	Cases	Per cent
15–19	12	11
10–14	18	17
5–9	33	30
0–4	46	42
	109	100

* After Friedlander, J. W., and Sarbin, T. R. (1938). "The depth of hypnosis," *J. abnorm. soc. Psychol.*, **33**, 281–294.

To compare the results that were obtained following the renewed interest in measuring hypnotic susceptibility, the distributions from a few representative studies have been converted in Table 6 to a scale similar to that of Table 3. The story that is told is not very different, although the typical findings are of a higher proportion of refractory subjects and a lower proportion of somnambulistic ones than in the nineteenth-century reports.

Table 6
Distribution of Susceptibility to Hypnosis: Some Twentieth-Century Studies

INVESTIGATORS	DATE	SCALE	SUBJECTS	CASES	DISTRIBUTION OF CASES (IN PER CENT)*			
					REFRACTORY: NONSUS-CEPTIBLE	DROWSY: LIGHT	HYPOTAXY: MODERATE	SOMNAM-BULISTIC: DEEP
Barry, MacKinnon, and Murray	1931	Own	College students	73	16	37	29	18
Davis and Husband	1931	Own	College students	55	9	47	15	29
Friedlander and Sarbin	1938	Own	College students	57	33	50	12	5
Eysenck and Furneaux	1945	Own	Neurotic patients	60	37	38	17	8
Weitzenhoffer	1956	†	College students	200	23	59	15	3
Hilgard, Weitzenhoffer, and Gough	1958	†	College students	74	3	51	30	16
Total cases				519				
Range of percentages					3–37	37–59	15–30	3–29
Mean of percentages					20	47	20	13

* The original data have been redistributed according to the most comparable categories.
† Friedlander-Sarbin scale, as modified slightly by Weitzenhoffer (1956).

CURRENT HYPNOTIC SUSCEPTIBILITY SCALES

Owing to some dissatisfaction with the existing scales, particularly with the form of distribution resulting, Weitzenhoffer and Hilgard undertook an extensive revision and expansion of the Friedlander-Sarbin type of scale. Many of the Friedlander and Sarbin items were retained, buteasier items were added to reduce the number of zero scores; and modifications were made in the scoring basis for other items. The Stanford Hypnotic Susceptibility Scale was at first prepared in two forms, Form A and Form B, essentially equivalent forms to permit before-and-after studies (Weitzenhoffer and Hilgard, 1959). An additional form, Form C, was later added, meeting some new specifications (Weitzenhoffer and Hilgard, 1962). Finally, the Stanford Profile Scales were prepared to emphasize the differentiated aspects of hypnotic behavior (Weitzenhoffer and Hilgard, 1963; Hilgard, Lauer, and Morgan, 1963). Form A of the Stanford Hypnotic Susceptibility Scale was adapted at Harvard for group administration, and is known as the Harvard Group Scale of Hypnotic Susceptibility (Shor and Orne, 1962). A scale closely related to the Stanford one was developed at the University of Illinois for use with children by London (1962a) and is known as the Children's Hypnotic Susceptibility Scale. An eight-item scale has been developed by Barber (Barber and Glass, 1962) to be used with or without prior hypnotic induction as a test of hypnotic-like behavior. These scales will be considered in some detail.

Stanford Hypnotic Susceptibility Scale (SHSS), Forms A and B

The scales have been published, with normative data on 124 college students, and with accompanying record and interrogatory blanks (Weitzenhoffer and Hilgard, 1959). Additional data have been given in Hilgard, Weitzenhoffer, Landes, and Moore (1961), and in Hilgard (1962).

The scale proposes that for psychometric purposes it is desirable to know what responses can be yielded following a standardized induction procedure. It is not assumed that this procedure will be optimal for all, or indeed, for any, of the subjects; yet if comparisons are to be made, uniformity of practice is desirable. Hence the two forms have similar induction procedures, both using eye fixation, eye closure, and relaxation suggestions, the two forms being varied enough in wording to avoid excessive monotony. Much of the Friedlander-Sarbin language is followed, but suggestions are continued beyond eye closure for those who close their eyes early to equalize the amount of time spent in induction. The subject is introduced to suggestion through postural sway prior to the induction; because this "waking suggestion" item correlates with responsiveness following induction it is included as one of the 12 scored items. Eye closure within induction becomes the second item, and it is followed then by ten additional opportunities to respond to suggestions in such a way as to receive a "pass" or "fail" score, passing in this case meaning responding in the manner of a hypnotized subject. The items, even of the so-called "challenge" type, are stated quite permissively, in keeping with contemporary trends in hypnotic induction. For example, the familiar finger-lock instructions are as follows:

Now let us try something else. Put your fingers together. Interlock your fingers. That's it. Press your hands tightly together. Notice how your fingers are becoming *tightly* interlocked together, more and more *tightly* interlocked together... *so* tightly interlocked together that you wonder very much if you could take your fingers and hands apart... Your fingers are interlocked, tightly interlocked... and I want you to try to take your hands apart... just try... (*Allow 10 sec*)

(*If taken apart:*) That's all right. You noticed how hard it was to get started. Now return your hands to their resting position and relax... just relax.

(*If not taken apart:*) Stop trying and relax... Your hands are no longer tightly clasped together... you can take them apart... Take them apart, return them to the arms of the chair and relax... just relax.

Although the instructions are stated firmly, there is no shouting of "You can't take them apart!" and no embarrassment to the hypnotist when the subject fails to follow the suggestion.

The 12 items of Form A and Form B are given in Table 7 along with the criteria of passing.

The original norms of the Stanford Hypnotic Susceptibility Scale are based on the results of 124 Stanford students, half tested first with Form A, half with Form B. Because the two forms were found to be strictly comparable, the reported norms were based on the initial induction, regardless of which form was given first. The score distributions are presented in Table 8. In the use of these norms it must be kept in mind that these are based on a student population in a single university, sampled from a psychology class in a special way. The norms therefore lack full generality, but they provide a useful standard by which to determine whether or not a given sample lies above or below this reference sample.[3] When "volunteers" at Stanford have been used, their scores average higher than for subjects selected in the more standardized fashion (Boucher and Hilgard, 1962).

[3] The norms have shown satisfactory stability for Stanford samples selected in the same way during subsequent years. For example, the mean for 533 cases from Stanford samples, all tested originally with Form A, is 5.62 (SD 3.27), differing by less than half a point from the original standardization sample, and with nearly identical standard deviations.

Table 7
Items in the Stanford Hypnotic Susceptibility Scale: Forms A and B*

ITEM	FORM A	FORM B	CRITERION OF PASSING
1. Postural sway	Backwards	Backwards	Falls without forcing
2. Eye closure	Form A induction	Form B induction	Eyes close without forcing
3. Hand lowering	Left	Right	Lowers at least 6 in. by end of 10 sec.
4. Arm immobilization	Right arm	Left arm	Arm rises less than 1 in. in 10 sec.
5. Finger lock	Before chest	Overhead	Incomplete separation of fingers at end of 10 sec.
6. Arm rigidity	Left arm	Right arm	Less than 2 in. of arm bending in 10 sec.
7. Moving hands	Together	Apart	(A) Hands close as 6 in. (B) Hands apart at least 6 in.
8. Verbal inhibition	Name	Home town	Name unspoken in 10 sec.
9. Hallucination	Fly	Mosquito	Any movement, grimacing, acknowledgment of effect
10. Eye catalepsy	Both eyes closed	Both eyes closed	Eyes remain closed at end of 10 sec.
11. Posthypnotic suggestion	Changes chairs	Rises, stretches	Any partial movement response at signal
12. Amnesia	Recall of items 3 to 11	Recall of items 3 to 11	Recall of 3 or fewer items

* From: Weitzenhoffer, A. M., and Hilgard, E. R. (1959). *Stanford Hypnotic Susceptibility Scale, Forms A and B.* Palo Alto, Calif.: Consulting Psychologists Press.

Table 8
Norms for Initial Induction, Standardization Forms Sample, Stanford Hypnotic Susceptibility Scale (SHSS), A and B*

GENERAL LEVEL	RAW SCORES	NUMBER OF CASES		PER CENT OF CASES		CENTILE EQUIVALENT	STANDARD SCORE†
High	12	3	31	2	24	99	73
	11	6		5		95	67
	10	9		7		89	63
	9	5		4		84	60
	8	8		6		78	58
Medium	7	11	39	9	31	71	56
	6	10		8		62	53
	5	18		14		51	50
Low	4	13	54	11	45	38	47
	3	12		10		28	44
	2	13		11		18	41
	1	9		7		9	37
	0	7		6		3	31
		$N = 124$		100			

* From: Weitzenhoffer and Hilgard (1959).
† Mean of 50, standard deviation of 10.

The total scores have proved to yield quite satisfactory retest reliabilities, with alternate forms being used in the retesting, and different hypnotists serving the second time. The retest reliability reported in the original standardization sample ($N = 124$) was $r = .83$; the following year, a new sample of 96 cases yielded a retest reliability of $r = .90$. If one combines the two days of testing, these reliabilities become $r = .91$ and $r = .95$ for these two samples (Hilgard, 1962).

The individual items also turn out to be quite reliable in retesting, as shown in Table 9.

Table 9
Contributions of Each Item Within the Total Stanford Hypnotic Susceptibility Scale (SHSS), Forms A and B*

ITEM	PER CENT PASSING	RELIABILITY (DAY 1 VERSUS DAY 2) TETRACHORIC *r*'S	CORRELATION WITH TOTAL SCALE MINUS THIS ITEM: BISERIAL *r*'S
1. Postural sway	69	.96	.38
2. Eye closure	58	.78	.57
3. Hand lowering	81	.83	.63
4. Arm immobilization	14	.74	.75
5. Finger lock	32	.83	.72
6. Arm rigidity	32	.88	.83
7. Moving hands	70	.75	.51
8. Verbal inhibition	23	.94	.79
9. Hallucination	35	.71	.55
10. Eye catalepsy	30	.94	.79
11. Posthypnotic suggestion	49	.60	.60
12. Amnesia	32	.77	.69

* From: Weitzenhoffer and Hilgard (1959).

Among the advantages of the SHSS Forms A and B are their ease of administration, their lack of needed equipment, and their nonthreatening nature, to both subject and hypnotist. They are therefore useful with beginners in hypnosis, as well as for more advanced workers.

Harvard Group Scale of Hypnotic Susceptibility (HGS)

To introduce the economies of group administration, Shor and Emily C. Orne have developed a group adaptation of the Stanford Hypnotic Susceptibility Scale, Form A, arranged for self-scoring (Shor and Orne, 1962). It is thus possible to test a whole class for hypnotic susceptibility at a single sitting; this is useful for demonstration purposes as well as in the selection of subjects for further hypnotic experimentation.

Table 10
Items in the Harvard Group Scale of Hypnotic Susceptibility (HGS) Compared with Those in the Stanford Hypnotic Susceptibility Scale (SHSS), Form A*

STANFORD SCALE FORM A (SHSS)	EQUIVALENT ITEM IN HARVARD GROUP SCALE (HGS)	SCORING CRITERION, HARVARD GROUP SCALE (HGS)
1. Postural sway	1. Head falling	Head falls forward at least 2 in.
2. Eye closure	2. Same	Eyelids closed before told to close them deliberately
3. Hand lowering	3. Same	Lowered at least 6 in. before told to let hand down deliberately
4. Arm immobilization	4. Same	Hand not lifted more than 1 in. when told to stop trying
5. Finger lock	5. Same	Fingers incompletely separated when told to stop trying
6. Arm rigidity	6. Same	Arm bent less than 2 in. before being told to stop trying
7. Moving hands together	7. Same	Hands not more than 6 in. apart when told to return them to resting position
8. Verbal inhibition (name)	8. Communication inhibition (head-shake, "No")	Did not shake head before told to stop trying
9. Fly hallucination	9. Same	Outward acknowledgment of effect
10. Eye catalepsy	10. Same	Eyes remained closed
11. Posthypnotic suggestion (changes chairs)	11. Posthypnotic suggestion (touches ankle)	Makes at least observable partial movement to touch ankle
12. Amnesia	12. Same	Three or fewer items listed in 3 min, before amnesia lifted

* From: Shor, R. E., and Orne, Emily C. (1962). *Harvard Group Scale of Hypnotic Susceptibility*. Palo Alto, Calif.: Consulting Psychologists Press; SHSS, see Table 7.

The items are very similar to those of Form A, SHSS, as shown in Table 10. Several experiments have shown the high correspondence between the group form and the individual form of the test (Shor and Orne, 1963; Bentler and Hilgard, 1963; Bentler and Roberts, 1963).

In using the procedure with a large group, it is usually desirable to have not only an experienced person conducting the session, but an experienced observer free to move about the room and handle individual matters as they arise. There are seldom problems, but occasionally a subject ceases to cooperate in the midst of the session, and needs to be warned not to disturb the others. Someone may fall asleep, and no longer attend to instructions; this is relatively unimportant unless it becomes disturbing to others during the interrogation. Some subjects are slow to throw off the effects of the hypnotic experience. It is our practice at Stanford to offer the opportunity to discuss the experience afterwards, in case any sequelae should arise, though care is taken not to suggest that there will be any aftereffects. The Form A content is so innocuous that few problems are likely to arise.

Table 11
Scores on Harvard Group Scale (HGS) Compared with Scores Based on Individual Testing

	GROUP ADMINISTRATION			INDIVIDUAL ADMINISTRATION			
	N	MEAN	SD		*N*	MEAN	SD
1. Three samples compared: control sample, participating first in nonhypnotic experiment; individual sample of volunteers; group sample of volunteers*	152	7.41	3.04	Control	54	6.63	2.96
				Volunteer	115	8.68	2.64
2. Subjects tested in small groups with both observer-scoring and self-scoring (omitting amnesia)							
Observer-scored	45	6.56	2.41				
Self-scored	45	6.71	2.43				
Subjects tested individually and scored as usual; then self-scored as a test of the adequacy of self-scoring†				Objective scoring	34	6.44	2.54
				Self-scoring	34	6.64	2.26
3. Subjects tested in large groups; some returned for individual testing‡							
Selected volunteers	19	10.11	1.45		19	9.16	2.21
Unselected "coerced" volunteers	22	6.00	3.23		22	5.73	3.58

* Shor, R. E., and Orne, Emily C. (1963). "Norms on the Harvard Group Scale of Hypnotic Susceptibility, Form A," *Int. J. clin. exp. Hyp.*, **11**, 39–48; supplemented by data supplied by D. N. O'Connell.

† Bentler, P. M., and Hilgard, E. R. (1963). "A comparison of group and individual induction of hypnosis with self-scoring and observer-scoring," *Int. J. clin. exp. Hyp.*, **11**, 49–54.

‡ Bentler, P. M., and Roberts, Mary R. (1963). "Hypnotic susceptibility assessed in large groups," *Int. J. clin. exp. Hyp.*, **11**, 93–97.

The comparability between self-scoring and observer-scoring has been studied in the case of both group and individual administration. It comes as something of a surprise that a subject can, in retrospect, score himself on 12 items essentially as the observing hypnotist scores him, but this is found to be the case, even when the subject is not informed in advance that he will be expected to do this (Bentler and Hilgard, 1963). Self-scoring tends to yield scores averaging a fraction of a point higher than observer-scoring (Shor and Orne, 1963), but self-scoring and observer-scoring correlate from .83 to .89 in different comparisons. It is not unreasonable that self-scoring should be a little higher: there are often genuine self-observed effects that do not quite meet the psychometric criteria when precise times or precise measures of movement are used. Some results are summarized in Table 11.

Self-scoring is necessary when subjects are tested in large groups. It might be true that the scoring was adequate but that the group induction produced changes significantly different from individual induction. This turns out not to be the case, and group results are quite comparable to individual ones. The most stringent comparison is that between self-scores on the group test and observer scores on a subsequent individual test; the correlation for 45 subjects turns out to be $r = .74$ (Bentler and Hilgard, 1963). In general, this means that for three-fifths of the subjects their self-scores on the group form will lie within one point of later objective scores by the hypnotist in an individual session, and over 90 per cent will have scores falling within three points of each other on the two occasions.

Stanford Hypnotic Susceptibility Scale (SHSS) Form C

The earlier Forms A and B served their intended purposes rather well, as indicated by satisfactory reliabilities, validities, and convenience, including the adaptation for group testing. There are, however, various purposes that such tests can serve, and Form C was developed to serve some additional purposes. For one thing, some richer item content was desired, and Form C includes a number of hallucinatory items, age regression, and dreaming within hypnosis, supplementing the predominantly motor items of Forms A and B. It was also desirable to have a scale not linked to a specific technique of induction; although the Form B induction is normally used in Form C, eye closure within induction is not one of the scored items, and the Form C test can be used with other inductions, or, indeed, without any induction at all. Finally, convenience in administration is offered by having the items arranged strictly in order of difficulty. Because the scale is sufficiently unidimensional, a short form of scoring is provided, so that it is not necessary to take subjects through the whole scale in order to get an estimate of their final scores. It has turned out, as we shall see later, that Form C serves somewhat more satisfactorily than Form A as a criterion measure when personality tests are used in prediction. For many purposes it would be most economical to test subjects first on the Harvard Group Scale (HGS) and then to test selected subjects on Form C individually, using the short form. This would yield a good deal of information about a subject's hypnotic abilities without an undue amount of experimenter time involved.

Table 12
Items of Stanford Hypnotic Susceptibility Scale (SHSS), Form C, with Scoring Criteria*

ITEM	CRITERION OF PASSING
0. Eye closure during induction	(As in Form B, but not counted)
1. Hand lowering (right hand)	Lowers at least 6 in. in 10 sec.
2. Moving hands apart	Hands 6 in. or more apart after 10 sec.
3. Mosquito hallucination	Any acknowledgment of effect
4. Taste hallucination (sweet, sour)	Both tastes experienced *and* one strong or with overt movements
5. Arm rigidity (right arm)	Less than 2 in. of arm bending in 10 sec.
6. Dream	Dreams well; experience comparable to a dream
7. Age regression (school) (5th and 2nd grades)	Clear change in handwriting between present and one regressed age
8. Anosmia to ammonia	Odor of ammonia denied and overt signs absent
9. Arm immobilization (left arm)	Arm rises less than 1 in. in 10 sec.
10. Hallucinated voice	Subject answers voice realistically at least once
11. Negative visual hallucination: two of three boxes	Reports seeing only two boxes
12. Posthypnotic amnesia	Subject recalls 3 or fewer items before "Now you can remember everything"

* From: Weitzenhoffer, A. M., and Hilgard, E. R. (1962). *Stanford Hypnotic Susceptibility Scale, Form C.* Palo Alto, Calif.: Consulting Psychologists Press.

To permit Form C to be used as an alternate to Form B, the Form B induction is provided (though it is optional), and a number of Form B items are repeated, so that retest comparisons can be made with results on Form A. The new items, giving greater richness to Form C, are: taste hallucination, age regression, dream within hypnosis, anosmia, hallucinated voice, and negative visual hallucination (seeing only two of three boxes). The items, with their scoring criteria, are presented in Table 12. Except for the amnesia item, necessarily at the end, the items are arranged in the order of increasing difficulty as expressed by percentage passing.

The score distribution on Form C, as obtained from 203 Stanford students, is reported as the basis for normative data (Weitzenhoffer and Hilgard, 1962). It turns out to be very similar to the distribution for scores on Form A. A shorter form is made possible by the item order. The test is a moderately satisfactory Guttman-type scale, although some of the middle items are too nearly equal in difficulty to meet criteria of desirable scaling, and the extreme items are both too easy at the one end and too hard at the other. By continuing to test until the third item failure is reached (whether or not the failures are consecutive), and adding one point for a possible later success, the defects in scaling are overcome, and a short-form score is yielded which is found to correlate .94 with the long form. The saving of time is, of course, primarily with those who make low scores; the full scale is used for those who score 9 or more. Norms for the short form are also included in the published scale.

The item difficulty, estimated reliability, and contribution of each item to the total scale, are given in Table 13. The reliabilities are retest reliabilities for those cases in which the same or equivalent items appear in Form A and Form C; for three items (anosmia, dream, and age

Table 13

Item Difficulty, Correlation of Item with Total Score, and Estimated Reliability of Individual Items, Stanford Hypnotic Susceptibility Scale (SHSS), Form C*

ITEM	PER CENT PASSING, $N = 203$	CORRELATION WITH TOTAL SCORE MINUS THIS ITEM (BISERIAL r's) $N = 203$	RELIABILITY COEFFICIENTS (TETRACHORIC r's)
1. Hand lowering	92	.60	.77 (N=307)
2. Moving hands apart	88	.49	.65 (N=307)
3. Mosquito hallucination	48	.80	.76 (N=307)
4. Taste hallucination	46	.75	.60 (N=35)
5. Arm rigidity	45	.76	.67 (N=307)
6. Dream	44	.57	.63 (N=58)
7. Age regression	43	.68	.69 (N=58)
8. Arm immobilization	36	.81	.60 (N=307)
12. Amnesia†	27	.85	.74 (N=307)
9. Anosmia to ammonia	19	.65	.65 (N=58)
10. Hallucinated voice	9	.63	.70 (estimated)‡
11. Negative visual hallucination (sees 2 of 3 boxes)	9	.87	.60 (N=35)

* From: Weitzenhoffer and Hilgard (1932); and Hilgard, E. R. (1965). *Hypnotic susceptibility*, p. 238. New York: Harcourt, Brace & World.

† Amnesia out of order of difficulty because necessarily at end of administration.

‡ Estimated on basis of correlation of +.70 with music hallucination (N= 58).

regression) the same items appear in the profile scales, which followed for some of the same subjects. For taste hallucination, the hallucinated voice, and the negative visual hallucination, not repeated in the testing program, the reliability is an estimate. Because no other item falls below a reliability of .60, and because the correlation of these items with the total is substantially the same as the others, the figure of .60 is not an unreasonable estimate of minimum reliability.[4]

Because there is only one Form C, retest reliability for the whole scale was not available as with Forms A and B. Recourse was had, therefore, to the Kuder-Richardson formula 20. This led to an estimated reliability of $r = .85$ ($N = 203$) comparable to that of Forms A and B.

Form C thus preserves the desirable features of high internal consistency, and overall reliability characteristic of Forms A and B, and adds the greater richness of item content and some other technical advantages through independence of a particular form of induction and short-form scoring.

Children's Hypnotic Susceptibility Scale (CHSS)

A scale designed especially for children, classified into two age categories (ages 5 to 0 through 12 to 11 and ages 13 to 0 through 16 to 11) has been prepared by London (1962a). Part I of the scale is very comparable to Form A of the Stanford Hypnotic Susceptibility Scale; it is a 12-item scale with items chosen to parallel those of the Stanford Form A Scale, though adaptations have been made to ease the use with children. Part II consists of items that were originally part of the depth scale being tested at Stanford, most of which are now found in Form C or in Forms I and II of the Stanford Profile Scales of Hypnotic Susceptibility, to be discussed later.[5] Each item is presented as a four-point scale (0 to 3), convertible to a $\pm$ scale by considering scores of 2 to 3 to be + and of 0 to 1 to be —. London believes that it is important to record qualitative observations along with the quantitative ones, and provision is made on the scoring forms for doing this.

The items of the Children's Hypnotic Susceptibility Scale, with the minimum responses required for a score of 2 (that is, +) are given in Table 14.

[4] Another method of estimation involves correlation with related items of the profile scale. The taste hallucination, a positive hallucination, correlated .31 with the positive olfactory hallucination—a different sense but a related function; the two-of-three boxes negative visual hallucination correlates .55 with the missing watch hand, a different form of negative visual hallucination, and the hallucinated voice correlates .68 with another form of positive auditory hallucination, that of heard music. Because these correlations involve some generalized validity in addition to reliability, they make the estimated reliabilities within reason. The number of cases was 58 for each of these three correlations.

[5] Some of the items are also in the 17-point scale described by Weitzenhoffer and Sjoberg (1961).

Table 14
Items on the Children's Hypnotic Susceptibility Scale (CHSS)*

PART I		PART II	
ITEM	MINIMUM FOR PLUS SCORE	ITEM	MINIMUM FOR PLUS SCORE
1. Postural sway	Loses balance and recovers without falling	13. Posthypnotic suggestion (reinduction)	Closes eyes; eyes open but glazed
2. Eye closure	Eyes close within 10 sec. of final instruction before request to close eyes	14. Visual and auditory hallucination (television)	Sees TV set, turns it on; may fail to see picture clearly
3. Hand lowering	Hand moves through 30 degrees arc or more	15. Cold hallucination	Appropriate verbal response
4. Arm immobilization	Hand rises from 1 in. to 3 in.; or with effortful movement, up to 4 in.	16. Anesthesia	May be aware of stimulus but unable to describe it
5. Finger lock	Incomplete separation of fingers; little effort	17. Taste hallucination	Experiences at least slight or vague taste sensations
6. Arm rigidity	Arm bends less than 2 in., with little effort	18. Smell hallucination (perfume)	Affirms odor of perfume
7. Hands together	Hands move to within 2 in. of each other	19. Visual hallucination (rabbit)	Sees rabbit, describes it; may not pick it up
8. Verbal inhibition (name)	Name not spoken; little effort	20. Age regression	Changes writing of name or figure drawing appropriately
9. Auditory hallucination	Appropriate movement	21. Dream	Perfunctory report, but does not appear to be composing story during the report
10. Eye catalepsy	Eyes remain closed; little effort		
11. Posthypnotic suggestion (standing up, stretching)	Remains seated and stretches; or, stands but does not stretch	22. Awakening and posthypnotic suggestion	Completes significant portion of suggested sequence seeing rabbit posthypnotically
12. Amnesia	3 or fewer items recalled with relative ease		

* From: London, P. (1962a). *The Children's Hypnotic Scale*. Palo Alto, Calif.: Consulting Psychologists Press.

Note: The items and scoring standards of Parts I and II are alike for older and younger children, but the items are worded somewhat differently in the two forms.

It is said that the first part of the test (Part I) requires about 20 minutes of actual testing time. If a child has been generally unresponsive, it may not be desirable to go on to Part II. The remaining items of Part II require about 30 minutes to administer.

In reporting preliminary work on the scale, London (1962b) has distinguished between the overt behavior that a scale such as this measures, and the "subjective involvement" in hypnosis that accompanies these performances, but may differ from one child to another. The tendency for these two aspects to be highly correlated attests to the validity of the objective scores. Norms are promised shortly from the Illinois laboratory.

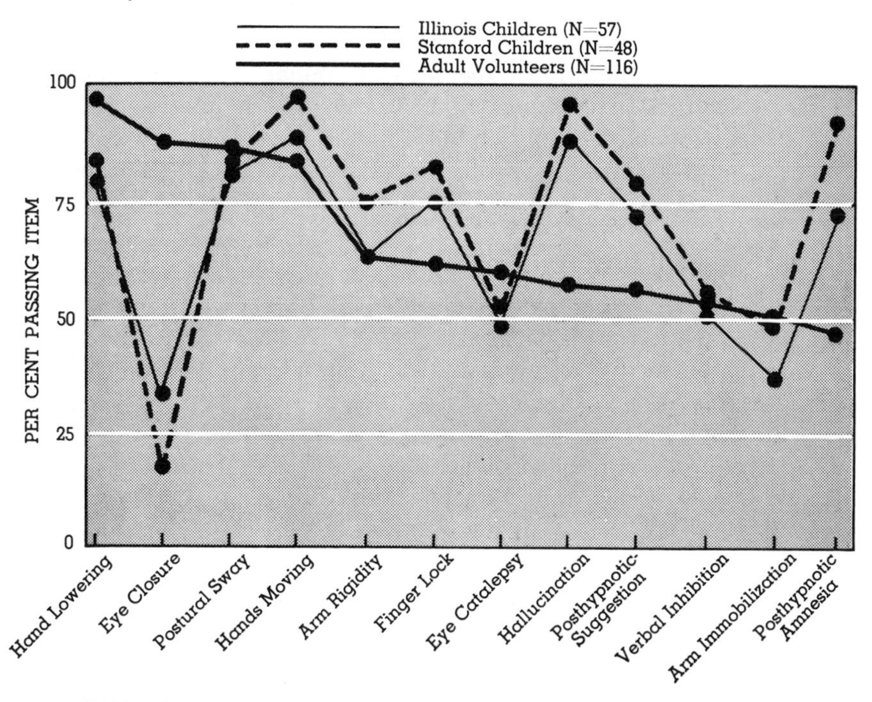

Figure 1. Item difficulty for children compared with that for adult volunteers. The adult volunteers include both Harvard and Stanford samples; the children samples are those from Illinois and Stanford. From: Moore, Rosemarie K., and Lauer, Lillian W. (1963), "Hypnotic susceptibility in middle childhood," *Int. J. clin. exp. Hyp.*, **11**, 167–174.

Although early results show that the children's samples score higher than the standardization sample of adults for SHSS, Form A, they do not score significantly higher than volunteer samples of adults with which they should perhaps be compared. An important discrepancy between children's scores and adult volunteer scores has been pointed out by Moore and Lauer (1963). They show that the profile of item difficulty is quite different for the two kinds of samples, with compensatory difficulty accounting for the lack of differences in mean score. Children find it particularly difficult to keep their eyes closed (possibly in part a result of something internal to the children's scale); in any case, they do poorly on both eye closure and eye catalepsy, relative to adult volunteers. At the same time, they are superior to the adult volunteers particularly on the hallucinatory and amnesia items. A comparison of item difficulty for the two children's samples and adult volunteers from the Stanford and Harvard laboratories is given in Figure 1.

Further studies are needed to clear up the differences in performance between children and adults, and the transitional stages. Despite some of the difficulties in working with children, the hypnotic scores are satisfactorily reliable. A retest on the Children's Hypnotic Susceptibility Scale, using a plus-minus scoring of all 22 items with 39 children, yielded a reliability of .92 (London, 1962b).

Barber Suggestibility Scale (BSS)

A scale that has been extensively used by Barber and his associates (Barber and Glass, 1962; Barber and Calverley, 1963) differs from those previously discussed in that it is intended to test hypnotic-like behaviors *without prior induction* of hypnosis. It can, of course, be used following induction, and has been used in that way to study the effects of induction procedures. As pointed out earlier, the SHSS, Form C, can also be used in this manner, but norms are not available on it for responses without prior induction. The items of Barber's scale are given in Table 15, with their scoring standards summarized.

In calling attention to normative data on this scale, it must be noted that these data were gathered *without prior attempted induction of hypnosis.* The preliminary instructions, substituting for induction, were as follows:

> These are all tests of imagination. The better you can imagine and the harder you try, the more you'll respond. Try as hard as you can to concentrate, and to imagine the things I tell you to. (Barber and Glass, 1962.)

Data for 462 adults can be found in Barber and Glass (1962) and for 724 subjects, ages 6 to 22, in Barber and Calverley (1963).

It is important to know that a considerable fraction of the responses to suggestion that are associated with hypnosis can be obtained from susceptible subjects who have not gone through the usual induction procedures. The problems involved will be discussed later. Responses without prior induction correlated with responses following induction

Table 15
Items of the Barber Suggestibility Scale (BSS)*

ITEM	SCORING CRITERIA
0. Chevreul pendulum	Not scored
1. Arm lowering (eyes open)	1 point for 4 in. or more
2. Arm levitation from horizontally extended position (eyes open)	1 point for response of 4 in. or more
3. Hands locked in lap (eyes open)	1/2 point for incomplete separation after 5 sec. of effort, or 1 point for incomplete separation after 15 sec. of effort
4. Suggestion of extreme thirst (eyes closed)	1/2 point for swallowing, lip moistening, etc., and 1/2 point for indication, during post-hypnotic interview, that subject became thirsty
5. Verbal inhibition (name) (eyes closed)	1/2 point if name not said after 5 sec. of effort, or 1 point if name not said after 15 sec. of effort
6. Body immobility (inability to stand up) (eyes closed)	1/2 point if not completely standing after 5 sec. of effort, or 1 point if not completely standing after 15 sec. of effort
7. Posthypnotic response (cough to a click) (suggested while eyes closed; tested with eyes open)	1 point if coughs to click
8. Selective amnesia (to remember all tests except arm moving up) (suggested while eyes closed; tested with eyes open)	1 point if recalls all other tests but Test 2 and recalls it in response to cue words
Total possible score: 8 points	

* From: Barber, T. X., and Glass, L. B. (1962). "Significant factors in hypnotic behavior," *J. abnorm. soc. Psychol.*, **64**, 222–228.

to the extent of .85 (Spearman rank-correlation, $N = 30$) (Barber and Glass, 1962).

Although the percentage passing each item tends to be less than following a usual hypnotic induction, some 14 to 15 per cent of the subjects were found by Barber and Glass to pass even the items considered to be more difficult, such as verbal inhibition and selective amnesia.

Stanford Profile Scales of Hypnotic Susceptibility (SPS) Forms I and II

It became evident, in working with the earlier constructed susceptibility scales, that despite a strong common factor in hypnotic responsiveness, some high-scoring subjects had clear gaps in their scores. For example, some who yielded high scores on the various motor items failed to respond to posthypnotic amnesia instructions, whereas for others the converse was true.[6] Hence it became clear that some sort of scale diagnostic of the special abilities associated with hypnotic performance would be valuable, a scale which minimized the common factor in hypnosis in favor of a profile of special abilities. The Stanford Profile Scales of Hypnotic Susceptibility were standardized to meet this need (Weitzenhoffer and Hilgard, 1963; Hilgard, Lauer, and Morgan, 1963). Such scales yield a profile of scores instead of a single score of hypnotic susceptibility, thus showing areas of special strength and weakness.

Table 16
Items of Stanford Profile Scales of Hypnotic Susceptibility (SPS), Forms I and II*

FORM I: INDUCTION BY HAND LEVITATION (NOT SCORED)		FORM II: INDUCTION BY HAND LOWERING (NOT SCORED)	
1. Hand analgesia	0–3	1. Heat hallucination	0–3
2. Music hallucination	0–3	2. Selective deafness	0–3
3. Anosmia to ammonia	0–3	3. Hallucinated ammonia	0–3
4. Recall of meal	0–3	4. Regression to birthday	0–3
5. Hallucinated light	0–3	5. Missing watch hand	0–3
6. Dream I: topic unspecified	0–3	6. Dream II: about hypnosis	0–3
7. Agnosia I: house	0–3	7. Agnosia II: scissors	0–3
8. Joke	0–3	8. Personality alteration	0–3
9. Posthypnotic verbal compulsion	0–3	9. Posthypnotic automatic writing	0–3
Total	0–27	Total	0–27

* From: Weitzenhoffer, A. M., and Hilgard, E. R. (1963). *Stanford Profile Scales of Hypnotic Susceptibility, Forms I and II.* Palo Alto, Calif.: Consulting Psychologists Press.

Considering the Profile Scales first as simply another form of hypnotic susceptibility scale, the total scores can be used similarly to the total scores on Forms A, B, and C. Then Forms I and II are each total scales with maximum scores of 27 each. The items involved are given in Table 16. Note that motor items and amnesia, prominent in Forms A, B, and C of SHSS have been left out; for some purposes, as we shall see later, the scores on these items from Form A enter into extended profile scale scores. Norms for the Stanford sample ($N = 112$), based on subjects who scored 4 or more on Form A are given in the Manual (Hilgard, Lauer, and Morgan, 1963). This somewhat curtailed sample showed a

[6] Some such cases were reported earlier by Hilgard and Hilgard (1962).

correlation between Forms I and II of $r = .72$. This is a reliability-validity coefficient, because the items are quite different in substance on the two days, although they are similar in topic; if one considers the two-day scores to be a single test, the reliability, as estimated by the Spearman-Brown formula, becomes .86.

Table 17
Intercorrelations of scores on SHSS, Forms A and C, and SPS, Forms I and II*

	FORM C (SHSS)	FORM I (SPS)	FORM II (SPS)
Form A (SHSS)	.82	.64	.62
Form C (SHSS)		.71	.72
Form I (SPS)			.78

* From: Hilgard, E. R. (1965). *Hypnotic Susceptibility*, p. 251. New York: Harcourt, Brace & World.
Note: Stanford students, $N = 59$. In this sample all subjects were tested on all scales; that is, those scoring low on Form A were not eliminated from the profile scale testing.

The common factor that runs through all hypnotic scales is attested by the intercorrelations between scores on Forms A, C, I, and II, Table 17, based on a new sample in which the distributions were not curtailed. In some cases, several months elapsed between the testing on Forms A and C and the later Profile Scale testing on Forms I and II. The generally satisfactory correlations, despite differences in test content, induction procedures, and changing hypnotists, give assurance that the criteria of hypnotic susceptibility are reasonably stable. At the same time, the correlations are not so high as to preclude subordinate factors.

Although the individual items of the SPS can be plotted to yield an individual item profile, greater profile stability is achieved by combining the items into subscales. For this purpose the items of Forms I and II are grouped into four subscales of four items each, and two additional subscales are devised by combining the results from Form A with the remaining items of Forms I and II. The subscale rationale is presented in Table 18.

Because of the differing content between Forms I and II, reliabilities of subscales obtained by correlating two items of Form I with two items of Form II confound reliability and validity. Nevertheless, such correlations yielded reliability estimates lying between .65 and .80 where such estimates could be made (Hilgard, Lauer, and Morgan, 1963). In order to make a more direct approach to the reliability problem, alternate forms for Form I and Form II were prepared for use in a retest program, so that Form Ia paralleled Form I very closely and

Table 18
Rationale of Subscales Derived from Profile Scales Form I and II and Selected Items from Form A*

ADOPTED NAME AND INITIALS OF SUBSCALE	FUNCTIONS INTENDED TO BE TESTED	ITEM CONTENT OF TESTS IN SUBSCALE
AG: Agnosia and cognitive distortion	Distortion of meaning and value, rather than of sense-perception	I: 7 Agnosia I: House I: 8 Joke (affective distortion) II: 7 Agnosia II: Scissors II: 8 Personality alteration (reduced intelligence)
HP: Hallucinations: positive	The experiencing of sensory and perceptual phenomena in the absence of appropriate stimuli	I: 2 Music hallucination I: 5 Hallucinated light II: 1 Heat hallucination II: 3 Hallucinated ammonia
HN: Hallucinations: negative	Lack of awareness of stimulation that would normally be perceived	I: 1 Hand analgesia to shock I: 3 Anosmia to ammonia II: 2 Selective deafness II: 5 Missing watch hand (visual)
DR: Dreams and regressions	Memory revival and fantasy production, including fantasied "reliving" of events in the past	I: 4 Recall of meal I: 6 Dream I: General II: 4 Regression to birthday II: 6 Dream II: About hypnosis
AM: Amnesia and posthypnotic compulsions	Behavior suggested during hypnosis but carried out after arousal from hypnosis, usually with forgetting of the instructions	Amnesia: Rescored from Form A I: 9 Posthypnotic verbal compulsion II: 9 Posthypnotic automatic writing
MC: Loss of motor control	Motor responses carried out automatically as a result of direct suggestion; loss of volitional control over movement as a result of suggestion	Motor Pool (a) from Form A 1. Postural sway 2. Eye closure 4. Arm immobilization 5. Finger lock Motor Pool (b) from Form A 6. Arm rigidity 7. Hands moving together 8. Verbal inhibition 10. Eye catalepsy

* From: Hilgard, E. R., Lauer, Lillian W., and Morgan, Arlene H. (1963). *Manual for Stanford Profile Scales of Hypnotic Susceptibility, Forms I and II.* Palo Alto, Calif.: Consulting Psychologists Press.

Form IIa paralleled Form II very closely, modifying such items as would be inappropriate for direct retest. All the 60 subjects who participated in this retest program had earlier been tested with Forms A and C. Now they were tested on the profile scales half in the order

Ia-I-II, half in the order IIa-II-I. Thus half the subjects furnished a test-retest comparison of the items of Form I, half of Form II, and all permitted a study of some of the characteristics of Forms I and II when given in the order I-II or the order II-I. The total results of this analysis have not yet been published; some of the data have been used in the previous Table 17, and the retest reliability data are given in Table 19.

Table 19
Stanford Profile Scales of Hypnotic Susceptibility: Subscale Reliabilities as Determined by Retests*†

SUBSCALE	FORM I VS. Ia (TWO-ITEM SCALE) ($N = 22$)	FORM II VS. IIa (TWO-ITEM SCALE) ($N = 22$)	ESTIMATED RELIABILITY (FOUR-ITEM SCALE)‡
AG: Agnosia	.50	.73	.77
HP: Hallucinations: positive	.41	.63	.69
HN: Hallucinations: negative	.53	.84	.84
DR: Dreams and Regression	.68	.75	.84
AM: Amnesia and posthypnotic compulsion	.61	.83	.85**
MC: Loss of motor control	.62	.59	.76**

* From: Hilgard (1965), p. 257.

† For this purpose, only those subjects in the retest experiment are included who scored 4 or more on Form A.

‡ The reliabilities of the two-item subscales were averaged by first transforming the r's to z's, and then the average r stepped up by the Spearman-Brown formula to estimate the four-item reliability.

** In computing reliabilities, use was made of scores available from Form C to provide equivalent forms for these subscales for Forms I and Ia and II and IIa.

For this purpose the 16 subjects who scored below 4 on Form A have been eliminated, in order to have the reliabilities based on a sample similar to that used in standardizing the profile scales. The correlations are somewhat unstable in view of the limited numbers of cases, but the orders of magnitude are sufficiently representative to show that one can make use of the individual subscale scores with some assurance, even though each subscale is composed of but four items. The reliabilities shown in Table 19, estimated by the retest procedure, are of about the same order of magnitude as those reported in the manual, obtained by correlating the two subscale items of Form I with the two corresponding subscale items of Form II.

The method of preparing a profile based on subscale scores is as follows. First, the raw scores from SHSS Form A and SPS Forms I and II are assembled on standard forms that are provided. From these, subscale scores are obtained by adding the scores for the individual items composing the subscales. These raw scores are then plotted on forms provided and thus converted to standard scores by a graphical method. Two specimen profiles are shown in Figure 2, one of a subject (No. 795) above the mean of the standardization group on all subscales except AM (amnesia and posthypnotic compulsion), the other of a subject

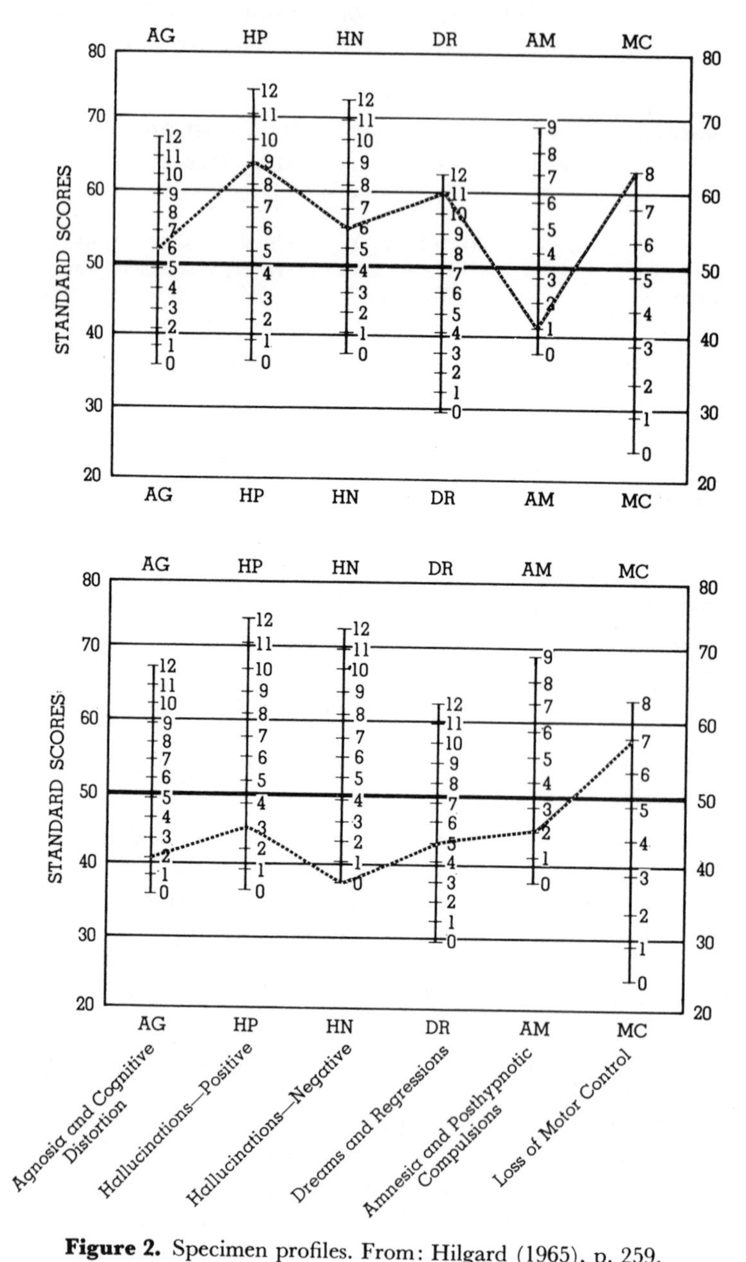

Figure 2. Specimen profiles. From: Hilgard (1965), p. 259.

(No. 966) particularly high in motor control, while below the mean in everything else. A number of other specimen profiles are given in the Manual (Hilgard, Lauer, and Morgan, [1963]).

THE COMPOSITION OF HYPNOTIC ABILITIES

The profile scales are based on the assumption that there are significant differences in the hypnotic performances of individuals going beyond the unidimensional one of "hypnotic depth" or "hypnotic involvement." That this is indeed the case has often been pointed out by earlier investigators, often through a factor analysis of scores of hypnotic susceptibility.

Eysenck (1943) in a factorial study of eight tests of suggestibility showed that two orthogonal factors accounted for the correlations. These he interpreted as *primary suggestibility*, based on ideomotor performances of which body sway is typical, and *secondary suggestibility*, or indirect suggestibility of the kind represented by the progressive weights test of Binet (1900). In repeating and extending a similar type of investigation, Eysenck and Furneaux (1945) confirmed the two clusters of tests, the tests of primary suggestibility correlating among themselves with an average of +.50, those of secondary suggestibility with an average of +.15, while the average intercorrelation between tests of primary and secondary suggestibility was +.02. An additional distinction was proposed somewhat tentatively, that between two types of those who responded to suggestion, the "active" and the "passive" responders. This distinction was made earlier by White (1937), but we have been unable to establish it through observations upon our normal subjects (Hilgard, Weitzenhoffer, Landes, and Moore, 1961). The Eysenck-Furneaux subjects were neurotic male army patients; what difference that makes is at present unknown.

A number of further factor analytic studies have been made of hypnosis, for example, those of Ås and Lauer (1962), Das (1958), Hammer and Evans (1963), Moore (1961), and Stukat (1958). They typically find a strong first factor, corresponding to Eysenck and Furneaux's primary suggestibility, and a number of subordinate factors depending upon the composition of the battery used. The Stanford studies have restricted the number of factors by using only test items with some saturation on the first factor. Thus a test of arm catalepsy (passively raising the forearm with the elbow resting on the arm of the chair, and scoring as a pass if the arm remained up when released) was eliminated from Form A because, although satisfactorily reliable ($r_t = .92$), its biserial correlation with the total score minus that item was negligible ($r = -.14$). Retaining such an item would, of course, have changed the factor structure of the battery. Other tests of "secondary suggestibility," such as progressive weights, have not been included in our scales. Hence the elimination of "secondary suggestibility" means that our subordinate factors are essentially specific factors found within tests whose total scores are still weighted with the common factor. It is to be expected, therefore, that SHSS Forms A, B, and C, will be unusually highly loaded with a common factor; the profile scales, Form I and II, should give more prominence to secondary factors because the inert low-scoring subjects are eliminated, and the tests are scored so as to be of more nearly equal difficulty throughout (Hilgard, 1965).

Factor Analyses

SHSS, Form A. The scores of 402 subjects, male and female students, were intercorrelated, using tetrachoric correlations. The only arbitrary practice adopted was to add enough cases to yield 1 per cent of the cases in a near-empty cell if less than 1 per cent of the cases fell in that cell; by keeping the margins as they were, this meant displacing at most four of the 402 cases, and made the tetrachoric correlation determinate for these cases.

The obtained matrix was then factor-analyzed by the principle components method, using the facilities of the Stanford Computation Center.[7] The first three unrotated factors accounted for 53, 10, and 6 per cent of the variance, respectively, a total of 69 per cent.[8] None of the remaining factors accounted for more than 3 per cent of the variance, so they are ignored.

Graphical rotation to maximize the factor loadings on the first three orthogonal factors yielded the item clusters shown in Table 20.

The results are quite clear-cut. The first factor, on which all tests are substantially loaded, is best represented by the five "challenge" or "negative suggestion" items, representing *loss of voluntary control* over musculature in hands, arms, eyelids, and vocal mechanisms. These five items all load from 85 to 90 on the first factor.

The second factor consists of *direct suggestion* motor items, in which there is a muscular response to the direct suggestion that the body is swaying, the eyes are closing, or the hands are moving. These are also the easiest items of the scale, and two additional interpretations of this factor are possible: one, that it is a "difficulty" factor with high loadings on "easy" items; two, that it represents a waking suggestion factor, of items that can be passed by those who do not enter into the

[7] Supported by a grant from the National Science Foundation (NSF-GP948).

[8] An earlier factor analysis of Forms A and B combined, based on the standardization sample of 124 cases, had yielded three unrotated factors accounting for 51, 12, and 6 per cent of the variance, also totaling 69 per cent. Therefore the replication appears to be quite satisfactory.

Table 20
Stanford Hypnotic Susceptibility Scale (SHSS), Form A: Factor Loadings After Rotation*

ITEM	FACTOR I	FACTOR II	FACTOR III
Most representative of Factor I:			
5. Finger lock	90	11	05
10. Eye catalepsy	88	16	15
4. Arm immobilization	86	09	−14
8. Verbal inhibition	86	05	−02
6. Arm rigidity	85	34	00
Most representative of Factor II:			
7. Moving hands	42	80	10
3. Hand lowering	38	71	23
2. Eye closure	48	49	13
1. Postural sway	33	48	28
Most representative of Factor III:			
11. Posthypnotic suggestion (changing chairs)	30	17	68
12. Suggested amnesia	58	00	56
9. Hallucination (fly)	53	18	37
Variance	43	15	09
Cumulative variance	43	58	67

* From: Hilgard (1965), p. 221.
Note: $N = 402$.

hypnotic state to any appreciable extent. The difficulty interpretation is supported by the rank order correlation of $r_s = .85$ between the item difficulty expressed as percentage passing and the weight on this factor. Interpreting this as a difficulty factor does not mean that it is an artifact of item scoring; there may very well be psychological meaning to the gradation of items according to the ease with which the suggestions can be followed. A high loading on this factor means that this is the kind of test passed by those unable to pass the more difficult ones. Hence the various interpretations of this factor are all compatible with each other.

The third factor is represented by the most *cognitive* items in Form A, that is, items involving hallucinations and amnesia, and the following of posthypnotic suggestions. These items also load substantially on the first factor. In some sense these items most represent the kinds of experience associated with the historical conception of deeper hypnosis, and their correlation with the first factor validates the whole scale; at the same time, the presence of the third factor indicates that a completely motor scale would miss some aspects of hypnotic experience. It was in part our awareness of these special factors, little represented in Form A, that led to the construction of Form C.

Of course, additional factors can be extracted, but none accounts for more than 3 per cent of the variance, so that this analysis has been limited to the first three factors.

SHSS, Form C. A similar factor analytic procedure was carried out with Form C, using the scores of 307 subjects, students of both sexes, all members of our regular samples. The factor loadings on the first three orthogonal factors, computed by the principal components method, and rotated graphically, are given in Table 21.

Table 21
Stanford Hypnotic Susceptibility Scale (SHSS), Form C: Factor Loadings After Rotation*

ITEM	FACTOR I	FACTOR II	FACTOR III
Most representative of Factor I:			
12. Amnesia	90	12	−02
11. Negative visual hallucination	84	06	−16
5. Arm rigidity	79	26	10
8. Arm immobilization	74	30	21
9. Anosmia	58	22	−36
Most representative of Factor II:			
1. Hand lowering	10	80	20
2. Moving hands apart	19	77	21
6. Dream	54	46	−05
7. Age regression	68	35	23
Most representative of Factor III:			
10. Hallucinated voice	66	00	39
3. Mosquito hallucination	72	37	30
4. Taste hallucination	70	36	26
Variance	44	17	05
Cumulative variance	44	61	66

* From: Hilgard (1965), p. 242.
Note: $N = 307$.

The results are not as clear-cut as for Form A, but an interpretable pattern emerges. The first factor is again prominent with ten of the 12 items loading at least 50 on it, even after rotation, and it accounts for about the same amount of variance (44 per cent) as the first factor of Form A. This time the items representative of it include the two challenge items (arm rigidity and arm immobilization) as before, but amnesia becomes the most representative item, and two negative hallucination items also enter. Hence, this can be interpreted as some sort of *ideomotor inhibition*, affecting both the control of voluntary muscles, and the inhibition of sensory impressions and recall. Too much must not be made of this special interpretation, because many positive items (positive hallucinations and dreams) also load on this first factor.

The second factor, as before, includes the direct suggestion motor items (hand lowering and hands moving apart), but now includes two quite different items: dreams and age regression. It will be noted that dreams and age regression load substantially on the first factor, whereas the motor items do not. In this case the *difficulty* interpretation is even more cogent than in the case of Form A, for the loadings on Factor II correlate $r_s = .91$ with item difficulty. This high correlation with item difficulty ought to be reflected in analysis of scores because the items in Form C are arranged in an ascending order of difficulty, so that those who are able to enter hypnosis very lightly, if at all, are faced with the easy items early, and those who can go on are perhaps encouraged by their passing of these easy items.[9]

The items assigned as representative of the third factor include all items that load highest on the factor, except for the negative loading of anosmia, although all load higher on the first factor and two of them load higher on the second factor. Hence this is a weak specific factor; but its psychological meaning is rather clear, because all items represent *positive hallucinations*, and negative hallucination items load negatively on it. It can therefore be interpreted as a bipolar factor of hallucinatory ability, with a high loading representing capacity for positive hallucinations.

The general conclusions of both Form A and Form C are that there is a strong first factor running through both scales, that there is a factor related to item difficulty, which may have meaning in the contrast between waking suggestibility and trance suggestibility, and some special factors are associated with cognitive distortion, possibly differentiating positive from negative hallucinations.

SPS, Forms I and II. To assess the variety of special abilities tested by the profile scales, the 18 items from the two forms of the scale were all treated as coming from one test. The subjects were the 112 students, men and women, from the standardization sample, selected as having scored at least 4 on Form A. This analysis will differ from the others, then, in having neither motor items nor amnesia represented, and having a somewhat curtailed sample. Although the items of the profile scale are scored on a 0 to 3 basis, to keep the same order of magnitude and to include in this analysis whatever artifacts are produced by the use of tetrachoric correlations, the scores were dichotomized before the correlations were computed.[10]

[9] The first factor also correlates moderately with item difficulty, $r_s = -.58$, but the structure of the factor weights indicates that we are dealing also with item content. The possibility of some artifacts in correlations based on fourfold tables with items of extreme dichotomies is inescapable.

[10] For other purposes, the extended profile scales, including the motor items and the amnesia items, have been factor-analyzed, using product-moment correlations. Some of these results are being incorporated in a doctoral dissertation being prepared by Lillian W. Lauer and will eventually be published. See Hilgard (1965), pp. 264–270.

The results of factor analysis are given in Table 22. The first factor, as anticipated, is somewhat reduced in weight, now accounting for but 31 per cent of the variance. The three factors together account for 62 per cent of the variance, perhaps a little less of the variance than the three factors of the other two scales.

Table 22
Stanford Profile Scales of Hypnotic Susceptibility (SPS), Forms I and II: Factor Loadings After Rotation*

ITEM	FACTOR I	FACTOR II	FACTOR III
Most representative of Factor I:			
Heat: II	84	36	16
Agnosia: II	82	18	39
Lights: I	80	45	01
Verbal compulsion: I	72	−08	16
Missing watch hand: II	65	38	42
Selective deafness: I	64	44	19
Agnosia: I	61	43	26
Hand analgesia: I	57	25	−31
Joke: I	49	−07	00
Anosmia, ammonia: I	46	48	06
Most representative of Factor II:			
Dream: General, I	00	70	44
Ammonia: II	42	66	−01
Regression to birthday	35	64	24
Recall of meal: I	42	64	08
Dream: re Hypnosis, II	17	58	53
Music hallucination: I	44	51	12
Most representative of Factor III:			
Automatic writing: II	54	05	64
Personality alteration: II	38	33	63
Variance	31	20	11
Cumulative variance	31	51	62

* From: unpublished data.
Note: $N = 112$.

In terms of the subscales, the ten items selected as most representative of Factor I include all four of the negative hallucinations (HN subscale), in this way corresponding to *the inhibitory nature of the first factor* of SHSS, Form C. Also included are three of the four agnosia items (AG subscale), two of which (agnosia I and II) are inhibitory-type items. The remaining items are positive: two positive hallucinations (HP subscale), and the verbal compulsion item from the AM subscale.

The second factor includes all four of the items of the DR subscale, dreams and regression, plus two positive hallucination items, ammonia and music hallucinations. This second factor is best identified with dreams and regression, perhaps interpreted as *availability of realistic self-aroused fantasies and memories* (thus including the ammonia and music hallucinations).

The third factor is best represented by two items that involve both a considerable amount of distortion and the maintaining of a hypnotic role through time when suggestions are no longer being given. The automatic writing involves a contradiction between what is being said and what the hand is writing; the personality distortion involves a change in the self that contradicts actual social status and intelligence. Hence a major cognitive distortion is involved; it is not surprising that the two agnosia items, the missing watch hand and the dreams, also have positive loadings on this factor. Perhaps this can be called *ability to maintain a generalized reality distortion.*

The tendencies for individual items to load on all three factors means that the tests themselves are by no means "pure" representatives of the factor to which they happen to be assigned. It seemed wise, however, to assign each test to the one factor that it would most help make explicit. In Table 22 all tests were assigned to the factor where the loading is largest, with the exception of anosmia, placed with the other negative hallucination items in Factor I although its weight in Factor II (.48) is numerically larger than its weight in Factor I (.46). The difference in weights is trivial, and the content suggested that Factor I would be a better place for it to fit.

Correspondence Among Factors of SHSS Forms A and C and SPS Forms I and II

Any one item in a hypnotic susceptibility scale is likely to reflect more than one of the factors included in the scale. Hence factor scores on any one factor that are estimated from the scores on combinations of individual items will correlate with scores on another factor obtained in this way, even though the pure factors are orthogonal. It is of some interest to know the interrelationships of such factor scores, because they help us to understand to what extent the factor interpretation has empirical significance.

The factor analyses of SHSS Forms A and C and SPS Forms I and II were made on separate but overlapping samples. That is, there were different numbers of cases in each analysis. Factor scores were determined for the factors of each scale by adding the scores for those items which best represented the particular factors, as classified in Tables 20, 21, and 22.

To compare the factors across tests a number of techniques are available, including, of course, a factor analysis in which all the test items are thrown together in one large matrix. There is some advantage, from the point of view of one who is to use the separate tests empirically, in determining the factor scores separately for the factors discovered within each test, and then correlating these factor scores across tests. Because the profile scale sample was a curtailed one, dropping the subjects scoring 0 to 3 on Form A, it was felt desirable to make this across-test comparison on the new sample, in which the profile scale was administered to all subjects. The tests included in the factor scoring are those determined from the original factor analysis (with the restricted sample in the case of Forms I and II) but the scores on these tests are from a sample in which all subjects were included.

In the common factor that runs throughout these scales we have a kind of validation for their content as representing something that has historically been called hypnosis. The secondary factors show the usefulness of analyses of this kind; of course, the results presented do not exhaust the possible refinements that could be made.

Table 23
Factors in Common Between SHSS Forms A and C, and SPS Forms I and II: Loadings After Orthogonal Rotation*

SUBSCALE	FACTOR I	FACTOR II	FACTOR III
A-I	82	−04	−10
C-I	82	06	−19
A-III	78	−07	−17
C-III	66	−04	01
P-I	70	54	−10
P-II	59	49	03
P-III	62	61	−03
A-II	54	00	43
C-II	47	12	45
Variance	49	07	05
Cumulative variance	49	56	61

* From: unpublished data. Although the items representative of each factor were determined from other samples, separately for Forms A, C, and I-II, these same items were scored for a new sample given all the tests. For this purpose, subjects who scored 0 to 3 on Form A remained in the sample, thus raising the correlations somewhat through the increase in range of scores over what they would have been had these cases been omitted.

Note: The scores entering the correlation matrix were scores based on the three most representative factors for each scale, A-I, II, and III; C-I, II, and III; P-I, II, and III. ($N = 59$ throughout.)

In Table 23 the results of this factor analysis of factor scores is presented. The three subscales of Form A, based on items grouped as representing factors, are designated as A-I, A-II, and A-III; for Form C the factor subscales are C-I, C-II, and C-III; for Forms I and II of the profile scales the factor subscales are designated as P-I, P-II, and P-III.

Table 23 results from the orthogonal rotation of the correlation matrix based on the intercorrelations of these nine subscales.

The first factor, accounting for 49 per cent of the variance, runs through all of the subscales, and supports the contention that there is a heavy common factor within various hypnotic susceptibility scales. The heavy loadings on A-I, C-I, A-III, C-III, and P-I show that this general factor receives a heavy contribution from items reflecting loss of voluntary motor control (A-I, C-I), amnesia (C-I, A-III), and loss of cognitive capacities, agnosia, and negative hallucinations (C-III, P-I). The historical resemblance between hypnosis and hysteria is implied in these weights, for the classical hysteric was often both paralyzed (loss of voluntary control) and anesthetic (loss of cognitive capacity).

The second factor is exclusive to the profile scales, and runs through the three of them; it supplements, rather than replaces, the common factor. The profile scales differ from Forms A and C in having no strictly motor items; and the second factor probably reflects also the weightings in those scales of fantasy material, and the maintaining of reality distortion through time.[11]

Finally, Factor III, representing A-II and C-II, is the familiar easy-item factor, with high weights for items such as postural sway, eye closure, hand lowering, and moving hands. These waking suggestion items nevertheless also have appreciable weights on the first factor, and legitimately remain within the battery.

THE STABILITY OF HYPNOTIC SUSCEPTIBILITY

Whenever a human ability is subjected to measurement, the question arises as to how stable that ability is, how enduring it is through time. The historical studies of the constancy of the IQ are addressed to this problem, and we face the same kind of problem concerning the stability of the ability to enter hypnosis and to respond to tests of hypnotic susceptibility. The evidence thus far presented, based on retest reliabilities, shows that under standard conditions hypnotic susceptibility is a quite dependable trait, with retest correlations commonly lying in the 80's and 90's. Like the IQ, which also shows such retest reliabilities, there is a good deal of room for individual variation, and the assertion of stability is not the whole story.

It is commonly assumed that hypnotic performance depends upon at least two underlying conditions: one, a kind of basic and enduring hypnotic ability; and second, a more readily modifiable attitudinal component. Thus the capacity to resist hypnosis, on the part of a hypnotizable person, is recognized; if this is the case, subjects may presumably

[11] When Factors I and II are plotted, it is evident that their relationship is oblique; an oblique rotation would separate them further, but would conceal the fact that the profile scales are also heavily loaded on Factor I.

show varying degrees of resistance, depending upon circumstances, and underestimates of potential hypnotizability may therefore result from testing under unfavorable circumstances. There is also the other side of the coin, that is, a capacity to simulate hypnotic performances, and test results may occasionally be contaminated by scores that indicate a higher hypnotic susceptibility than is actually present. On strictly logical grounds it would seem that an attempt to measure susceptibility is very precarious indeed, and some writers are strongly of this opinion (such as Dorcus, 1963). In practice, the situation is not so bad, with most subjects being fully cooperative, as, indeed, they usually are on interest and personality tests, which are subject to the same possibilities of falsification.

Let us now turn to some empirical approaches to the question of stability of performance.

Hypnotic Performances as a Function of Trance Induction

Our characterization of hypnosis is as a state of heightened responsiveness to certain kinds of suggestions, such as those sampled in the various tests of hypnotic susceptibility. Usually these tests are given after the hypnotic state has been induced through eye fixation and closure, arm levitation, relaxation, or other of the so-called induction procedures.

It is well known that suggestions similar to those given following induction are also responded to in the waking state, and they are commonly called waking suggestions to distinguish them from suggestions within the hypnotic state. Although this continues in words the outworn waking-sleeping dichotomy between the ordinary state and the hypnotic state, little confusion results because the operations specified are quite clear. Waking suggestions are merely suggestions given before an induction is attempted; they are distinguished from the suggestions responded to after induction has been attempted without begging the question as to the differences involved.[12]

In SHSS, Forms A and B, and the corresponding HGS, one of the scored items is a body-sway item, tested prior to attempted induction. It is included because it correlates with the subsequent responsiveness to suggestions. Hence the constructors of these tests recognized a correspondence between waking suggestibility and suggestibility after induction. The question was unanswered, however, as to how much difference induction made. Empirical answers have been given by Weitzenhoffer and Sjoberg (1961) and Barber and Glass (1962).

Weitzenhoffer and Sjoberg (1961) found that responsiveness to a series of typical hypnotic suggestions increased following hypnotic

[12] Weitzenhoffer (1963) discusses some of the differences.

induction, although responsiveness to suggestion without induction correlated with responsiveness after induction $r_s = .54$ for 60 subjects tested before and after attempted induction. Some 57 per cent of the subjects showed little or no gain with induction; the remaining 43 per cent showed appreciable gain; 17 per cent gained five or more points on a 17-point scale. Correspondingly, Barber and Glass (1962) found a significant gain among a group of 30 subjects on their eight-point scale. Some 50 per cent showed score increases following induction, with 27 per cent showing gains of 1.5 to 3 points on the eight-point scale. They found a rank correlation of .85 between the two sessions.

One important finding on which both studies agree is that a few highly susceptible subjects yield all the phenomena of hypnosis *without* a formal induction. This shows the importance of subject selection when hypnotic phenomena are demonstrated, and why stage hypnotists, having selected a good subject, can appear to be essentially magicians in producing trance effects.

Another finding, stated clearly in the Weitzenhoffer and Sjoberg report, is that the amount of gain with induction is relatively independent of the level of suggestibility in the waking state. That is, some subjects who were quite unresponsive to suggestions prior to trance induction were moderately responsive subjects following induction; whereas some rather successful subjects changed very little with induction. The correlation between initial status and gains was but .17, nonsignificant.[13]

When a test of hypnotic susceptibility is given, using a standardized induction procedure, these studies imply that for about half the subjects the induction procedure will be without effect, for one of two reasons, either (1) that they were not susceptible to the induction procedure and failed to enter the hypnotic state; or (2) that they entered the hypnotic state without requiring the induction procedure. These differences need to be understood, for they affect the interpretation of studies such as that by Barber and Calverley (1963) in which subjects are selected who are unusually high in responsiveness to waking suggestion for comparison with the results with and without induction. It may be that such a selection will bring in many subjects who do not require an induction procedure to enter the hypnotic state, thus attenuating the differences between induction and noninduction.

These studies on the effectiveness of induction tend to confirm the usefulness of hypnotic susceptibility scales, regardless of how the substantive issue comes out, by showing the high correlations between

[13] This correlation is still of interest, because, with the ceiling effect, there is often a *negative* correlation between initial status and gains, the lower scorers having so much more room to improve. The obtained correlation, although not significant, is at least not negative.

responsiveness to suggestions under the two circumstances. Were correlations with outside measures (such as personality tests) under consideration, it might not matter too much whether or not the person was responsive to the particular induction procedure used.

Attitude and Expectation About Hypnosis

Dorcus (1963) gives five cases of subjects who presumably would have scored as insusceptible on standard tests, yet who became good subjects when a sensitive hypnotist adapted his method to their needs. Although his interpretations are sensible, in none of the cases was a standard method actually tried, so we have no genuine before-and-after measures. The case that came nearest to meeting these requirements was that of an Italian woman for whom a passive induction seemed ineffective, though she then responded to an authoritarian induction, felt to be more in accordance with her cultural background.

That expectation of hypnosis is an important aspect of entering the hypnotic state has been well attested in several experiments. Weitzenhoffer, Gough, and Landes (1959) showed that with an eye-fixation method similar to that used originally by Braid (1843), subjects not expecting to be hypnotized showed very little effect; only 5 per cent of 42 cases responding above 5 on the Friedlander-Sarbin scale; when there was eye fixation combined with the expectation of hypnosis, 33 per cent of 27 cases responded with scores above 5 on the scale, yielding essentially the same scores that they achieved on a later regular induction of hypnosis by the Friedlander-Sarbin method. Glass and Barber (1961) found that for 12 subjects whose nonhypnotic control scores fell below their scores following trance-induction, the expectation of hypnosis, induced by giving a placebo, which they were told would facilitate hypnosis, led to hypnotic scores *without* induction equal to those *with* induction.

Expectations about the nature of hypnosis, for those who have not been hypnotized, tend to correlate with their subsequent hypnotic scores. When such expectations were obtained by questionnaire in a psychology class, prior to any indication that opportunities would be provided for hypnosis, the expectations, scored on an attitude dimension as giving a favorable or unfavorable picture of hypnosis, led to a correlation for female subjects of $r = +.37$ ($N = 125$) with later hypnotic susceptibility scores on Form A (Melei and Hilgard, 1963). Attitude scores for male subjects were, however, not predictive of their hypnotic scores ($r = .07$, $N = 161$).

Attempts to Modify Susceptibility

It is commonly believed that hypnotic susceptibility is readily modified with practice. This belief may come about because of the greater speed with which the hypnotic state can be induced with practice, so that, for example, a signal set up in advance can be used to bring on the state at once. It would be entirely possible for hypnotic susceptibility to remain unchanged while speed of entering the state was reduced; thus a person unable to have positive hallucinations might remain unable to have them.

Studies addressed to this problem have led to somewhat contradictory results, and more evidence is needed. Orne reports (personal communication) little success in modifying susceptibility; the same is true of Gill and Brenman (1961). Wiseman and Reyher (1962) have reported a technique for using dreams to deepen the hypnotic trance. Their success was attested by the number of subjects who became completely amnesic following their method; after using the method, 70 per cent of 30 subjects experienced complete amnesia as contrasted with 33 per cent before the method was used. They point out that the method is more successful in developing complete amnesia among those who already experienced partial amnesia than in converting a totally nonamnesic subject into an amnesic one. Blum (1963, p. 137) reports choosing three subjects, one scoring low, one medium, and one high in SHSS, Form A. After a dozen hours of training, both medium and low subjects were reported to have scored in the high range on SHSS, Form B. This is his answer to the objection to using hypnosis in personality investigations because such investigations are limited to "good" subjects: if any subject can be converted to a usable subject, this objection does not hold. If his finding is generalizable, it shows the limitations in any attempt to correlate persisting personality characteristics with hypnotizability.

A study dealing with this problem has been reported by Ås, Hilgard, and Weitzenhoffer (1963). Selecting subjects who scored in the middle ranges of SHSS, Form A, they attempted by the use of various techniques to modify hypnotizability. Considerable freedom was exercised, some of the time being spent in psychotherapeutic attitude discussions, some in building upon the achieved successes to obtain further gains, some in a variety of induction techniques, such as fractionation methods and induction-within-induction. Despite this freedom of methods, the three experienced hypnotists involved achieved only very slight gains as revealed by before-and-after tests of susceptibility. The main limitation of the study is that the repeated sessions numbered only four to ten, and a fuller test would perhaps require many more sessions. The general conclusion was that hypnotic susceptibility, as measured by the existing scales, is at least fairly stable, and little likely to change dramatically. This conclusion is, of course, contradictory to that of Blum, and, to a lesser extent, of Wiseman and Reyher.

A cautious interpretation of the evidence would lead to the moderate conclusion that, without special intrusion, hypnotic susceptibility is reasonably stable; with intrusions of various kinds, with repeated inductions running upwards of a dozen or so, some dramatic changes may occur, including loss of susceptibility as well as increase. Hypnotic scales do not rest for their usefulness on the persistence of a dead-level of susceptibility: they are equally useful in studying such fluctuations as may occur, and in specifying the amount of change from time to time.

CORRELATES OF HYPNOTIC SUSCEPTIBILITY

To characterize the hypnotically susceptible and the hypnotic non-susceptible has turned out to be a far more difficult problem than might be expected on the basis of the satisfactory criterion measures of susceptibility. One possibility is to reject the whole attempt as essentially illusory, because hypnotic susceptibility is an individual matter depending upon ability, attitude, hypnotist, hypnotic technique, and so forth, thus too whimsical and ephemeral to be caught by correlation coefficients. Still, as in the study of personality generally, there are some persistent low correlations that encourage the seeker to raise them; if there is a little demonstrated order, there may very well be more underlying order if we are imaginative enough to find it.

In what follows, I shall give some representative results on various topics that have interested those seeking to understand the nature of hypnotic susceptibility. The literature is large, and no effort will be made to be exhaustive.

Age

A collection of 744 cases by Liébeault, summarized by Beaunis (1887), covers the age span from under 7 through 63 and up. No child below 14 was found uninfluenced by hypnotic procedures, and between the ages of 7 and 14, more than half were termed somnambulistic. This was the period of maximum susceptibility; beyond that there was little change, with possibly a slight decline in susceptibility with age. Later quantitative studies are few. Messerschmidt (1933) found high points in responsiveness to postural sway at ages 6 to 8, with decline thereafter. Stukat (1958), in a thorough study of suggestibility in children and adults, found an age trend in "secondary suggestibility" (a reduction in effectiveness from grades 1 through 7) but no age trend in "primary suggestibility," which is most closely related to hypnosis. London (1962) and Moore and Lauer (1963), using London's CHSS, found no consistent trends with age in childhood, although their children's samples differed from adult samples in showing higher amounts of amnesia and hallucination, and more resistance to keeping eyes closed. In view of the role of amnesia in the estimation of somnambulism, this high amnesia among children may be concordant with the high susceptibility report of Liébeault.

Barber and Calverley (1963) report the largest sample to date of children tested by a standard test of hypnotic-like suggestions (BSS); although the test was given *without* administering a formal induction procedure, the results may not be too different from those that would be found following trance induction. They found with 724 subjects of ages 6 to 22 that highest susceptibility was between the ages of 8 and 10, with a decrease thereafter; the leveling-off point was approximately ages 14 to 15, when adult scoring was reached. The contradiction between these results and those of Stukat (1958) remains unexplained. In agreement with the results of London and those of Moore and Lauer, they found the most striking change in amnesia, which was among the upper half of items in ease of passing at ages 8 to 10, and the most difficult item beyond age 14.

The practical success of dentists and anesthetists in hypnotizing children shows that, in general, they make good subjects, but the quantitative aspects need further study. It is usually assumed that hypnosis fails with very young children because of their inadequate experience with words, but adequate studies, in which verbal ability is controlled, are lacking, so that we know little about the lower limits.

Sex

Probably because of its association with hysteria (Charcot), it has long been supposed that women are more hypnotizable than men, but this conjecture has also been denied for many years. Weitzenhoffer (1953), reviewing earlier evidence, agreed that women tend often to score as more suggestible or susceptible to hypnosis than men, many studies reporting slight but nonsignificant differences in this direction. Later studies, however, have tended to deny these differences. In a study comparing the results for 100 men and 100 women, half of each sex hypnotized by a male hypnotist, half by a female hypnotist, no sex difference was demonstrated (Weitzenhoffer and Weitzenhoffer, 1958). The results from repeated testing in our laboratory have failed to reveal any sex differences, beyond an initial study in which such differences were reported (Hilgard, Weitzenhoffer, and Gough, 1958). For example, the mean of Form A for 272 males from our regular samples is 5.59 (SD 3.12), for 261 females 5.65 (SD 3.42), a nonsignificant difference between means of but .06 points on a 12-point scale. Although some subtle sex differences will doubtless be discovered in time, the general burden of evidence at present is that men and women are equally susceptible to hypnosis.

Intelligence

Weitzenhoffer (1953) in reviewing the evidence believed that it demonstrated a small correlation between intelligence as measured by tests of hypnotizability. Our unpublished data show essentially zero correlations between SHSS Forms A and C with scholastic aptitude tests taken prior to college entrance: for 313 subjects the correlation between Verbal Scholastic Aptitude scores and Form A is −.10, and Form C, −.02; between Mathematical Scholastic Aptitude scores and Form A, −.07, and Form C, −.02.

The question of the hypnotizability of the mentally defective is unsettled; this is assumed to rest upon sufficient verbal ability and capacity to attend to instructions. Sternlicht and Wanderer (1963) found 12 of 20 mentally defective children hypnotizable (ages 7 to 16; MA 3.3 to 9.0). Within this small sample, the correlation between MA and subjective hypnotic depth was $r_s = +.52$, with IQ, $r_s = +.77$. Of the six scores of 8 to 10 (on a 12-point scale), five were made by those with MA's of 6 and above, one only with an MA as low as 5.0 (CA 9, IQ 56). Thus the minimum intellectual level needed for satisfactory hypnosis appears to correspond to the verbal abilities of an elementary school child.

Projective Tests of Personality

Efforts to use the Rorschach test in discriminating between the hypnotic susceptible and the nonsusceptible have led to contradictory results; some hopeful indicators noted by Sarbin and Madow (1942) and different indicators by Brenman and Reichard (1943) were contradicted by Shafer (1947), working under Brenman; Shafer's very limited results were but partially reproduced when tried on another small sample. Steisel (1952) fared no better.

Results with the Thematic Apperception Test, particularly card 12M, which can be interpreted as a hypnotic interaction, appear to measure a favorable attitude to hypnosis, correlated with susceptibility (White, 1937; Rosenzweig and Sarason, 1942). Because, as previously noted, a verbal report of attitude also correlates with susceptibility, this does not appear to be a very profound finding.

Personality Inventories

A great number of attempts have been made to correlate the self-reports from standard inventories with hypnotic susceptibility. Because these tests have a great many scales, it is often found that one or more of the scales will yield a correlation that, taken alone, meets the standards of statistical significance. When the test is repeated on a new sample, the previous correlation commonly disappears, in favor of some other significant one. With many correlations, chance factors enter; because of the complex interrelationships within personality inventories, it is difficult to state precisely what standards should be met to find any one of many correlations significant, but they should in any case be higher than suggested by the usual formulas for the standard error of a single correlation. In view of these uncertainties, replicated results can be the only source of confidence. When these replicated findings are looked for, the yield of the standard inventories, such as the Guilford-Zimmerman, CPI, MMPI, MPI, is very slight.

Among more recent studies, the positive results of Furneaux and Gibson (1961), with the Maudsley Personality Inventory (MPI), were not confirmed by Hilgard and Bentler (1963); and Hilgard and Lauer (1962) failed to find reproducible correlations with the California Psychological Inventory (CPI). In some unreported studies from the Stanford laboratory, the Minnesota Multiphasic Personality Inventory (MMPI) has shown some slight promise, but chiefly in the form of the "yea-saying" score (the sum of all "Yes" answers, regardless of how keyed in the test). This has been found to yield a small, but consistent, positive correlation with scores on SHSS, Form C, between .20 and .30 on various samples. The Myers-Briggs Type Indicator (Myers, 1962) has shown little promise.

The Semantic Differential (Brightbill and Zamansky, 1963) has been found to point up some differences between a group of more susceptible and less susceptible subjects, but there is little indication that it would be at all powerful in selecting individual subjects as more or less susceptible.

Neuropsychiatric Diagnosis

Despite the many years that hypnosis has been used in psychotherapy, little is known about the relative hypnotizability of patients falling into the various categories. Charcot's contention that only hysterics could be hypnotized was refuted by many of the early writers on hypnosis. The general summary by Gill and Brenman (1959) was to the effect that neurotics are less hypnotizable than normal individuals, whereas hysterics are perhaps more hypnotizable than other neurotics. On the whole, psychotics are not supposed to be very hypnotizable. The evidence on all these matters is very scanty. The neurotic sample of Eysenck and Furneaux (1945) had a score distribution essentially like those of Friedlander and Sarbin (1938) and Weitzenhoffer (1956) with unselected college students. Most of the studies recently reported show psychotics more hypnotizable than older conjectures led one to expect. These studies of psychotics have shown substantial numbers to be susceptible (Wilson, Cormen, and Cole, 1949; Gale and Herman, 1956; Heath, Hoakin, and Sainz, 1960). A recent study by Kramer and Brennan (1964), has tested 25 hospitalized schizophrenic women on SHSS, Form A, with a resulting mean score of 8.00, SD 1.83, as high a mean as found for volunteer samples of normal college students. In this sample scores below 5 were absent, and six of the 25 cases scored between 10 and 12, with 12 the maximum possible. The best present summary would be that there are no clearly demonstrated differences in mean susceptibility of normals, neurotics, and psychotics, provided, of course, that the psychotics are sufficiently in contact for hypnosis to be attempted at all.

Inventories of Hypnotic-like Experiences

The conjecture is plausible that susceptibility to hypnosis, because it can be so quickly revealed under appropriate circumstances, should also show itself in ordinary life experiences. Basing an inventory upon this conjecture, Shor (1960) asked students questions about hypnotic-like experiences in daily life, and then proceeded to correlate these with susceptibility to hypnosis. A satisfactory positive relationship resulted, which held up on replication (Shor, Orne, and O'Connell, 1962). Following his lead, Ås developed a related questionnaire, incorporating 18 of Shor's items, and his instructions, in a 60-item questionnaire (Ås, O'Hara, and Munger, 1962). This became the basis for a number of reports in which responses on the inventory were related to hypnotic susceptibility scores (such as, Ås, 1962; Ås and Lauer, 1962; Ås, 1963). The work started by Shor and Ås has been carried a step further by Lee-Teng (1965). It is evident that this method yields a consistent moderate correlation with hypnotic susceptibility, the correlation with Form C being around $r = .30$ in most samples. One of the technical defects is the number of items keyed in the "Yes" direction, so that there is some contamination with "yea-saying"; this may account for the difficulty found in raising the correlations through item-analysis.

Behavioral Tests

Because hypnotic responsiveness tends to be active, including bodily movements and postures, altered perceptions of presented stimuli, and so on, measurements that include more than replies to questions would seem to be promising.

Moore (1964) used various behavioral tests of social suggestibility to explore the "suggestion" interpretation of hypnotic susceptibility. She found, in keeping with other studies of "secondary suggestibility," that there was little relationship between a kind of social "gullibility" and hypnosis. Roberts (1963) employed various laboratory tests of attention to investigate the "attention" theory of hypnosis, and also found little relationship. She did, however, find a correlation of —.30 with some scores of the Witkin rod-and-frame test for 30 female subjects, although the relationship was not significant for 30 males ($r = -.10$). The correlation indicates that the more field dependent subjects are less hypnotizable.

Sarbin and Lim (1963) had members of the Dramatic Art Department at the University of California rate the improvisations on a stage of subjects who had previously been hypnotized. The ratings of role-taking ability correlated rho = .39 for a first sample of 13, and rho = .52 for a second sample of 20. It was reported that all those rated high in role-taking ability were above the mean in hypnotizability, although some low on role-taking ability were also hypnotizable.

In general, unless the tests are very similar to those that have conventionally been included as part of hypnosis ("primary suggestion" items) little relationship is found, no matter how plausible the conjectures are that such relationships ought to exist.

Developmental Background and Interview Data

The Stanford laboratory has been conducting a long-term study of the personality background of college subjects of varying degrees of hypnotic susceptibility, utilizing interviews prior to hypnosis in the attempt to predict hypnotic susceptibility.[14] The purpose of the prediction is not to produce an efficient predictive instrument—a work sample of hypnosis is likely to remain much more efficient than any type of indirect aptitude-for-hypnosis measure—but rather to alert the interviewers to subtleties in the personality-susceptibility relationship through the effort to predict. The interview data, obtained prior to the hypnotic sessions, can then be coded and analyzed, regardless of the successes or failures in global predictions.

Unfortunately the data thus far collected are still in process of analysis and the results unpublished. The following specimen of data is merely a hint of the kinds of relationships that appear.

It becomes evident from the interviews that there is no one "typical" personality for the hypnotically susceptible; the low correlations that are found consistently with personality tests and other instruments of prediction arise because subjects enter hypnosis with widely divergent backgrounds, and thus to some extent cancel each other out on scores on standard inventories. To illustrate this, we may take childhood fantasy and involvement in reading as related to hypnotic susceptibility (Table 24). We find a barely significant correlation between interviewer ratings of fantasy and SHSS Form C scores of $r = .23$ ($N = 104, p = .05$). Now consider the interviewer ratings of adventuresomeness and non-caution, chiefly in outdoor activities, but in general, in willingness to "live dangerously." This, too, correlates $r = .26$ ($N = 104$, $p = .01$). Now we have two low correlations, and it might be assumed that combining these two "predictors" we would improve our correlation with hypnosis. Because these two predictions are uncorrelated ($r = .08$), a multiple-correlation would, in fact, yield an $r = .33$ ($N = 104$, $p = .01$)

[14] The interview studies, mostly unpublished, are under the direction of Josephine R. Hilgard. A preliminary report, indicative of the kinds of information sought, appears in Hilgard and Hilgard (1962); see also Hilgard (1965), Chapter 18.

Table 24
Adventuresomeness and Childhood Fantasy as Moderators of the Correlations Between These Ratings and Hypnotic Susceptibility*

ITEMS CORRELATED	PRODUCT MOMENT CORRELATIONS	
Adventuresomeness vs.		
hypnotic susceptibility		
All subjects	.26‡	($N = 104$)
Low fantasy subjects	.32‡	($N = 67$)
High fantasy subjects	.03	($N = 37$)
Fantasy vs.		
hypnotic susceptibility		
All subjects	.23†	($N = 104$)
Low adventure subjects	.34†	($N = 49$)
High adventure subjects	.11	($N = 55$)

* From: Hilgard, E. R. (1964). "The motivational relevance of hypnosis," *Nebraska Symposium on Motivation*, **12**, 29.
† $p < .05$.
‡ $p < .01$.

through the most favorable combination of these two. This implies some sort of additive relationship between the items, so that scores can be combined in a regression equation. But suppose, instead, we see the items as alternative. In that case, we can use one item as a moderator for the other. Then we would hypothesize that for those *low in fantasy* there will be a *higher* correlation between adventuresomeness and hypnosis than for those high in fantasy, and *for those low in adventuresomeness* there will be a higher correlation between hypnosis and fantasy than for those high in adventuresomeness. Both of these conjectures turn out to be true, as shown in Table 24. Although the yields of the multiple correlation method and the moderator method in this case turn out to be very similar, the contrasts within the moderator method invite the interpretation that fantasy and adventure are alternate routes into hypnosis.

The "trait" analysis implied in Table 24 is being supplemented by a developmental analysis. That is, some kinds of childhood backgrounds are favorable to producing the kind of person who is adventurous or cautious, or who has a rich or limited fantasy life. Such an analysis will provide the empirical background for a developmental-interactive theory of hypnosis, that is, one that emphasizes both the history of the individual, and the influence of contemporary features of the hypnotic transaction (Hilgard, 1962; Hilgard and Hilgard, 1962).

As in all problems of individual differences, in the understanding of hypnotic susceptibility there is a residual problem of innate, congenital, and acquired abilities. Adequate twin studies have not yet been conducted to throw light on the possible inheritance of hypnotizability, and there are few statistics on either sibling or parent-child resemblances. It always needs to be pointed out that these interpretations need not be black-or-white; there may, in fact, be a hereditary component to hypnotic susceptibility, even though hypnotic ability is also a matter of child-rearing practices, identification with parents, and other developmental influences whose results come about largely through learning.

CONCLUSION

The development of scales for measuring hypnotic susceptibility have shown that (1) reliable scales can be constructed; (2) hypnotic ability, although subject to some degree of modification, tends to be quite stable over time; and (3) there is a high common factor to tests of hypnotizability that conform to the types of behavior commonly included in the social definition of hypnosis (responsiveness to ideomotor suggestions, positive and negative hallucinations, dreams and regression, amnesia, posthypnotic suggestions, and so on). Specific factors can also be identified, but the weight of the common factor is most impressive.

This rather favorable state with respect to the criterion of hypnotizability encourages the attempts to find personality correlates. The results to date seem rather skimpy in view of the efforts expended, but at least we know that some behavior outside hypnosis is rather closely related to behavior within hypnosis (particularly responses to waking suggestion, and role-taking behavior) and some responses on attitude questionnaires and personality inventories show a modest correlation with susceptibility, particularly attitudes giving a favorable evaluation of hypnosis, and "yea-saying" on inventories. Beyond this, it appears from interview studies that global, one-dimensional approaches are likely to yield limited results because there are alternative paths into hypnosis, as illustrated by the roles of adventuresomeness and fantasy. These are illustrative only, and other paths may be available, or these may be partial descriptions of a more fundamental dichotomy.

REFERENCES

Ås, A. (1962). "Non-hypnotic experiences related to hypnotizability in male and female college students," *Scand. J. Psychol.*, **3**, 112–121.

——— (1963). "Hypnotizability as a function of nonhypnotic experiences," *J. abnorm. soc. Psychol.*, **66**, 142–150.

Ås, A., Hilgard, E. R., and Weitzenhoffer, A. M. (1963). "An attempt at experimental modification of hypnotizability through repeated individualized hypnotic experience," *Scand. J. Psychol.*, **4**, 81–89.

Ås, A., and Lauer, Lillian W. (1962). "A factor-analytic study of hypnotizability and related personal experiences," *Int. J. clin. exp. Hyp.*, **10** (3), 169–181.

Ås, A., O'Hara, J. W., and Munger, M. P. (1962). "The measurement of subjective experiences presumably related to hypnotic susceptibility," *Scand. J. Psychol.*, **3**, 47–64.

Barber, T. X., and Calverley, D. S. (1963). "'Hypnotic-like' suggestibility in children and adults," *J. abnorm. soc. Psychol.*, **66**, 589–597.

Barber, T. X., and Glass, L. B. (1962). "Significant factors in hypnotic behavior," *J. abnorm. soc. Psychol.*, **64**, 222–228.

Barry, H., MacKinnon, D. W., and Murray, H. A., Jr. (1931). "Studies on personality: A. Hypnotizability as a personality trait and its typological relations," *Hum. Biol.*, **13**, 1–36.

Beaunis, H. (1887). *Le somnambulisme provoqué.* Paris: Bailière.

Bentler, P. M., and Hilgard, E. R. (1963). "A comparison of group and individual induction of hypnosis with self-scoring and observer-scoring," *Int. J. clin. exp. Hyp.*, **11**, 49–54.

Bentler, P. M., and Roberts, Mary R. (1963). "Hypnotic susceptibility assessed in large groups," *Int. J. clin. exp. Hyp.*, **11**, 93–97.

Bernheim, H. (1891). *Hypnotisme, suggestion, psychothérapie: Etudes nouvelles.* Paris: Doin.

Binet, A. (1900). *La suggestibilité.* Paris: Schleicher Frères.

Blum, G. S. "Programming people to simulate machines." In Tomkins, S. S., and Messick, S. (Eds.) *Computer Simulation of Personality.* New York: Wiley.

Boucher, R. G., and Hilgard, E. R. (1962). "Volunteer bias in hypnotic experiments," *Amer. J. clin. Hyp.*, **5** (1), 49–51.

Braid, J. (1843). *Neurypnology: Or the Rationale of Nervous Sleep Considered in Relation to Animal Magnetism.* London: Churchill.

Bramwell, J. M. (1903). *Hypnotism.* Reissued (1956). New York: Julian.

Brenman, Margaret, and Reichard, Suzanne. (1943). "Use of the Rorschach test in the prediction of hypnotizability," *Bull. Menninger Clin.*, **7**, 183–187.

Brightbill, R., and Zamansky, H. S. (1963). "The conceptual space of good and poor hypnotic subjects: A preliminary exploration," *Int. J. clin. exp. Hyp.*, **11**, 112–121.

Charcot, J. M. (1882). "Physiologie pathologique. Sur les divers états nerveux determinés par l'hypnotization chez les hystériques," *CR Acad. Sci., Paris*, **94**, 403–405.

Das, J. P. (1958). "Factor analysis of a hypnotic scale," *Indian J. Psychol.*, **33**, 97–100.

Davis, L. W., and Husband, R. W. (1931). "A study of hypnotic susceptibility in relation to personality traits," *J. abnorm. soc. Psychol.*, **26**, 175–182.

Dorcus, R. M. (1963). "Fallacies in predictions of susceptibility to hypnosis based on personality characteristics," *Amer. J. clin. Hyp.*, **5**, 163–170.

Eysenck, H. J. (1943). "Suggestibility and hypnosis—an experimental analysis," *Proc. Roy. Soc. Med.*, **36**, 349–354.

EYSENCK, H. J., and FURNEAUX, W. D. (1945). "Primary and secondary suggestibility: An experimental and statistical study," *J. exp. Psychol.*, **35**, 485–503.

FRIEDLANDER, J. W., and SARBIN, T. R. (1938). "The depth of hypnosis," *J. abnorm. soc. Psychol.*, **33**, 281–294.

FURNEAUX, W. D., and GIBSON, H. B. (1961). "The Maudsley Personality Inventory as a predictor of susceptibility to hypnosis," *Int. J. clin. exp. Hyp.*, **9**, 167–177.

GALE, C., and HERMAN, M. (1956). "Hypnosis and the psychotic patient," *Psychiat. Quart.*, **30**, 417–424.

GILL, M. M., and BRENMAN, MARGARET (1959). *Hypnosis and Related States: Psychoanalytic Studies in Regression.* New York: Intern. Univ. Press.

GILLES DE LA TOURETTE (1889). *L'hypnotisme et les états analogues au point de vue médico-légal.* Paris: Plon, Nourrit, & Cie.

GLASS, L. B., and BARBER, T. S. (1961). "A note on hypnotic behavior, the definition of the situation, and the placebo effect," *J. nerv. ment. Dis.*, **132**, 539–541.

HAMMER, A. G., EVANS, F. J., and BARTLETT, MARY (1963). "Factors in hypnosis and suggestion," *J. abnorm. soc. Psychol.*, **67**, 15–23.

HEATH, E. S., HOAKIN, P. C. S., and SAINZ, A. A. (1960). "Hypnotizability in state-hospitalized schizophrenics," *Psychiat. Quart.*, **34**, 65–68.

HILGARD, E. R. (1962). "Lawfulness within hypnotic phenomena." In Estabrooks, G. H. (Ed.) *Hypnosis: Current Problems.* New York: Harper & Row.

——— (1964). "The motivational relevance of hypnosis." In *Nebraska Symposium on Motivation*, **12**, 1–46.

——— (1965). *Hypnotic Susceptibility.* New York: Harcourt, Brace, and World.

HILGARD, E. R., and BENTLER, P. M. (1963). "Predicting hypnotizability from the Maudsley Personality Inventory," *Brit. J. Psychol.*, **54**, 63–69.

HILGARD, E. R., and HILGARD, JOSEPHINE R. (1962). "Developmental–interactive aspects of hypnosis: Some illustrative cases," *Genet. Psychol. Monogr.*, **66**, 143–178.

HILGARD, E. R., and LAUER, LILLIAN W. (1962). "Lack of correlation between the California Psychological Inventory and hypnotic susceptibility," *J. consult. Psychol.*, **26**, 331–335.

HILGARD, E. R., LAUER, LILLIAN W., and MORGAN, ARLENE H. (1963). *Manual for Stanford Profile Scales of Hypnotic Susceptibility, Forms I and II.* Palo Alto, Calif.: Consulting Psychologists Press.

HILGARD, E. R., WEITZENHOFFER, A. M., and GOUGH, P. (1958). "Individual differences in susceptibility to hypnosis," *Proc. Nat. Acad. Sci.*, **44**, 1255–1259.

HILGARD, E. R., WEITZENHOFFER, A. M., LANDES, J., and MOORE, ROSEMARIE K. (1961). "The distribution of susceptibility to hypnosis in a student population: A study using the Stanford Hypnotic Susceptibility Scale," *Psychol. Monogr.*, **75**, (8, Whole No. 512).

HULL, C. L. (1933). *Hypnosis and Suggestibility: An Experimental Approach.* New York: Appleton-Century-Crofts.

KRAMER, E., and BRENNAN, E. P. (1964). "Hypnotic susceptibility of schizophrenic patients," *J. abnorm. soc. Psychol.*, **69**, 657–659.

LECRON, L., and BORDEAUX, J. (1947). *Hypnotism Today.* New York: Grune & Stratton.

LEE-TENG, EVELYN (1965). "Trance-susceptibility, induction-susceptibility, and acquiescence as factors in hypnotic performance," *J. abnorm Psychol.*, **70**, 383-389.

LIÉBEAULT, A. A. (1889). *Le sommeil provoqué et les états analogues.* Paris: Doin.

LOEWENFELD, L. (1901). *Der hypnotismus.* Wiesbaden: Bergmann.

LONDON, P. (1962a). *The Children's Hypnotic Susceptibility Scale.* Palo Alto, Calif.: Consulting Psychologists Press.

——— (1962b). "Hypnosis in children: An experimental approach," *Int. J. clin. exp. Hyp.*, **10** (2), 79–91.

MELEI, JANET, and HILGARD, E. R. (1964). "Attitude toward hypnosis, self-predictions, and hypnotic susceptibility," *Int. J. clin. exp. Hyp.*, **12**, 99–108.

MESSERSCHMIDT, R. (1933). "Response of boys between the ages of 5 and 16 years to Hull's postural suggestion test," *J. genet. Psychol.*, **43**, 405–421.

MOORE, ROSEMARIE K. (1964) "Susceptibility to hypnosis and susceptibility to social influence," *J. abnorm. soc. Psychol.*, **68**, 282-294.

MOORE, ROSEMARIE K., and LAUER, LILLIAN W. (1963). "Hypnotic susceptibility in middle childhood," *Int. J. clin. exp. Hyp.*, **11**, 167–174.

MYERS, ISABEL B. (1962). *The Myers-Briggs Type Indicator.* Princeton: Educational Testing Service.

PITRES, A. (1891). *Lectures cliniques sur l'hystérie et l'hypnotisme.* Vol. 2. Paris: Doin.

RICHER, P. (1885). *Études cliniques sur la grande hystérie ou hystéro-épilepsie.* Paris: Delahaye & Lecrosnier.

RICHET, C. (1884). *L'homme et l'intelligence.* Paris: Alcan.

ROBERTS, MARY R. (1963). *Attention and Related Abilities as Affecting Hypnotic Susceptibility.* Unpublished doctoral dissertation, Stanford Univ.

ROSENZWEIG, S., and SARASON, S. (1942). "An experimental study of the triadic hypothesis: Reaction to frustration, ego-defense, and hypnotizability. I. Correlational approach," *J. Pers.*, **11**, 1–19.

SARBIN, T. R., and LIM, D. T. (1963). "Some evidence in support of the role-taking hypothesis in hypnosis," *Int. J. clin. exp. Hyp.*, **11**, 98–103.

SARBIN, T. R., and MADOW, L. W. (1942). "Predicting the depth of hypnosis by means of the Rorschach test," *Amer. J. Orthopsychiat.*, **12**, 268–271.

SCHMIDKUNZ, H. (1894). "*Zur statistik des hypnotismus,*" *Wien. med. Wschr.*, **23**, 1022–1024.

SHAFER, R. (1947). *A Study of Personality Characteristics Related to Hypnotizability.* Unpublished master's thesis, Univ. of Kansas.

SHOR, R. E. (1960). "The frequency of naturally occurring 'hypnotic-like' experiences in the normal college population," *Int. J. clin. exp. Hyp.*, **8**, 151–163.

SHOR, R. E., and ORNE, EMILY C. (1962). *Harvard Group Scale of Hypnotic Susceptibility.* Palo Alto, Calif.: Consulting Psychologists Press.

Shor, R. E., and Orne, Emily C. (1963). "Norms on the Harvard Group Scale of Hypnotic Susceptibility, Form A," *Int. J. clin. Hyp.*, **11**, 39–48.

Shor, R. E., Orne, M. T., and O'Connell, D. N. (1962). "Validation and cross-validation of a scale of self-reported personal experiences which predicts hypnotizability," *J. Psychol.*, **53**, 55–75.

Steisel, I. M. (1952). "The Rorschach test and suggestibility," *J. abnorm. soc. Psychol.*, **47**, 607–614.

Sternlicht, M., and Wanderer, Z. W. (1963). "Hypnotic susceptibility and mental deficiency," *Int. J. clin. exp. Hyp.*, **11**, 81–92.

Stukat, K.-G. (1958). *Suggestibility: A Factorial and Experimental Analysis.* Stockholm: Almqvist & Wiksell.

Watkins, J. G. (1949). *Hypnotherapy of the War Neuroses.* New York: Ronald.

Weitzenhoffer, A. M. (1953). *Hypnotism: An Objective Study in Suggestibility.* New York: Wiley.

——— (1956). *Hypnotic Susceptibility as Related to Masculinity-Femininity.* Unpublished doctoral dissertation, Univ. of Michigan.

——— (1963). "The nature of hypnosis: Part II," *Amer. J. clin. Hyp.*, **6**, 40–72.

Weitzenhoffer, A. M., Gough, P. B., and Landes, J. (1959). "A study of the Braid effect: Hypnosis by visual fixation," *J. Psychol.*, **47**, 67–80.

Weitzenhoffer, A. M., and Hilgard, E. R. (1959). *Stanford Hypnotic Susceptibility Scale, Forms A and B.* Palo Alto, Calif.: Consulting Psychologists Press.

———, (1962). *Stanford Hypnotic Susceptibility Scale, Form C.* Palo Alto, Calif.: Consulting Psychologists Press.

——— (1963). *Stanford Profile Scales of Hypnotic Susceptibility, Forms I and II.* Palo Alto, Calif.: Consulting Psychologists Press.

Weitzenhoffer, A. M., and Sjoberg, B. M., Jr. (1961). "Suggestibility with and without 'induction of hypnosis'," *J. nerv. ment. Dis.*, **132**, 204–220.

Weitzenhoffer, A. M., and Weitzenhoffer, Geneva B. (1958) ."Sex, transference, and susceptibility to hypnosis," *Amer. J. clin. Hyp.*, **1**, 15–24.

White, M. M. (1930). "The physical and mental traits of individuals susceptible to hypnosis," *J. abnorm. soc. Psychol.*, **25**, 293–298.

White, R. W. (1937). "Two types of hypnotic trance and their personality correlates," *J. Psychol.*, **3**, 265–277.

Wilson, C. P., Cormen, H. H., and Cole, A. A. (1949). "A preliminary study of the hypnotizability of psychotic patients," *Psychiat. Quart.*, **23**, 657–666.

Wiseman, R. J., and Reyher, J. (1962). "A procedure utilizing dreams for deepening the hypnotic trance," *Amer. J. clin. Hyp.*, **5** (2), 105–110.

14

"Hypnotic" Phenomena: A Critique of Experimental Methods

THEODORE X. BARBER[1]
The Medfield Foundation

ALTHOUGH the phenomena of "hypnosis"—limb and body rigidity, analgesia, hallucinations, deafness, amnesia—are legendary, very few carefully controlled experiments have been conducted in this area. In the majority of studies, the behavior of subjects who were said to be "hypnotized" was not compared with the behavior of "waking" controls. In the relatively small number of experiments that included a comparison group, the "awake" subjects tended to differ from the "hypnotized" subjects on such critical factors as prior practice and training on the criterion tasks. This chapter first analyzes the variables that need to be controlled in "hypnosis" research and,

[1] From the Medfield Foundation, Harding, Massachusetts, and the Division of Psychiatry, Boston University School of Medicine. Work on this chapter was supported by research grants (MY4825 and MH7003) from the National Institute of Mental Health, United States Public Health Service.

The chapter constitutes a revision and extension of a previous paper by the writer, entitled "Experimental Controls and the Phenomena of 'Hypnosis': A Critique of Hypnotic Research Methodology," published in the *Journal of Nervous and Mental Disease*, volume 134, pages 493–505, copyright © 1962 by the Williams & Wilkins Co. Permission to rewrite the previous paper has been granted by the copyright holder.

secondly, presents evidence indicating that, when rigorous controls are instituted in this area, researchers may find that suggestions of analgesia, hallucinations, deafness, time distortion, and so on, given either to "hypnotized" or to "awake" subjects, produce similar overt behaviors and similar reports of subjective experiences.

WHAT IS MEANT BY "HYPNOTIC STATE"?

When experimenters state that subjects were "hypnotized" or placed in a "hypnotic state" or in "trance," they appear to be referring to the following: (1) one of various types of procedures that have been traditionally categorized as "hypnotic inductions" or "trance inductions" was administered; and (2) the subjects manifested one or more signs or characteristics that have been traditionally presumed to signify that a person is no longer "normally awake" but has entered a hypothesized state of "trance." These two interrelated referents can be spelled out as follows:

First, investigators agree that numerous procedures can be categorized as "hypnotic inductions" or "trance inductions." At present such procedures typically include suggestions that the subject is becoming relaxed, drowsy, and sleepy and is entering a hypnotic state. Pattie (1956) and Weitzenhoffer (1955, 1957) have comprehensively described other types of "induction" procedures including "passes" or hand gestures, stimulation of "hypnogenic" areas of the body, and use of metronome, pendulum, rotating mirrors, "hypnodisks," and so on. The administration of one of these "induction" procedures is generally assumed to be necessary to induce an inexperienced subject to enter the "hypnotic state;" however, a consensus exists that after a subject has had training in "hypnosis," he may be induced to enter "trance" by a drastically abbreviated "induction" consisting of a prearranged signal or cue word.[2]

Second, numerous attempts have been made to find physiological indices of the hypothesized state of "trance" that is said to be produced when the "induction" procedure is effective. These studies, reviewed elsewhere (Barber, 1961b), have failed to yield an acceptable physiological criterion; and hypnotists at present, as in the past, typically infer the presence of "trance" from observation of relatively subtle signs manifested by the subject. According to Erickson, Hershman, and Secter (1961), these signs of "trance" include loss of mobility, tonicity throughout the body, rigid facial expression, and literalness in response. Pattie (1956) lists similar indices: "passivity... disinclination to

[2] Although "induction" procedures differ widely, on close inspection they all seem to include at least one common denominator; namely, explicit or implicit suggestions that the subject is entering a state that differs from the "normal waking" state.

talk. . . literal-mindedness, and a lack of spontaneity and initiative." Gill and Brenman (1959, pp. 38–39) write that "hypnotized" subjects show ". . . momentary lapses into somewhat stiff or frozen postural attitudes. . . an impression of a slight slowing down of the pace of bodily movement. . . [and] a fleeting glazing of the eyes, the 'unseeing look' normally found in reverie or in a 'brown study.'" Weitzenhoffer (1957, p. 212) has succinctly summarized the apparent consensus of investigators in this area, writing that: "There seems to be some agreement that hypnotized individuals, even when behaving in a most natural manner, still show a constriction of awareness, a characteristic literal-mindedness, some psychomotor retardation, and possibly a degree of automatism."

Hull (1933), Weitzenhoffer (1957), and others also include heightened suggestibility as an index of the presumed "hypnotic state." In practice, however, hypnotists claim that they are able to judge whether the subject is in "hypnotic trance" by subtle signs such as those mentioned above without determining whether the subject's level of suggestibility has been elevated above the "waking" level.[3] Furthermore, including enhanced suggestibility as a referent for the word "hypnosis" or "hypnotic trance" begs a crucial question: namely, *is heightened responsiveness to suggestions, if and when it can be demonstrated, causally related to the "hypnotic induction" procedure and to the presumed "hypnotic state" or is it produced by other factors in the situation?* To answer this question it is necessary to compare response to standardized test-suggestions in a "hypnotized" group and an "awake" group while exercising rigorous control over the following variables: (1) subject variables (differences between subjects assigned to the "hypnosis" and "awake" treatments); (2) instructions and suggestions per se; (3) interpersonal variables; (4) motivational variables; and (5) the manner in which the situation is defined to the subject. These critical variables are discussed in turn below.

SUBJECT VARIABLES

Fisher (1955) has emphasized that "the good hypnotic *S* in many respects closely resembles an extremely eager and cooperative laboratory *S* (in the normal waking state) who, prior to the experiment, alertly awaits *E*'s instructions." Some "good" hypnotic subjects are apparently so eager and cooperative that they "strive" to produce the effects desired by the experimenter. An example of such "striving" is found in Pattie's (1935) report of an attempt to produce uniocular

[3] In fact, because hypnotists in most instances do *not* assess the subject's response to standardized test-suggestions prior to and after the induction of "trance," they are unable to state whether "trance" has elevated the subject's suggestibility.

blindness in five selected subjects. After the subjects were placed in "trance," they were given the suggestion that they were blind in one eye. A battery of visual tests was then administered including opthalmological examination, plotting of the blind spot in the "good" eye, and tests using the stereoscope and Flees' box with crossed images. Four of the five subjects responded to the tests with normal vision in both eyes. However, one subject, who claimed that one eye was blind even though it could distinguish light from dark, responded to all tests given over a series of sessions as though she were actually blind in one eye. In the final session the subject was given a complicated visual test designed to detect malingering; the results showed that the "blind" eye was not impaired "to the slightest degree" and Pattie concluded that "The results of all former tests were thus invalidated." In a subsequent hypnotic session the subject stated, after much resistance, that she had given a convincing demonstration of unilateral blindness because of the following: "she knew all the time that she could see, but since [the experimenter] had said she could not, she acted as if she did not"; during the stereoscopic test the two images were separated for a second after exposure and this gave her the knowledge needed to respond as if she were unable to see with one eye; when tested with the Flees' box she "saw there were mirrors in there and figured somehow that the one on the left was supposed to be seen with the right eye"; after the experimenter had first attempted to plot the blind spot, she practiced plotting it at home with the aid of a friend. (The named friend corroborated the latter statement.)

Wolberg (1948, p. 49) presented comparable data, which suggest that some "good" hypnotic subjects may go to extremes to comply with the requests or suggestions of the experimenter. A "hypnotized" subject was given the posthypnotic suggestion that hives would develop over his forearm. At the next session the subject showed a markedly irritated skin but no evidence of hives. Although the subject at first denied that he had irritated the skin, he confided under "trance" that immediately after the previous session he had taken a walk through the woods, had picked poison ivy leaves, and had rubbed them vigorously over his forearm. Along similar lines, von Schrenck-Notzing (1896) noted that a "good" hypnotic subject, who was given the posthypnotic suggestion that a blister would form on a specified area, tried to comply with the suggestion by deliberately injuring the area in which the blister was supposed to appear.

The "Good" Hypnotic Subject "As His Own Control"

These and other investigations (such as Barber, 1958), which appear to indicate that some "good" hypnotic subjects "strive" to produce the effects expected or desired by the experimenter, raise a serious question concerning the use of a single group of "good" hypnotic subjects under both the experimental and control treatments. "Good" subjects may correctly or incorrectly surmise that the experimenter desires or expects better results under "hypnosis" and to fulfill these desires or expectations may deliberately give an inferior performance when "awake" (see Sutcliffe, 1960). To illustrate this contention let us examine two experiments, one on "hypnotic anesthesia" presented by R. R. Sears (1932) and one on "hypnotic color blindness" presented by Erickson (1939). Additional experiments that could serve as illustrative cases (Gidro-Frank and Bowersbuch, 1948; Klein, 1930; Kline and Guze, 1951) are discussed by the writer elsewhere (Barber, 1962a, 1962c).

Sears (1932) administered a "hypnotic induction" procedure to seven selected "good" hypnotic subjects. When the subjects appeared to be in "trance," it was suggested that the left leg was insensitive. A sharp steel point was then pressed alternately against the "anesthetic" left leg and the control right leg for one second without breaking the skin. The results were: (1) The "hypnotized" subjects flinched when the stimulus was applied to the normal right leg but not when applied to the "anesthetic" left leg. (2) They showed less physiological reactivity—such as less variability in respiration and less galvanic skin response—when the "anesthetic" leg was stimulated than when the normal leg was stimulated. Subsequently the same subjects were instructed under "waking" conditions to inhibit all responses to pain and the noxious stimulus was reapplied. The "awake" subjects flinched when the stimulus was applied and also manifested the normally expected degree of physiological reaction to the painful stimulus. Sears concluded from these observations that "voluntary inhibition of reaction to pain does not present a picture that even remotely resembles the reaction under true hypnotic anesthesia." However, this conclusion is rendered questionable by the subjects' failure to inhibit flinching when they were instructed under the "waking" condition to inhibit responses to painful stimulation. In pilot studies Sears had found that most people could easily prevent themselves from flinching when stimulated by the sharp steel point. Hull (1933, p. 267) pointed out that because flinching can be inhibited voluntarily, it appears that the "good" hypnotic subjects participating in the Sears experiment might not have tried to suppress reactions to pain when they were instructed to do so under the "waking" condition.

To investigate "hypnotic color blindness" Erickson (1939) selected six "good" hypnotic subjects possessing normal color vision. Each subject was placed in "trance" and given suggestions of color blindness. (Red, green, red-green, and total color blindness were suggested to each subject in random order.) Following each suggested color deficiency, the Ishihara Test of Colorblindness was administered. Under each of the suggested color-blind conditions the "hypnotized" subjects responded to some or many of the Ishihara cards in the manner expected from persons who possess the color deficiency. The following controls were used in the experiment:

1. After amnesia was suggested for the events occurring during "trance," the subjects were told under "waking" conditions that it is possible to perceive different numerals, additional numerals, or to see the Ishihara plates as having no numerals, and they were "admonished to exercise much effort to read the plates in an entirely new fashion." The "awake" subjects did not give any of the responses expected from the color-blind, reading each Ishihara card in the normal manner.

2. The "awake" subjects were next shown how the color-blind perceive the Ishihara cards by exhibiting the cards under red, blue, green, and yellow lights; the Ishihara was then readministered under instructions to detect the numerals perceived by color-blind individuals. Erickson writes that "despite their sophistication by the exhibition of the cards under colored lights, the subjects were unable to do more than confirm their previous normal responses."

Because many apparent "color-blind" responses were given under "trance" but not under the "waking" condition, Erickson concluded that deficiencies in color vision comparable with those found in congenital color blindness can be elicited by suggestions given under "trance."

To check the above findings, Barber and Deeley (1961) asked ten unselected subjects who possessed normal color vision to respond to the Ishihara test first by trying not to see the color red and, second, by trying not to see green. This "waking" group read some of the Ishihara cards in the manner expected from individuals with red or green color blindness. Rock and Shipley (1961) carried out a similar study with eight subjects. The Ishihara was administered under "waking" conditions six times in one experimental session. On the first four trials the subjects were asked to imagine that they were green, red, red-green, and totally color blind. On the fifth trial they were asked to give their normal responses. On the sixth trial they were asked to report all of the numerals that they could detect on the Ishihara cards. On the first four trials the subjects responded to many of the Ishihara cards in the manner expected from the congenitally colorblind. (These "awake" subjects gave approximately as many "color-blind" responses as had Erickson's "hypnotic color-blind" subjects.) The fifth trial showed that the subjects possessed normal color vision. The sixth trial showed that seven of the eight subjects had no difficulty in detecting all of the numerals seen by color-blind individuals. Along similar lines, Bravin (1959) found that some subjects who received suggestions of color blindness under "trance" and some subjects who received instructions to role-play color blindness under "waking" conditions responded to the Pseudoisochromatic test and the colored yarn sorting test of color blindness in the manner expected from the congenitally color-blind. (Under ordinary conditions, Bravin's subjects manifested normal color vision.)

In brief, Erickson found that a selected group of "good" hypnotic subjects was unable when "awake" to detect any of the figures on the Ishihara, which are seen by the color-blind individual even when the "color-blind" figures had been exhibited under colored lights. In contrast, Barber and Deeley, Rock and Shipley, and Bravin found that unselected "awake" subjects could detect many of the figures seen by the color-blind individual. Although we cannot state with certainty why Erickson's subjects were unable when "awake" to detect any of the "color-blind" figures that had been explicitly pointed out to them, the marked discrepancy between the "waking" performance of Erickson's selected "good" hypnotic subjects and the "waking" performance of the unselected subjects participating in the other investigations appears to support the following contention: if a single group of "good" hypnotic subjects is tested under both the "hypnosis" and the control condition, as in Erickson's experiment, it is difficult to exclude the possibility that the subjects may deliberately give an inferior performance under the control condition to comply with what they correctly or incorrectly surmise are the desires or expectations of the experimenter.

Additional objections to using a single group of "good" hypnotic subjects "as their own controls" have been presented by Pattie (1935) and by Sutcliffe (1960) (see also Lindquist, 1953, pp. 160–161). The general conclusion indicated is that the same "good" hypnotic subjects should not constitute both the experimental group and the control group; the performance of subjects assigned to the "hypnosis" treatment should be compared with the performance of an independent group assigned to the control treatment.

Use of an Independent Control Group

Although an experimental design that includes an independent control group is strongly recommended for research in "hypnosis," the design involves at least two potential pitfalls:

1. Investigators using independent control and experimental groups almost always assign "good" hypnotic subjects to the experimental treatment. To ascertain that the subjects are actually "good" subjects, preliminary selection or practice sessions are conducted with them. In many instances, haphazardly selected subjects who have not participated in preliminary sessions are allocated to the control treatment. This procedure is open to the criticism that discrepancies in performance

on the criterion tasks are not contingent upon the experimental group being in the "hypnotic state" and the control group being in the "awake state," but upon the experimental group having acquired useful experience or training. In the preliminary sessions, the experimental group may have: (1) formed a friendly relationship with the investigator; (2) become familiar with the experimental situation; and (3) received practice in responding to the criteria suggestions or to related suggestions. These and possibly other factors carried over from the selection or training sessions to the experiment proper could have the general effect of making the experimental group more at ease or less anxious in the situation and enhancing its motivation and its ability to give a "good" performance.

2. In most experiments employing an independent control group, "good" hypnotic subjects were assigned to the experimental treatment and unrated subjects or "poor" hypnotic subjects were allocated to the control treatment. The explicit criterion for selection of the experimental group—that the subjects were the most "hypnotizable" or most capable of entering "trance"—appears difficult to differentiate from an interrelated implicit criterion, namely, that the subjects were the most willing or the most motivated (irrespective of "hypnotic trance") to yield to the wishes of the investigator or to try to carry out his instructions or suggestions.

A recent experiment by Salzberg (1960a, 1960b) may serve to illustrate these contentions. This investigator gave suggestions for enhanced learning performance to a "hypnotized" group and to an independent control group. The suggestions facilitated learning proficiency in the "trance" subjects but not in the "awake" subjects. It should be noted, however, that the subjects were not assigned at random to experimental and control treatments. On the contrary, subjects allocated to the "hypnosis" treatment were preselected as meeting criteria for high suggestibility; whereas subjects assigned to the control treatment were not required to meet these criteria. By thus confounding the experimental treatments with pre-existing differences among subjects with respect to suggestibility, Salzberg was unable to determine whether the "hypnosis" group was more responsive than the control group to suggestions for improved performance because it was in "hypnotic trance" or because it was composed of subjects who were more suggestible to begin with.

To illustrate further the above contentions let us examine a study by Orne (1959) in which "good" hypnotic subjects who had participated in preliminary training sessions were assigned to the experimental treatment and "poor" subjects, who were instructed to "fake hypnosis," were assigned to the control treatment. Orne found that although the overt experimental behaviors of the "fake" subjects were similar to the behavior of the "real" subjects, the two groups differed in reports of subjective experiences. For instance, when given suggestions that a finger was insensitive to pain, there were no noticeable differences between the experimental "hypnosis" group and the "fake" control group in overt responses to such noxious stimuli as electric shock and painful heat; however, on postexperimental inquiry, the experimental subjects stated that they had experienced little or no discomfort, whereas the controls stated that they had experienced pain. It may be, as Orne implied, that such differences in subjective experiences were due to one group being in "trance" and the other group being in the "awake" state. An alternative possibility, however, is that differences in subjective reports with respect to pain experienced were due to such uncontrolled factors as the following: (1) Irrespective of "trance" and irrespective of prior training, the "good" subjects in the experimental group may have been more willing or more motivated than the "poor" subjects in the control group to try to imagine vividly that a finger was numb or insensitive to pain. (2) The experimental group but not the control group had participated in preliminary practice or training sessions. In these sessions, the experimental group had not only received general practice in complying with experimental instructions and suggestions but had also received specific practice in trying to respond to suggestions of "analgesia" or numbness. (3) An additional criticism appears applicable specifically to the use of a "faking" control group; pre-experimental instructions given to the "fake" subjects—such as, to continue to "fake" when they received a "somewhat painful electric shock"—could have precluded their perceiving or reporting the noxious stimulation as nonthreatening or nonpainful.

In brief, assigning "good" hypnotic subjects to the experimental treatment and unrated subjects or "poor" hypnotic subjects to the control treatment is contraindicated in "hypnosis" research. When randomization procedures are not used in assigning subjects to treatments, as in the Salzberg and Orne experiments, differences on the criterion measures can be attributed to pre-existing differences between subjects allocated to experimental and control groups rather than to the presence of the "hypnotic state" in one group and its absence in the other.

EFFECTS OF DIRECT INSTRUCTIONS AND SUGGESTIONS

The effects of direct suggestions to perform the criterion behaviors have at times been confounded with the effects of "hypnotic trance." In a number of studies the "hypnotized" group, but not the "waking" control group, was given suggestions to show certain effects, for example, suggestions of analgesia or deafness. Finding that the "hypnotized" group showed less response than the "waking" group to noxious stimulation or to auditory stimulation, it was concluded that alterations in sensory-perceptual functions can be produced by suggestions given under "trance." These studies, however, failed to exclude the possibility that the effective factor in ameliorating pain or in producing apparent "deafness" was not "hypnotic trance" but the suggestions of analgesia or deafness per se; if the "waking" group had received suggestions of analgesia or deafness it may have shown similar effects. To illustrate these contentions let us examine a few studies concerned with "hypnotic analgesia," "hypnotic deafness," "hypnotic time distortion," and the effects of "hypnosis" on physiological functions.

"Hypnotic Analgesia"

With few exceptions experimental studies concerned with the effects of "hypnosis" on pain compared pain reactivity under "hypnotically suggested analgesia" with reactivity under an uninstructed "waking" condition. Although some studies (Doupe, Miller, and Keller, 1939; Dynes, 1932; West, Niell, and Hardy, 1952) found that suggestions of analgesia given under "hypnotic trance" were effective, as compared to the uninstructed "waking" condition, in reducing subjective and physiological responses to noxious stimulation, this does not demonstrate that "hypnotic trance" was necessary to produce the effects. As Brown and Vogel (1938) hypothesized, it may be possible to produce a similar reduction in response to pain stimuli by instructing a "waking" group to try to imagine that a noxious stimulus is nonpainful.

Barber and Hahn (1962) designed an experiment to test the Brown and Vogel hypothesis. Specifically, these investigators asked: Is "hypnotically suggested analgesia" more effective than "waking-imagined analgesia" in attenuating subjective and physiological responses to painful stimulation? Water near the freezing point applied to the hand for three minutes was selected as the pain stimulus. Previous investigators (Benjamin, 1958; Kunkle, 1949; McMurray, 1950; Wolf and Hardy, 1941) had reported that "aching pain" is produced within 10 to 60 seconds after a limb is immersed in ice water; if the freezing water is not removed, pain continues for two to four minutes before adaptation occurs; and the intensity of the pain experienced is related to increments on such physiological variables as heart rate, systolic and diastolic pressure, and respiratory variability.

Subjects for the Barber-Hahn experiment were chosen as follows: The Barber Suggestibility Scale (Barber and Calverley, 1963b; Barber, Karacan, and Calverley, 1964) was administered to 192 female students under a "direct suggestions" condition, that is, without a preceding "hypnotic induction." The 48 most responsive subjects (ranking in the upper quartile with respect to scores on the suggestibility scale) were selected to participate in the experiment. These subjects, who were homogeneous with respect to sex, age, social background, and level of pre-existing suggestibility, were allocated at random to the following four experimental treatments with 12 subjects to each treatment: Hypnotically Suggested Analgesia; Uninstructed treatment; Control treatment; and Waking-Imagined Analgesia.

Subjects assigned to the Hypnosis treatment were given a standardised 20-minute "induction" procedure patterned after the hypnotic procedures of Friedlander and Sarbin (1938), Marcuse (1959, pp. 52–53), and Weitzenhoffer and Hilgard (1959, pp. 13–18). Following the "hypnotic induction" the subjects were given a series of tests to assess suggestibility. All subjects in this group appeared to enter "trance;" they showed psychomotor retardation and lack of spontaneity and initiative, and responded positively to the test-suggestions. Suggestions were then given for a period of one minute to induce anesthesia of the left hand. Following the anesthesia suggestions the "hypnotized" subjects immersed the "anesthetic" hand in water at 2 degrees C for three minutes.

Subjects assigned to the Uninstructed, Control, and Waking Imagination treatments were not given a "hypnotic induction." Under the Uninstructed and Control treatments the subjects were simply asked to immerse the left hand in water; the Uninstructed group immersed the hand in water at 2 degrees C for three minutes and the Control group immersed the hand in water *at room temperature* for the same period of time. Subjects allocated to the Waking-Imagined Analgesia treatment were instructed for a period of one minute to imagine a pleasant situation when the noxious stimulation (water at 2 degrees C) was applied ("...When your hand is in the water, try to imagine that it is a very hot day, that the water feels pleasantly cool, and that your hand is relaxed and comfortable...").

Soon after stimulation all subjects completed a standardized questionnaire designed to assess the degree to which discomfort or pain was experienced. This questionnaire yielded the following findings: (1) The Hypnosis and Waking-Imagination groups did not differ in subjective testimony, stating that the stimulus was experienced as uncomfortable but not painful. (2) The Hypnosis and Waking-Imagination groups differed significantly from the Uninstructed group, which rated the stimulus as painful, and from the Control group, which rated the stimulus as not uncomfortable.

Physiological variables (forehead muscle tension, respiration, heart rate, and skin resistance) monitored prior to and during stimulation were analyzed in terms of Lacey's (1956) Autonomic Lability Scores to control for differences in basal (prestimulus) levels of physiological functioning. These analyses showed the following: (1) The Hypnosis group and the Waking-Imagination group did not differ significantly on any physiological response to the noxious stimulus. (2) Compared to the Uninstructed condition, both "hypnotically suggested analgesia" and "waking-imagined analgesia" were effective in reducing forehead muscle tension and respiratory irregularities during the noxious stimulation. (3) Neither "Hypnotically Suggested Analgesia" nor "Waking-Imagined Analgesia" affected heart rate or skin resistance; under the Hypnotic Analgesia, Waking-Imagined Analgesia, and Uninstructed treatments subjects showed significantly faster heart rate and significantly lower skin resistance than under the Control treatment.

In brief, Barber and Hahn found that "Waking-Imagined Analgesia" and "Hypnotically Suggested Analgesia" had a similar effect in producing a reduction in subjective pain experience and in reducing some but not all physiological responses to noxious stimulation. Further studies are needed to confirm and extend these findings.

"Hypnotic Deafness"

General treatises on hypnotism (Estabrooks, 1943; Moll, 1889; Weitzenhoffer, 1953) assert or imply that suggestions of deafness are often effective with "hypnotized" subjects but are ineffective with nonhypnotized subjects. This assertion appears to derive from unsystematic observations rather than from carefully controlled experimental studies. Although a number of experimenters (Erickson, 1938a, 1938b; Kline, Guze, and Haggerty, 1954; Malmo, Boag, and Raginsky, 1954; Sutcliffe, 1961) administered suggestions of deafness to selected "trance" subjects, no one, to my knowledge, gave similar suggestions to a "waking" control group. Barber and Calverley (1964b) recently conducted an experiment to fill this lacuna and to answer the following questions:

1. Are suggestions of deafness more effective when given under hypnotic conditions than under nonhypnotic conditions in producing total or partial "subjective deafness," that is, in eliciting testimony that auditory stimuli either were not perceived or were perceived as reduced in intensity?

2. Does "subjective deafness" produce *objective* consequences that are similar to or identical with the objective effects of actual deafness?

Barber and Calverley assessed the objective effects of suggested deafness by the delayed auditory feedback (DAF) method in which the subject's utterances are recorded, delayed for a fraction of a second, amplified, and returned to his ears through a headphone. Prior studies had shown that the speech of a person with normal hearing, but not of a deaf person, is impaired when his voice is returned to his ears within .1 to .8 seconds after uttering. This impairment typically includes: (1) speech disturbances such as stuttering and mispronunciations:

(2) increased loudness of voice; and (3) decreased rate of speaking (Black, 1951; Chase, Sutton, and First, 1959; Lee, 1950; Yates, 1963).

The Barber and Calverley experiment involved analysis of covariance for a randomized groups design.[4] Forty-two women college students were first tested individually with DAF on Form 1 of a standardized oral reading test. In the same session, each subject was tested individually with DAF on Form 2 of the oral reading test under one of three experimental treatments with 14 subjects randomly assigned to each treatment. Subjects assigned to Treatment A read Form 2 after receiving a standardized hypnotic induction procedure plus suggestions of deafness for the feedback of their voice ("... When you put the earphones on this time you will be deaf to your voice, you will not hear your voice coming back to you, you will not hear anything at all..."). Subjects assigned to Treatment B were given "waking" suggestions of deafness ("... This time I want you to ignore and be deaf for your voice coming back to you..."). Subjects allocated to Treatment C read Form 2 without receiving either a "hypnotic induction" or suggestions of deafness.

The dependent variables consisted of scores on a standardized questionnaire designed to assess "subjective deafness" and scores on the following: time required to read the standardized material; loudness of voice when reading the material; and number of speech disturbances—such as mispronunciations, repetition of words, stuttering—per unit of reading. The results were:

1. The suggestions of deafness had an effect on approximately two-thirds of the subjects in Treatment A and almost all the subjects in Treatment B. Nine subjects (64 per cent) in Treatment A (Hypnotic Induction Plus Suggestions of Deafness), 13 subjects (93 per cent) in Treatment B (Waking Suggestions of Deafness), and one subject (seven per cent) in Treatment C (Control) stated in response to the questionnaire that, when reading Form 2 aloud with feedback of their speech, they either did not hear anything coming through the earphones or the sounds seemed muffled, far away, or not as loud or intense.

[4] In the covariance design, as used in this experiment and in other experiments discussed subsequently in the present chapter (Barber and Calverley, 1963e; 1964a; Parker and Barber, 1964), a measure is obtained of subjects' responses to the dependent variable prior to random assignment of subjects to experimental and control treatments (Edwards, 1960, Chap. 11; McNemar, 1955, Chap. 17; Ray, 1960, Chap. 10; Winer, 1962, Chap. 11). The covariance design has the advantage but not the disadvantage of the "subject as his own control" design. Both the covariance method and the "subject as his own control method" reduce the estimate of the experimental error. However, the "subject as his own control" design, as pointed out, has a serious disadvantage in hypnotic research in that the same subjects compose both the experimental group and the control group and the subjects can vary their performance to meet the desires or expectations of the experimenter. In the covariance design this possibility is minimized by testing different subjects under the experimental and control treatments.

2. Although the suggestions of deafness were effective with the majority of hypnotic and nonhypnotic subjects in eliciting reports of altered auditory perception, analyses of covariance showed that the suggestions of deafness did not produce noticeable *objective* effects on performance. Subjects claiming total "subjective deafness," subjects claiming partial "subjective deafness," and subjects stating that they heard normally all showed about the same number of speech disturbances, the same loudness of voice, and the same slowness of speech when reading aloud with delayed feedback of their vocalizations.

The Barber and Calverley findings suggest that previous studies in this area may have confounded two independent variables: (1) the "hypnotic trance state"; and (2) suggestions of deafness. In prior investigations suggestions of deafness were given subsequent to the administration of a "hypnotic induction" and when the subjects showed characteristics that are presumed to indicate the presence of "trance." Suggestions of deafness were not given to comparable subjects under "waking" conditions. Apparently, it was assumed that suggestions of deafness would have an effect only with "hypnotized" subjects. The results of the Barber and Calverley experiment indicate that this assumption is open to question: many experimental subjects who have received suggestions of deafness will report some alteration in auditory perception or some degree of "subjective deafness." These subjective reports can be elicited with or without the prior administration of one of the procedures traditionally labeled as a "hypnotic induction" and with or without the subjects manifesting signs that are supposed to indicate that they are in "hypnotic trance."

"Hypnotic Time Distortion"

In a series of studies Cooper and Erickson (1954) found that "time distortion"—that is, subjective testimony that a brief period seemed to be a very long period of time—could be produced in selected "good" hypnotic subjects by suggestions given under "trance." In discussing this finding, they implicitly contended that "time distortion" is very difficult if not impossible to produce in unselected subjects under "waking" conditions. To confirm the results and to test the implicit contention of Cooper and Erickson, Barber and Calverley (1964d) carried out an experiment as follows.

To cross-validate the finding that "time distortion" can be produced in selected subjects under "trance," 16 "good" hypnotic subjects (Group A) were placed in "hypnotic trance" and given suggestions that five minutes would seem to be five hours. (The suggestions for time distortion were closely patterned after those used by Cooper and Erickson.) To test the tacit contention that "time distortion" is difficult if not impossible to produce in unselected "waking" subjects, 16 subjects who had not been pretested for suggestibility or hypnotizability (Group B) were given similar suggestions for time distortion under "waking" conditions. A third group of 16 unselected subjects (Control) was not given suggestions for time distortion. Following the experimental treatments, all subjects were given a learning task for a five-minute period and then given a standardized questionnaire designed to assess the "seeming duration" of the learning period. On the average, the "seeming duration" of the five-minute period was judged as 89 minutes by Group A ("good" hypnotic subjects given suggestions for time distortion under "trance"), 47 minutes by Group B (unselected subjects given suggestions for time distortion under "waking" conditions), and four minutes by Group C (Control). Although there appeared to be a trend for Group A to give reports of more extended "seeming duration" than Group B, the variability in both groups was so large that the differences between the means fell short of statistical significance.

In brief, the study by Barber and Calverley confirmed Cooper and Erickson's finding that "time distortion" can be produced by suggestions given to selected subjects under "hypnotic trance." However, the Barber and Calverley findings also indicate that "time distortion" can be produced by suggestions given to unselected subjects under "waking" conditions. Further studies are needed that will be conducted along similar lines as the Barber and Calverley study but will differ from it in that suggestions for time distortion are given to subjects *assigned at random* to "hypnosis" and "waking" treatments.

Physiological Effects Produced Under "Hypnosis"

A number of investigations that reported that physiological alterations can be produced by suggestions given under "hypnotic trance" failed to use a control group given similar suggestions without "trance" (see Barber, 1961b). To illustrate, let us examine briefly a few reports concerned with elevation of gastric acidity, enhancement of inflammatory reaction to injury, acceleration of the heart, and reduction of warts.

Elevation of Gastric Acidity. Heyer (1925), Ikemi (1959), and others reported that suggestions of eating a meal given to "hypnotized" subjects produced an elevation in gastric acidity somewhat comparable to that observed when an actual meal is ingested. A "waking" control group was not used in these studies. Because other investigators (Luckhardt and Johnston, 1925; Wolf and Wolff, 1947) reported that gastric acidity can be augmented in some "awake" subjects by the "mere discussion" of eating a delicious meal, carefully controlled studies may find that suggestions of eating food given to "hypnotized" and "awake" subjects produce a comparable elevation in stomach acidity. Experiments are needed to assess this possibility.

Enhancement of Inflammatory Reaction to Injury. Chapman, Goodell, and Wolff (1959) placed 13 selected subjects in "a state of moderate to deep hypnosis" and suggested to them that one arm was very sensitive and the other arm was either normal or insensitive. A standard heat stimulus was then applied alternately to the two arms. The results indicated that suggestions of sensitivity given under "hypnosis" enhanced the inflammatory reaction to thermal injury. However, because suggestions of sensitivity were not given to a "waking" group, it cannot be concluded that "hypnotic trance" was either necessary or helpful in producing the effect. Further studies are required that will repeat the procedures of Chapman *et al.* but that, in addition, will use a control group selected from the same population as the "hypnosis" group *and is given the same suggestions of limb sensitivity.*

Heart Acceleration. Van Pelt (1954) placed a "good" hypnotic subject in "trance" and suggested to him that his heart was beating faster. The electrocardiogram showed that cardiac rate increased from 78 to 135 beats per minute. Although the study indicated that heart acceleration can be produced by suggestions, it did not demonstrate that "hypnotic trance" was instrumental in producing the effect. If, instead of first "hypnotizing" the subject, Van Pelt had given the suggestions of tachycardia under "waking" conditions, similar results might have been obtained. Because some apparently normal persons can produce tachycardia at will (Favill and White, 1917; King, 1920; Koehler, 1914; Pease, 1889; Taylor and Cameron, 1922; Van de Velde, 1897), the writer will venture to predict that, in future research, suggestions of heart acceleration will prove to be effective with a small number of "hypnotized" subjects and also with a comparable small number of "waking" controls.

Reduction of Warts. Sinclair-Gieben and Chalmers (1959), Ullman and Dudek (1960), and others reported that wart remission could be produced in some subjects by suggestions given under "trance." As in the above studies, an independent "waking" control group was not employed. Judging from a series of investigations (Bloch, 1927; Bonjour, 1929; Grumach, 1927; Memmescheimer and Eisenlohr, 1931; Sulzberger and Wolf, 1934; Vollmer, 1946), which found that various suggestive procedures that did not involve "hypnotic trance," such as, painting the warts with an innocuous brightly colored dye, were ostensibly effective in some instances in producing wart regression, we can hypothesize that suggestions of wart disappearance are effective with a comparable proportion of "hypnotized" and "waking" subjects. Experiments are needed to test this hypothesis.

Experimenter's Tone and Manner

These considerations suggest that in further research the same instructions or suggestions to carry out the criterion behaviors or to show specified physiological effects should be given to a "hypnotized" group and to an independent control group. It should be emphasized that the suggestions should be worded identically and should be given in the same tone of voice to both groups. Some of the differences in response to suggestions observed in "hypnotized" and "waking" subjects may be due to differences in the way the suggestions are presented (see Barber and Calverley, 1963a). Because, with few exceptions, researchers in this area seem to believe that suggestions are more effective when given under "hypnosis," they may inadvertently communicate their beliefs to the subjects by giving suggestions in an emphatic and expectant manner to those that are "hypnotized" and in a hesitating, less forthright, and less effective manner to the controls. Further studies are needed that will focus on the experimenter's tone of voice and his inflections, gestures, and demeanor when giving suggestions. Well-planned studies along these lines may find that the experimenter's beliefs and expectations affect the results by influencing the way in which he administers the instructions and suggestions to "hypnotized" and "awake" subjects.

In brief, experiments in "hypnosis" have at times failed to control for the effects of instructions or suggestions per se. Suggestions to carry out certain behaviors were given under "hypnotic trance" but not under "waking" conditions and the resultant behaviors were illogically attributed to the effects of "trance." There is sufficient evidence to indicate that in some of these experiments similar performances could have been elicited in both "hypnotized" and "waking" subjects if all subjects had been given the same suggestions or instructions to perform the criterion behaviors. In further work, suggestions or instructions to perform the criterion acts should be given in the same words and in the same tone of voice to both "trance" and "waking" groups, preferably by administering the suggestions by a tape recording (see Barber and Calverley, 1964c).

INTERPERSONAL VARIABLES

The sufficient conditions for the production of some so-called "hypnotic" phenomena may consist of direct verbal suggestions that the effects are forthcoming, which are given to the subject by a prestigeful person in a close interpersonal setting. To illustrate this possibility let us examine a few clinical reports concerned with the relief of pain by "hypnosis."

Butler (1954) attempted to relieve pain associated with carcinoma in 12 selected "hypnotizable" patients. Each patient received suggestions of pain relief in a series of "hypnosis" sessions held daily and sometimes two to four times per day. Ten of the 12 patients stated that their pain was reduced during and, at times, for a brief period following the "trance" sessions. However, when "hypnosis" and the relationship between patient and physician were terminated, the patients showed a return of severe pain. The important finding in these cases was that when "hypnosis" was discontinued, but the physician continued to give the same amount of personal attention to the patient, the patient continued to show pain relief. Butler emphasized that in treating pain by "hypnosis" the physician "gives of himself to the patient. . .and, as the sympathetic bond between the two grows stronger, the hypnologist may even 'feel' the symptoms he is trying to eradicate from the patient."

Marmer (1959) also pointed to the attention and support given to the patient as a major variable, writing that "the realization that the anesthesiologist is willing to invest time, effort, warmth, and understanding in an attempt of hypnosis will give most patients added security and trust in the physician and will result in decreased tension and anxiety." Lea, Ware, and Monroe (1960) presented similar observations in a study that set out to assess the effects of "hypnosis" on chronic pain: "At times it was hard to decide whether benefit was actually being derived from hypnosis itself or such extraneous factors as the secondary gain a patient would derive from an unusual amount of personal attention from the hypnotherapist."

Comparable data have been obtained in obstetrical settings. In a study with 200 patients, Winkelstein (1958) found that to produce a measure of pain relief during parturition it was necessary for the physician to devote much time and personal attention to each patient. This investigator de-emphasized the importance of "hypnotic trance," pointing to the following variables as crucial: (1) suggestions of pain relief per se; (2) the mental attitude of the patient toward pregnancy and delivery; (3) the will to succeed; (4) the confidence of the patient in the procedure as well as in the obstetrician; and (5) the patient-obstetrician rapport. Along similar lines, Chlifer (1930) observed that the effectiveness of suggestions of pain relief is not related to the "depth of trance;" labor pain can at times be ameliorated by suggestions given without "trance;" and "the success of verbally induced analgesia is closely related to the personality of the subject and the relationship established between the doctor and the parturient woman."

These clinical reports suggest an experiment in which obstetrical patients (or postoperative patients or other patients in pain) are assigned at random to a "hypnosis" and a "waking" control treatment. If both the "hypnosis" and control groups are given a comparable opportunity to interact with and to form a "close" relationship with the physician-experimenter, it appears possible that suggestions of pain relief given under the "waking" condition will be as effective as suggestions given under the "trance" condition (see Barber, 1963a).

Uncontrolled interpersonal variables may have influenced the results in other studies. As noted above, in many experiments the "hypnosis" group had participated in preliminary practice or training sessions in which it had interacted with the experimenter and had an opportunity to form a social relationship with him. In contradistinction, the control group had not participated in preliminary sessions or had participated in fewer preliminary sessions than the "hypnosis" group. Furthermore, during the treatment sessions the "hypnosis" group generally received more of the experimenter's time and interest than the control group. Because the experimental group had interacted more extensively with the experimenter and had possibly formed a closer relationship with him, it appears possible that it was more willing to comply with his wishes or suggestions. To control this factor it is necessary for both experimental and control groups to be given comparable opportunity to interact with the experimenter or for both groups to be tested by an experimenter with whom they are not acquainted.

MOTIVATIONAL VARIABLES

As noted previously in this chapter, in many instances a single group served as its own control and no attempt was made to motivate the subjects to perform to the best of their ability under both the "trance" *and the control treatments.* When independent control and "hypnosis" groups were used, the experimental situation was typically defined to the control group as an ordinary experimental situation and to the "hypnosis" group as an important situation or as a situation in which "unprecedented kinds of experiences" were to be expected (Gill and Brenman, 1961, pp. 10–11). It appears possible that differences in performance were due to the discrepant expectations of the two groups, and to differential motivation and interest in the experiment, rather than to the presence or absence of "hypnotic trance."

To illustrate the importance of motivational variables, let us examine recent experiments by Weitzenhoffer and Sjoberg (1961) and Barber and Glass (1962) in which a series of standardized test-suggestions were administered under a "waking" condition and following a "hypnotic induction." The results of both experiments showed that a standardized procedure of the type traditionally labeled a "hypnotic induction" is effective in producing a statistically significant enhancement of suggestibility. Both experiments, however, are open to the same criticism: although an attempt was made to produce positive task motivation under the "hypnosis" treatment, that is, instructions and suggestions were given to the subject to "try his best," "to let things happen," and "to cooperate," no attempt was made to produce positive task motivation under the "waking" treatment. Does a standardized "hypnotic induction" give rise to heightened response to suggestions when an attempt is made to motivate both the experimental and the control group to perform maximally on suggested tasks? Barber and Calverley (1962, 1963d, 1963f) conducted a series of experiments to answer this question.

In the first experiment (Barber and Calverley, 1962), 138 college students were allocated at random to six experimental groups with 23 subjects to each group. The criterion measure consisted of response to the following eight standardized test-suggestions, which are included in the Barber Suggestibility Scale: Arm Lowering; Arm Levitation; Inability-to-Unclasp-Hands; Thirst "Hallucination"; Inability-to-Speak-Name; Body Immobility; "Posthypnotic-Like" Response; and Selective Amnesia. Subjects allocated to the "hypnosis" treatment were assessed on response to the eight test-suggestions immediately upon completion of a standardized 15-minute "hypnotic induction," which included eye fixation on a light blinking in synchrony with the sound of a metronome, repetitive suggestions of relaxation, drowsiness, sleep, and of entering a hypnotic state, and suggestions that a high level of performance was expected on forthcoming tasks. The other groups were assessed on response to the test-suggestions without receiving a "hypnotic induction." Subjects assigned to an Uninstructed Control group, for example, were told that they were to be tested for imaginative ability and then were assessed on the criterion suggestions without receiving further instructions. Another group (Task Motivation) was assessed on response to the test-suggestions after receiving brief instructions (for 60 seconds) designed to produce positive motivation to perform well in a situation defined as a test of imagination; subjects in this group were told that others had performed well on the tasks; they also could perform well if they tried to imagine vividly; if they did not try to the best of their ability to cooperate and to imagine, the experiment would be worthless and the experimenter would be disappointed. The results showed that although the Hypnotic Induction treatment was significantly more effective than four of the five nonhypnotic treatments in producing a high level of response to the test-suggestions, it was not significantly more effective than the Task Motivation treatment. Furthermore, assessment of reports of subjective experiences indicated that subjects given task-motivating instructions under "waking" conditions experienced a significantly greater number of the suggested effects than subjects given the "hypnotic induction."

Barber and Calverley (1963d, 1963f) obtained comparable results in two cross-validation experiments. Both experiments were similar to the above in that subjects from a homogeneous population were randomly assigned to at least three treatment groups: a group given a standardized "hypnotic induction" procedure for 15 minutes; a group given task-motivating instructions for one minute; and a control group given no instructions. The two experiments yielded very similar findings: (1) Both the Hypnotic Induction treatment and the Task Motivation treatment were more effective than the Uninstructed Control treatment in producing a high level of suggestibility. (2) The group given the "hypnotic induction" and the group given brief task-motivating instructions did not differ significantly from each other in overt response to the eight test-suggestions or in subjective testimony that the suggested effects were experienced.

The Barber and Calverley experiments support the contention that when an attempt is made to motivate an "awake" group to perform well on suggested tasks, the null hypothesis of no difference in response to suggestions in the "awake" group and a group given a "hypnotic induction" is difficult to disconfirm. To further illustrate the significance of motivational variables, let us consider an experiment by A. B. Sears (1955) in which subjects who learned the Morse Code under "hypnotic trance" made significantly fewer errors when subsequently tested in the "awake" state than a group of controls who learned the code under "waking" conditions. Data presented in the report suggest that motivation to learn the code, which apparently varied independently of the "hypnotic state," may have been the critical variable in producing the better learning performance in the experimental group. Before the experiment was completed, 44 per cent of the original subjects in the control group had dropped out as compared to only 24 per cent in the "hypnosis" group. The large number of drop-outs in the control group appeared to be due to lack of motivation to perform the learning task. Sears writes that "the control group complained of boredom and loss of interest, while the experimental group admitted they had no real goal in learning the code but were interested in knowing how well and how fast they could learn it." This, together with additional data presented in Sears' report, suggests that subjects assigned to the "trance" treatment were aware that the experiment was designed to test the effect of "hypnosis" on learning and were interested to see what effects "hypnosis" would actually have; consequently, they apparently maintained an interest in the experiment and learned better than the control subjects who were not interested and not motivated to carry out the learning assignment.

The above considerations raise the following question: When investigators (such as Hammer, 1951, 1954) find that enhanced learning proficiency can be produced by task-motivating suggestions given under "trance," is this effect partly due to the presence of "trance" or is it solely due to the task-motivating suggestions? To answer this question, Parker and Barber (1964) conducted an experiment as follows.

Forty subjects were selected from a pool of more than 200 college students who had been rated on the Barber Suggestibility Scale under a "waking suggestions" condition. Of the 40, 30 had been rated as highly suggestible and ten as nonsuggestible. In the experiment proper all subjects were first tested in the same way on Form I of three cognitive-learning tasks: Digit Symbol Substitution; Memory for Words; and Abstract Reasoning. Retests on an equivalent form (Form II) of the three tasks were then given as follows. The 30 suggestible subjects were assigned at random to three treatment groups with ten subjects to each group: Group A (Task-Motivating Instructions); Group B (Hypnotic Induction Procedure Plus Task-Motivating Instructions); and Group C (Uninstructed Control). The ten nonsuggestible subjects (Group D) were retested subsequent to receiving task-motivating instructions in the same way as Group A. Groups A and D (Task-Motivating Instructions) were told that they could improve their performance and were expected to improve their performance on Form II of the three learning tasks; others had been able to raise their scores by trying harder; and if they did not try to the very best of their ability, the experiment would be worthless and the experimenter would be disappointed. Subjects in Group B were given a "hypnotic induction" and, when they appeared to be in "trance," were given similar task-motivating instructions as Groups A and D. Group C (Uninstructed Control) was retested on Form II without receiving preliminary instructions or suggestions. Analyses of covariance indicated that: (1) neither task-motivating instructions given alone nor a "hypnotic induction" given together with task-motivating instructions significantly affected performance on the more difficult tasks (Memory for Words and Abstract Reasoning); however, (2) task-motivating instructions produced a comparable enhancement of performance on the Digit Symbol Substitution task in Groups A, B, and D, that is, in "hypnotized" and "awake" subjects and in suggestible and non-suggestible subjects.

The Parker and Barber findings suggest a new perspective toward previous studies (such as Hammer, 1951; Salzberg, 1960a; Sears, 1955), which found that suggestions given under "hypnotic trance" facilitated performance on learning or cognitive tasks. Referring to the Parker-Barber findings with the Digit Symbol Substitution test consider the following:

1. If the "trance" group had been used as its own control or if it had been compared with Group C (Uninstructed Control) Parker and Barber might have concluded that "hypnotic trance" improves learning proficiency.

2. However, by including two additional groups that received task-

motivating instructions without "hypnotic induction" (Groups A and D), they found that whatever improvement in performance was manifested by the "hypnotized" subjects was also manifested by both suggestible and nonsuggestible subjects who had received brief task-motivating instructions *without* a "hypnotic induction"; and the task-motivating instructions appeared to be sufficient, whereas the "hypnotic induction" procedure and the presumed "state of trance" appeared to be unnecessary for producing enhanced learning proficiency.

Uncontrolled motivational factors may have also influenced the results in some of the studies that were conducted to test the popular belief that "hypnosis" increases physical strength and endurance. A number of experiments in this area apparently confounded two independent variables: (1) the "hypnotic trance state"; and (2) task-motivating suggestions, that is, instructions or suggestions stating that the subject could perform at a very high level on strength and endurance tasks. For instance, Ikai and Steinhaus (1961), Roush (1951), and Wells (1947) gave task-motivating suggestions to "hypnotized" subjects but not to "waking" controls. They found that performance on strength tasks was enhanced by suggestions given under "hypnotic trance." However, because they failed to give similar suggestions to "awake" subjects, they did not demonstrate that "hypnotic trance" was either necessary or helpful in producing the effect.

London and Fuhrer (1961) recently designed a study to disentangle the effects produced by "hypnotic trance" from the effects produced by task-motivating instructions. Thirty-two female subjects were tested on strength of grip and weight-holding endurance under two "hypnosis" and two "waking" conditions. Task-motivating instructions were given under one but not the other "hypnosis" condition and under one but not the other "waking" condition. The results indicated that: (1) "hypnotic trance" by itself (without task-motivating instructions) did not affect either strength or endurance; and (2) strength and endurance were facilitated by task motivating instructions given with and also without "trance."

Barber and Calverley (1963e) recently conducted an experiment to cross-validate London and Fuhrer's findings. Sixty female volunteers were pretested and then retested in single individual sessions on grip strength (hand dynamometer) and weight-holding endurance. The pretests were given to all subjects in the same way under ordinary experimental conditions. The retests were given after the administration of one of the following four experimental treatments with 15 subjects allocated at random to each treatment: Task-Motivating Instructions Alone; Hypnotic Induction Procedure Alone; Hypnotic Induction Procedure Plus Task-Motivating Instructions; and Control. Analyses of covariance for the 2×2 factorial showed the following:

1. Grip strength was not significantly affected by the experimental variables (hypnotic induction, task-motivating instructions, or hypnotic induction together with task-motivating instructions).

2. The "hypnotic induction" procedure by itself produced a decrement in weight-holding endurance, whereas task-motivating instructions given alone and task-motivating instructions given subsequent to a "hypnotic induction" resulted in significantly enhanced weight-holding endurance.

Barber and Calverley concluded that: (1) task-motivating instructions are instrumental variables in the experimental production of enhanced endurance; and (2) "hypnosis" (that is, the administration of a procedure of the type traditionally labeled a "hypnotic induction" and the appearance of those characteristics on the part of the subject that have been traditionally presumed to signify the presence of "hypnotic trance") is irrelevant to the experimental elicitation of heightened endurance.

DEFINITION OF THE SITUATION

Defining the situation as "hypnosis" may be sufficient to arouse the subject's curiosity, to enhance his interest in the experiment, and to motivate him to perform well on the criterion tasks, irrespective of whether the subject enters "trance" (see Barber and Calverley, 1963c; Glass and Barber, 1961). By defining the situation as "hypnosis" additional factors are introduced that could bias the results. For instance, implicit aspects of the subject-experimenter contract in a "hypnosis" situation may include the following message: the subject is expected to carry out suggested acts to the best of his ability, including acts that under other circumstances might appear unusual or odd, and the experimenter in turn is expected to assume responsibility for the consequences of the acts that he instructs the subject to perform. In contrast, the control treatment is almost always defined explicitly or implicitly as an ordinary situation in which the subject is not expected to perform unusual behaviors. These contrasting definitions of the situation may have biased the results in experiments that found that suggestions given under the "trance" treatment, but not under the control treatment, were effective in eliciting ostensibly antisocial acts such as attempting to injure another (Rowland, 1939) or exhibiting oneself sexually (Kline, 1958). Further research is needed in which both "hypnotized" and "awake" subjects are explicitly informed that they are expected to carry out all instructions and suggestions no matter how odd or unusual they may appear with the implication that, in the final analysis, the experimenter will be responsible for any untoward consequences. A critical analysis of research in this area (Barber, 1961a) suggests that if the situation is defined in the same way to "hypnosis" and "waking" groups and if interpersonal and motivational variables are controlled, the "waking" group will respond in a similar manner as the "hypnotized" group to instructions or suggestions to perform ostensibly antisocial acts.

The word "hypnosis" possesses additional connotations that can influence the outcome of experimental studies. Dorcus, Brintnall, and Case (1941) administered a questionnaire concerning beliefs about hypnosis to 669 college students; and London (1961) administered a similar questionnaire to 645 students. To the question, "Will people remember what took place under hypnosis?" 64 per cent of the first sample and 74 per cent of the second answered that they would not remember. Is "spontaneous hypnotic amnesia," as Weitzenhoffer (1953, p. 176) contends, "probably a natural concomitant of very deep hypnosis," or is it a function of subjects' beliefs that after having participated in a "hypnosis" experiment they should behave as if they do not remember what occurred? Studies are needed that will manipulate beliefs concerning "the amnesia of hypnosis" prior to the experimental sessions. For instance, if subjects are told in a pre-experimental lecture given by a prestigeful person that when amnesia is not specifically suggested, hypnotized persons always remember what occurred, the writer will venture to predict that "trance" subjects will manifest no more spontaneous amnesia than "waking" controls (see Barber, 1962b).

To many present-day experimental subjects the word "hypnosis" connotes a condition resembling sleep. This implication of the word may have biased the outcome of some experiments, such as those assessing the effects of suggestions to dream. When an experimental subject, who may or may not be in "trance," is given the suggestion to dream in a situation defined explicitly as "hypnosis" and implicitly as a situation involving a sleeplike state, he probably does not view the suggestions as odd or inappropriate. In contradistinction, when a control subject is told to dream, he may perceive the instructions as incongruous in the "waking" situation. Experiments that found that suggestions to dream were effective in producing "dream" reports under the "trance" treatment but not under the "waking" treatment (such as Klein, 1930), require replication with an additional control: the situation should be defined to the "waking" group as one in which it is not incongruous to dream. It may be possible to accomplish this by informing the control group that scientific studies with the electroencephalograph demonstrate that it is possible to dream without actually being asleep. Data presented in a recent review of research in this area (Barber, 1962c) suggest that if the situation is defined to both a "hypnotized" group and a "waking" group as one in which it is not odd to dream and if both groups are instructed to dream, the two groups will report similar "dreamlike" experiences and a comparable proportion of subjects in both groups will define their experiences as "dreams."

AN ILLUSTRATION: "HYPNOTIC HALLUCINATION"

To further underscore the importance of controlling the variables discussed in this chapter, let us briefly examine work concerned with the "hypnotic hallucination."

General treatises on hypnotism (Bernheim, 1886; Bramwell, 1903; Moll, 1889; Weitzenhoffer, 1953) assert or imply that visual and auditory "hallucinations" can be elicited by suggestions given to "hypnotized" subjects but are very difficult if not impossible to elicit in subjects who are not "hypnotized." This assertion appears to derive from unsystematic observations, not from rigorously controlled experimental studies (see Barber, 1963b). The following question is pertinent: Is a "hypnotized" group more responsive to suggestions to hallucinate than a control group when subject variables, instructional variables, interpersonal variables, and motivational variables are controlled? To answer this question, Barber and Calverley (1964a) proceeded as follows.

To control subject variables, Barber and Calverley worked with 78 volunteers from a homogeneous population of female secretarial students who had not participated in previous experimental studies. To control instructional variables, both the "hypnosis" group and the control groups were given the same instructions to hallucinate. To control motivational variables, both the "hypnosis" group and one of the control groups were given task-motivating instructions. Interpersonal variables were controlled to the extent that the experimenter was unacquainted with any of the subjects prior to the experimental sessions.

The subjects were first tested individually in the same way on direct instructions to hallucinate. This pretest had four parts: (1) Immediately after entering and being seated in the experimental room, the subject was informed that the experiment would begin at once and was told, firmly and seriously, to close her eyes and to hear a phonograph record playing "White Christmas." (2) After 30 seconds she was asked to open her eyes and to check a standardized rating scale with respect to the vividness and realism of the suggested auditory hallucination. (3) The subject was next instructed in a firm tone of voice to see a cat sitting on her lap and; finally, (4) she was asked to check a second rating scale with regard to the vividness and realism of the suggested visual hallucination.

In the same experimental session each subject was retested on equivalent hallucination instructions (to hear a record playing "Jingle Bells" and to see a dog sitting on her lap) after the administration of one of three experimental treatments with 26 subjects assigned at random to each treatment. Subjects allocated to Treatment 1 were given a standardized "hypnotic induction" for 15 minutes which included eye-fixation, suggestions of relaxation, drowsiness, and sleep, and suggestions to the effect that a high level of performance was expected on forthcoming tasks. Subjects assigned to Treatment 2 were given brief task-motivating instructions under "waking" conditions (such as "... everyone is able to do this... to see an animal sitting on their lap and to hear a phonograph record playing, if they really try.... This time I want you to really try to see and to hear the things I ask you to"). The remaining subjects, assigned to the control treatment, were retested on the hallucination suggestions without receiving either a "hypnotic induction" or task-motivating instructions. The results were:

1. On the pretest (base-level test), 54 per cent of the subjects stated that they "heard" the suggested sounds and 33 per cent testified that they "saw" the suggested object.

2. Analyses of covariance indicated that: (a) response to the hallucination instructions was facilitated by the administration of the "hypnotic induction" procedure and also by the administration of brief task-motivating instructions; (b) the group given the "hypnotic induction" and the group given task-motivating instructions did not differ significantly from each other in response to the hallucination instructions; and (c) both of these groups were significantly more responsive than the uninstructed control group.

The first finding—that one third to one half of the subjects responded positively on the pretest—indicates that, among volunteer female subjects, base-level response to direct instructions or suggestions to see and to hear objects and sounds that are not present may be higher than has been assumed. This finding raises an important question: To what extent are previous reports concerned with "hypnotic hallucinations" (such as Erickson *et al.*, 1961; Halpern, 1961) invalidated by failure to obtain base-level data from an independent control group? With few if any exceptions, prior investigators in this area failed to test a control group, apparently assuming that subjects in the "waking" state would not testify that they saw objects and heard sounds that were not present.

The second finding of this experiment indicates that when an attempt is made to control subject variables, instructional variables, interpersonal variables, and motivational variables, it is difficult to reject the null hypothesis of no difference in response to instructions to hallucinate in a "hypnotized" group and a "waking" group. This is in line with the results of a series of recent experiments (Barber and Calverley, 1962, 1963d, 1963e, 1963f, 1964a, 1964b, 1964c; Barber and Hahn, 1962; Barber and Parker, 1964), some of which were described earlier in this chapter, which found that a standardized "hypnotic induction" procedure was more effective than no instructions but not noticeably more effective than brief task-motivating instructions in facilitating response to suggestions of limb and body rigidity, analgesia to noxious stimulation, dreaming on a specified topic, amnesia, deafness, enhanced endurance, enhanced learning proficiency, and so on.

CONCLUSION

Further studies are needed that will control the following variables: (1) pre-existing differences among subjects in responsiveness to suggestions; (2) the wording of instructions and suggestions and the tone of voice in which suggestions are presented; (3) the relationship between subject and experimenter; (4) subjects' motivation to perform well on experimental tasks; and (5) the manner in which the situation is defined to the subject.

To control subject variables, it is recommended that "hypnosis" and "awake" groups be drawn at random either from subjects rated high on a suggestibility scale or from subjects not rated on suggestibility (see Sutcliffe, 1960). Both groups should participate in the same number of preliminary practice sessions. Both groups should be tested in the criterion situation by an experimenter with whom each group has had a comparable degree of previous acquaintance or by an experimenter with whom neither group is acquainted. Both groups should be motivated to perform well on the experimental tasks. The instructions or suggestions to perform the criterion behaviors should be given to both groups in the same words and in the same tone of voice. Because in the treatment sessions the experimental subjects will be informed that they are to be "hypnotized," their interest and curiosity may be aroused; the experiment should be defined to the control subjects in a manner that may also arouse their interest. We can hypothesize, from the data presented in this chapter, that when these variables are controlled, suggestions of analgesia, color blindness, dreaming, hallucinations, and so on, given to "hypnotized" subjects and to "awake" subjects will produce similar overt behaviors and similar reports of subjective experiences.

This hypothesis can be stated differently: Response to suggestions of analgesia, amnesia, hallucinations, and so on, is a function of such variables as the manner in which the situation is defined to the subject; the relationship between subject and experimenter; the subject's interest in the experiment and his attitude toward the test situation; the subject's motivation to perform well on assigned tasks (see Barber, 1964). Postulating a "hypnotic state" that gives rise to a high level of response to suggestions is misleading and unparsimonious. Although some subjects who respond to suggestions manifest characteristics that are supposed to signify the presence of "hypnotic trance," such as "...disinclination to talk... literal-mindedness... lack of spontaneity and initiative" (Pattie, 1956), these "trancelike" characteristics can be removed by instructing the subject not to show them; and if the subject has positive attitudes toward the experimenter and toward the test situation and is motivated to perform well on assigned tasks, he will continue to manifest a high level of response to suggestions. Further, it needs to be emphasized that: (1) Some subjects who have been given a "hypnotic induction" and who appear to be in "trance" do not respond to suggestions of analgesia, amnesia, hallucinations, and so on; and (2) some subjects who have not been given a "hypnotic induction" and who do not show characteristics that are presumed to signify the presence of "trance" respond to many or all suggestions.

Further research aiming to delineate the factors making for high response to suggestions should be careful not to confound the variable labeled as "trance" with such variables as instructions designed to produce positive motivation to perform well on assigned tasks and instructions or suggestions to perform the criterion behaviors. We can predict that when the variables discussed in this chapter are kept distinct and unconfounded, the variable labeled "hypnotic trance" will prove to be extraneous to producing "analgesia," "hallucinations," "amnesia," and so on.

This prediction is not as controversial as may at first appear. Many investigators pay only lip service to the "hypnotic state" or "trance" as a factor in producing enhanced response to suggestions. In fact, some investigators will state that by the term "hypnotic state" or "trance" they refer, not to the condition produced by a successful "hypnotic induction" and associated with passivity, disinclination to talk, lack of spontaneity and iniative, and so on, but to such variables as a close relationship between subject and experimenter and positive motivation on the part of the subject to respond to the best of his ability on assigned tasks. To these investigators, we can say that the term "hypnotic state" or "hypnotic trance" historically and traditionally has had many more connotations and denotations than they give it; and if by this term they refer to interpersonal and motivational variables, their statements would be more parsimonious and more within the scientific tradition if they dropped the concept of "hypnotic trance," which is loaded with surplus-meaning, and spoke in terms of the concrete empirical variables with which they are concerned. Other investigators seem to use the term "hypnotic state" or "trance" whenever a subject manifests a high level of response to test-suggestions irrespective of whether the subject has been given a procedure of the type traditionally labeled a "hypnotic induction" and irrespective of whether he shows any of the signs that have been traditionally presumed to signify the presence of "trance." When used in this manner the term "hypnotic trance" is synonymous with the term "high suggestibility." Again, since the term "hypnotic state" or "trance" has many more connotations and denotations than these investigators mean to give it, it would be more parsimonious and more scientific if they did not use the term but spoke simply of a high level of response to test-suggestions.

SUMMARY

Most of the data presented in general treatises on hypnotism derive from studies that did not include a control treatment. In the majority of instances, "hypnotized" subjects, but not "waking" subjects, were given suggestions of analgesia, deafness, hallucinations, amnesia, and so on. Although some of the "hypnotized" subjects manifested the suggested effects, it was not demonstrated that the "hypnotic state" was either necessary or helpful in their production. There is evidence to indicate that if "waking" control subjects had been given suggestions of analgesia, deafness, hallucinations, and so on, some of them may also have manifested the effects shown by the "hypnotized" subjects.

The relatively few experiments that included a "waking" control group are criticized as having failed to exercise sufficient control over important experimental variables. These variables are as follows: (a) In most experiments a single group of "good" hypnotic subjects was tested under both the "hypnosis" and the "awake" treatments. In some of these experiments it appears that the "good" hypnotic subjects, in striving to comply with what they correctly or incorrectly surmised were the expectations or wishes of the experimenter, deliberately gave their best performance under the "hypnosis" condition and deliberately gave an inferior performance under the "waking" condition. This factor was not controlled in other studies that used "good" hypnotic subjects "as their own controls." (b) In studies employing independent experimental and control groups, the "hypnosis"–"waking" comparisons were often biased by the following factors:

1. The experimental group, but not the control group, had participated in preliminary selection or training sessions in which it had received practice or experience in performing tasks that were similar to or identical with the criterion tasks.

2. The experimental group consisted of highly selected individuals who were judged to be "good" hypnotic subjects. In many instances the control group was selected from individuals who were rated as

"poor" subjects or from unrated subjects. The explicit criterion for selection of the experimental group—that the subjects were "hypnotizable"—appears difficult to differentiate from an interrelated implicit criterion, namely, that the subjects were the most willing or most motivated (irrespective of "hypnotic trance") to comply with the wishes of the experimenter or to try to carry out his instructions or suggestions.

3. A positive relationship between subject and experimenter was at times established in the preliminary practice or training sessions that were held with the experimental group but not with the control group. This relationship was strengthened during the treatment sessions when the "hypnosis" group received more of the experimenter's time and interest than the control group. Because the experimental group had interacted more extensively with the experimeter, and had possibly formed a closer relationship with him, it may have been more willing (with or without "hypnotic trance") to comply with his instructions or suggestions.

4. To the experimental group the situation was explicitly defined as "hypnosis" and explicitly or implicitly defined as an important and unusual situation in which interesting events were to be expected. In addition, special efforts were usually made to motivate the experimental group to perform well on the criterion tasks. In contrast, the situation was typically defined to the control group as an ordinary experimental situation and no effort was made to arouse interest or to motivate the subjects to perform maximally. Discrepancies in expectancies, interest, and motivation may have been sufficient to produce some of the observed differences in performance, independently of the presence or absence of "hypnotic trance."

It is concluded that:

1. Further studies are needed that will rigorously control the variables discussed in this chapter. When these variables are carefully controlled, researchers may find that "awake" subjects are as responsive to suggestions as "hypnotized" subjects.

2. Further studies are needed in which the variables discussed in this chapter will be varied systematically. When the effects of these variables have been systematically assayed, investigators may conclude that it is unnecessary and unparsimonious to postulate a "hypnotic trance state" to explain response to suggestions of analgesia, time distortion, color blindness, deafness, amnesia, hallucinations, and so on. Response to suggestions of this type may be found to be a function of the manner in which the situation is defined to the subject; the relationship between subject and experimenter; the subject's interest in the experiment and his attitude toward the immediate test situation; and the subject's motivation to perform well on assigned tasks.

REFERENCES

BARBER, T. X. (1958). " Hypnosis as perceptual-cognitive restructuring: IV. "Negative hallucinations," *J. Psychol.*, **46**, 187–201.

——— (1961a). "Antisocial and criminal acts induced by 'hypnosis': A review of experimental and clinical findings," *Arch. gen. Psychiat.*, **5**, 301–312.

——— (1961b). "Physiological effects of 'hypnosis,'" *Psychol. Bull.*, **58**, 390–419.

——— (1962a). "Hypnotic age regression: A critical review," *Psychosom. Med.*, **24**, 286–299.

——— (1962b). "Toward a theory of hypnosis: Posthypnotic behavior," *Arch. gen. Psychiat.*, **7**, 321–342.

——— (1962c). "Toward a theory of 'hypnotic' behavior: The 'hypnotically induced dream'," *J. nerv. ment. Dis.*, **135**, 206–221.

——— (1963a). "The effects of 'hypnosis' on pain: A critical review of experimental and clinical findings," *Psychosom. Med.*, **25**, 303–333.

——— (1963b). "Toward a theory of 'hypnotic' behavior: Positive visual and auditory hallucinations," Harding, Mass: Medfield Foundation (mimeo).

——— (1964). "Hypnotizability, suggestibility, and personality: V. A critical review of research findings," *Psychol. Rep.*, **14**, 299–320.

BARBER, T. X., and CALVERLY, D. S. (1962). " 'Hypnotic behavior' as a function of task motivation," *J. Psychol.*, **54**, 363–389.

——— (1963a). "Experimenter's tone of voice as a variable affecting 'hypnotic-like' suggestibility." Harding, Mass: Medfield Foundation.

——— (1963b). " 'Hypnotic-like' suggestibility in children and adults," *J. abnorm. soc. Psychol.*, **66**, 589-597.

——— (1963c). "Toward a theory of 'hypnotic' behavior: Effects on suggestibility of defining the situation as hypnosis and defining response to suggestions as easy." Harding, Mass: Medfield Foundation.

——— (1963d). " Toward a theory of hypnotic behavior: Effects on suggestibility of task motivating instructions and attitudes toward hypnosis," *J. abnorm. soc. Psychol.*, **67**, 557-565.

——— (1963e). "Toward a theory of 'hypnotic' behavior: Enhancement of strength and endurance," Harding, Mass: Medfield Foundation.

——— (1963f). "The relative effectiveness of task-motivating instructions and trance-induction procedure in the production of 'hypnotic-like' behaviors," *J. nerv. ment. Dis.* **137**,107–116.

——— (1964a). "An experimental study of 'hypnotic' (auditory and visual) hallucinations," *J. abnorm. soc. Psychol.*, **68**, 13–20.

——— (1964b). "Experimental studies of 'hypnotic' behavior: Suggested deafness evaluated by delayed auditory feedback," *Brit. J. Psychol.*, **55**, 439–446.

——— (1964c). "The comparative effects on 'hypnotic-like' suggestibility of recorded and spoken suggestions," *J. consult. Psychol.*, **28**, 384.

——— (1964d). "Toward a theory of 'hypnotic' behavior: An experimental study of 'hypnotic time distortion,'" *Arch. gen. Psychiat.*, **10**, 209-216.

BARBER, T. X., and DEELEY, D. C. (1961). "Experimental evidence for a theory of hypnotic behavior: I. 'Hypnotic color-blindness' without 'hypnosis'." *Int. J. clin. exp. Hyp.*, **9**, 79–86.

BARBER, T. X., and GLASS, L. B. (1962). "Significant factors in hypnotic behavior," *J. abnorm. soc. Psychol.*, **64**, 222–228.

BARBER, T. X., and HAHN, K. W., Jr. (1962). "Physiological and subjective responses to pain producing stimulation under hypnotically-suggested and waking-imagined 'analgesia'," *J. abnorm. soc. Psychol.*, **65**, 411–418.

BARBER, T. X., KARACAN, I., and CALVERLY, D. S. (1964). "'Hypnotizability' and suggestibility in chronic schizophrenics," *Arch. gen. Psychiat.*, **11**, 439–451.

BENJAMIN, F. B. (1958). "Effect of aspirin on suprathreshold pain in man." *Science*, **128**, 303–304.

BERNHEIM, H. (1886). *Suggestive Therapeutics.* Westport, Conn.: Associated Booksellers (Republished 1957).

BLACK, J. W. (1951). "The effect of delayed side-tone upon vocal rate and intensity," *J. speech hear. Disord.*, **16**, 56–60.

BLOCH, B. (1927). "Ueber die Heilung der Warzen durch Suggestion" *Klin. Wschr.*, **6**, 2271–2275, 2320–2325.

BONJOUR, J. (1929). "Influence of the mind on the skin," *Brit. J. Dermatol.*, **41**, 324–326.

BRAMWELL, J. M. (1903). *Hypnotism: Its History, Practice, and Theory.* New York: Julian (Republished, 1956).

BRAVIN, M. (1959). *Role-play and Direct Suggestion in Hypnotically Induced Color Blindness.* Unpublished doctoral dissertation, University of Denver.

BROWN, R. R., and VOGEL, V. H. (1938). "Psychophysiological reactions following painful stimuli under hypnotic analgesia contrasted with gas anæsthesia and novocain block," *J. appl. Psychol.*, **22**, 408–420.

BUTLER, B. (1954). "The use of hypnosis in the care of the cancer patient," *Cancer*, **7**, 1–14.

CHAPMAN, L. F., GOODELL, H., and WOLFF, H. G. (1959). "Increased inflammatory reaction induced by central nervous system activity," *Trans. Ass. Amer. Physicians*, **72**, 84–109.

CHASE, R. A., SUTTON, S., and FIRST, D. (1959). "Bibliography: Delayed auditory feedback," *J. speech hear. Disord.*, **24**, 193–200.

CHLIFER, R. I. (1930). "Verbal analgesia in childbirth," *Psychotherapia*, Kharkov, 307–318. Quoted in Chertok, L. (1959). *Psychosomatic Methods in Painless Childbirth.* New York: Pergamon.

COOPER, L. F., and ERICKSON, M. H. (1954). *Time Distortion in Hypnosis.* Baltimore: Williams & Wilkins.

DORCUS, R. M., BRINTNALL, A. K., and CASE, H. W. (1941). "Control experiments and their relations to theories of hypnotism," *J. gen. Psychol.*, **24**, 217–221.

DOUPE, J., MILLER, W. R., and KELLER, W. K. (1939). "Vasomotor reactions in the hypnotic state," *J. Neurol. Psychiat.*, **2**, 97–102.

DYNES, J. B. (1932). "An experimental study of hypnotic anesthesia," *J. abnorm. soc. Psychol.*, **27**, 79–88.

EDWARDS, A. L. (1960). *Experimental Design in Psychological Research.* Revised Ed. New York: Rinehart.

ERICKSON, M. H. (1938a). "A study of clinical and experimental findings on hypnotic deafness: I. Clinical experimentation and findings," *J. gen. Psychol.*, **19**, 127–150.

——— (1938b). "A study of clinical and experimental findings on hypnotic deafness: II. Experimental findings with a conditioned response technique." *J. gen. Psychol.*, **19**, 151–167.

——— (1939). "The induction of color blindness by a technique of hypnotic suggestion," *J. gen. Psychol.*, **20**, 61–89.

ERICKSON, M. H., HERSHMAN, S., and SECTER. I. I. (1961). *The practical Applications of Medical Dental Hypnosis.* New York: Julian.

ESTABROOKS, G. H. (1943). *Hypnotism.* New York: Dutton.

FAVILL, J., and WHITE, P. D. (1917). "Voluntary acceleration of the rate of the heart beat," *Heart*, **6**, 175–188.

FISHER, S. (1955). "An investigation of alleged conditioning phenomena under hypnosis," *J. clin. exp. Hyp.*, **3**, 71–103.

FRIEDLANDER, J. W., and SARBIN, T. R. (1938). "The depth of hypnosis," *J. abnorm. soc. Psychol.*, **33**, 453–475.

GIDRO-FRANK, L., and BOWERSBUCH, M. K. (1948). "A study of the plantar response in hypnotic age regression," *J. nerv. ment. Dis.*, **107**, 443–458.

GILL, M. M., and BRENMAN, M. (1961). *Hypnosis and Related States.* New York: International Universities Press.

GLASS, L. B., and BARBER, T. X. (1961). "A note on hypnotic behavior, the definition of the situation and the placebo effect," *J. nerv. ment. Dis.*, **132**, 539–541.

GRUMACH, L. (1927). "*Ueber Suggestivbehandlung von Warzen.*" *Münch. med. Wschr.*, **74**, 1093–1094.

HALPERN, S. (1961). "On the similarity between hypnotic and mescaline hallucinations," *Int. J. clin. exp. Hyp.*, **9**, 139–149.

HAMMER, E. F. (1951). *The Effects of Post-hypnotic Suggestion on Some Aspects of Learning Performance and Certain Other Intellectual and Psychomotor Tasks.* Unpublished doctoral dissertation. New York University.

——— (1954). "Post-hypnotic suggestion and test performance," *J. clin. exp. Hyp.*, **2**, 178–185.

HEYER, G. R. (1925). "*Psychogene Functionsstörungen des Verdauungstraktes.*" In O. Schwarz (Ed.) *Psychogenese und Psychotherapie Körperlicher Symptome*, Wien: Springer. pp. 229–257.

HULL, C. L. (1933). *Hypnosis and Suggestibility: An Experimental Approach.* New York: Appleton-Century-Crofts.

IKAI, M., and STEINHAUS, A. H. (1961). "Some factors modifying the expression of human strength," *J. appl. Physiol.*, **16**, 157–163.

IKEMI, Y., AKAGI, M., MAEDA, J., FUKUMOTO, T., KAWATE, K., HIRAKAWA, K., GONDO, S., NAKAGAWA, T., HONDA, T., SAKAMOTO, A., and KUMAGAI, M. (1959). "Hypnotic experiments on the psychosomatic aspects of gastro-intestinal disorders," *Int. J. clin. exp. Hyp.*, **7**, 139–150.

KING, J. T., Jr. (1920). "An instance of voluntary acceleration of the pulse," *Bull. Johns Hopkins Hosp.*, **31**, 303–304.

Klein, D. B. (1930). "The experimental production of dreams during hypnosis," *Univ. Texas Bull.*, No. 3009, 5–71.

Kline, M. V. (1958). "The dynamics of hypnotically induced anti-social behavior," *J. Psychol.*, **45**, 239–245.

Kline, M. V., and Guze, H. (1951). "The use of a drawing technique in the investigation of hypnotic age regression and progression," *Brit. J. med. Hyp.*, **3**, 1–12.

Kline, M. V., Guze, H., and Haggerty, A. D. (1954). "An experimental study of the nature of hypnotic deafness: Effects of delayed speech feedback," *J. clin. exp. Hyp.*, **2**, 145–156.

Koehler, M. (1914). "*Ueber die willkürliche Beschleunigung des Herzschlages beim Menschen.*" *Arch. ges. Physiol.*, **158**, 579–622.

Kunkle, E. C. (1949). "Phasic pains induced by cold," *J. appl. Physiol.*, **1**, 811–824.

Lacey, J. I. (1956). "The evaluation of autonomic responses: Toward a general solution," *Ann. N. Y. Acad. Sci.*, **67**, 123–164.

Lea, P. A., Ware, P. D., and Monroe, R. R. (1960). "The hypnotic control of intractable pain," *Amer. J. clin. Hyp.*, **3**, 3–8.

Lee, B. S. (1950). "Effects of delayed speech feedback," *J. acoust. Soc. Amer.*, **22**, 824–826.

Lindquist, E. F. (1953). *Design and Analysis of Experiments in Psychology and Education.* Boston: Houghton Mifflin.

London, P. (1961). "Subject characteristics in hypnosis research. I. A survey of experience, interest, and opinion," *Int. J. clin. exp. Hyp.*, **9**, 151–161.

London, P., and Fuhrer, M. (1961). "Hypnosis, motivation, and performance," *J. Pers.*, **29**, 321–333.

Luckhardt, A. B., and Johnston, R. L. (1924). "Studies in gastric secretions: I. The psychic secretion of gastric juice under hypnosis," *Amer. J. Physiol.*, **70**, 174–182.

Malmo, R. B., Boag, T. J., and Raginsky, B. B. (1954). "Electromyographic study of hypnotic deafness," *J. clin. exp. Hyp.*, **2**, 305–317.

Marcuse, F. L. (1959). *Hypnosis: Fact and Fiction.* Baltimore: Penguin Books.

Marmer, M. J. (1959). *Hypnosis in Anesthesiology.* Springfield, Ill.: C. C. Thomas.

McMurray, G. A. (1950). "Experimental study of a case of insensitivity to pain," *Arch. Neurol. Psychiat.*, **64**, 650–677.

McNemar, Q. (1955). *Psychological Statistics.* Second Ed. New York: Wiley.

Memmescheimer, A. M., and Eisenlohr, E. (1931). "*Untersuchungen über die Suggestivebehandlung der Warzen,*" *Dermatol. Z.*, **62**, 63–68.

Moll, A. (1889). *Hypnotism.* London: Scott.

Orne, M. T. (1959). "The nature of hypnosis: Artifact and essence," *J. abnorm. soc. Psychol.*, **58**, 277–299.

Parker, P. D., and Barber, T. X. (1964). "'Hypnosis,' task motivating instructions, and learning performance," *J. abnorm. soc. Psychol.*, **69**, 499–504.

Pattie, F. A. (1935). "A report on attempts to produce uniocular blindness by hypnotic suggestions," *Brit. J. med. Psychol.*, **15**, 230–241.

PATTIE, F. A. (1956). "Methods of induction, susceptibility of subjects, and criteria of hypnosis." In Dorcus, R. M. (Ed.) *Hypnosis and Its Therapeutic Applications*. New York: McGraw-Hill.

PEASE, E. A. (1889). "Voluntary control of the heart," *Boston med. surg. J.*, **120**, 525–529.

RAY, W. S. (1960). *An Introduction to Experimental Design*. New York: Macmillan.

ROCK, N. L., and SHIPLEY, T., Jr. (1961). "Ability to 'fake' color blindness in the waking state: A control for suggested color blindness under hypnosis," Philadelphia: Dept. of Psychiatry, Temple University.

ROUSH, E. S. (1951). "Strength and endurance in the waking and hypnotic state," *J. appl. Physiol.*, **3**, 404–410.

ROWLAND, L. W. (1939). "Will hypnotized persons try to harm themselves or others?" *J. abnorm. soc. Psychol.*, **34**, 114–117.

SALZBERG, H. C. (1960a). *An Experimental Investigation of the Differential Effects of Hypnotic, Post-Hypnotic and Waking Suggestion on Learning, with Tasks Varied in Complexity*. Unpublished doctoral dissertation, University of Tennessee.

——— (1960b). "The effects of hypnotic, post-hypnotic and waking suggestion on performance using tasks varied in complexity," *Int. J. clin. exp. Hyp.*, **8**, 251–258.

VON SCHRENCK-NOTZING, A. F. (1896). "*Ein experimenteller und kritischer Beitrag zur Frage des suggestiven Hervorrufung circumscripter vasomotorischer Veränderungen auf der äusseren Haut.*," *Z. Hypn.*, **4**, 209.

SEARS, A. B. (1955). "A comparison of hypnotic and waking learning of the International Morse Code," *J. clin. exp. Hyp.*, **3**, 215–221.

SEARS, R. R. (1932). "An experimental study of hypnotic anesthesia," *J. exp. Psychol.*, **15**, 1–22.

SINCLAIR-GIEBEN, A. H. C., and CHALMERS, D. (1959). "Evaluation of treatment of warts by hypnosis," *Lancet*, **2**, 480–482.

SULZBERGER, M. B., and WOLF, J. (1934). "The treatment of warts by suggestion," *Med. Rec.*, **140**, 552–557.

SUTCLIFFE, J. P. (1960). "'Credulous' and 'skeptical' views of hypnotic phenomena: A review of certain evidence and methodology," *Int. J. clin. exp. Hyp.*, **8**, 73–101.

——— (1961). "'Credulous' and 'skeptical' views of hypnotic phenomena: Experiments in esthesia, hallucination, and delusion," *J. abnorm. soc. Psychol.*, **62**, 189–200.

TAYLOR, N. B., and CAMERON, H. G. (1922). "Voluntary acceleration of the heart," *Amer. J. Physiol.*, **61**, 385–398.

ULLMAN, M., and DUDEK, S. (1960). "On the psyche and warts: II. Hypnotic suggestion and warts," *Psychosom. Med.*, **22**, 68–76.

VAN DE VELDE, T. H. (1897). "*Ueber willkürliche Vermehrung der Pulsfrequenz beim Menschen*," *Arch. ges. Physiol.*, **66**, 232–240.

VAN PELT, S. J. (1954). "The control of heart rate by hypnotic suggestion." In LECRON, L. M. (Ed.) *Experimental Hypnosis*, New York: Macmillan, pp. 268–276.

VOLLMER, H. (1946). "Treatment of warts by suggestion," *Psychosom. Med.*, **8**, 138–142.

WEITZENHOFFER, A. M. (1953). *Hypnotism: An Objective Study in Suggestibility.* New York: Wiley.

——— (1955). "The induction of hypnosis: History and methodology." In KLINE, M. V. (Ed.), *Hypnodynamic Psychology.* New York: Julian.

——— (1957). *General Techniques of Hypnotism.* New York: Grune & Stratton.

WEITZENHOFFER, A. M., and HILGARD, E. R. (1959). *Stanford Hypnotic Susceptibility Scale.* Palo Alto: Consulting Psychologists Press.

WEITZENHOFFER, A. M., and SJOBERG, B. M., Jr. (1961). "Suggestibility with and without 'induction of hypnosis'." *J. nerv. ment. Dis.*, **132**, 204–220.

WELLS, W. R. (1947). "Expectancy versus performance in hypnosis," *J. gen. Psychol.*, **35**, 99–119.

WEST, L. J., NIELL, K. C., and HARDY, J. D. (1952). "Effects of hypnotic suggestions on pain perception and galvanic skin response," *Arch. neurol. Psychiat.*, **68**, 549–560.

WINER, B. J. (1962). *Statistical Principles in Experimental Design.* New York: McGraw-Hill.

WINKELSTEIN, L. B. (1958). "Routine hypnosis for obstetrical delivery: An evaluation of hypnosuggestion in 200 consecutive cases," *Amer. J. obstet. Gynec.*, **76**, 152–160.

WOLBERG, L. R. (1948). *Medical Hypnosis.* Vol. 1: *The Principles of Hypnotherapy.* New York: Grune & Stratton.

WOLF, S., and HARDY, J. D. (1941). "Studies on pain: Observations on pain due to local cooling and on factors involved in the 'cold pressor' response," *J. clin. Invest.*, **20**, 521–533.

WOLF, S., and WOLFF, H. G. (1947). *Human Gastric Function: An Experimental Study of a Man and His Stomach.* Second Ed. New York: Oxford University Press.

YATES, A. J. (1963). "Delayed auditory feedback," *Psychol. Bull.*, **60**, 213–232.

They are ill discoverers that think there is no land, when they can see nothing but sea.

Francis Bacon, *Advancement of Learning*, II:VII, 5.

15

On the Social Psychology of Hypnosis Research

DAVID ROSENHAN[1]

Educational Testing Service

THE social psychology of hypnosis research comprises a vast domain of extra-experimental influences that are not unique to hypnosis and that derive from many sources. They derive from the very fact that one is conducting an experiment, with all that that implies. They derive from the attitudes and expectancies held by the experimenter and the subject, from the implicit and explicit cues that are emitted and responded to by each. They derive from the personal properties of subjects and experimenters: their personalities, their motivations, and possibly even their physical characteristics. And, of course, they derive from the traditional sources of sample bias. Much of this terrain is yet unexplored, for hypnosis as for other kinds of research. Thus, our discussion of the

[1] This paper owes much to friends and colleagues, particularly to conversations with G. S. Blum, E. R. Hilgard, S. Messick, and M. T. Orne. Their interest in the problems may be taken for granted, though not, of course, their sympathy with the arguments. J. E. Gordon, R. E. Shor, and S. S. Tomkins carefully reviewed a draft of the manuscript and offered many helpful comments. Finally, the energetic assistance of Sydell Carlton in assembling the materials cannot be be acknowledged too deeply, and the final manuscript benefited greatly from her concrete and kindly criticisms.

social psychology of the hypnosis experiment must be more often speculative than empirical, more often suggestive than definitive.

This chapter is addressed to the following issues: If hypnosis exists, how shall we know it? How shall we isolate those behaviors that uniquely accompany hypnosis from those that may be otherwise induced? And what precautions can be taken to ensure that behaviors that are termed "hypnotic" are truly so and not merely by-products of other determinants? We will consider the possibility that subjects' motivations and behaviors in hypnosis are similar to their motivations and behaviors in the waking state; this would make it difficult to elicit performances that are clearly a function of hypnosis. We will also investigate the role of the hypnotist: his properties, particularly his experience, biases, and motivations. And finally, we will examine the nature of the population that volunteers for hypnosis experiments: its attitudes, its expectancies, and the ways in which it differs from the population that fails to volunteer for these experiments. In short, we will be investigating the ambience into which the hypnosis experiment is placed.

Because the hypnosis literature is large, we will limit ourselves to recent studies, primarily to experimental rather than clinical reports. This limitation has been imposed because of the need to set some boundaries for this chapter and because the relatively recent literature exhibits refinements in technique and controls that were not often present in earlier studies.

HYPNOSIS AND EXPERIMENT-ELICITED BEHAVIOR

One source of difficulty in understanding the nature of hypnosis is that the pursuit of such understanding must take place within the context of an experiment. Experiments, however, are themselves artificial situations that evoke in subjects dramatic behaviors that those subjects might not ordinarily display. An experiment has a "back-action effect" on subjects' behavior that reaches beyond the effects of the particular experimental procedure. The matter reduces to one of separating experiment-elicited behavior from hypnotic behavior.

The tacit assumption that commonly guides an experimenter in his relations with a subject is that the latter is, for purposes of the experiment, a passive organism, wholly within the control of the experimenter's manipulations. The experiment itself determines the subject's behavior. Whenever the needs of the experiment dictate that the subject be ignorant of the hypotheses or of the reinforcement contingencies, the subject is assumed to be ignorant; subsequent postexperimental inquiry, deriving as it does from such an assumption, tends most often to bolster rather than to question this assumption.

From the subject's point of view, the matter is quite different. The contemporary status of research is such that performance for Science appears to elicit from subjects the same attitudes and energies that performance for God and for Country once aroused. This "Giving for Science" is evident at several interrelated levels. At the *behavioral* level, the subject manifests extensive obedience. At the *motivational* level, he has the heightened desire to perform and to please, along with a degree of trust invested in the experimenter that is rarely invested in a stranger. Finally, there are *cognitive* components to this "giving" that manifest themselves in a muted but sensitive awareness of what is going on and, more especially, of which behaviors are desirable in terms of the hypotheses of the experiment. These behavioral, motivational, and cognitive manifestations are in part derived from what Orne (1959) has called the "demand characteristics of an experiment."

It is important to note that the same variables that seem to underlie performance in any psychological experiment are precisely those that are viewed as underlying hypnosis. *Obedience*, for example, has been widely viewed as a concomitant of hypnosis (Hull, 1933; Janet, 1920; McDougall, 1926; White, 1941; Wolberg, 1948). Both White (1941) and Sarbin (1950) have described hypnosis in terms of the subject's "heightened motivation" to perform and to please the hypnotist. And although "muted awareness" is not a term that has been traditionally associated with hypnosis theory, it bears more than a casual resemblance to the concept of "altered state of consciousness," which, as a description of hypnosis, is much in favor in current theory (White, 1941; Orne, 1959; Shor, 1959a, 1962b; Sutcliffe, 1960, 1961).

Obedience

It is evident that an experiment often elicits from a subject behavior that in other settings would be regarded as aberrant. Two examples will suffice. Orne (1962b) attempted to develop a series of psychologically noxious, meaningless, or boring tasks that subjects either would refuse to perform or would perform for only a short time. Each subject was given sheets of random numbers and asked to add serially each adjacent pair of numbers. After he finished the additions on each page, the subject was instructed to pick up a card that told him to tear up the sheet of paper he had just finished into a minimum of 32 pieces, to go on to the next sheet, and, when it was finished, to pick another card. All cards had the same instructions—to tear up the work that had just been completed. After departing with the comment that he would return "eventually," the experimenter waited to see how long the subjects would persist. Quite to Orne's surprise, subjects stayed with the task for several hours with relatively few signs of overt hostility. When asked about their performance, subjects tended to attribute considerable meaning to the task, viewing it as a test of endurance or the like.

Milgram (1965) reports a series of experiments that again demonstrate the degree to which subjects will obey an experimenter. Performing as teachers who were to train "students" to errorless performance, the subjects were instructed to administer to their students increasing amounts of quite painful electric shock, up to a maximum of 450 volts. Milgram's subjects protested vigorously throughout. Some evidenced serious psychological disintegration. Yet the majority continued to shock their subjects right up to the limit merely because the experimenter had told them to continue the experiment. Despite their overt and substantial distress at having to persist, none of the subjects terminated the experiment before they had administered 300 volts.

Antisocial Behavior

The most dramatic instances of obedience in hypnosis are found in the reports of hypnotically induced antisocial behavior. We shall not deal here with the rather large literature in this area because several reviews have recently been published (Barber, 1961a; Orne, 1962a; Young, 1958). A discussion of just a few critical instances will serve to illustrate the issues at hand.

Among the most famous of the clinical instances is the Heidelberg case (Mayer, 1937), in which a young lady was induced to give large amounts of money to her hypnotist, to engage in sexual relations with him and with his friends, and to make several attempts on her own life and on her husband's life. Reiter (1958) reports on a subject who was induced to rob a bank by a hypnotist and who was apprehended only after he had killed two men. In another case described by Reiter (1958), a schoolteacher was induced to shoot himself in the arm, among other criminal acts.

These instances are often cited to indicate the degree to which hypnosis can extend behavior beyond the ordinary limits. One can, of course, ask whether these same obedient behaviors could not have been produced in the waking state and in other contexts. Each of them appears to have derived from a long-standing relationship between the hypnotist and his subject, which might alone have evoked the behavior. Furthermore, there is evidence that many of the subjects were in one way or another psychologically disturbed; this too might alone account for the behavior. These alternative interpretations have constituted the core of the objections to relying seriously on the clinical literature. They point to the possibility that extreme obedience is not unique to the hypnotic state (nor, in these instances, to behavior during experiments). Compliance is widespread, and its appearance in the context of hypnosis may merely be another instance of its ubiquity.

The experimental literature also provides striking instances of obedience during the hypnotic state. Here too, however, the studies do not commonly address the question of whether such behavior could be otherwise obtained. Consider the following experiment by Young (1958), one that is similar to those performed by Rowland (1939) and by Lyon (1954). Young asked eight somnambulistic subjects to throw nitric acid at a research assistant and to handle an apparently poisonous snake. Half of his subjects were separated from the assistant by an invisible glass partition; half were not. And half of the subjects were told that the snake was dangerous; whereas half were informed that it was quite harmless. Neither partition nor instructions appeared to make a difference. Seven of his eight subjects willingly reached for the snake and threw the acid. The same subjects, when serving as their own waking controls, however, refused to engage in either behavior. Furthermore, Rowland (1939) reports that his unhypnotized colleagues who saw the apparatus were also quite unwilling to touch the snake. Both Young and Rowland ascribe the greater willingness of experimental subjects to engage in dangerous behavior to the fact that they had been hypnotized.

Orne and Evans (1963) have recently undertaken a careful replication of Young's and Rowland's experiments. Subjects were hypnotized and then told that they had an irresistible urge to carry out all the suggestions given to them. They were then asked to pick up a number of innocuous objects and a harmless lizard and snake. Following this, they were asked to handle an extremely venomous snake, to remove a penny from a powerful nitric acid solution, and to throw the acid in an assistant's face. Five of six deeply hypnotizable subjects carried out all the suggested activities; because the sixth became disturbed at the sight of the harmless lizard, further tests were not conducted with her. Serving as their own controls in the waking state, only two subjects were willing to pick up the snake and to throw the acid, and only one attempted to remove the coin from the acid. Moreover, in the waking state these subjects were more hesitant than they had been while hypnotized. Thus, Young's findings (and Rowland's) were, by and large, replicated.

Orne and Evans (1965), however, are skeptical of the interpretation that is commonly given to such experimental demonstrations: that it is hypnosis that brings about the antisocial behavior. They raise the "fundamental question [of] whether the apparently antisocial behavior elicited under hypnosis *exceeded* behavior which is legitimized by the experimental situation per se. It is still necessary to examine whether the apparently antisocial and self-injurious acts exceed the limits of social and behavioral control which implicitly exist in the experimental situation. It is only if behavior lies outside the range of social control legitimized by the experimental situation, qua situation, that the production of the antisocial behavior can be attributed to the experimental variable, in this case hypnosis" (p. 191).

To examine this issue, Orne and Evans used three additional control groups. First, a group of unhypnotizable subjects was asked to simulate hypnosis, that is, to attempt to fool the hypnotist by pretending to be deeply hypnotized. The hypnotist was unable to distinguish between really hypnotized subjects and simulating subjects. And although there were some qualitative differences between the simulators and the "reals" in the experimental situations, no differences were evident in their tendencies to carry out the antisocial behavior. A second group was told that it was a control group in a study employing normal and simulating subjects. Here too, five of the six subjects attempted to carry out the two tasks involving acid; and although two of them refused to handle the poisonous snake, the performance of this group as a whole was only slightly inferior to that of the simulators. Thus, it was clear that simulating subjects were not necessary to demonstrate the point of this study. Normal, waking controls, treated in all other ways like the hypnotized and simulating groups, willingly engaged in these apparently dangerous tasks. Finally, a number of subjects, colleagues of the experimenters, were informally asked to carry out the experimental tasks. They uniformly refused and remained unresponsive to pressure and persuasion. These subjects did not perceive themselves as participants in a formal experiment, nor did they experience the experimenter-subject relationship that is peculiar to all psychological experiments. Hence, they did not obey.

Thus, we find that each group of subjects performed as it might have been expected to perform on the basis of the demand characteristics associated with its task and status. As long as waking subjects (simulators and simple controls) felt that they were part of a scientific endeavor, their trust in the experimenter permitted them to engage in the apparently dangerous tasks, presumably because they felt that the experimenter in some way protected them from the apparent consequences of their behavior. Informal control subjects, however (such as colleagues of the experimenter), experienced no such trust. They were dealing with the experimenter outside of the formal context of Science, where no guarantees for their safety were implicit. Finally, hypnotic subjects serving as their own controls presumably obeyed a different set of cognitions. They may have understood that the performance expected of them in the waking state was different from that expected in hypnosis. If hypnosis connotes a capacity to transcend normal waking powers, then the demand characteristics implied for the waking state require the comparatively inferior performance that they gave.

In general, then, these experiments demonstrate that obedience to the demand characteristics implied in an experiment may be a pervasive aspect of all psychological experiments. Hypnosis does not appear to add markedly different ingredients to obedience behavior, and thus it is difficult at this level to distinguish the effects of hypnosis from those of ordinary experiment-elicited behavior. For precisely this reason, Orne and Evans suggest that it may not be possible to examine the effects of hypnosis on antisocial behavior in an experimental setting.

Muted and Sensitive Awareness

The term "muted awareness" designates the phenomenon whereby subjects in many experiments sense what is expected of them, sense also that they are not supposed to have this awareness, and behave accordingly. Thus, on brief or unsophisticated inquiry, subjects will often deny that they have "intuited" the main hypotheses of the experiment or that they have understood the purpose of the experimental manipulations. This denial satisfies their need to be "good" subjects and at the same time satisfies the experimenter that he has concealed his biases. Thus, a pact of naïveté is established (Orne [1962b] terms it a pact of ignorance), with both parties sufficiently invested to play their roles well and to retain their secrets.

This issue was recently explored in a symposium on behavior without awareness (Eriksen, 1962). The evidence seemed to indicate that such phenomena as the Greenspoon effect, wherein verbal behavior was presumably altered even though subjects were apparently unaware of the reinforcement contingencies, could be accounted for by such pacts of naïveté. Rosenthal, Persinger, Vikan-Kline, and Fode (1963) have recently shown that certain kinds of interviews are more successful than others in eliciting the degree to which subjects are aware of the experimental contingencies. Indeed, experimenters have for a long time been mutedly aware that although their subjects insist that they understand nothing of an experiment, somehow the precise contents of the experiment gets around to other potential subjects!

These matters are relevant to the social psychology of hypnosis experiments for several reasons. In the first place, they imply that subjects will be alert to cues that can direct their behavior and verbalizations. Moreover, it is unlikely that subjects will report these cues during the postexperimental interview, because such disclosure would destroy the pact of naïveté. Finally, just as hypnotic subjects will be sensitive to information that can direct their performance, so too will control subjects look for cues that can direct theirs.

This last issue has not been given sufficient attention in the recent experimental literature on hypnosis. Consider the following possibility. Many recent reports, particularly those that compare the performances of simulating and real subjects, have noted that the outstanding feature of hypnosis appears to reside in subjective experience. Sutcliffe (1961), for example, locates the distinguishing feature of hypnosis in "the subject's emotional conviction that the world is as suggested by the hypnotist." Orne (1959) has coined the term "trance logic" to describe the ability of the hypnotic subject to "mix freely his perceptions derived from reality with those which stem from his imagination and are perceived as hallucinations. These perceptions are fused in a manner that ignores everyday logic." The "observations" of the cognitive operations of hypnotic subjects have been made through a comparison of the behavior and verbalizations of these subjects with those of simulators. Yet the simulators have been told only to "behave" as though they were hypnotized. No set has presumably been given to them to "think" as though they were hypnotized. It is not altogether unlikely that were such cognitive sets given to simulators, their cognitive behavior would be quite similar to that of the hypnotized subjects. Indeed, because knowledge of the way a hypnotized person thinks is as much a part of the folklore as knowledge of the ways he acts, there is no reason to believe that trance logic could not be elicited on demand from a simulator.

In the absence of substantive experimental data, the issue of whether there are unique subjective experiences associated with hypnosis remains conjectural. Considerably more work needs to be done on the problems of awareness, both in hypnotic and in other psychological research, before one can conclude that certain kinds of awareness are or are not differentially present in hypnosis. For the moment, though, let us note that the muted awareness that is found in many areas of psychological research may have its analogue in "trance logic" (Orne, 1959), "dissociated consciousness" (Janet, 1920; Prince, 1916), and altered or "dissociated awareness" (Weitzenhoffer, 1953). Separating the limited awareness that accompanies a person's experience in many psychological experiments from the particular brand that accompanies hypnotic experiences is a matter for future research.

Heightened Motivation

Several theories view heightened motivation as the distinguishing component of hypnosis (McDougall, 1926; Sarbin, 1950; White, 1941). White (1941), for example, has argued that the phenomena of hypnosis result from the subject's motivation to behave like a hypnotized person as defined by the hypnotist and understood by the subject. Orne (1959) has demonstrated the degree to which the desire to behave like a hypnotized person influences hypnotic performance. In his study, subjects who had seen catalepsy of the dominant hand occur as part of a hypnosis demonstration subsequently exhibited the same phenomenon themselves, even though such a phenomenon never occurs spontaneously.

In hypnosis literature, the motivation to comply is nowhere clearer than in Pattie's attempt to produce uniocular blindness by hypnotic suggestion (1935). Pattie used five somnambulist subjects, the first four of whom were rapidly disqualified on the basis of their performance on tests of binocular rivalry and visual acuity. The fifth "was so clever at malingering that for several months I believed that the phenomena in her case were not simulated" (p. 231). This subject produced apparently genuine blindness on the stereoscope, on several tests of perimetry, in red and green filter experiments, on image reversal and the plotting of blind spot, and in actual ophthalmological examination. The fact that she reported unimpaired light perception strengthened the impression that her blindness was real, for otherwise she would have "lied" about this aspect of vision as well as about her acuity. Only a quite complicated filter test determined that the subject was indeed not blind. Pattie then persuaded her to reveal to some extent the methods she had used to "malinger." These included rapid and brief eye movements in the stereoscope to separate the images momentarily, practicing the "blind spot" at home with the help of a friend to simulate it in the test, the clever and sensitive use of her extensive knowledge of vision mechanics, and considerable alertness to the limitations of the apparatus. Thus, in the image reversal test, for example, she was able to detect that mirrors were being used and she responded accordingly.

Pattie (1935) refers to this behavior as "malingering," whereas it might equally well be interpreted as an instance of heightened motivation, one that led the subject to employ all her resources to behave as she thought she was expected to behave by the experimenter. Other studies support this view. Fisher (1954), for example, found that subjects exhibited posthypnotically suggested ear-scratching only when they believed that the experiment was still in progress. Subjects who were led to believe that the experiment was over failed to exhibit the suggested behavior. In both instances, subjects behaved as they thought they were expected to behave.

Without exception, the well-controlled experimental evidence reveals no difference between the performance of hypnotized subjects and either their own or others' waking motivated performance. In his replication of the Ashley, Harper, and Runyon (1951) study, in which subjects were hypnotized and "inoculated" with either rich or poor life histories and then asked to perform a coin size-estimation task, Orne (1959) employed simulating subjects as controls. These subjects were simply told to *act* as if they were rich or poor, and their performance on the size-estimation task was compared with that of hypnotized subjects. No performance differences were found.

Orne (1959) hypnotized nine subjects and compared their ability to hold a kilogram weight aloft with their performance during a motivated waking state. Waking performance *exceeded* hypnotic performance. As noted above, Orne and Evans (1965), found that simulating subjects and even nonsimulating, nonhypnotized controls were willing to engage in the same antisocial behavior as hypnotized subjects.

In experiments on esthesia and hallucination, Sutcliffe (1961) was unable to find differences between hypnotic and waking performance. Barber and Hahn (1962), in comparing subjects who had been asked to imagine analgesia with those who had been suggested analgesia under hypnosis, found no differences in responsiveness to pain stimulation. In another study Barber and Hahn (1963) found that hypnosis was no more effective in inducing relaxation (as measured by muscle action potentials, respiration, heart rate, and skin potential) than simple instructions to relax. Subjects who were given a placebo and told that it was a powerful hypnotic drug performed neither better nor worse on the Barber Suggestibility Scale than they had with trance induction (Glass and Barber, 1961). Shor (1962a) examined the responses of real and simulating hypnotic subjects to painful stimulation. Under conditions designed to minimize anxiety, the characteristically heightened physiological responsiveness to such stimulation failed to occur. Thus, neither hypnosis nor simulation contributed additionally to this diminished sensitivity. London and Fuhrer (1961) studied the physical performance of relatively good and poor hypnotic subjects, all of whom were exposed to hypnosis, nonhypnotic exhortation to perform, and hypnosis plus exhortation. Hypnosis had considerably less effect on performance than did exhortation. Using the same design, Rosenhan and London (1963a) replicated the general findings that the physical performances during hypnosis of good and poor subjects were not significantly different. In another report, Rosenhan and London (1963b) found no differences between hypnotizable and nonhypnotizable subjects (again, both groups were "hypnotized") with respect to their memory for nonsense syllables. Finally, a study of both sense and nonsense learning (Schulman and London, 1963) yielded no differences between tranceable and nontranceable subjects who had been exposed to the hypnotic induction.

Weitzenhoffer and Sjoberg (1961) and Barber and Glass (1962) report that with regard to items traditionally employed in measures of hypnosis, trance induction significantly facilitates performance relative to slightly motivated nontrance conditions. These findings could be interpreted to mean that for such items, trance induction adds significantly to the motivation ordinarily associated with psychological experiments. The issues here, however, are not clear, because in both studies subjects were aware that at some point the experiment would involve hypnosis. In anticipation of that event, subjects might have depressed the rates of nonhypnotic performance in order to do well under hypnosis (see Evans, 1963; Rosenhan and London, 1963a). In subsequent experiments Barber and Calverley (1962, 1963) report that brief motivating instructions do heighten responsiveness to items traditionally employed in assessing susceptibility, so that no significant differences obtain between subjects who have been motivated and those who have undergone the traditional trance induction.

Motivational Differences Between Relatively Good and Poor Hypnotic Subjects. Recently, some evidence has been accumulated to the effect that in the waking state good hypnotic subjects are *not* as motivated to perform as poor hypnotic subjects. London and Fuhrer (1961) found that people who are relatively unsusceptible to hypnosis are *superior* in their *base rate* physical performance to people who are highly susceptible. Concerned that these findings might be due to the possibility that highly susceptible subjects unconsciously depress their base rate performance to show great improvement during the hypnosis part of the experiment, Rosenhan and London (1963a) obtained measures of base rate physical performance before their subjects knew that the experiment involved hypnosis. If anything, the findings were more dramatic, demonstrating even greater differences between relatively good and poor hypnotic subjects than had been found in the London-Fuhrer experiment. Gordon and Freston (1964) found that relatively unsusceptible subjects are better able to give childish verbal associations when instructed to do so than are waking hypnotizable subjects. Orne (1963) reports that somnambulistic subjects who should be highly motivated, tend not to return to the laboratory for further experiments, whereas unsusceptible subjects are more reliable and punctual. Finally, in an experiment that required subjects to set the level of shock that they would be willing to tolerate, Shor (1959a) found that poor hypnotic subjects selected considerably higher intensity levels than good subjects.

There also appears to be some evidence that good hypnotic subjects are not especially motivated to comply with posthypnotic suggestions when compared with subjects who were not hypnotized but given the same instructions (Orne, 1963). In a study that investigated the persistence of posthypnotic suggestions, Patten (1930) asked each subject to press his forefinger down when the names of animals appeared on a list that was revolving on a memory drum. Subjects who had been given the suggestion to perform this task posthypnotically exhibited a greater decrement in performance over time than did waking control subjects. Kellogg (1929) gave subjects the posthypnotic suggestion that when they were reading sonnets printed on even-numbered pages, they would breathe twice as rapidly as they usually did, and that they would breathe twice as slowly when reading sonnets printed on odd-numbered pages. Although the performance of waking subjects showed no decrement over time, the performance of the hypnotic subjects was, in all cases, lower at the end of the test period than it had been on the first trial. Thus it would seem that not only on base rate measures, but also in posthypnotic waking behavior, good hypnotic subjects may be less motivated to perform than controls.

Controls for Experiment-Elicited Behavior

Given the variety of factors that can affect hypnotic behavior and the evidence suggesting that hypnotic behavior can be simulated, it is not a simple matter to suggest controls for hypnosis experiments. For tests of the "skeptical" versus "credulous" views of hypnosis, Sutcliffe (1960, 1961) has offered a complex design that compares somnambulists with nonsomnambulists in four experimental conditions: waking control, hypnotic trance, hypnotic trance plus suggestions, and waking simulation of hypnosis. In addition, for each of these conditions subjects are tested for the presence or absence of the experimental stimulus (that is, whether one group can, say, hallucinate the presence of an object, while another group can hallucinate its absence). Thus, we have 16 independent conditions, for which 16 independent random samples are required. Moreover, Sutcliffe suggests that independent hypnotists be used for each of the eight hypnotic conditions.

One could add to the complexity of this design. Several experiments have already demonstrated that untranceable subjects (that is, subjects who obtain very low scores on standard measures of hypnotic susceptibility) are also quite responsive to the trance induction procedure and subsequent suggestions (London and Fuhrer, 1961; Rosenhan and London, 1963a, 1963b). One might thus require that a third group, untranceables, be studied along with those who are deeply hypnotizable (somnambulists) and those who are only moderately hypnotizable (nonsomnambulists). Moreover, because it is quite likely that different hypnotists can elicit different kinds of hypnotic behavior from subjects, one would want to be sure, in the ideal experiment, either that (a) all of the hypnotists employed in the experiment had similar properties and skills or that (b) several hypnotists were used in each of the hypnotic conditions.

Clearly, this design is too cumbersome to permit an extensive examination of the many issues involved in hypnosis. And although its validity is not seriously debated, its utility is quite questionable. It is hardly necessary that each scientist achieve the true cosmology all at once, or that a research strategy deal with all the possibilities in one experiment. For many of the problems associated with hypnosis, two simpler designs will suffice.

Simulation Design. Orne (1959) has suggested that to compare the motivation engendered by hypnosis with that which could be provided in the waking state, hypnotic subjects need to be compared with waking ones who have been asked to behave as if they were hypnotized. The design requires that the request to simulate be made by one experimenter and the actual simulation be performed with a second experimenter, who should not know who is "real" and who is "simulating." The combined motivation that derives from satisfying one experimenter while fooling another is thought to be sufficient to elicit from simulators performances that are motivationally comparable to those elicited from hypnotized subjects.

The similarity of performance elicited from "reals" and simulators does not, of course, mean that their motivations are identical in either content or degree. The respective motivations are brought about by clearly different means. Nor does it imply that motivation is somehow artifactual to hypnosis, as Orne has stated. In the first place, in the absence of a known "essence" of hypnosis (to use Orne's terms), it is not possible to stipulate the "artifacts" of hypnosis. Moreover, because the motivations achieved in simulators and reals are not identical, they are not comparable insofar as the "reality" of hypnosis is concerned. The simulator design offers us a comparison rather than a true control group, permitting us to examine whether another motivational state can yield the same performance as hypnosis does. When we find that it can, we learn only that hypnosis is not unique with regard to eliciting a particular performance. If we find that it cannot, we can argue that hypnosis is superior to this kind of motivation in eliciting the performance in question.

Tranceable-Untranceable Design. Young (1925, 1926) was the first to compare the performance of hypnotized subjects with that of unhypnotizable subjects who had, however, been exposed to the hypnotic "patter." This design had the apparent advantage of exposing the control group to the identical conditions as the experimental groups.

The procedure was refined by London and used in several studies (London and Fuhrer, 1961; Rosenhan and London, 1963a, 1963b; Schulman and London, 1963). In three of these studies, however, it was found that hypnosis does affect the performance of relatively unhypnotizable subjects. In some cases, it improves their performance more than it improves the performance of hypnotizable subjects! Thus, the use of relatively poor hypnotic subjects is no longer a useful control for experimental conditions, because both poor and good hypnotic subjects respond to hypnotic induction techniques. (It remains, however, an interesting technique for examining subject differences in relation to hypnosis.) By the same token, it would no longer appear justifiable to use untranceable subjects as simulators unless base rate performance for hypnotizable and simulating subjects proved to be no different from each other.

EXPERIMENTER PROPERTIES

Although a great deal of attention has been focused on subject variables in hypnosis experiments, researchers have barely attended to *experimenter properties*. We use this phrase to include two kinds of properties. First, there are the personal attributes of the experimenter—in the case of hypnosis, his skill and ability, his personality, and a large number of currently unspecifiable characteristics that may interact with the experimental variable under consideration. Second, there is experimenter bias, which refers to the ways in which the experimenter's hypotheses and expectancies affect his data.

Experimenter's Attributes

The effects of the attributes of the experimenter on data are not often considered in an experimental design. McGuigan (1963) has recently pointed out that as long as differences exist among experimenters, the data from any one study may have limited generality, particularly when such differences are likely to interact with experimental conditions or subject variables. In a study of verbal conditioning, for example, Sarason (1962) found that the personality of the experimenter interacted with the personality of his subjects and with the experimental task. Generalizations about conditioning from the behavior of subjects in one task, without considering other tasks and experimenter characteristics, would have led to unwarranted conclusions. (For a thorough examination of the effects of the experimenters' personal characteristics on subjects' performance in verbal learning experiments, see Krasner [1962].)

It may well be that insofar as the administration of the standardized hypnotic susceptibility scales is concerned—the Stanford Scale (Weitzenhoffer and Hilgard, 1959), the Harvard Group Scale (Shor and Orne, 1964), and the Children's Scale (London, 1962)—experimenter attributes may have little or no effect relative to the effects produced by the induction itself (although London [1963], in the standardization of the Children's Scale, took care to use many hypnotists of both sexes). Once, however, we move away from the susceptibility scales (which can, as a matter of fact, be tape-recorded) to the depth scales (which are quite difficult to tape-record), or begin to work with the clinical induction of somnambulistic states, it is quite possible that experimenter attributes (such as skill and personality) play a sizable role in the hypnotic outcome. Differences in experimenter skill might well account for the controversy about the stability of hypnotic susceptibility (see, in particular, Ås, Hilgard, and Weitzenhoffer, 1963; Blum, 1961; Hilgard, *et al.*, 1961).

It would lend greater substance to this discussion if one could suggest the likely ways in which experimenter attributes other than skill might affect hypnotizability. One might hypothesize that female hypnotists would in general be less successful than males (because the available subject population overwhelmingly prefers male hypnotists) and that older and more authoritative men would be more effective than peers. But these are merely speculations, for we have not given much thought to conceptualizing the problems of experimenter attributes, beyond those involved in skill. It is quite likely that the "personality" of the hypnotist might significantly affect subject performance, even on standardized scales of susceptibility. But how and in what ways is by no means clear.

Experimenter Bias

We have long been aware that scientists "are imperfect instruments in the quest for lawful relationships" (Rosenthal, 1963). Errors in observation, in recording data, and in interpretation have, through the years, led to the establishment of systems and procedures whereby some of these difficulties can be avoided. Our use of the phrase "experimenter bias" is meant to highlight another related source of error, quite commonly overlooked in psychological as in other research areas: the influence of the experimenter's expectancies and hypotheses on the data he obtains.

Much of the recent research in this area has been conducted by Rosenthal and his associates. Experimenters who were given the task of obtaining ratings of success and failure on a group of relatively neutral pictures and who were told to expect high (success) ratings tended to obtain such ratings. Told to anticipate low or failure ratings, they tended to obtain failure ratings (Rosenthal and Fode, 1963a). Instances of bias are found not only with human subjects but also with planaria (Rosenthal, 1963) and rats (Rosenthal and Fode, 1963b). Thus, when experimenters were told that their animal subjects were "maze bright," their rats learned a maze more rapidly than did the rats run by experimenters who believed them to be "maze dull." Moreover, an experimenter's bias is not limited only to the data he himself collects, but is also communicated to his assistants and affects their data as well (Rosenthal, Persinger, Vikan-Kline, and Mulry, 1963).

We mentioned earlier that the expectancy of an experimenter regarding the degree to which his subjects are aware of the experimental contingencies can have important implications for the problems involved in learning without awareness and may be relevant to the study of the role of awareness in hypnosis. In his paper on the demand characteristics of the experimental situation, Orne (1959) raised the question of whether the expectancies of the experimenter might in some manner be communicated to the subject, thereby enabling the subject to behave as a "good" subject was supposed to behave.

The degree to which experimenter bias has, however subtly, pervaded the hypnosis literature is hard to specify, because to date only one study has attempted to investigate this problem. Rosenhan (1963) studied the relationship between hypnosis and conformity and obtained results that indicated that hypnotizable subjects conform on certain kinds of content but resist conforming on other kinds. These findings were, by and large, replicated in a subsequent experiment conducted by the author. Another replication was, however, conducted concomitantly by a female research assistant. Prior to that replication, she had been shown the data from the first experiment, except that the direction of the correlations was reversed. Thus, if the correlation was positive in the original study, it was represented to her as negative, and vice versa. A reasonably plausible rationale for the reversed findings was given to her, and she was furthermore "protected" from the literature. There is sufficient independent evidence that she was both totally convinced of the verity of the data to which she had been exposed and ignorant of other studies. Her data (which were scored twice by other assistants who had no knowledge of the experiment) yielded correlations that were significantly different from those obtained by the principal investigator and that were in most cases opposite in sign. Thus, where significant negative correlations had been obtained between hypnotizability and "aggression" conformity in the first experiment and in its replication, the assistant obtained significant positive relationships. And whereas the first experiments yielded positive correlations between conformity on an acquiescence scale and hypnotizability, the last experiment yielded negative correlations.

It is clear from this study that two different experimenters can obtain significantly different results despite identical procedures. Because, however, the experimenters differed not only with regard to their hypotheses, but also with regard to age, sex, authority among the subjects, and experimental experience, it cannot be determinately stated that the obtained differences were entirely a function of the fact that they held different hypotheses. At the same time, one must consider these findings in light of the fact that many experiments in psychology are conducted by research assistants who differ in personal characteristics from the principal investigator but whose hypotheses are consistent with his; the data of the assistants do not usually differ from that of the main experimenter. It seems far more likely that the differences obtained in the hypnosis-conformity study were a function of the different expectations and hypotheses held by the experimenters.

The data from this experiment and the issues generally involved in experimenter bias invite discussion of the ways in which conceptions of hypnosis affect the obtained data. Consider the positions of Barber (see 1957, 1961a, 1961b; Barber and Calverley, 1962) and Blum (1961, 1963), for example. Barber and his associates have surrounded the word "hypnosis" with quotation marks, and implied that the term is neither useful nor meaningful. Practically all of the research that has come from their laboratory appears to support this conclusion. Blum, on the other hand, reports remarkable alterations in personality, memory, performance, and perception as at least a partial result of hypnosis. One may wonder whether the expectancies of these experimenters have directly affected their obtained results. For Barber's subjects, the demand characteristics of the experimental situation may require that they perform in such a way as to discredit the existence of hypnosis. For Blum's subjects, on the other hand, the experimental situation may be structured so that subjects perform in ways that appear to exceed dramatically their capacities in the waking state.

Support for these hypotheses can be seen in the case of "Subject J." Barber (1957) reported that this subject was quite capable of entering a self-induced hypnotic trance but was a poor "heterohypnotic" subject. It appears that the subject had taken a tutorial in hypnosis and, Barber argued, having read widely in the area, Subject J arrived at the conclusion that "the hypnotist does not possess any special 'power' or ability, that a subject induces the phenomena in himself, and that a subject does not have to accept the hypnotist's statements as true and valid" (p. 302). Thus, according to Barber, Subject J could hypnotize himself but could not be hypnotized by another person.

On the face of it, Barber's argument seems perfectly reasonable. But the fact that Barber's conceptions of hypnosis appeared to be consistent with the subject's performance is more important for the purposes of this analysis. For, as Shor and Schatz (1960) made clear, it simply was not true that Subject J was unable to enter into hypnosis with another person. Shor, who was Subject J's instructor in the hypnosis tutorial, had specifically taught him to be able to produce "profound autosuggestive phenomena in himself while retaining a choice of whether or not to respond to heterosuggestions." Schatz, who was Subject J, reports that "an insufficient effort was made to elicit his wish to enter a heterohypnotic relationship with the experimenter." The report makes clear that under cooperative conditions Subject J was quite able to enter deeply into a heterohypnotic trance and to manifest the behaviors that are consistent with depth in such a trance state. It seems reasonable to infer that Barber's hypotheses regarding the nature of hypnotic behavior prevented him from eliciting a performance from Subject J that might nullify these hypotheses.

In this same vein, Duke (1964) surveyed the several hundred correlations between hypnosis and tests of primary suggestibility that have been obtained over the past 50 years. Among other findings, he notes that the experience of the investigator is related to the magnitude of the correlations obtained between the primary tests. Thus, the mean correlations obtained by investigators who were engaged in their first study of these relationships tended to be of the order of .32. However, in second study efforts, the mean correlation rose significantly to .69. Duke suggests that either the suggestors improved with experience or the investigators did in fact alter the procedures in the later experiments.

However, an equally plausible explanation derives from current work in experimenter bias. That is, because "good early returns" on data tend to lead to further good returns, whereas poor early returns tend also to confirm themselves later, one might expect investigators to "improve" on their performances the second time around. In interpreting the zero order correlations among tests of primary suggestibility reported by Benton and Bandura (1952), Duke makes a similar suggestion. He argues that the study "seemed to betray a strong disbelief in the functional unity of both the primary and secondary suggestibility tests," implying that their disbelief created a bias in the direction of no relationship and thus no relationship was found.

The effects of experimenter bias are pervasive and appear to have important implications for hypnosis, as for general psychological research. Yet, the processes by which these biases are communicated have not been illuminated. It is quite likely that the experimenter's expectations are communicated through a multitude of subtle cues, which together demand particular forms of behavior from subjects. These experimenter-emitted cues affect not only mean scores but also the relationships between performances.

Research in the area of experimenter bias may raise some further interesting questions for hypnosis research. For example, are the hypnosis data obtained by experimenters who have themselves been able to experience deep trance (and are therefore more convinced of the phenomena of hypnosis) different from those obtained by experimenters who are relatively immune to hypnosis procedures? Does the tranceability of the experimenter interact with that of the subject, such that a highly tranceable hypnotist elicits a better performance from a low tranceable subject than does a low tranceable experimenter? And does the hypnotist's expectations regarding the subject's tranceability interact with his own hypnotic susceptibility, such that a hypnotist who is himself a poor subject elicits worse performances from people whom he thinks are poor subjects than would a hypnotist who is a good subject? Answers to these questions might illuminate the nature of the hypnosis relationship, in addition to shedding light on other significant aspects of experimenter properties.

Control of Experimenter Properties. It is difficult to stipulate controls in this area when the processes by which such biases are communicated are still unclear. Rosenthal (1963) suggests the use of automated apparatus; and taped instructions have been used to assess hypnotic susceptibility. But these possibilities have only limited merit for hypnosis experiments, particularly those in which hypnotic depth is being assessed, because many of these experiments require face-to-face contact. The use of many experimenters, all of whom are relatively uninformed with regard to the hypotheses of the study, is another possibility, but its utility, in terms of both time and expense, is quite limited. It may be possible to limit experimenter bias and perhaps to avoid some of these contaminants that arise from other experiment properties by instructing the experimenters about the possibilities of such effects and of their danger. Because it appears that biases are communicated from the principal investigator to his assistants, and thence to the subjects, it would be important for the principal investigator to attempt to "remain objective" and to communicate objectivity to his laboratory. This is obviously more easily advised than done. We need further data from those who are engaged in the problem of experimenter properties before we can make more specific recommendations. For the moment, it seems that we can only rely on the presumed self-correcting tendencies of science, which is only to say that we will have to go about our business as usual.

POTENTIAL SOURCES OF SAMPLE BIAS

The problem of sample bias is a difficult one for psychological research in general, but it is an especially knotty one for hypnosis research. For hypnosis wears many halos: of danger, of drama, of the mysterious, of pseudoscience, and of others less well defined. And one may at least suspect that these halos are attractive to some people, who then volunteer for hypnosis experiments, and less attractive to others, who avoid such experiments. Because hypnosis researchers rely almost wholly on volunteer subjects, whether or not volunteers are representative of the total population is a serious question.

The issues involved in sample bias are receiving attention in the general psychological literature. Reviews by Bell (1961, 1962) make it clear that significant differences do exist between volunteers and nonvolunteers for psychological experiments. In general, the data demonstrate that volunteers tend to be less conventional in their attitudes and behavior than nonvolunteers; they tend to be more maladjusted and, in some studies, more anxious; they are less sociable and more self-absorbed; and they seem to be higher in need achievement. In addition, volunteers may be more intelligent and may differ on a wide variety of personality measures. The issue is complicated by the fact that differences between volunteers and nonvolunteers tend to be experiment-specific. Thus, subjects who volunteer for hypnosis experiments appear to be more intelligent than those who do not volunteer, but such differences are not found between volunteers and nonvolunteers for studies in "learning," "personality," or "attitudes toward sex" (Martin and Marcuse, 1958).

Martin and Marcuse (1957) found that subjects are quite reliable in their willingness to volunteer for hypnosis experiments. Subjects who were asked to volunteer for a two-hour experiment were informed one week later that the experiment had been redesigned and that it was necessary to ask again for volunteers. Subjects who volunteered the first time volunteered the second time ($r = .97$). In addition, the authors reported that volunteers were more intelligent than nonvolunteers; that male volunteers were significantly less anxious and ethnocentric and that they obtained higher dominance-submission scores on the Bernreuter than male nonvolunteers. Female volunteers appeared to score higher in sociability than female nonvolunteers. Brady, Levitt, and Lubin (1961) reported that apprehension at the prospect of being hypnotized prevented some student nurses from volunteering for hypnosis, but Levitt, Lubin, and Zuckerman (1962) found that financial incentives and knowledge about hypnosis did *not* affect volunteering behavior.

Most studies take verbal acquiescence with regard to hypnosis experiments as equivalent to actual volunteering. There is some evidence, however, that many people who say they will show up for an experiment never do. Levitt, Lubin, and Brady (1962) found that nearly 30 per cent of students who had said that they would volunteer failed to come for their appointments. It is not clear from the data whether these "pseudovolunteers" differed significantly from either the volunteers or the nonvolunteers, but the kinds and numbers of significant comparisons between the volunteers groups varied depending upon whether pseudovolunteers were included with the volunteers (because they indicated that they would participate) or with the nonvolunteers (because they didn't show up). When the pseudovolunteers were included with the volunteers, only two of the 38 volunteers-nonvolunteers comparisons were significant at the .05 level. When, however, they were included with the nonvolunteers, eight comparisons achieved significance. Although even eight (and certainly two) "significant" comparisons out of a possible 38 could occur by chance, the authors conclude that where one puts the pseudovolunteer leads "to very different inferences concerning the personalities of volunteers and nonvolunteers."

There does not yet appear to be consensus on whether or not attitudes toward, and prior experience with, hypnosis affect hypnotizability. Melei and Hilgard (1964) report that those who volunteered for hypnosis were more favorable in attitude toward hypnosis than those who did not volunteer. London, Cooper, and Johnson (1962) find no relationships, at least for the attitudes and experiences that they surveyed. Moreover, in their study of a wide variety of personality scales, only the Socialization scale on the California Psychological Inventory correlated with willingness to volunteer for hypnosis, and that correlation was quite low. Hilgard *et al.* (1961) reported that female volunteers obtained lower scores on the Self-Control scale of the CPI than did nonvolunteers, but this finding was not substantiated in the London, Cooper, and Johnson study (1962). Lubin, Brady, and Levitt (1962) found that among student nurses, volunteers for hypnosis experiments had higher scores on the Rorschach dependency ratio and on the Edwards Personal Preference Schedule Aggression and Exhibitionism scales than did nonvolunteers. The latter, on the other hand, obtained higher scores on the Guilford-Zimmerman factor scales of objectivity, friendliness, and personal relations and higher scores on the Edwards Order scale.

These studies of volunteer-nonvolunteer differences, although interesting in themselves, cast little light on a central problem of sample bias for hypnosis research: are the differences between volunteers and nonvolunteers significant with regard to *actual hypnotic performance*? The question has two parts. First, does volunteering or nonvolunteering affect hypnotic performance? And second, are the trait, experience, or attitude differences between volunteers and nonvolunteers predictive of hypnotic performance?

The answer to the first question appears to be affirmative: it makes a difference with regard to hypnotic performance whether or not the subjects are volunteers. Boucher and Hilgard (1962) compared ordinary volunteers, who had responded to an advertisement in the student newspaper, with "coerced volunteers," who had chosen the hypnosis experiment in preference to others to satisfy requirements for a psychology course. They found that both male and female coerced volunteers obtained significantly lower scores than did ordinary volunteers on the Stanford Hypnotic Susceptibility Scale (Weitzenhoffer and Hilgard, 1959). And among the coerced volunteers, those who had indicated prior to the call for subjects that they would be unwilling to serve in hypnosis experiments (and who presumably changed their minds when confronted with a choice of other unfavorable alternatives) scored significantly lower than did other coerced volunteers.

In three independent studies, Dermen (1964), Melei and Hilgard (1964), and Rosenhan and Tomkins (1964) found that preference for hypnosis correlates positively with hypnotizability for females but not for males. The very fact that this finding was replicated twice is quite remarkable for research in hypnosis. But the consistently obtained sex differences are not thereby made easier to interpret. Melei and Hilgard (1964), finding that females use more negative adjectives in describing hypnosis, argue that the range of preference scores is greater for females than for males. Those females who view hypnosis negatively and then participate in hypnotic experiments tend to be relatively unhypnotizable, thus producing the moderate correlations between attitude and susceptibility. Rosenhan and Tomkins (1964) suggest that insofar as hypnosis often implies giving up control and putting oneself in the control of another person, preference for hypnosis may stimulate greater conflict in males than females for the reason that these implications are less consistent with the male sex role. Thus, the correlation between preference and hypnotizability would be constricted for males but more substantial for females.

Melei and Hilgard (1964) further reported that inexperienced subjects' self-predictions of hypnotizability tend to correlate slightly but significantly with their actual hypnotic performance. Among experienced subjects, however, females' self-predictions correlate quite strongly with actual performance ($r = .65$), whereas males' do not. A selective factor, presumably greater for males than for females, may be operating here, so that causal strands are difficult to disentangle.

With regard to the second question, whether the traits that distinguish volunteers from nonvolunteers are predictive of hypnotizability, the answer appears to be a tentative "No." Rosenhan and Tomkins (1964) found that those subjects who preferred hypnosis experiments were distinguishable from those who did not on a variety of personality traits and on birth order; yet none of these characteristics correlated significantly with hypnosis scores. Here, as in many other studies, the problem of personality correlates of hypnotizability continues to be an elusive one (see Hilgard and Lauer, 1962).

London and Rosenhan (1964), reviewing the problem of biased sampling in hypnosis as in other research areas, point out that any analysis of the problem is faced with the psychological equivalent of the Heisenberg principle. On the one hand, unless nonvolunteers are forced to participate in an experiment, one cannot make generalizations regarding the total population. On the other hand, if they *are* forced, then one is faced with the problem of samples coming from known different populations. The problem is not easily resolvable.

In sum, it is clear that there are differences between volunteers and nonvolunteers for hypnosis research, and this evidence is consistent with studies of volunteer bias in other areas of psychological research. In addition, "coerced" volunteers differ in their hypnotizability from ordinary volunteers, and female subjects who prefer to be hypnotized are more hypnotizable than those who do not have such preferences. But the personality and other differences that distinguish volunteers from nonvolunteers are not predictive of hypnotic susceptibility.

POPULAR ATTITUDES TOWARD HYPNOSIS

A description of the social psychology of hypnosis requires some consideration of the attitudes toward hypnosis that are found in the general population from which we draw our experimental samples. Oddly enough, despite the fact that there presumably exists a widespread folklore about hypnosis, we have little formal information in this area. When one considers White's (1937) hypotheses about the relations between attitude and hypnotizability, Orne's (1959) demonstration of how prior observation of hypnosis shapes hypnotic behavior, and the possibility that prior experience of either the direct or the observational sort might influence subjects' performance, the absence of data on attitudes, experience, and exposure is quite surprising.

London (1961) and London, Cooper, and Johnson (1962), using a questionnaire that was intended to assess direction of popular prejudice rather than accuracy of knowledge, surveyed interest and opinion among 645 college males and females. They reported that direct personal experience with hypnosis was quite limited in their sample (6.8 per cent) but that observational experience, primarily with entertainers as hypnotists, was quite extensive (60 per cent). London concludes that "there is sufficiently wide knowledge of what it looks like to be hypnotized so that the responses of experimental subjects to the hypnotic state are likely to be considerably colored by their expectations of how a hypnotized person acts" (1961). Such knowledge may also be available to younger subjects through the mass entertainment media.

About one quarter of their sample estimated that they could easily be hypnotized; another quarter felt that they could not be easily hypnotized; the remainder were doubtful about their susceptibility to hypnosis. These proportions are quite similar to the incidence of susceptibility reported by Hilgard *et al.* (1961).

More than half of London's sample expressed willingness to volunteer for hypnosis, with males being slightly more eager than females. The majority of the respondents expressed no preference with regard to the sex of the hypnotist. Among those who did have preferences, however, both males and females preferred a male hypnotist.

Some interesting data emerge from their survey of attitudes toward hypnosis. Subjects were given the opportunity to state, in a true or false format, both their own opinion of many popular conceptions about hypnosis and also what they felt would be the opinion of the public at large. Of the subjects, 86 per cent felt that people could *not* be hypnotized against their will, and 65 per cent felt that the public would feel the same way. A majority of the subjects denied a relationship between gullibility and hypnotizability but viewed the public as believing that such a relationship exists. Some 41 per cent believed that when hypnotized, "people . . . lose control over themselves, so that they will do or say things that they would normally restrain." (This finding, incidentally, suggests that the assurances given to subjects that they will not be asked to do anything that would embarrass or harm them in any way are well warranted and perhaps ought to be expanded.)

A large majority of potential subjects (81 per cent) believed that "it is difficult for a hypnotized person to resist obeying a hypnotic suggestion," but a smaller number (56 per cent) held that "hypnotized people are not aware of what they are doing during trance." More than one quarter of the respondents thought that "a real danger of hypnosis is that it may be impossible to get people out of the trance." Finally, females tended in general to be more cautious than males about the dangers of hypnosis and about the possible loss of volition in the hypnotic state.

CONCLUSIONS

We have considered here the effects of several potential sources of bias in the data obtained from hypnosis experiments. These have included the effects of experiment-elicited behaviors, experimenter properties, and the attitudes and biases of potential subjects. Throughout the discussion, it has been easier to point to problems than to indicate their solutions, and if the reader is left with the sense that there are too many problems and too few solutions to permit adequate research into hypnotic phenomena, this conclusion was not intended. Indeed, by borrowing quite heavily from other areas of psychological research, even by paraphrasing a chapter title that had been used previously in illuminating these problems for psychological research (see Orne, 1962; Rosenthal, 1963), we have intended to imply that these problems are not unique to hypnosis experiments. Many areas of psychology, including those that possess long histories and respected traditions (such as conditioning and animal learning), are prone to similar difficulties.

With regard to experiment-elicited behavior, to the demand characteristics of the experimental situation, and to experimenter properties, although it is clear that we cannot always control for them within the limits of either reason or economy, we can at least be on the lookout for them. It is possible to question a subject thoroughly following an experiment or to have a "stooge" of the experimenter (who is also a peer of the subject) question the subject. These are not expensive procedures. Orne (1962) has suggested that "dry runs" be conducted before each experiment, in which subjects would be exposed to the experimental instructions and asked what *they* think the hypotheses of the experiment are. One can keep the characteristics of one's assistants in mind, observing their hypotheses and inquiring carefully into their behavior. For crucial experiments, one can use an assistant whose hypotheses run counter to those held by the others, merely to see if his data are consistent nevertheless. None of these suggestions constitute controls in the true sense of the word. Rather, they are procedures that may be used in the course of any experiment to indicate whether further controls are necessary in subsequent research. And they are likely to save considerable time and effort.

Finding more precise controls for demand characteristics will further tax our experimental ingenuity. Orne's simulation technique has several obvious and important advantages. But since London and his co-workers have shown that subjects who obtain low scores on standardized scales of hypnotic susceptibility (that is, subjects who are untranceable) as well as subjects who obtain high scores are responsive to the hypnotic procedures, it is hard to know where to find subjects for simulations. On the other hand, London's procedure, which exposes untranceable subjects to exactly the same procedures as tranceable ones, possesses theoretical appeal but is open to the same kind of criticism: both types of subjects appear to be responsive to trance inductions. The fact that they are *differentially responsive* permits us to study subject differences in response to hypnotic instructions, but it does not take care of the problems of demand characteristics. Clearly, however, either of these techniques is more likely to shed light on hypnotic processes than no controls at all, and we simply need further experience with both of them before we can be certain of their precise characteristics.

We have noted previously that controls for experimenter differences are simply uneconomical for experiments in hypnosis. This is not to say, however, that we do not require more information on whether, and in what ways, experimenters differ by virtue of experience or other personal attributes. An experimental program directed toward illuminating this problem would likely be of great value both for itself and for stipulating controls for other kinds of hypnotic research.

We began this inquiry by asking: If hypnosis exists, how shall we know it? Are there behaviors that uniquely accompany hypnosis and that are separable from those behaviors that are otherwise induced? Current knowledge would indicate that there are not such unique behaviors, at least insofar as the broad array of behaviors that have been examined hypnotically and with adequate controls is concerned. We now have greater reason to believe that the phenomena of hypnosis are not isolated or encysted, but rather appear to bear striking similarities to other kinds of experimental behavior. Moreover, consideration of the social psychology of hypnosis experiments has yielded tempting hypotheses for future research, including the possibility of reconciling quite divergent points of view regarding what can and what cannot be performed in hypnosis. If there are not, right now, many answers to the questions we began with, there is at least the greater likelihood that definite answers will be forthcoming—which is a rather optimistic view of the Gordian knot.

REFERENCES

Ås, A., Hilgard, E. R., and Weitzenhoffer, A. M. (1963). "An attempt at experimental modification of hypnotizability through repeated individualized hypnotic experience," *Scand. J. Psychol.*, **4**, 81–89.

Ashley, W. R., Harper, R. S., and Runyon, D. K. (1951). "The perceived size of coins in normal and hypnotically induced economic states," *Amer. J. Psychol.*, **54**, 564–592.

Barber, T. X. (1957). "Hypnosis as perceptual-cognitive restructuring: III. From somnambulism to autohypnosis," *J. Psychol.*, **44**, 299–304.

——— (1961a). "Antisocial and criminal acts induced by 'hypnosis'," *Arch. gen. Psychiat.*, **5**, 301–312.

——— (1961b). "Physiological effects of 'hypnosis'," *Psychol. Bull.*, **58**, 390–419.

Barber, T. X., and Calverley, D. S. (1962). "'Hypnotic behavior' as a function of task motivation," *J. Psychol.*, **54**, 363–389.

——— (1963). "The relative effectiveness of task-motivating instructions and trance-induction procedure in the production of 'hypnotic-like' behaviors," *J. nerv. ment. Disord.*, **137**, 107–116.

Barber, T. X., and Glass, L. B. (1962). "Significant factors in hypnotic behavior," *J. abnorm. soc. Psychol.*, **64**, 222–228.

Barber, T. X., and Hahn, K. W., Jr. (1962). "Physiological and subjective responses to pain producing stimulation under hypnotically-suggested and waking-imagined 'analgesia'," *J. abnorm. soc. Psychol.*, **65**, 411–418.

——— (1963). "Hypnotic induction and 'relaxation'," *Arch. gen. Psychiat.*, **8**, 295–300.

Bell, C. R. (1961). "Psychological versus sociological variables in studies of volunteer bias in surveys," *J. appl. Psychol.*, **45**, 80–85.

——— (1962). "Personality characteristics of volunteers for psychological studies," *Brit. J. soc. clin. Psychol.*, **1**, 81–95.

Benton, A. L., and Bandura, A. (1952). "'Primary' and 'secondary' suggestibility," *J. abnorm. soc. Psychol.*, **48**, 336–340.

Blum, G. S. (1961). *A Model of the Mind.* New York: Wiley.

——— (1963). "Programming people to simulate machines." In S. S. Tomkins and S. Messick (Eds.). *Computer Simulation of Personality*, New York: Wiley, pp. 127–157.

Boucher, R. G., and Hilgard, E. R. (1962). "Volunteer bias in hypnotic experimentation," *Amer. J. clin. Hyp.*, **5**, 49–51.

Brady, J. P., Levitt, E. E., and Lubin, B. (1961). "Expressed fear of hypnosis and volunteering behavior," *J. nerv. ment. Disord.*, **133**, 216–217.

Dermen, D. (1964). *Correlates of Hypnotic Susceptibility.* Unpublished master's thesis, Univer. of Illinois.

Duke, J. D. (1964). "Intercorrelational status of suggestibility tests and hypnotizability," *Psychol. Rec.*, **14**, 71–80.

Eriksen, C. W. (Ed.) (1962). "Behavior and awareness," *J. Pers.*, **30**, 1–158.

Evans, F. J. (1963). "Behavioral changes produced by hypnosis: A methodological contribution." Paper presented at meetings of the Society for Clinical and Experimental Hypnosis, New York, October, 1963.

FISHER, S. (1954). "The role of expectancy in the performance of posthypnotic behavior," *J. abnorm. soc. Psychol.*, **49**, 503–507.

GLASS, L. B., and BARBER, T. X. (1961). "A note on hypnotic behavior, the definition of the situation and the placebo effect," *J. nerv. ment. Dis.*, **132**, 539–541.

GORDON, J. E., and FRESTON, M. (1964). "Role-playing and age regression in hypnotized and nonhypnotized subjects," *J. Pers.*, **32**, 411–419.

HILGARD, E. R., and LAUER, LILLIAN W. (1962). "Lack of correlation between the California Psychological Inventory and hypnotic susceptibility," *J. consult. Psychol.*, **26**, 331–335.

HILGARD, E. R., WEITZENHOFFER, A. M., LANDES, J., and MOORE, ROSEMARIE K. (1961). "The distribution of susceptibility to hypnosis in a student population: A study using the Stanford Hypnotic Susceptibility Scale," *Psychol. Monogr.*, **75**, 8 (Whole No. 512).

HULL, C. L. (1933). *Hypnosis and Suggestibility: An Experimental Approach.* New York: Appleton-Century-Crofts.

JANET, P. (1920). *Major Symptoms of Hysteria.* New York: Macmillan.

KELLOGG, E. R. (1929). "Duration and effects of post-hypnotic suggestions," *J. exp. Psychol.*, **12**, 502–514.

KRASNER, L. (1962). "The therapist as a social reinforcement machine." In Strupp, H. H., and Luborsky, L. (Eds.). *Research in Psychotherapy*, Washington, D.C.: American Psychological Association, pp. 61–94.

LEVITT, E. E., LUBIN, B., and BRADY, J. P. (1962). "The effect of the pseudovolunteer on studies of volunteers for psychology experiments," *J. appl. Psychol.*, **46**, 72–75.

LEVITT, E. E., LUBIN, B., and ZUCKERMAN, M. (1962). "The effect of incentives on volunteering for an hypnosis experiment," *Int. J. clin. exp. Hyp.*, **10**, 39–41.

LONDON, P. (1961). "Subject characteristics in hypnosis research: Part I. A survey of experience, interest, and opinion," *Int. J. clin. exp. Hyp.*, **9**, 151–161.

——— (1962). *The Children's Hypnotic Susceptibility Scale.* Palo Alto, Calif.: Consulting Psychologists Press.

——— (1963). "Experiments in hypnosis with children." Paper presented at symposium on "The New 'Hard-Nosed' Approach in Hypnosis Research," American Psychological Association Meetings, Philadelphia, Pa., September, 1963.

LONDON, P., COOPER, L. M., and JOHNSON, H. J. (1962). "Subject characteristics in hypnosis research. II. Attitudes towards hypnosis, volunteer status and personality measures. III. Some correlates of hypnotic susceptibility," *Int. J. clin. exp. Hyp.*, **10**, 13–21.

LONDON, P., and FUHRER, M. (1961). "Hypnosis, motivation and performance," *J. Pers.*, **29**, 321–333.

LONDON, P., and ROSENHAN, D. (1964). "Personality dynamics," *Ann. Rev. Psychol.*, **15**, 447–492.

LUBIN, B., BRADY, J. P., and LEVITT, E. E. (1962). "A comparison of personality characteristics of volunteers and nonvolunteers for hypnosis experiments," *J. clin. Psychol.*, **18**, 341–343.

Lyon, W. (1954). "Justification and command as techniques for hypnotically induced antisocial behavior," *J. clin. Psychol.*, **5**, 288–290.

Martin, R. M., and Marcuse, F. L. (1957). "Characteristics of volunteers and nonvolunteers for hypnosis," *Int. J. clin. exp. Hyp.*, **4**, 176–180.

——— (1958). "Characteristics of volunteers and non-volunteers in psychological experimentation," *J. consult. Psychol.*, **22**, 475–479.

Mayer, L. (1937). *Das Verbrechen in Hypnose und seine Auflärungsmethoden.* München: Lehmanns. Cited by Orne, M. T. (1962). "Antisocial behavior and hypnosis: Problems of control and validation in empirical studies." In Estabrooks, G. H. (Ed.), *Hypnosis: Current Problems.* New York: Harper & Row.

McDougall, W. (1926). *Outline of Abnormal Psychology.* New York: Scribner.

McGuigan, F. J. (1963). "The experimenter: A neglected stimulus object," *Psychol. Bull.*, **60**, 421–428.

Melei, Janet P., and Hilgard, E. R. (1964). "Attitudes towards hypnosis, self-predictions, and hypnotic susceptibility," *Int. J. clin. exp. Hyp.*, **12**, 99–108.

Milgram, S. (1963). "Behavioral study of obedience," *J. abnorm. soc. Psychol.*, **67**, 371–378.

——— (1965). "Some conditions of obedience and disobedience to authority," *Hum. Relat.*, **18**, 57–76.

Orne, M. T. (1959). "The nature of hypnosis: Artifact and essence," *J. abnorm. soc. Psychol.*, **58**, 277–299.

——— (1962a). "Antisocial behavior and hypnosis: Problems of control and validation in empirical studies." In Estabrooks, G. H. (Ed.). *Hypnosis: Current Problems*, New York: Harper & Row, pp. 137–192.

——— (1962b). "On the social psychology of the psychological experiment: With particular reference to demand characteristics and their implications," *Amer. Psychologist*, **17**, 776–783.

——— (1963). "The nature of the hypnotic phenomenon: Recent empirical studies." Paper presented at symposium on "The New 'Hard-Nosed' Approach in Hypnosis Research," American Psychological Association Meetings, Philadelphia, Pa., September, 1963.

Orne, M. T., and Evans, F. J. (1965). "Social control in the psychological experiment: Antisocial behavior and hypnosis," *J. pers. soc. Psychol.*, **1**, 189–200.

Patten, E. F. (1930). "The duration of post-hypnotic suggestions," *J. abnorm. soc. Psychol.*, **25**, 319–334.

Pattie, F. A., Jr. (1935). "A report of attempts to produce uniocular blindness by hypnotic suggestion," *Brit. J. med. Psychol.*, **15**, 230–241.

Prince, M. (1916). *The Unconscious.* New York: Macmillan.

Reiter, P. J. (1958). *Antisocial or Criminal Acts and Hypnosis: A Case Study.* Springfield, Ill.: C. C. Thomas.

Rosenhan, D. (1963). "Hypnosis, conformity, and acquiescence," *Amer. Psychologist*, **18**, 402. (Abstract)

Rosenhan, D., and London, P. (1963a). "Hypnosis: Expectation, susceptibility, and performance," *J. abnorm. soc. Psychol.*, **66**, 77–81.

ROSENHAN, D., and LONDON, P. (1963b). "Hypnosis in the unhypnotizable: A study in rote learning," *J. exp. Psychol.*, **65**, 30–34.

ROSENHAN, D., and TOMKINS, S. S. (1964). "On preference for hypnosis and hypnotizability." *Int. J. clin. exp. Hyp.*, **12**, 109–114.

ROSENTHAL, R. (1963). "On the social psychology of the psychological experiment: The experimenter's hypothesis as unintended determinant of experimental results," *Amer. Scientist*, **51**, 268–283.

ROSENTHAL, R., and FODE, K. L. (1963a). "Psychology of the scientist: V. Three experiments in experimenter bias," *Psychol. Rep.*, **12**, 491–511.

——— (1963b). "The effect of experimenter bias on the performance of the albino rat," *Behav. Sci.*, **8**, 183–189.

ROSENTHAL, R., PERSINGER, G. W., VIKAN-KLINE, LINDA L., and FODE, K. L. (1963). "The effect of experimenter outcome-bias and subject set on awareness in verbal conditioning experiments," *J. verb. Learn. verb. Behav.*, **2**, 275–283.

ROSENTHAL, R., PERSINGER, G. W., VIKAN-KLINE, LINDA L., and MULRY, R. C. (1963). "The role of the research assistant in the mediation of experimenter bias," *J. Pers.*, **31**, 313–335.

ROWLAND, L. W. (1939). "Will hypnotized persons try to harm themselves or others?" *J. abnorm. soc. Psychol.*, **34**, 114–117.

SARASON, I. G. (1962). "Individual differences, situational variables, and personality research." *J. abnorm. soc. Psychol.*, **65**, 376–380.

SARBIN, T. R. (1950). "Contributions to role-taking theory: I. Hypnotic behavior," *Psychol. Rev.*, **57**, 255–270.

SCHULMAN, R. E., and LONDON, P. (1963). "Hypnosis and verbal learning," *J. abnorm. soc. Psychol.*, **67**, 363–370.

SHOR, R. E. (1959a). *Explorations in Hypnosis: A Theoretical and Experimental Study.* Unpublished doctoral dissertation, Brandeis Univer.

——— (1959b). "Hypnosis and the concept of the generalized reality-orientation," *Amer. J. Psychother.*, **13**, 582–602.

——— (1962a). "Physiological effects of painful stimulation during hypnotic analgesia under conditions designed to minimize anxiety," *Int. J. clin. exp. Hyp.*, **10**, 183–202.

——— (1962b). "Three dimensions of hypnotic depth," *Int. J. clin. exp. Hyp.*, **10**, 23–38.

SHOR, R. E., and ORNE, EMILY C. (1964). *The Harvard Group Scale of Hypnotic Susceptibility, Form A: An adaptation for group administration with self-report scoring of the Stanford Hypnotic Susceptibility Scale, Form A.* Palo Alto, Calif.: Consulting Psychologists Press.

SHOR, R. E., and SCHATZ, J. (1960). "A critical note on Barber's case-study on 'Subject J'," *J. Psychol.*, **50**, 253–256.

SUTCLIFFE, J. P. (1960). "'Credulous' and 'skeptical' views of hypnotic phenomena, a review of certain evidence and methodology," *Int. J. clin. exp. Hyp.*, **8**, 73–101.

——— (1961). "'Credulous' and 'skeptical' views of hypnotic phenomena: Experiments on esthesia, hallucination, and delusion," *J. abnorm. soc. Psychol.*, **62**, 189–200.

WEITZENHOFFER, A. M. (1953). *Hypnotism: An Objective Study in Suggestibility.* New York: Wiley.

WEITZENHOFFER, A. M., and HILGARD, E. R. (1959). *Stanford Hypnotic Susceptibility Scale.* Palo Alto, Calif.: Consulting Psychologists Press.

WEITZENHOFFER, A. M., and SJOBERG, B. M., Jr. (1961). "Suggestibility with and without 'induction of hypnosis'," *J. nerv. ment. Dis.*, **132**, 204–220.

WHITE, R. W. (1937). "Prediction of hypnotic susceptibility from a knowledge of subject's attitude," *J. Psychol.*, **3**, 265–277.

——— (1941). "A preface to the theory of hypnotism," *J. abnorm. soc. Psychol.*, **36**, 477–505.

WOLBERG, L. R. (1948). *Medical Hypnosis.* Vol. I: *The Principles of Hypnotherapy.* New York: Grune & Stratton.

YOUNG, P. C. (1925). "An experimental study of mental and physical functions in the normal and hypnotic states," *Amer. J. Psychol.*, **36**, 214–232.

——— (1926). "An experimental study of mental and physical functions in the normal and hypnotic states: Additional results," *Amer. J. Psychol.*, **37**, 345–356.

——— (1958). "Antisocial uses of hypnosis." In LeCron, L. M. (Ed.). *Experimental Hypnosis*, New York: Macmillan, pp. 376–409.

16

Physiological Effects of Painful Stimulation During Hypnotic Analgesia[1]

RONALD E. SHOR[2]
Harvard Medical School

THIS chapter reviews the experimental literature on the physiological effects of painful stimulation during hypnotic analgesia. Except for occasional relevant passages, it does not review the larger question of the physiology of hypnotic analgesia, nor does it survey the clinical literature on hypnotic analgesia and anesthesia.

Other than the writer's own studies (Shor, 1959; 1962b), six experiments have been reported on the topic under review since 1930[3] (Brown

[1] This work was supported in part by grant AF49 (638)–728 from the Air Force Office of Scientific Research, and by grants from the Human Ecology Fund, and the Institute for Experimental Psychiatry.

[2] I wish to thank my colleagues in the Studies in Hypnosis Project, Harvard Medical School, Massachusetts Mental Health Center—Martin T. Orne, Donald N. O'Connell, Emily Carota Orne, and Frederick J. Evans—for their critical comments and editorial assistance in the preparation of this manuscript. I am also indebted in this regard to Ulric Neisser, Walter Toman, Ricardo B. Morant, and Harry Rand of Brandeis University.

[3] Although recently revised, the bulk of this review was first completed a number of years earlier (Shor, 1959.) Two relevant experimental reports with null findings have since appeared (Sutcliffe, 1961; Barber and Hahn, 1962) and the reviewer knows of a few additional studies incompleted at this time. A supplementary report eventually will be written to cover these further developments.

and Vogel, 1938; Doupe, Miller, and Keller, 1939; Dynes, 1932; Levine, 1930; Sears, 1932; and West, Neill, and Hardy, 1952).[4]

The writer has already published a brief summary report in which a number of methodological problems were illustrated by examples selected from the six experiments (Shor, 1962a). The present, more exhaustive review critically examines the basic issues and logic of the area of inquiry. It is written primarily for the investigator concerned with designing further research in this area.

Both in the writer's brief summary report and in the original research reports themselves, valuable prospects for further research have remained obscure. Especially serious misunderstandings result if one accepts the original research reports generally at face value, as many reviewers have done (see, for example, Barber, 1959; Gorton, 1949; Heron, 1954–1955; Kirkner, 1956; Raginsky, 1951; Young, 1941; Weitzenhoffer, 1951). An important critical appraisal on the other hand is given in the report by Sutcliffe (1960).

The review is not concerned with evaluating the present state of the evidence, although it will become clear in reading this exposition that the evidence is so equivocal that it is best not to draw generalizations at this time except as hypotheses for further research.

First, a detailed review will be made of each of the six studies taken separately. Second, a number of further, more general methodological issues will be discussed. And last, a brief résumé will be given of the writer's own experimental work in the area of inquiry.

LEVINE (1930)

The effects of painful stimulation on the psychogalvanic reflex (GSR) was studied in one female *S* who was capable of achieving profound hypnotic anesthesia. Three indices of pain were used: (1) *S*'s report, (2) gross bodily movement, and (3) GSR potential differences between the palm and back of one hand.

Procedure: Deep hypnosis was induced; then, without warning, a venipuncture needle was struck through the skin of the *S*'s arm. Hypnotic anesthesia was induced and the skin unexpectedly punctured again. Records were taken during both conditions. This sequence was repeated on three separate days.

[4] Reports appearing before 1930 will not be reviewed here because the studies were insufficiently systematic by modern standards. Peiper (1924) in four cases, and Prince and Peterson (1908) in one case reported that stimulation of an hypnotically anesthetized area produced a normal GSR. Georgi (1921) in three cases and Moravcsic (1921) in one case reported that hypnotic anesthesia eliminated entirely the usual GSR deflection to painful stimulation. Bechterev (1905) cited several Russian references in which it was allegedly demonstrated that during hypnotic anesthesia pricking did not elicit the normal respiratory, cardiac, or pupillary reactions to painful stimulation.

Results: During the nonanesthetized condition *S* reported feeling pain; she gasped, made sudden withdrawal movements from the stimulus. Large GSR deflections were also apparent. During the hypnotic anesthesia condition verbal reports of pain and bodily movements did not occur, but large GSR deflections continued. Although no quantitative analysis was made of the data, specimen record tracings give no reason to suppose that the GSR deflections in the two conditions were of different magnitudes.

Additional findings: Levine also had the *S* hallucinate a skin puncture without actual stimulation. All three indices (including GSR) appeared similar to those following actual pain.

A record was also secured from a second *S* who had a persistent hysterical anesthesia of her arms and legs. The record was taken in the waking state. When stimulated unexpectedly (eyes closed), *S* reported no pain and made no movement, but sizable GSR deflections occurred.

In reviewing Levine's experiment, Hull (1933) considered it one of the better of the early studies, and concluded:

> In judging the significance of these results, it should be remembered that Levine, like his predecessors in this field, appears to have been looking for some kind of all-or-none relationship, and it seems not to have occurred to him to make systematic measurements to determine whether the anesthetic condition might not have been associated with a certain amount of weakening of the reaction.[5] It is true that his published records offer slight basis for such a conjecture. It must be remembered, on the other hand, that a tendency of moderate amount can be neither proved nor disproved by the mere inspection of a small number of records. Accidental elements of unknown nature within the immensely complex mechanism of man are such that tendencies of moderate strength may be either simulated or entirely masked in any individual record. It is only when careful objective measurements have been made and the data subjected to statistical treatment which will permit the accidental elements to neutralize each other that a really convincing comparison can be made between an experimental (anesthetic) series and its (normal) control (1933; pp. 255–256, parentheses his).

DYNES (1932)

Three physiological variables—respiratory rate, heart rate, and GSR —were measured before and after stimulation in both the normal waking state and after suggestions of analgesia while *S*'s were in hypnosis. Three stimuli were used: the noise of a blank cartridge pistol, a pin prick, and a pinch.[6] Order of stimulus administration was not noted. Six *S*'s achieved somnambulism; the seventh entered only light hypnosis.

[5] Levine has since pointed out that he wanted to make such quantitative comparisons, but that they were not practical at the time (personal communication).

[6] Wording suggests that only one measure was taken for each stimulus condition, but later Dynes thought it more likely that he averaged the results of a number of stimuli of each type (personal communication).

The light hypnosis *S* was not identified. During training sessions *S*'s became familiar with the apparatus and experimental situation.

Upon arrival, *S*'s first rested for a few minutes, then were told to close their eyes and relax, but no hypnotic suggestions were given. Then the pistol shot and the two pain stimuli were given while a continuous record was taken of *S*'s responses. Bodily mechanisms were allowed to quiet down in resting intervals given between the stimulations. Dynes observed that the pinch produced considerable pain and that the pin prick was less painful but more sudden and unexpected. It was noted that none of the *S*'s could repress a sudden inspiratory gasp in the waking state when the pistol was fired.

After the waking record was secured, hypnosis was induced and aversive stimuli again administered. Before each stimulus, suggestions were made of feeling no pain. *S*'s were also told that they would not hear the report of the gun. The waking state always preceded the hypnotic state.

S's were made fully cognizant of the purpose of the experiment and were informed before each stimulus both in hypnosis and in the waking state about the kind of stimulation to expect. They did not know exactly when it would occur in either state, however (personal communication).

Because four of the seven *S*'s had complete amnesia for the hypnotic period, subjective reports were available from only the remaining three. The light hypnosis *S* reported partial analgesia for the pain stimuli; the two somnambulists reported complete analgesia. The noise of the pistol was reported as softer during hypnosis by the light hypnosis *S*; the two somnambulists reported that the sound was so far away that it did not startle them in the least.

No gross bodily movements were observed in hypnosis. In the waking state withdrawal from the painful stimuli and startle responses to the pistol shot were observed.

Results: Dynes presented a general summary of results shown in Table 1. Because tracing patterns were in essential agreement for all three stimuli, these effects were averaged. A before-stimulation and an after-stimulation score was reported for each *S* in both the waking and the hypnotic states. Means were reported separately for the three physiological variables. Each set of before-stimulation scores was compared with the corresponding set of after-stimulation scores. Small but significant differences in the expected directions emerged for respiratory rate and heart rate. Although difference for GSR was also in the expected direction, it was statistically nonsignificant.

Additional control: Dynes also investigated the possibility of voluntary simulation of reactions by the inclusion of two special *S*'s who were required to "fake" hypnosis. These were *S*'s whom Dynes had trained in hypnosis, but were asked by a third party supposedly without Dynes' knowledge, really not to enter hypnosis in the experiment.

Table 1
General Table*

	MEAN RESPIRATORY RATE PER MI.				MEAN HEART RATE PER MI.				MEAN PSYCHOGALVANIC DEFLECTION	
Subject	Waking		Trance		Waking		Trance		Waking	Trance
	Before	After	Before	After	Before	After	Before	After		
No. I	16.5	24.4	17.20	16.3	89.2	99.0	96.0	96.0	6.80	5.00
No. II	17.7	21.0	16.25	17.3	69.5	72.5	70.7	70.1	3.25	4.26
No. III	15.0	16.3	14.20	14.6	78.3	81.9	77.2	78.9	4.60	4.20
No. IV	13.0	13.7	12.70	13.2	69.0	69.2	72.0	72.0	5.67	4.02
No. V	13.8	16.2	17.20	16.6	76.6	77.7	74.7	73.9	5.70	4.80
No. VI	20.5	22.5	20.70	18.7	85.5	89.0	89.0	86.5	6.50	6.25
No. VII	17.75	20.0	19.25	19.5	76.0	73.0	68.0	67.0	3.58	4.41
Sums	114.25	134.1	117.50	116.2	544.1	562.3	547.6	544.4	361.0	319.4
Means	16.32	19.15	16.78	17.60	77.73	80.33	78.23	77.77	5.16	4.56
Differences	+ 2.83		+ 0.82		+ 2.6		− 0.46			− 0.6

* From: Dynes, J. B. (1932). "Hypnotic anesthesia," *J. abnorm. soc. Psychol.*, **27**, 82.

(Actually, however, Dynes had full knowledge of which *S*'s were faking.) Although the data on these two special *S*'s were too meager for statistical analysis and were not presented, it is noted that the faking records appeared indicative of heightened tension and excitement.[7]

The feature of having the waking trials always precede the hypnotic trials in this study must be viewed as a methodological shortcoming. Further comment on the problem of failure to randomize order will be made in discussing the study by West *et al.* (1952).

BROWN AND VOGEL (1938)

Following Hull's suggestion (1933, p. 253), hypnotic analgesia was compared with two types of chemical anesthetics. Four other variations were included in the design to make seven conditions, as follows: (1) the normal waking state, (2) the hypnotic state with suggestions of complete analgesia, (3) the normal waking state with the request to imagine analgesia, (4) nitrous oxide general anesthetic, (5) local Novocain block, (6) the hypnotic state with suggestions of hyperalgesia, and (7) the normal waking state with the request to imagine hyperalgesia.

Three pain stimuli were used in all conditions. Sharp pain was produced with a blood lancet; continuous pain, with a weighted thumbtack. Hot water at 49 degrees C was the third stimulus. Conditions 6

[7] Dynes has since commented that he was so familiar with his *S*'s real hypnotic reactions that their simulation was easy to recognize. He added, however, that if the *S*'s had been strangers they might have been hard to detect (personal communication).

and 7 were run twice: once with the three pain stimuli, and once with comparable but painless stimuli. The order of these conditions was varied for each *S*.

Polygraphic tracings were abstracted into six physiological indices: (1) GSR conductance change, (2) GSR recovery ratio, (3) pulse rate ratio, (4) change in relative blood pressure, (5) respiration time for five breaths, and (6) the relationship between expiration and inspiration amplitudes of respiration.[8] Except for the two respiration measures, indices were computed by relating the level of reactivity before-stimulation to the level after-stimulation.

Three somnambulistic *S*'s were used, carefully preselected for hypnotic depth and hypnotic analgesic effect. Only one measure per stimulus was taken for each *S* so that no estimate was provided of response consistency within data cells.[9]

Pain stimuli were applied to both legs. Suggestions of normal feeling in the left control leg were made throughout.

Before the main experiment a few preliminaries familiarized *S*'s with the situation and provided some estimate of general reactivity level. From this pilot work it became clear that suggested analgesia (or suggested deafness) did not abolish all possible reactions to stimuli, but it could not be ascertained whether a *lessening* of reactivity might have occurred.

The use of waking imagination categories (that is, conditions where the *S* was required to imagine analgesia or hyperalgesia in the waking state) is a noteworthy procedure. In describing these imagination categories, however, no information was provided on whether the waking, voluntary attempts to imagine analgesia (or hyperalgesia) actually resulted in diminished (or heightened) subjective pain perception. Only if there was an alteration in reported subjective pain perception would it be plausible to relate any observed physiological effects to waking analgesia or hyperalgesia. If, however, the subjective perception of painfulness appeared to remain the same, it might be better to consider the waking analgesia category an indirect way of *inhibiting* or *suppressing* physiological responses, and to consider the waking hyperalgesia category an indirect way of attempting to call forth emotional overreactions.

Results: Only raw, uncondensed numerical data were furnished. A number of specimen polygraphic tracings were also presented.

Although the data were few, we have made a descriptive condensation to help illuminate possible trends. For each variable and condition there were nine units of data for each leg. These nine numbers represented

[8] Not to be confused with the I/E time ratio.

[9] An exception was the lancet stimulus in the local block condition where two measures were taken on two of the three *S*'s.

the three stimuli for the three *S*'s.[10] By subtracting each control (left) leg score from its comparable experimental (right) leg score, a total of nine difference scores has been derived for each variable and condition. Means were then computed for each of the three *S*'s and graphs were prepared from these means. Abstracts of these graphs are shown in Figure 1. For simplicity, only the means for the normal waking state (WC), waking analgesia (WA), hypnotic analgesia (HA), and the painful stimulus condition under the local block (LB) condition have been included. Lower scores indicate correspondingly lesser physiological effect after stimulation of the right (experimental) leg than after stimulation of the left (control) leg.

Although there are some interesting trends in one or another graph, the data are too sparse and inconsistent to suspect the operation of other than chance influences.

As noted, Brown and Vogel also presented a set of specimen polygraphic tracings. Unfortunately the impression generated is that these tracings were typical and unambiguous. Conclusions were then drawn from both the numerical table and the tracings with no apparent recognition of their disparity. By preceding the conclusions with the statement, "Within the limits of our experimental conditions," the authors felt justified in examining their data for trends without concern for the question of statistical significance. Unfortunately, the examination was not clearly labeled as pure conjecture, and the wording can easily be misinterpreted as generalizations from evidence.

The major conclusions drawn from the study follow with needed critical appraisal.

1. It can be observed that scores in the waking imagination category vary at least as much as in hypnotic analgesia. In analyzing individual records it was concluded:

> There appears to be no marked difference between the physiological reactions to pain under hypnotically induced analgesia and that under imagined analgesia in the normal waking state, although only a tentative conclusion can be made on the basis of our present study. . . . It appears . . . that in the subjects which we have observed imagination in the normal waking state may be just about as effective with respect to influencing the physiological reactions to pain as that which may be observed following suggestions in the trance state. . . . The effects produced by imagination in the normal waking state are of significance in demonstrating the possibility of *voluntarily* influencing those physiological processes which have generally been considered as autonomous . . . the influence of unconscious activity upon these processes has perhaps been frequently overemphasized. (pp. 413 and 418)

These statements suggest the unwarranted conclusion that both waking imagination and hypnotic analgesia are effective in influencing

[10] These comments are generally true even though some of the data are missing.

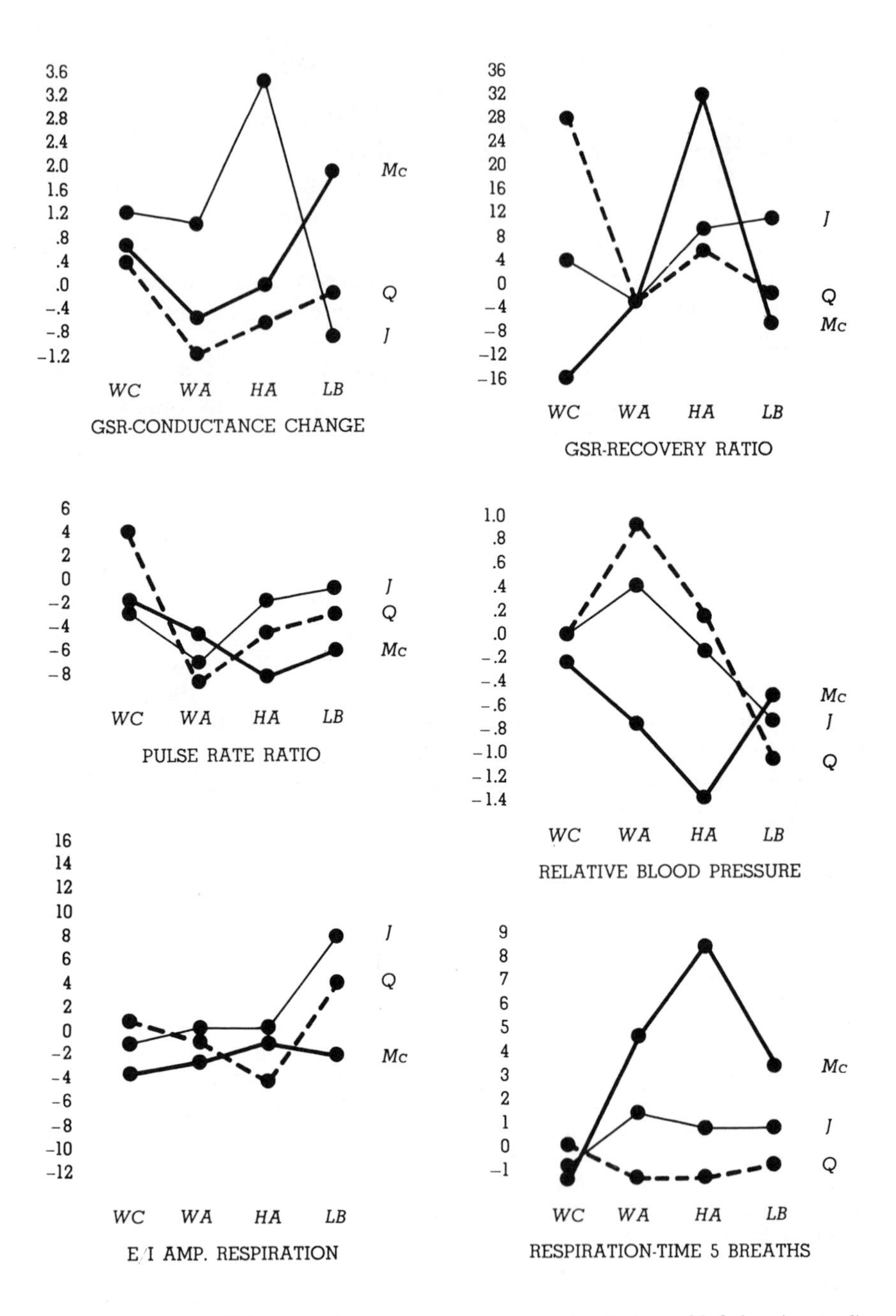

Figure 1. Mean differences between responses to stimulation of left leg (control) and right leg (experimental) in Subject *J*, Subject *Q*, and Subject *Mc*. (After Brown and Vogel, 1938.)

physiological reactions to pain, but that both are about equally effective. Because neither had a measurable effect does not mean that both had about equal effectiveness. Simply because neither was shown effective under these experimental conditions does not mean that they would appear even similar in a more sensitive test.

2. Another major conclusion was that there were no physiological reactions to the painful stimuli that could serve as reliable indicators of the painful experience:

> [There was] marked variability of reaction to painful stimuli both with respect to extent and direction of effect. Although the stimuli were judged to be quite painful, there seemed to be no physiological signs of sufficient significance for determining the presence of pain. . . . Quantitative changes in physiological reactions to painful stimuli are not reliable indicators of painful experience. (pp. 412 and 420)

The statement was unfortunately allowed to stand without further discussion even though it contradicted many other statements in the report. For example, the statement under Conclusion 1 above contradicts it, as do the following two statements:

> In the control record [of figure 3-b] . . . it is obvious that the physiological reactions are affected, although the changes are not as great as those observed in the trance state. (pp. 416–417)
>
> Physiological reactions to moderate and mild sensory stimuli may be affected by suggestion in the hypnotic state and by imagination in the normal state. (p. 420)

If physiological reactions are not reliable indicators of painful experience, then conclusions cannot be drawn that various conditions affect the pain responses differentially. Without physiological indices that are reliably responsive to pain the study loses its avowed purpose. There is reason, however, to be skeptical of a literal interpretation of the statement. As already noted, specimen polygraphic tracings are presented in the report. Visual appraisal of these tracings shows consistent changes in response to the pain stimuli on at least the GSR channel, and frequently on others.

This visual appraisal of the tracings is corroborated in an analysis of the table. Interpreted literally, the statement that there are no reliable physiological indicators of painful experience refers to a comparison between the level of physiological reaction before stimulation and the level after stimulation. If consistent pre-post stimulus differences occur in Brown and Vogel's tabular data, then the statement must be incorrect. Because the two respiration measures were recorded without noting prestimulation level, it is not possible now to specify whether a change in reaction occurred as a result of stimulation. The other four variables were recorded taking initial level into account, however, and it therefore is possible to look for consistent pre-post stimulation changes. A score of zero on GSR Conductance Change indicates no pre-post difference. Because most scores are above zero, it is clear that changes did take place. A similar result holds for GSR Recovery Ratio. Pulse Rate Ratio is consistent with Brown and Vogel's statement in that it varies around an approximate average of 100. Changes in Relative Blood Pressure are in all instances greater than zero and positive in direction. On three of the six physiological variables, therefore, the statement about no reliable indicators is incorrect; it is probably true for one variable, and information is unavailable for the remaining two. What the authors perhaps intended to convey is that the reactions to pain in the two legs (experimental and normal control) were not sufficiently unalike to yield significant differences or even visible trends; that is, a recognition of null findings. Such null findings may be (a) due to a lack of such differences, or (b) due to the use of an experimental design too insensitive to capture existing differences. Given the great variability in measurement apparently noted by the authors, an experiment with only one measurement per cell for three *S*'s seems of dubious statistical power to rely on to discern differences.

3. It is concluded that nitrous oxide anesthesia has no similarity to hypnotic analgesia:

> We were unable to observe any physiological responses to painful stimuli while the subjects were under gas anesthesia. The application of nitrous oxide is associated with marked physiological changes, the nature of which is quite dissimilar to those observed following hypnotic analgesia. There appears to be no point of similarity between these two states. . . . Nitrous oxide anesthesia abolishes physiological reactions to moderately intense sensory stimuli. (Severe stimuli were not used.) (pp. 419–420; authors' parentheses)

To the extent that this quotation is based upon clinical observations, it appears highly relevant. To the extent, however, that the quotation is meant to refer to the polygraphic data reported in the table, its factual basis needs re-examination. Data are reported for only two of the three *S*'s in the nitrous oxide condition. As noted above, the left leg obviously could not be used as a nonanesthetized control during this session. The essential finding was that when stimuli were applied there was no GSR reaction. This is sufficiently atypical of the data as a whole to be judged a special kind of event. The remaining variables, however, yield scores that are closely congruent with scores during other conditions. As far as reported data are concerned then, the statement about the uniqueness of nitrous oxide anesthesia refers only to a disappearance of the GSR to painful stimuli.[11]

[11] The only further comment made to this point is that in one *S* (Q) there was a continuous rise in blood pressure from 106/74 to 195/100 and in pulse rate from 79 to 117 (p. 414). However, this was later described as a function of the nitrous oxide and not of stimulation (Brown, personal communication).

Whatever the deficiencies of this study as a source of evidence, it has a number of important features that would be valuable to incorporate into future research. Perhaps the most intriguing feature of the design was the inclusion of tests with indifferent stimuli in the hyperalgesia conditions. (West *et al.* [1952] also included stimuli at zero intensity but did not analyze them separately.) Indifferent stimuli could be used to advantage, moreover, in other conditions besides hyperalgesia —perhaps by intermixing them randomly with actual pain stimuli. It would be of major interest, for example, to compare the differential physiological effect to an anesthetized leg of two stimuli—one noxious and the other indifferent—neither of which at the time is subjectively experienced as painful. It would be necessary, of course, to take cognizance of conditioning and expectancy in such a design, but it would allow the use of one segment of the *S*'s anatomy as its own control without altering instructions.

DOUPE, MILLER, AND KELLER (1939)

Vasoconstriction of the cutaneous blood vessels was the physiological index used in this study. Eight *S*'s were run; four were graduate students and four were patients with no evidence of organic nervous disease. A series of eleven single *S* experiments was described. Three *S*'s were only in one experiment each. One *S* was in three experiments, and another was in five. Data were not reported on the other three *S*'s.

At the beginning of each experiment, the *S* was seated comfortably in a quiet, temperature-controlled room of 22 to 24 degrees C. *S* was allowed to rest for a few minutes after the physiological recording devices were attached to his body. Hypnosis was then induced and deepened until a criterion of adequate depth was reached. Criterion was defined in terms of *S*'s reported inability to feel a deep pin prick on an hypnotically anesthetic arm.[12]

After a few preliminaries *S*'s arms (or legs) were placed in warm water of 45 degrees C to produce dilation of the peripheral blood vessels. Once dilated, the vessels remained stable, providing a base-line of vasoconstriction. Hypnotic suggestions were then given for one of the two immersed limbs to become analgesic with the implication that normal feeling would remain in the other limb. Six to 40 pain stimuli then were given to each of the limbs, applied alternately. Seven of the 11 experiments were run using moderately painful stimuli; the remainder with severely painful stimuli. These two intensities—moderate and severe—were established in terms of *S*'s report. Moderate intensity was defined as those stimuli that the *S* in the waking state could bear with

[12] It is unclear whether the criterion was anesthesia or analgesia.

equanimity; severe, as those stimuli that the *S* in the waking state was hardly able to endure. Pin pricks were used as moderate stimuli. A special stylus was used to maintain approximately equal intensities throughout any given experiment. Two kinds of severe stimuli were used: (a) deeper pin pricks, and, occasionally, (b) the prolonged application of ice. The trials where one or the other were applied were not identified. Time intervals between stimuli were not noted, nor was it made clear whether cues were given for *S*'s to anticipate stimuli. After termination of hypnosis the various stimuli were repeated but these data were not reported. Further information on the effectiveness of hypnosis was then secured in terms of amnesia and the *S*'s failure to appreciate the passage of time.[13]

Results: Results of the first seven experiments are presented in Table 2. It will be observed that two of the *S*'s participated in two experiments. In five experiments the analgesic limb means are lower than the normal limb means. It should be noted that both experiments in which the normal limb means are higher were the second experiments for the respective *S*'s. Statistical significance was achieved only in A. B.'s first experiment. In A. B.'s second experiment the mean difference was both nonsignificant and in the opposite direction. These findings were interpreted as follows:

> In one experiment (A. B. 1) . . . the average response . . . was 37 per cent less when the analgesic right leg was stimulated, and the . . . difference was significant. When the experiment was repeated (A. B. 2) with the suggestion that the formerly normal left leg was not analgesic, greater constrictions were still obtained from stimulation of the left leg. The value of *P*, however, showed that this result was much less significant than the former, and it was explicable on the basis of the persistence of the suggestion from the previous experiment. (p. 99)

This interpretation requires rephrasing because it was overstated in two ways. First, the statement that the probability value was "much less significant" in the second experiment can refer in this context only to statistical significance and not clinical significance. It means that one can be *more confident* in generalizing about the reality of the observed differences in the first experiment than in the second. No proof was given, however, that there was less of an effect in the second experiment than in the first. A direct test of this contingency is possible by comparing the analgesic-minus-normal difference scores in the two experiments, reversing the signs of the differences for the second experiment. This method of comparison tests whether the differences in the first experiment were larger than in the second, ignoring the fact that the mean differences were in opposite directions. In performing this analysis we

[13] It was observed that hypnotic induction as such did not affect the peripheral vessels. Data were not presented to quantify this generalization, however.

Table 2
Responses to Moderate Stimuli*

	R. L.		A. R.		C. M.		J. L. (EXP. 1)		J. L. (EXP. 2)		A. B. (EXP. 1)		A. B. (EXP. 2)	
	NORMAL	ANALGESIC	NORMAL	ANALGESIC	NORMAL	ANALGESIC	NORMAL	ANALGESIC	NORMAL	ANALGESIC	NORMAL	ANALGESIC	NORMAL	ANALGESIC
	L. arm	R. arm	R. leg	L. leg	R. arm	L. arm	L. leg	R. leg	R. leg	L. leg	L. leg	R. leg	R. leg	L. leg
	1.9	2.8	2.7	2.7	1.0	0.7	1.6	1.2	2.5	4.0	2.5	1.0	0.0	1.3
	2.9	1.6	1.7	1.7	0.6	0.6	1.2	2.0	1.5	1.0	0.0	0.0	0.0	0.7
	1.3	0.8	5.0	5.0	0.5	0.5	2.1	1.2	3.0	4.5	2.7	1.6	0.6	0.0
	1.0	1.0	3.7	2.5	1.0	1.0	1.0	0.9	5.0	4.5	2.9	1.5	0.2	0.0
	0.9	1.2	3.8	2.3	0.9	0.8	2.8	2.1	5.5	5.0	2.8	2.2	0.5	0.0
	1.0	0.7	2.0	3.8	0.5	0.5	2.9	2.2	5.0	5.0	3.2	2.8	1.7	3.6
	1.7	0.9					2.2	3.2			4.6	2.2	0.9	2.8
	1.6	1.9									2.5	3.1	1.5	0.0
											2.0	0.0	0.4	0.7
											3.1	2.1	0.3	1.8
											3.8	2.1	1.0	4.1
													6.0	4.5
													0.8	5.0
													1.0	5.0
													1.6	1.4
													7.0	1.2
													3.8	4.7
													0.8	1.5
													6.0	3.0
Mean	1.54	1.36	3.15	3.00	.75	.68	1.97	1.83	3.75	4.00	2.74	1.71	1.79	2.23
Difference	− 11.6%		− 4.8%		− 9.3%		− 7.1%		+ 6.6%		− 37.6%		+ 29.7%	
P†	0.6		0.8		0.6		0.9		0.8		0.02		0.5	

* From: Doupe, J., Miller, W. R., and Keller, W. K. (1939). "Vasomotor reactions in the hypnotic State," *J. neurol., neuros. and Psychiat.*, **2**, 100. Reprinted by permission of the British Medical Association.

† P = Computed according to Mainland (1938) indicates the probability of the difference in means being significant. When P is 0.9 the difference might be expected in 9 out of 10 samples chosen from similar material. When P is 0.02 the difference would be expected to arise by chance only twice in 100 samples.

Note: The figures represent the vertical distance in cm between the diastolic phase of the pulse wave before and that during the time of greatest constriction as measured on the original record.

found nonsignificant differences between the means but quite significant differences between the variances. The variance in the second experiment is over seven times larger than in the first.

Second, it is problematic to say that the change in direction of mean differences in the two experiments is due to the suggestion's persistence. No documentation is given for the speculation.

Additional rephrasings also are needed of the following generalizations:

> Disregarding these two results (the two experiments of subject A. B.) the other experiments all showed a negative difference which, though separately of little significance, together implied that stimulation of the analgesic limb was slightly but definitely less effective in producing a vasoconstriction than similar stimulation of the normal limb. (p. 99)

Two comments again are required. (1) As noted earlier, it is a mistake to say that excluding subject A. B. all directions of difference were negative. The second experiment for J. L. also had a positive mean difference. (2) No substantiation is given for the statement that the analgesic limb was slightly but definitely less effective in producing a vasoconstriction. Our own analysis of these data using a t test for correlated samples between the pairs of means of the seven experiments on Table 2, and again for the first five experiments excluding A. B. failed to achieve statistical significance.

The remaining four experiments were run with the severe stimuli, and the results are shown in Table 3. The first of these experiments was on J. L., his third participation. The difference was in the expected direction and significant ($p < .02$ level). A. B., who had already participated in two experiments, was again run in the three final experiments. Mean differences in all three of these final experiments were in the expected direction. Only the last of these, however, reached statistical significance. In regard to this last experiment it was learned from A. B. that repeated reinforcements (repetitions) of the suggestion of analgesia was an important part of the technique. The authors have been able to separate those stimuli given without reinforcement from those stimuli given with it. When these two sets of data were segregated and tested independently, it was observed that the mean difference with reinforcement was very significant ($p < .01$ level) and in the expected direction. However, the mean difference without reinforcement, although insignificant, was in the *opposite* direction. Further comment was not made on this discrepancy. It is instructive to display the means of this last experiment graphically, as is done in Figure 2.

It can be observed that although the total normal mean is higher than the total analgesic mean, their component means differ widely. The most striking feature of these relationships is the great discrepancy

Table 3
Responses to Severe Stimuli*

SUBJECT	J. L.		A. B. (EXP. 3)		A. B. (EXP. 4)				A. B. (EXP. 5)			
									(NO REINFORCEMENT)		(WITH REINFORCEMENT)	
	NORMAL	ANALGESIC	NORMAL	ANALGESIC	NORMAL	ANALGESIC	NORMAL	ANALGESIC	NORMAL	ANALGESIC	NORMAL	ANALGESIC
	L. leg	R. leg	R. leg	L. leg	R. leg	L. leg	R. leg	L. leg	R. leg	R. leg	L. leg	R. leg
	3.0	3.0	5.0	4.5	4.0	3.3	2.3	3.1	1.3	4.6	3.3	1.0
	3.2	2.3	5.0	5.0	3.3	3.5	1.6	2.6	0.6	1.8	2.5	1.8
	3.0	1.4	5.0	2.0	2.2	0.0	0.8	3.5	1.2	2.5	4.6	1.0
	3.5	2.1	1.0	2.5	1.1	1.0	4.8	3.4	6.0	1.3	5.0	4.3
	3.2	1.0	4.5	0.0	1.9	3.9	0.7	1.2	2.8	0.4	4.7	6.0
	1.7	1.5	3.5	3.6	4.4	4.6	1.2	0.8	1.5	5.0	7.0	5.6
			4.1	5.0	2.3	1.8	1.5	2.0	2.1	4.5	7.5	5.0
			3.8	3.0	2.2	1.5	2.1	2.6	3.4	5.0	4.7	6.0
			2.3	0.7	2.6	0.8	0.0	2.8	0.0	3.6	2.2	1.5
			2.1	0.8	2.8	0.9	3.2	3.1	0.8	1.8	3.7	3.3
			0.0	0.0	0.4	0.8	4.5	3.4	3.6	0.0	4.7	1.0
			4.0	3.0	1.5	3.4	4.6	2.2	1.4	1.2	3.6	2.0
			1.0	4.0	3.2	4.2	3.5	3.2	4.0	2.8	—	2.5
					2.3	2.1	1.4	3.1	4.1	5.0	4.1	4.3
					4.0	2.7	2.2	1.6	8.0	2.7	2.3	1.6
					1.7	3.3	1.5	2.6	1.8	5.6	2.8	0.5
					2.0	1.7	2.6	2.9			8.0	2.1
					2.2	1.3	2.4	3.2			3.2	1.0
					1.3	1.6					2.0	0.8
					0.3	0.5					4.0	1.0
					2.4	3.2					0.8	1.3
					3.4	2.4					1.4	0.5
											—	1.5
											5.5*A*	3.0
											4.0*C*	2.5*B*
											—	2.3*D*
											2.5	1.8
											—	0.7
Mean	2.93	1.88	3.18	2.62	—	—	2.31	2.19	2.64	2.99	3.92	2.35
Difference	− 35.8%		− 17.6%				− 5.2%		+13.2%		− 40.0%	
P	0.02		0.4				0.6		0.6		0.01	

* From: Doupe *et al.* (1939), p. 101.
Note: Figures obtained as in Table 2. Responses indicated by letters are shown in Fig. 2.

between the normal leg mean in the no-reinforcement condition as compared with the normal leg mean in the with-reinforcement condition. We have tested this difference and found it to be statistically significant. Assuredly this is a puzzling state of affairs. There is no reason to expect that increased suggestions of analgesia for the analgesic leg should in any way *heighten* the reaction to the *control leg* unless the so-called control leg is not functioning as a control. It thus seems a strong possibility that the overall significant difference that emerged in this experiment may have been due to an artificially raised response from the so-called

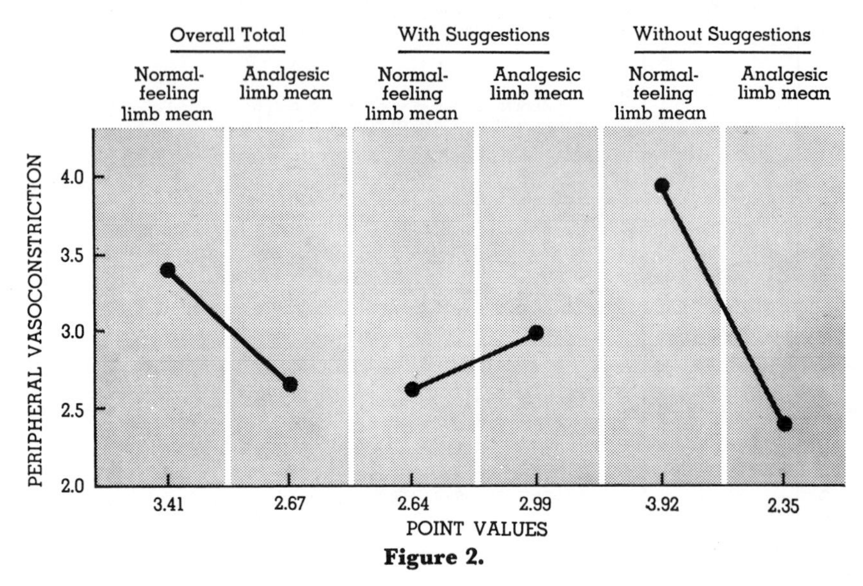

Figure 2.

normal limb rather than as a result of a diminished effect from the analgesic limb. Merely because the experimental design specifies that one limb is *supposed* to remain an unchanged control does not mean that this will occur. It must be remembered that A. B. had already taken part in four prior experiments before participating in this final one. Much of hypnosis can be understood as role-playing even when *S* is not consciously aware of how he is achieving a certain goal. Quite unwittingly, *S* may have produced an abnormally high "normal" response (hyperreaction), which by default gave a large mean difference. If this could be demonstrated, it would be interesting in its own right but should not be confused with an analgesic effect.

Although Doupe *et al.*'s evidence is weak, they offer a tentative theoretical interpretation of the analgesic effect, which is of interest in its own right:

> The different results produced by light and strong stimulation may be explained on the following basis. . . . The results reported above show that the autonomic

nervous system may be brought into activity by a noxious stimulus that is not consciously perceived and which apparently does not set up any associated emotional state. It has also been shown that mental activity alone or in association with suggestions of pain will activate the autonomic nervous system so that a vasoconstriction of the peripheral blood vessels ensues. The greater response which has been found on strongly stimulating the normal side may, therefore, be a summation of the results of the mental activity or emotional state caused by the appreciation of the pain, and of the other more direct results of the stimulus. Conversely, the greater similarity of the responses following light stimulation of either side is due to the fact that the stimuli were too slight to cause much mental anxiety. Bearing these considerations in mind, it would seem that stimulation of an hypnotically anaesthetized area produces the same involuntary reactions as does stimulation of an area of normal sensibility, except for those elements which are contributed by the associated mental state. (p. 105)

An important feature of this investigation was the use of both "moderate" and "severe" stimuli. Another important feature was that a few of the *S*'s were run a number of times, and the data from each session were treated separately. The investigation is of especial value, however, because it raises the important problem of possible hyperreactions in the control intervals.

WEST, NEILL, AND HARDY (1952)

The investigation was based on the Hardy-Wolff-Goodell technique for administration of painful stimuli in the form of known amounts of radiant heat. These known amounts were then correlated with subjective impressions of pain intensity, in terms of the dol scale (1947). The authors compared subjective pain thresholds and subjective changes in pain sensitivities above threshold in the waking condition and after suggestions of analgesia while *S*'s were in hypnosis. The GSR was the only physiological index used. During the experiment the *S*'s rested supine on a cot and the dolorometer was placed comfortably on the blackened back of the left hand and forearm; GSR electrodes were placed on the right hand. Skin resistance was recorded every two minutes during a ten-minute resting period. After threshold was determined, a series of stimuli of increasing intensities was administered. These were routinely at zero, threshold, and 2, 4, 6, and in some cases, 7 dols. GSR was measured in terms of percentage change.

Hypnosis was then induced and its depth estimated. After suggestions of analgesia (anesthesia), stimuli were repeated in the same order as in the waking control period. During hypnosis *S*'s were asked to report on the quality of the stimuli in terms of the dol scale, measurements were taken of pain threshold, and ability to discriminate between stimuli of various intensities was determined. Inquiry was continued afterwards in the waking state. Although West *et al.* originally stated, "For control purposes, the periods of hypnosis and control were occasionally reversed with four of the seven subjects," West has amended this remark: "To my recollection, we reversed the order of waking and hypnotic conditions in *all* subjects, irregularly but systematically" (personal communication). Under neither contingency, however, does the order appear to have been adequately randomized, with the result that the waking series seems usually to have preceded the trance series. Because it is known that GSR is likely to dampen over time with repeated pain stimulations, especially at low pain intensities, the failure adequately to randomize order is a methodological shortcoming.

Anywhere from ten to 118 observations were made on each *S*, a total of 478 stimuli for the seven *S*'s. There were 45 experimental sessions, an average of 6.4 sessions per *S*. As noted above, stimuli ranged from painless shutter clicks to blister-producing intensities. In any given session *S*'s received an identical series of stimulations in the waking and hypnotic states, so that properly paired statistical comparisons could be made.[14]

Results are summarized in Table 4. The seven *S*'s were ranked in terms of estimated depth of hypnosis. Four *S*'s were consistently in light hypnosis; none was consistently in deep hypnosis.

The results showed statistically significant reductions in GSR reactivity for all seven *S*'s during hypnosis as compared with the waking state. On a number of occasions in hypnosis, it was reported that there was no GSR reaction to intense stimulation at all. Positive correlations appear suggested between (a) highest achieved depth of hypnosis, (b) highest experienced reduction in pain perception, and (c) amount of GSR reduction. Statistical treatment was not given, however.[15] In regard to the physiological measurements it was concluded: "The experimental results leave no doubt that hypnotic suggestion of analgesia diminishes the galvanic skin response to noxious stimuli." (p. 559).

Although GSR reactivity was less in hypnosis than in the waking state, this has not actually been shown to be dependent upon the suggestions of analgesia. It is a common observation that unless special instructions are given, hypnotic *S*'s are often more relaxed and less tense the deeper their hypnosis, particularly as compared with their alert waking state. The observed changes in the GSR perhaps may be attributable

[14] West further notes, "We were careful to observe skin resistance *base-line* and found that it did not shift significantly from hypnotic to non-hypnotic periods during any given sessions. This is important in light of Lacey's law of initial values. Increased anxiety during hypnosis, if reflected in a considerable downward shift of skin resistance base-line, would lead to an apparently diminished magnitude of galvanic skin response to a given stimulation during the period of lowered base-line" (personal communication). See Wilder (1957).

[15] We have computed phi coefficients on these three variables with Fisher's Exact Method for testing the results. There is a perfect positive phi correlation between a and b that is significant at the .03 point (one tail). The other two correlations (b and c, and a and c) are both .67. With samples of only seven *S*'s the associated probabilities are nonsignificant ($p = .14$).

Table 4
Effect of Hypnotic Suggestion of Anesthesia on Pain Sensation and on the Galvanic Skin Response to Pain*

SUBJECT NUMBER	NUMBER OF OBSERVATIONS	DEPTH OF TRANCE	PAIN PERCEPTION	REDUCTION OF GALVANIC SKIN RESPONSE, %	DEGREE OF CONFIDENCE
1	28	Light	Unchanged	26	0.05
2	118	Light	Hypalgesia 0–2 dols	64	0.01
3	48	Light	Hypalgesia 0–4 dols	49	0.01
4	92	Light	Hypalgesia 0–6 dols	55	0.01
5	10	Light	Hypalgesia 5 dols	67	0.01
	100	Medium	Analgesia		
6	50	Medium	Hypalgesia 5 dols	57	0.01
		Medium	Analgesia		
7	42	Medium	Hypalgesia 6 dols	62	0.01
		Deep	Analgesia		

* From: West, L. J., Neill, K. C., and Hardy, J. D. (1952). " Effects of hypnotic suggestions on pain perception and galvanic skin response," *Arch. neurol. Psychiat.*, **68**, 555.

to the general state of greater relaxation in hypnosis rather than functionally dependent on the suggestions of analgesia. Missing is a control comparison in the hypnotic state *without* suggestions of analgesia.

The authors, aware of this shortcoming, reported that in the first stages of investigation they performed a few preliminary tests that led them to believe that hypnosis alone does not diminish GSR reactivity. Data were not presented, however. West has since elaborated:

> I fear that we did pass over this point lightly. However, we did so because our preliminary studies indicated clearly that hypnosis alone does not alter GSR to pain. An experiment with *two* controls, one waking and one in trance without suggestions of anesthesia, was done at the beginning of the study. This actually involved several subjects and we reversed the waking and hypnotic control session in each subject at least once. We found no difference between the response of a waking subject who was completely relaxed, and the same subject hypnotized but with no suggestions of anesthesia. The identification of noxious stimulation according to the dol scale was comparable in the two states and the degree of galvanic skin response correlated with the reported intensity of pain sensation (personal communication).

West then brings up an interesting theoretical issue:

> If an individual has the notion that the hypnotic state implies diminished or departed pain sensations, it may not even be necessary to make suggestions of anesthesia to him in order to achieve it. Of course this problem did not come up with our subjects who were very carefully instructed (personal communication).

Implicit in this statement is a recognition of what Orne has termed "demand characteristics" (1959). Human *S*'s always evolve some pattern of preconceptions and expectations in any experiment, although these may remain unverbalized unless *S*'s are carefully questioned. These preconceptions often have a most profound effect on *S*'s accomplishments.

West has thus reasoned that if an individual believes that hypnosis alone will diminish perception of pain, *then this in itself* may result in a "spontaneous" analgesia without suggestions of analgesia. His logic may be applied just as well backwards as forwards, however. If an individual believes that hypnosis alone will not diminish perception of pain, *then this in itself* may inhibit a lessening of the perception of painfulness, which might otherwise have occurred spontaneously. Carried another step, the argument works equally well for physiological responses as for perception of painfulness.

Is there any way out of this tangle? Can there *ever* be a hypnosis-alone condition in an hypnotic analgesia experiment without at the same time unwittingly structuring expectations one way or another?

Even if the experimental situation as such were somehow neutrally structured, how would one prevent (or account for) the preconceptions held by different *S*'s? In an hypnotic analgesia experiment two ways of dealing with this problem appear relevant. The first is independently to estimate *S*'s preconceptions about the hypnosis-alone condition and compare these estimates with the results. The second is deliberately to structure the experimental situation one way or the other (or both ways, by using two different groups) to see how differing preconceptions influence responses.

SEARS (1932)

Under Hull's direction (1933), Sears investigated three things: (1) if hypnotic analgesia decreases physiological reactivity to pain, (2) if *S*'s without hypnotic analgesia produce similar decrements in reactivity by deliberately suppressing their reactions, and (3) if hypnosis alone, without hypnotic analgesia, itself alters reactivity.

S's were seven male undergraduates, all somnambulists. The experiment was run in three series; order was not randomized. The purpose of the first series, Wake Control, was to determine whether or not the responses to pain stimuli in both legs was about the same when no differential instructions were given. During the second series, Hypnotic Analgesia, hypnosis was induced and the left leg was hypnotically rendered analgesic; the right leg, however, was required to remain normally sensitive to stimuli throughout. The final series, Voluntary Inhibition, was run partly in hypnosis and partly in the waking state.

S's were instructed to inhibit all reactions to left (experimental) leg stimulation and react normally to right (control) leg stimulation.

An *ABBA* order of stimulation for the two legs was always used. Stimuli were kept from 50 to 80 seconds apart. Sears avoided a definite rhythm so that each stimulus would have the same quality of unexpectedness. Also he wished to avoid problems of temporal conditioning. The pain stimuli used were pin pricks on the calves of the legs. A special stylus was constructed to deliver pin pricks at approximately 20 ounces of pressure without breaking the skin. Each stimulation lasted approximately one second.

In the Wake Control series four to ten stimulations were given in each of three experimental periods. In the Hypnotic Analgesia series eight to 16 stimulations were given. A moderate number of stimulations were also given in the Voluntary Inhibition series. Data were simultaneously recorded on a number of physiological variables and abstracted into six separate types of measurement: (1) Facial Grimaces, (2) Respiratory Oscillation, (3) Respiratory Variability, (4) Pulse Oscillation, (5) Pulse Variability, and (6) Galvanic Skin Response.[16]

Except for Facial Grimace (which is all-or-none), the variables were all processed by computing the before-stimulation minus after-stimulation difference scores for each leg.[17] The median was then used to represent all measures taken for any one condition. These median data are presented in Tables 5 through 7, taken from Hull (1933). The data were then analyzed in terms of critical ratios.

Results: As had been expected, for none of the variables were significant differences found between the means of the medians in the Waking Control series. In the Hypnotic Analgesia series, results showed less of a reaction to stimulation in the analgesic leg than in the control leg.

[16] The methods of abstraction were as follows: (1) Facial Grimace. The presence or absence of a facial flinch was measured by a simple levered device. (2) Respiratory Oscillation. The total relative amount of depth of breathing in a given period of time was measured by summating the total amount of vertical movement in respiratory tracings for the 20-second period before stimulation and the 20-second period after stimulation. (3) Respiratory Variability. The average amount of variation in depth of breathing between successive breaths was measured for the 20-second period before stimulation and the 20-second period after stimulation. It was equated for variations in numbers of breaths. (4) Pulse Oscillation. A blood pressure cuff attached to the arm was kept at a constant pressure below systolic. Pulse (heart) beat amplitude was thus a relative measure of blood pressure. The total amount of vertical amplitude was measured for all beats in the 7 1/2-second period before stimulation and the 7 1/2-second period after stimulation. (The arm had to be kept still as movement could influence cuff pressure.) (5) Pulse Variability. The average amount of variability in amplitude between successive pulse beats in the 7 1/2-second period before stimulation and the 7 1/2-second period after stimulation was measured and then equated for variations in number of beats. (6) Galvanic Skin Response. Vertical movement in skin resistance during the 20-second period after stimulation was compared with the normal galvanometric vertical drift movement in the 20-second period before stimulation. The data were not transformed nor was initial resistance level taken into account.

[17] Flinch response per cents were computed for Facial Grimace.

Table 5

Summary of Sears' Experimental Results on His Normal Control Series, in Which the Right and Left Legs Were Pricked in the Non-Trance State with No Suggestions Given Regarding Anaesthesia*

SUBJECT	NUMBER OF STIMULATIONS		PERCENTAGES OF FACIAL FLINCH		MEDIAN GAIN IN RESPIRATORY OSCILLATION		MEDIAN GAIN IN RESPIRATORY AMPLITUDE VARIABILITY		MEDIAN GAIN IN PULSE OSCILLATION		MEDIAN GAIN IN PULSE AMPLITUDE VARIABILITY		MEDIAN GAIN IN GALVANIC SKIN OSCILLATION	
	R.L.†	*L.L.*†	*R.L.*	*R.L.*	*R.L.*	*L.L.*	*R.L.*	*L.L.*	*R.L.*	*L.L.*	*R.L.*	*L.L.*	*R.L.*	*L.L.*
Cl	12	11	0	0	+14	− 4	+0.1	−0.4	− 3	−18	0	0	+ 6	+ 8
Co	6	6	33	33	+ 7	+ 9	−0.2	+0.2	+ 1	+11	+0.2	+0.2	+12	+ 7
L	10	9	30	11	+34	+33	+6.9	+3.7	−12	−24	+0.5	+1.0	+ 3	+ 2
M	7	7	86	100	+79	+22	+5.1	+4.0	+25	− 2	+0.8	+1.2	+16	+10
S	4	4	50	50	− 9	+ 6	−1.3	−2.6	+14	+ 3	0	−0.5	+ 5	+ 5
Ta	6	6	100	83	+59	+99	+1.2	+2.0	−28	− 8	+0.7	+1.4	+ 4	− 4
Tr	4	4	75	75	+41	+21	+0.1	+3.5	+ 6	+ 7	+0.2	+0.3	+31	+52
Mean			53.43	50.29	+32.1	+26.6	+1.70	+1.49	+0.43	−4.43	+0.343	+0.514	+11.0	+11.43
P.E.M			8.36	8.90	7.26	8.06	0.72	0.59	4.08	3.06	0.077	0.165	2.93	4.36
Difference			3.14		5.5		0.21		4.86		0.171		0.43	
P.E.D			2.78		6.93		0.50		3.55		0.09		3.09	
D/P.E.D			1.13		0.79		0.42		1.37		1.90		0.14	

* From: Hull, C. L. (1933). *Hypnosis and Suggestibility*, p. 266. New York: Appleton-Century-Crofts, compiled from Sears, R. R. (1932), "Experimental study of hypnotic anesthesia," *J. exp. Psychol.*, **15**, 1–22.

† R.L. = right leg; L.L. = left leg.

Table 6

Summary of Sears' Experimental Results Concerning the Influence of Hypnotically Suggested Anaesthesia upon Various Objective Reactions to a Twenty-Ounce Blunt Prick on the Calf of the Leg*

SUBJECT	NUMBER OF STIMULATIONS		PERCENTAGES OF FACIAL FLINCH		MEDIAN GAIN IN RESPIRATORY OSCILLATION		MEDIAN GAIN IN RESPIRATORY AMPLITUDE VARIABILITY		MEDIAN GAIN IN PULSE OSCILLATION		MEDIAN GAIN IN PULSE AMPLITUDE VARIABILITY		MEDIAN GAIN IN GALVANIC SKIN OSCILLATION	
	N.L.†	*A.L.*†	*N.L.*	*A.L.*	*N.L.*	*A.L.*	*N.L.*	*A.L.*	*N.L.*	*A.L.*	*N.L.*	*A.L.*	*N.L.*	*A.L.*
Cl	14	14	7	7	+5	−6	−1.4	−1.8	+11	+9	+0.1	0	+10	+5
Co	20	20	0	10	+31	+32	+0.3	−0.1	−3	−7	+0.3	+0.3	+3	+3
L	16	16	19	0	+51	−22	+4.8	−0.3	−40	−5	+0.4	+0.4	+3	+2
M	12	12	75	0	+24	+54	+3.6	−0.3	−3	−23	+0.7	+0.2	+16	+11
S	11	10	45	0	+4	+23	+0.8	+0.2	−1	+7	+0.3	−0.1	+3	+3
Ta	21	20	52	0	+109	−29	+2.0	−0.1	−32	0	+0.3	0	+10	+10
Tr	7	7	14	0	−7	−62	+2.9	+1.2	−5	+2	−0.1	+0.2	+10	+9
Mean			30.28	2.42	+31.0	−1.4	+1.86	−0.17	−10.43	−2.43	+0.286	+0.143	+7.85	+6.14
$P.E._M$			6.49	1.00	9.33	9.47	0.67	0.21	4.34	2.54	0.058	0.043	1.18	0.89
Difference			27.86		32.4		2.03		8.00		0.143		1.71	
$P.E._D$			7.19		6.23		0.56		4.59		0.047		0.58	
$D/P.E._D$			3.87		5.20		3.62		1.74		3.04		2.95	

* From: Hull (1933), p. 261.
† *N.L.* = normal leg; *A.L.* = anesthetic leg.

Table 7
Summary of Sears' Experimental Results on His "Voluntary" Control Series

SUBJECT	NUMBER OF STIMULATIONS		PERCENTAGES OF FACIAL FLINCH		MEDIAN GAIN IN RESPIRATORY OSCILLATION		MEDIAN GAIN IN RESPIRATORY AMPLITUDE VARIABILITY		MEDIAN GAIN IN PULSE OSCILLATION		MEDIAN GAIN IN PULSE AMPLITUDE VARIABILITY		MEDIAN GAIN IN GALVANIC SKIN OSCILLATION	
	R.L.†	*L.L.*†	*R.L.*	*L.L.*	*R.L.*	*L.L.*	*R.L.*	*L.L.*	*R.L.*	*L.L.*	*R.L.*	*L.L.*	*R.L.*	*L.L.*
Cl	12	12	8	8	+ 1	−34	−0.9	+1.7	−10	−5	0	0	+ 5	+ 4
Co	8	8	0	0	+ 7	+18	+0.3	−0.4	+ 1	+1	—	—	+ 5	+ 4
L	9	8	0	0	+43	− 7	+1.5	+1.5	0	−3	—	—	+ 1	− 1
S	12	10	50	30	−22	+41	+4.7	+0.4	− 9	−1	+0.1	+0.1	+ 8	+ 9
Ta	9	9	78	78	+57	+91	+1.2	+3.1	− 7	−6	+0.2	+0.4	+ 5	+ 8
Tr	9	10	78	90	+51	+53	+1.3	+1.2	+ 3	+5	+0.1	+0.3	+21	+22
Mean			35.66	34.33	26.2	27.0	+1.35	+1.25	−3.67	−1.50	+0.10	+0.15	+7.50	+7.67
P.E.$_M$			9.40	10.01	6.78	11.20	0.52	0.30	1.42	1.03	0.024	0.069	1.75	2.0
Difference			1.71		0.8		0.10		2.17		0.050		0.17	
P.E.$_D$			2.80		8.09		0.54		0.93		0.046		0.41	
D/P.E.$_D$			0.61		0.10		0.18		2.33		1.08		0.41	

Note: The subject in the nontrance state was instructed deliberately to repress or conceal so far as possible the reactions to the prick on his left leg, but to make no such attempt at the prick on the right. Subject M was not given this series.

* From: Hull (1933), p. 268.

† *R.L.* = right leg; *L.L.* = left leg.

All of these differences were significant except for the variable, Pulse Oscillation. In the Voluntary Inhibition series, however, none of the differences were significant. Indeed, the tendency (nonsignificant) was for the differences to be in the opposite direction, suggesting possible overreaction in the experimental leg rather than a suppression of reaction. In the analysis of hypnosis alone, without hypnotic analgesia, none of the differences were significant expect for Facial Grimace.

These results repay closer examination, however. They are reviewed again below in greater detail, taking separately each of Sears' original three questions.

1. *The Effect of Hypnotic Analgesia.* Hull summarized the analgesic effect evidence by computing the percentages of mean reduction of pain reactions in the two legs. All of these differences were statistically significant except for Pulse Oscillation. Hull ranked the six variables according to their supposed volitional character. This classification is presented in Table 8, from Hull (1933).

Table 8
Summary of the Percentage of Mean Reduction in the Amounts of Various Reactions to Pain Presumably Due to Hypnotically Suggested Anaesthesia*

VOLITIONAL CHARACTER OF REACTION	REACTION	PERCENTAGE MEAN REDUCTION ON ANAESTHETIC LEG
Wholly voluntary	Verbal report	95 ±†
Partially voluntary	Facial grimace	92
Partially voluntary	Respiratory oscillation	105
Partially voluntary	Respiratory variability	109
Nonvoluntary	Pulse, oscillation	77
Nonvoluntary	Pulse, variability	50
Nonvoluntary	Galvanic skin reaction	22

* From: Hull (1933), p. 264.
† Estimate given by Dr. Sears in a private communication.

Inspection of the table creates the unambiguous conclusions that hypnotic analgesia considerably reduces the physiological effects of painful stimuli and that the response is more reduced the larger the volitional component.

2. *The Effect of Hypnosis Alone, Without Hypnotic Analgesia.* To see if hypnosis alone altered reactivity, Sears compared responses in the Waking Control and Hypnotic Analgesia series using the right control leg only. Except for Facial Grimace, none of the differences was significant. Four out of five differences were in the expected negative direction,

however. Although statistically nonsignificant, Sears believed it probable "that the induction of analgesia to the left leg during trance [was] not completely differential; i.e., there may [have been] a faint 'spread' of decreased sensitivity throughout the organism." (p. 21)

3. *The Effect of Voluntary Suppression.* Commenting on the Voluntary Inhibition series, Hull drew attention to the paradoxical finding that although *S*'s were supposedly trying to inhibit their reactions, the Facial Grimace continued. Because Facial Grimace appeared completely voluntary at the pain intensities used by Sears, this incongruity threw doubt on the adequacy of the Voluntary Inhibition series as a meaningful test of voluntary suppression. Hull said:

> The results . . . seem on the surface to . . . indicate a capacity quite beyond the power of voluntary simulation. . . . A closer examination of the situation, however, gives rise to some doubt as to the significance of these results. Sears states, doubtless with truth, that the facial flinch can ordinarily be inhibited at will. Nevertheless, the mean flinch values . . . indicate practically no influence of voluntary inhibition whatever. The fact that in this portion of the experiment such an inhibition did not take place is accordingly extremely paradoxical and throws doubt upon the significance of the lack of differences. . . . Clearly this portion of the experiment ought to be repeated in such a way as to provide assurance that the subjects really exert themselves to the maximum to suppress the signs of pain. . . . Until this fundamental fact has been determined, only tentative conclusions concerning the relation of the voluntary mechanism and hypnotic analgesia will be possible (Hull [1933], p. 267).

Why did Facial Grimace persist during Voluntary Inhibition? A number of possible alternative explanations comes to mind. (a) It may be, as Sears generalized, that a deliberate suppression of these responses is impossible, and may even increase rather than decrease reactivity. (b) Perhaps *S*'s tried to inhibit in the wrong fashion. It is likely *S*'s tried to inhibit their responses by directly "fighting against" them. Had they tried to suppress in an indirect fashion, by controlling their emotions, they may have been more successful; that is, they may have succeeded, had they allowed themselves to feel the pain for what it was but tried to "passively accept" the stimulus by emotionally controlling the anxiety attached to it. (c) *S*'s may have perceived that Sears did not expect the voluntary suppression to work; that is, unwittingly it may have been indirectly suggested that the phenomenon would not (or should not) succeed. Because hypnotic occurrences are so very much dependent upon the subtle innuendoes of the experimental situation and operator attitudes, strict cognizance must be taken of the impressions given in regard to the experiment and the experimenter's wishes and expectations. It is quite possible that Sears communicated to his *S*'s the impression that he was not completely convinced that they would be able voluntarily to suppress their reactions (or perhaps that he *doubted* they could). If instead he had given the impression that he knew they would succeed, his findings on this issue might have been different.

SHOR (1959)

An attempt was made to replicate Sears' design with an added control group.[18] Only three somnambulistic *S*'s and two Simulators were run before the study was abandoned. Although the replication was not carried far enough to view the results as evidence,[19] it did illuminate a number of unrecognized problems in procedure and interpretation.

We first carefully fabricated a pain stimulator device according to Sears' specifications and then tried it out on ourselves. We were surprized to discover that the pain produced was minimal. Hull's assertion that it was "a decidedly unpleasant stimulus" appeared incomprehensible. In using the pain stimulator with *S*'s in the actual research situation, however, we observed that *S*'s certainly did consider the stimulus as painful as Hull and Sears had described it. It was our impression that the unexpectedness of the stimulus plus the anxiety and apprehension factors with which it became intermixed were more responsible for the interpretation of the stimulus as painful than the "actual" pain intensity involved. During our postexperimental inquiries, *S*'s stated this plainly. They said that it was the *shock* of the stimulation not the *pain* that was irritating. The waiting without knowing when the shock was coming was the worst part of the experience. Their impression was that this tenseness while waiting caused increased sensitivity to the stimulus rather than natural sensitivity. Trying to maintain the "set" of analgesia in the left leg while keeping "normal" sensitivity in the right leg (without knowing when and to which side the stimulus was coming) appeared to them to spread the inhibitory effect to both legs and the apprehension effect to the whole body. Perhaps, then, the control leg response was unduly high; perhaps also, with a less complex task, the analgesic effect would have emerged even stronger.[20]

S's also stated that they had tried to use verbal and auditory cues to guess when the stimulus was coming; they report modest success. The *E*, however, was not aware of having given any such cues.

It was observed, moreover, that the intensity of the pain produced by the stimulus on the two-square-inch area varied considerably. This wide variability seemed due to two factors. First, even with stimulation kept relatively constant the area struck yielded widely different pain intensities. Second, even though the *E* tried to give exactly one-second

[18] These were *S*'s simulating hypnosis without *E* knowing beforehand which *S*'s were real and which were simulators (Orne, 1959).

[19] The findings were entirely null; not even minor trends emerged.

[20] It is plausible, however, that more apprehension was provoked in our experimental situation than it was in Sears'. In our study the requirements of the Real-Simulation method prevented the *E* from getting to know *S*'s beforehand; Sears had worked with his *S*'s many times. Our study was run in a mental hospital research laboratory; Sears had worked in an experimental room at the *S*'s own university. Sears had a few pieces of simple equipment; we had complicated apparatus, plus a one-way vision mirror with hidden observers. These differences could have altered the phenomena.

stimulations at a constant 20-ounce pressure, it was observed by *S*'s and by occasional independent judges that *E* deviated from this by small but perceptible amounts. The *E* himself was hardly aware of this variability, and it is plausible that this could systematically vary in regard to *E*'s expectations, unwittingly confounding the results.

It was concluded that the pain stimulator device was inadequate for producing moderate pain under rigorously controlled conditions. Thus our replication of the Sears' design was abandoned.

Trying to replicate Sears' design also increased our awareness of some unrecognized problems in data analysis and interpretation. It was pointed out earlier that medians were computed to serve as the first-stage raw data. The reason for computing medians became apparent only after gathering similar data ourselves. Our data had such inherent variability and non-normality that parametric analyses were prohibited.

Sears later noted that his data had similar characteristics:

> My recollection of the data is that they were highly variable. I note that we used the median values for calculating each subject's results. Possibly this was because of the relatively small number of stimulations for each subject, but I suspect also it was a choice based on my feelings that the variability and irregularity of distributions were so great that a median was a more appropriate measure than a mean (personal communication).

Medians drawn from erratic data may themselves be quite nonerratic, but curiosity was aroused to inspect Sears' median data graphically. The set of graphs is presented in Figure 3. The first three columns of each graph represent the before-stimulation minus after-stimulation medians for each leg. The left (control) leg medians are to the left, and the right (experimental) leg medians are to the right. (It will be recalled that during the Hypnotic Analgesia series the left leg was rendered analgesic; during the Voluntary Inhibition series the *S*'s were told to inhibit reactions following stimulation of the left leg.) The remaining three columns represent each *S*'s left (experimental) leg median subtracted from his right (control) leg median. These latter three columns of difference scores are the clearest source for observing the hypnotic analgesic effect.

The most striking feature of the graphs is that except for two variables, Facial Grimace and Respiratory Variability, the hypnotic analgesic effect seems rather small and erratic. This impression is very different from the one created by inspecting Hull's table of percentage mean reductions shown in Table 8. The analgesic effect looked quite powerful there. Only one variable, GSR, had less than a 50 per cent reduction; more than half had over 90 per cent reductions. To understand why Hull's table suggested strong effect and the graphs do not, it must be kept in mind that Hull's percentages referred only to the most generalized of averages. In Respiratory Oscillation, for example, the mean of

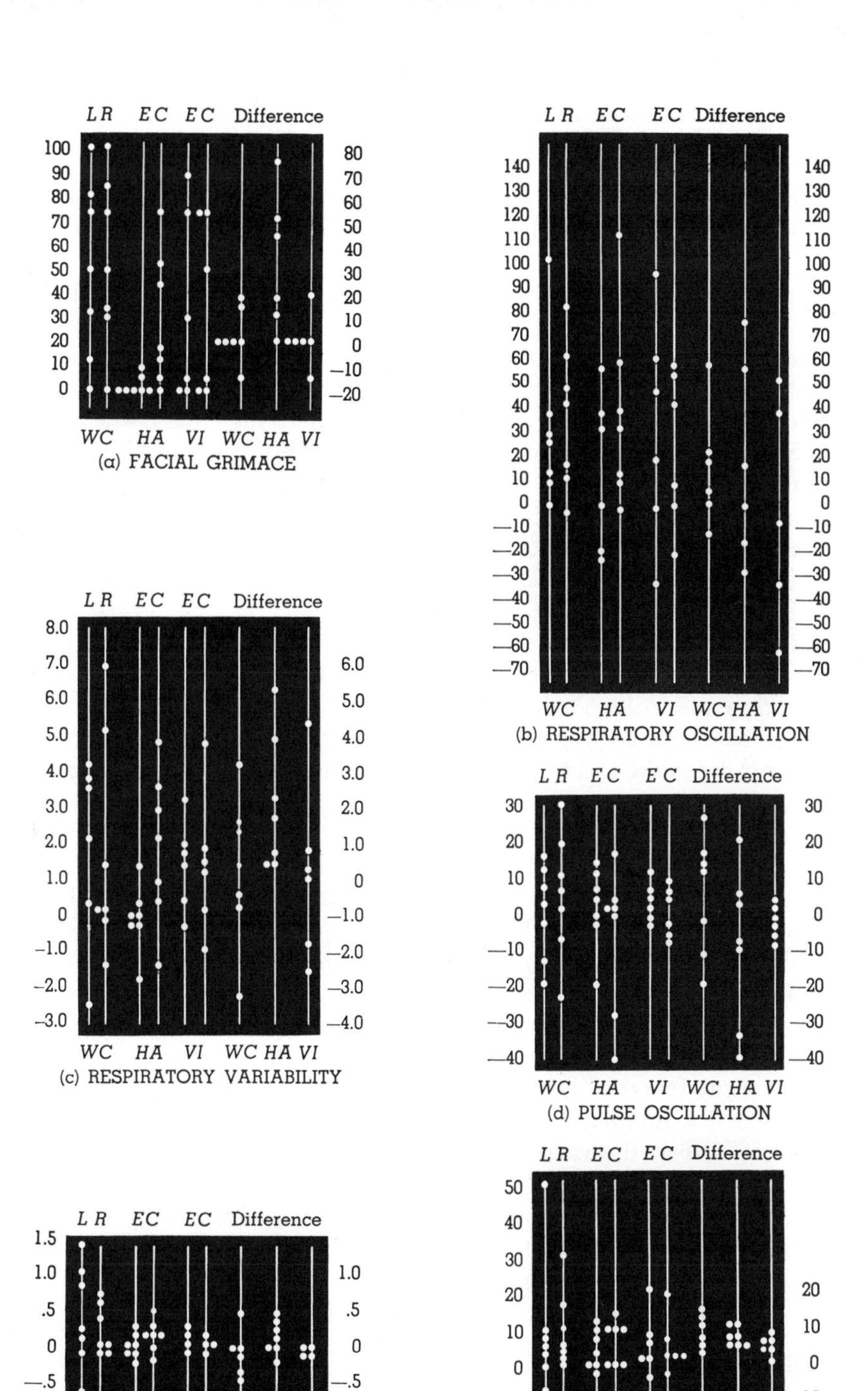
LR EC EC Difference
WC HA VI WC HA VI
(a) FACIAL GRIMACE
(b) RESPIRATORY OSCILLATION
(c) RESPIRATORY VARIABILITY
(d) PULSE OSCILLATION
(e) PULSE VARIABILITY
(f) GALVANIC SKIN RESPONSE

Figure 3.

the medians of the normal leg was +31.0; of the analgesic leg, —1.4. The percentage reduction was 105 per cent. The graphs show that these means were derived from distributions of medians with extensive overlap. These medians were themselves drawn from chaotically variable data. Most of the medians of the graph are similar, only a few are divergent.

Two different meanings of the phrase "strength of reaction" are useful to distinguish. The first meaning refers to an estimate of what the strength would be if all other factors are held constant. This meaning is illustrated by generalized averages, which ignore variability such as Hull's percentage mean reductions. The second meaning refers to strength *relative* to the other factors that contribute variance in the situation. Using the second meaning of strength, there is—except for Facial Grimace and Respiratory Variability—only a slight tendency for the analgesic leg's reaction to be less than the control leg's.

Inspection of these graphs also causes suspicion to be cast on the large critical ratios reported by Sears for such variables as Respiratory Oscillation and Pulse Variability. We have recomputed all of the probabilities on the analgesic effect using the modern comparable statistic (t for correlated data) and have found that some of the reported probabilities were incorrect.[21] According to our corrected figures, the analgesic effect in Facial Grimace and Respiratory Variability is significant ($p < .05$ and .025 points, respectively). Galvanic Skin Response is just barely significant ($p < .05$ point). Respiratory Oscillation, Pulse Variability, and Pulse Oscillation are nonsignificant.

This revision tends to undermine the firmness of Sears' results. We then discovered another problem, moreover, which tends to undermine them further. It will be recalled that the first type of statistical analysis that Sears performed was to see if the variables were reliable indices of physiological reaction to pain. It was reasoned that if no systematic difference was found in the physiological level before and after pain stimulation, then the variable was not useful as an index of pain. For these initial comparisons Sears selected the data for the right (control) leg in the Waking Control series. Analysis was performed by dividing the mean of the pre-post stimulation differences by the probable error (P. E.) of this mean. Findings were that GSR consistently rose in conductance after pain stimulation, meaning that GSR was a useful index of

[21] It will be observed that Sears used the now antiquated statistic based on the probable error (P. E.) to compute and test his critical ratios. Small sample statistics was in a rather crude stage of development for psychologists in 1932. The probabilities associated with these P. E. critical ratios did not take into account the number of degrees of freedom and thus consistently overestimated the level of significance as compared with the modern t test. Although this use of an antiquated statistic accounts for some of the discrepancy, it is not in itself incorrect. The major discrepancy and the source of the authentic errors was the result of arithmetical miscalculations.

response to pain. With only one exception, Pulse Oscillation, the mean differences of all other variables were at least two or more times their probable errors.[22]

Because computational errors had been found in the prior analysis, we recalculated these critical ratios and found them essentially correct. Some dissatisfaction was felt, however, in leaving the results in probable error form, because relevant probability tables are not commonly available. When the critical ratios are presented in the form of the modern t statistic, a problem in one of the variables, Respiratory Variability, becomes noticeable. The t ratio for Respiratory Variability is only 1.46. The probability associated with this ratio with six degrees of freedom is somewhere between the .10 and .05 points (one tail). Respiratory Variability therefore is of questionable adequacy as an index of physiological reaction to pain.

Respiratory Variability was Sears' best variable in the sense that it showed the most consistent, sizable hypnotic analgesic effect. Yet, the evidence is weak that Respiratory Variability is systematically responsive to pain stimulation. It must be concluded, therefore, that in the test of hypnotic analgesia the consistent and sizable effect on Respiratory Variability is quite possibly due to something other than a differential responsiveness to pain.

These many considerations make it advisable to reexamine Sears' results. Three out of six variables rather than five out of six yield significance in individual t tests, but one of these three, Facial Grimace, is hardly an autonomic variable, and another, Respiratory Variability, is doubtful as a useful index of response to pain to begin with.

All six directions of mean differences were correctly predicted (sign test, $p < .015$ point). Facial Grimace, however, is not autonomic and Pulse Oscillation was not found differentially responsive to pain. This leaves four out of four predicted directions of difference ($p = .06$ point). Further subtracting the dubious Respiratory Variability variable would leave but three out of three.

General Issues

Eight further, more general, issues emerge as relevant to all of the experiments in such a way that it is most useful to discuss them as separate topics.

1. *Extent of Apprehension and Anxiety as a Confounding Variable.* In a number of studies the hypothesis emerged that apprehension and anxiety arising from the general experimental situation may influence physiological reactivity. It is likely, moreover, that some mental stress may result directly, or be a concomitant of, the conscious experience of pain

[22] Facial Grimace could not be included in this analysis as there was no before-stimulation score.

(see discussion by Doupe *et al.*). Thus, it would seem necessary to distinguish sharply between this latter type of stress and the other sources of stress that might enter randomly within an experimental situation or that might inadvertently become entwined in a systematic fashion with one or another experimental condition. For example, if more soothing and ego-protective suggestions were given during the hypnotic analgesia condition than during the control conditions, one might predict that lessened physiological reactivity would be observed during hypnotic analgesia, yet this might nevertheless have no causal relationship to the lessened awareness of pain.

2. *Initial Physiological Level.* In the past few years increasing recognition has been given to the confounding effect of the initial physiological level on subsequent changes in level. Taking simple difference scores between initial and resultant level does not satisfactorily handle the problem. It is entirely possible that the physiological level *before* presentation of the pain stimulus (that is, initial level) may be systematically different in various experimental conditions. For example, the level before stimulation may be different when subjects are ready to experience pain in the waking state as compared with the level before stimulation in hypnosis while analgesic. Methodologically, it is necessary to establish that measurements of the effect of painful stimulation are free from any systematic bias due to initial physiological level, if one wishes to maintain that any observed effect refers to something other than initial levels. Of course, it would also be of interest to have separate comparisons of the initial levels for their own sake. (See the work of Wilder, 1957; Lacey, 1956; and Cogan, 1959.)

3. *Demand Characteristics.* Instances can be found in all of the studies where cognitive and moitvational factors (impressions and expectancies) might have influenced the results. To mention but one example, it is altogether possible that hypnotic analgesia in itself has no calming effect upon physiological reactivity, but if subjects *believe* that it has such a calming effect, this expectation in itself may be responsible for internal processes leading to a change in reactivity. It is well to refer here to Orne's valuable report (1959) where, under the concept of "demand characteristics," the important consequences of hypnotic subjects' motivations, cognitive expectancies, and the cueing character of the experimental situation were demonstrated.

4. *The Adequacy of Subjective Report.* Even if the subjective reality of hypnotic analgesia is accepted as a valid clinical fact, the question still remains of what techniques can be used in research to establish that in one specific instance analgesia has, in fact, phenomenologically occurred. Consider how Levine (1930) dealt with this problem. He apparently had some reservations about whether one can be certain of definite anesthesia during hypnosis: "In my experience, it is rarely possible to

be certain of definite anesthesia during hypnosis. Varying degrees of hypoesthesia can be obtained by suggestion with some frequency, but unmistakable anesthesia is rare" (p. 332).

One implication to be drawn from this is that some kind of rigorous clinical determination ought to be made of anesthesia (or analgesia) beyond the mere suggestion to subjects that anesthesia will occur. It is questionable, however, whether Levine's technique was itself adequate for this purpose. "[After] suggestions for deeper sleep. . . he said, 'Now you have lost all feeling in your right arm. If something touches it, you won't be able to feel it at all.' Then. . . the needle was stuck through the skin of the patient's arm. She did not move, and her facial expression did not change. Then she was asked 'Did you feel anything?' and she answered 'No'" (p. 336).

But can one trust a subject's bodily movements, facial expressions, and subjective reports either in hypnosis or later in the waking state, when the subject must recognize that the experimenter wants the anesthesia to have occurred? Levine took the only reasonable pragmatic approach: to define anesthesia operationally in terms of certain definite criteria—gross bodily movements and subject's report. In all likelihood, however, extensive inquiry is apt to be more accurate than minimal inquiry, and it is altogether possible that a subject will give a somewhat different report if he receives the impression that the experimenter wants only the exact truth no matter what that may be, rather than if he gets the impression that the experimenter will be disappointed if anesthesia did not take place. These considerations may apply both to the hypnotic and the waking state and do not necessarily imply conscious distortion of information.

5. *Statistical Sensitivity.* It is a common observation that psychophysiological data are quite erratic and that there are especially large differences between subjects. Given this state of affairs, it would seem futile to expect statistically significant differences even if differences do in fact exist, unless an experimental design is used that is elaborate enough so that reasonably extensive and reliable estimates can be made on a reasonably large number of subjects. With data that statistically require a microscope, one cannot search for effects with a magnifying glass. Although this consideration refers to experimentation in general, it deserves emphasis in this particular context because all of the studies cited suffer in one way or another from the defects of insensitivity. Brown and Vogel's research is the clearest example, but it is by no means alone. Much of the data from the various studies cannot be accepted as evidence as they remain in that statistical never-never land of seeming to show a trend yet coming within the confines of the null hypothesis.

6. *Pain Intensity and Duration.* Impressive claims for the clinical effectiveness of hypnotic analgesia and anesthesia have been made in regard

to the most profound pain intensities over long duration, but the experimental studies to date have dealt only with slight-to-moderate pain intensities of relatively short durations. West *et al.*, for example, have not often dared to go beyond 6 dols—and then for but moments. Even the so-called "severe" stimuli of Doupe *et al.* can hardly be compared with surgical intensities.

7. *The Fullest Development of the Anesthetic Condition.* A consideration of the historic development of the issue makes clear that Esdaile and the other mesmerists in the mid-nineteenth century did not induce hypnotic anesthesia in the modern sense (see, for example, Rosen, 1946). Using mesmeric passes and relying on preformed expectations of influence rather than verbal suggestion, they very slowly induced a state of profound stuporous slumber. Working in India, Esdaile's sober and well-documented descriptions record the performance of over 300 generally painless major surgical operations and thousands of minor ones. Esdaile found moreover that a strikingly high percentage of his patients could be rendered profoundly anesthetic.[23]

In the modern research laboratory, hypnotic anesthesia or analgesia is a faded version of what Esdaile and some others in the early years described. Perhaps these early descriptions were overstated. Another possibility is that certain laboratory and modern hypnotic techniques unwittingly inhibit the fullest development of the anesthetic condition. It is by means of verbal suggestions (which require that language functions must remain intact) that the modern research psychologist typically induces a relatively active and alert type of hypnosis compared with the very slowly induced, extremely detached, and nonverbal mesmeric stupor.

8. *Credence and Expectancy.* At about the same time as Esdaile's work (circa 1845) chemical anesthesics were discovered, soon overshadowing mesmeric anesthesia. Not long thereafter the crest of popular enthusiasm in mesmerism waned in Britain. As enthusiasm was replaced more and more by scorn and skepticism, mesmeric anesthesia was found less and less successful; again it became a rare event. Illuminating in this regard is a statement made by Elliotson near the end of his life:

> I believe I was not wrong; I believe that in what I originally saw, mesmerism played the parts precisely that I claimed for it. It is a wicked error to suppose that I was a party to a deception, or to a whole series of deceptions, if you like; but I candidly say . . . that mesmerism, at the present moment, has no power to remove pain. It is a mystery; it had power, and I once saw a leg painlessly removed under its influence; but we are now in another cycle, and it seems to me that there are special periods only in which mesmeric phenomena can be induced. (Quoted in Rosen, 1948.)

[23] Although, during periods of popular enthusiasm, frequent successes in induced surgical anesthesia have been reported in Europe and America, no one working in a Western cultural milieu has ever been quite as successful as was Esdaile working in India.

Research is needed into how firmly the subject believes prior to hypnosis that he will be rendered anesthetic, that is, into the factors of enthusiastic credence and firm expectancy of influence.

IMPLICATIONS FROM THE WRITER'S INVESTIGATION

Although the writer does not have sufficient detachment from his own experimental work on hypnotic analgesia (Shor, 1962b) to review it with critical perspective, it appears relevant to include a brief résumé of the study.

The research was designed to take more direct account of some of the unresolved issues. Primary attention was devoted to the question of whether *S*'s can voluntarily suppress their physiological responses while they are subjectively experiencing the pain-producing stimulus clearly and without analgesia. Another feature was the question of the possible physiological effect of hypnosis by itself, without analgesia. Attention was also devoted to helping produce conditions to keep the level of incidental anxiety minimal throughout.

It was our further objective to use a pain-producing stimulus that would be considerably more painful than those used in previous experiments. We wished to use the very highest pain intensity that could reasonably be achieved without at the same time so increasing stress as to vitiate the concomitant objective of keeping incidental anxiety minimal. Self-selected electric shock wattage was used.

In addition to real hypnotic *S*'s a special comparison group of *S*'s, unresponsive to hypnosis but required to simulate hypnosis throughout the experiment, was run according to the specifications of Orne's Real-Simulator method, described in detail elsewhere (Orne, 1959).

The five experimental conditions included were: (1) Wake Control, the effect of the wake state alone; (2) Hypnotic Control, the effect of hypnosis alone; (3) Wake Inhibition, the condition of voluntary suppression in the waking state; (4) Hypnotic Inhibition, voluntary suppression in the hypnotic state; and (5) Hypnotic Analgesia. The order of experimental conditions was counterbalanced, a wide variety of the most common physiological measures were used, and sufficient data were gathered to provide a highly sensitive statistical test.

Results: The first finding was that for this particular set of experimental conditions there were only tiny systematic physiological responses to pain in all of the five experimental conditions. Although highly significant statistically, the responses to the painful stimuli were very small in magnitude.

The second finding was that there were no measurable differences in response to shock in any of the five experimental conditions. In other words, Hypnotic Analgesia did not lessen physiological reactions to pain. Indeed, nothing did. Physiological reactions to pain were *just as slight* in the Wake Control condition as in any other condition.

Third, it was observed that *S*'s even in the Wake Control condition just sat through the shocks with an outward calm, which looked as if (even though they reported feeling the shock as very painful) they were not unduly upset by them. These findings certainly were contrary to our expectations; we thought Hypnotic Analgesia would have *some* minimizing effect on physiological reactivity to the pain, even though we expected Voluntary Inhibition might also.

Interpretation: To understand what these three findings mean, it is well to keep in mind that the entire experiment took place under conditions designed to minimize incidental anxiety throughout. It should be recalled in this regard that it had become obvious during our pilot work that in our experimental situation far larger physiological reactions to even perfunctorily painful stimuli occurred unless efforts were made to minimize this incidental anxiety.

A highly plausible interpretation of the results is that the lack of large effects anywhere may be the result of having succeeded in keeping incidental anxiety minimal. In other words, because incidental anxiety was *artificially* kept low, physiological responses to painful stimulation were very small. Under these circumstances neither hypnotic analgesia nor any other condition could show further, special effects on physiological reactivity.

In a scientific context this plausible interpretation must be regarded as tentative until it is confirmed in further investigations, especially because a direct comparison between the effects of high and minimal anxiety proved impracticable in this study given our other objectives. Nonetheless, three modestly compelling, clear-cut hypotheses may be drawn from the findings:

1. When the incidental anxiety component of the total pain experience is high, physiological responses to pain are large. Hypnotic analgesia is a means of reducing these responses.
2. When the incidental anxiety component of the total pain experience is low, physiological responses to even fairly intense pain are very small and hypnotic analgesia can effect no further measurable reduction in them.
3. Hypnotic analgesia is one means of eliminating the incidental anxiety component of the total pain experience.

In other words, these hypotheses advance the view that, inasmuch as the subjective experience of pain is eliminated during hypnotic analgesia, those physiological reactions do not occur that would otherwise ordinarily result from the stressful or threatening qualities of the painful stimulation. But *anything else* that minimizes the incidental anxiety component of the total pain experience—such as ego-protective procedures in the waking state—can have an effect on physiological responses similar to that of hypnotic analgesia.

A number of studies suggest that morphine relieves pain in a demonstrable fashion only when subjects are anxious (Hill, Kornetsky, Flanary, and Wikler, 1952a, 1952b; Kornetsky, 1954. Also see Beecher, 1959). Assuming that further experimentation will confirm that hypnotic analgesia reduces what we have called the "over-reactions" to pain under conditions of apprehension and stress, but that it has no effect on the generally subdued reactions to pain that occur under conditions of minimal anxiety, then the effects of hypnotic analgesia certainly should not be underestimated, for apparently even some of the most potent chemical analgesics (such as morphine) operate under similar conditions. Findings of this sort will be a clear demonstration of the objective physiological efficacy of hypnotic analgesia, especially for the clinical situation, because real-life pain almost always contains a sizable component of incidental anxiety. At the same time, these findings will tend to remove some of the urge to hypothesize peripheral neurophysiological changes. In a limited way the objective potency of hypnotic analgesia will be affirmed and, of greatest import, an understanding will have been achieved of at least some of the processes underlying the observed concomitant physiological changes.

REFERENCES

Barber, T. X. (1959). "Toward a theory of pain: Relief of chronic pain by leucotomy, opiates, placebos, and hypnosis," *Psychol. Bull*, **56**, 430–460.

Barber, T. X., and Hahn, K. W., Jr. (1962). "Physiological and subjective responses to pain producing stimulation under hypnotically-suggested and waking-imagined 'analgesia'," *J. abnorm. soc. Psychol.*, **65**, 411–418.

Bechterev, V. M. (1905). "*Des signes objectifs de la suggestion pendant le sommeil hypnotique*," *Arch. de psychol.*, **5**, 103–107.

Beecher, H. K. (1959). *Measurements of Subjective Responses: Quantitative Effects of Drugs.* New York: Oxford Univer. Press.

Brown, R. R., and Vogel, V. H. (1938). "Psychophysiological reactions following painful stimuli under hypnotic analgesia with gas anesthesia and Novocain block," *J. appl. Psychol.*, **22**, 408–420.

Cogan, E. A. (1959). *The Misuses of Compound Scores.* Unpublished manuscript.

Doupe, J., Miller, W. R., and Keller, W. K. (1939). "Vasomotor reactions in the hypnotic state," *J. neurol. Psychiat.*, **2**, 97–106.

Dynes, J. B. (1932). "Hypnotic anesthesia," *J. abnorm. soc. Psychol.*, **27**, 79–88.

Georgi, F. (1921). "*Bietrage zur Kenntnis des psychogalvanischen Phänomens*," *Arch. Psychiat.*, **62**, 571–578.

Gorton, B. E. (1949). "The physiology of hypnosis," *Psychiat. Quart.*, **23**, 317–343, 457–485.

HARDY, J. D., WOLFF, H. G., and GOODELL, H. (1947). "Studies on pain discrimination of differences in intensity of a pain stimulus as a basis of a scale of pain intensity," *J. clin. Invest.*, **26**, 1152–1175.

HERON, W. T. (1954–1955). "Hypnosis as an anesthetic," *Brit. J. med. Hyp.*, **6**, 1–7.

HILL, H. E., KORNETSKY, C. H., FLANARY, H. G., and WIKLER, A. (1952a). "Effects of anxiety and morphine on discrimination of intensities of painful stimuli," *J. clin. Invest.*, **31**, 473–480.

——— (1952b): " Studies on anxiety associated with anticipation of pain: I. Effects of morphine," *Arch. neurol. Psychiat.*, **67**, 612–619.

HULL, C. L. (1933). *Hypnosis and Suggestibility*. New York: Appleton-Century–Crofts.

KIRKNER, F. J. (1956). "Control of sensory and perceptive functions by hypnosis." In Dorcus, R. M. (Ed.). *Hypnosis and Its Therapeutic Applications*, New York: McGraw-Hill, Chap. 3.

KORNETSKY, C. (1954). "Effects of anxiety and morphine on the anticipation and perception of painful radiant stimuli," *J. clin. Invest.*, **47**, 130–135.

LACEY, J. I. (1956). "The evaluation of autonomic responses: Toward a general solution," *Ann. N. Y. Acad. Sci.*, **67**, 123–164.

LEVINE, M. (1930). "Pyschogalvanic reaction to painful stimuli in hypnotic and hysterical anesthesia," *Bull. Johns Hopk. Hosp.*, **46**, 331–339.

MORAVCSIC, E. E. (1921), "*Experimente über das psychogalvanische Reflexphänomen.*" *Jahrb. Psychiat. u. Neurol.*, **18**, 186–190.

ORNE, M. T. (1954). "The nature of hypnosis: Artifact and essence," *J. abnorm. soc. Psychol.*, **58**, 277–299.

PEIPER, A. (1924). "*Untersuchungen über den galvanischen Hautreflex (Psychogalvanishen Reflex) im Kindesalter, Jb. Kinderheilk*, **107**, 139–150.

PRINCE, M., and PETERSON, F. (1908). "Experiments in psychogalvanic reaction from co-conscious (subconscious) ideas in multiple personality," *J. abnorm. Psychol.*, **3**, 114–120.

RAGINSKY, B. B. (1951). "The use of hypnosis in anesthesiology," *J. Pers.*, **1**, 340–348.

ROSEN, GEORGE. (1946). "Mesmerism and surgery: A strange chapter in the history of anesthesia," *J. Hist. Med.*, **1**, 527–550.

——— (1948). "From mesmerism to hypnotism," *Ciba symp.*, **9**, 838–844.

SEARS, R. R. (1932). "Experimental study of hypnotic anesthesia," *J. exp. Psychol.*, **15**, 1–22.

SHOR, R. E. (1959). *Explorations in Hypnosis: A Theoretical and Experimental Study*. Unpublished doctoral dissertation, Brandeis Univer.

——— (1962). "On the physiological effects of painful stimulation during hypnotic analgesia: Basic issues for further research." In Estabrooks, G. H. (Ed.). *Hypnosis: Current Problems*, New York: Harper & Row, pp. 54–75.

——— (1962b). "Physiological effects of painful stimulation during hypnotic analgesia under conditions designed to minimize anxiety." *Int. J. clin. exp. Hyp.*, **10**, 183–202.

SUTCLIFFE, J. P. (1960). "'Credulous' and 'sceptical' views of hypnotic phenomena," *Int. J. clin. exp. Hyp.*, **8**, 73–101.

——— (1961). "'Credulous' and 'skeptical' views of hypnotic phenomena: Experiments on esthesia, hallucination, and delusion," *J. abnorm. soc. Psychol.*, **62**, 189–200.

WEITZENHOFFER, A. M. (1951). "The transcendence of normal voluntary capacities in hypnosis: An evaluation," *J. Pers.*, **1**, 272–282.

WEST, L. J., NEILL, K. C., and HARDY, J. D. (1952). "Effects of hypnotic suggestions on pain perception and galvanic skin response," *Arch. neurol. Psychiat.*, **68**, 549–560.

WILDER, J. (1957). "The law of initial value in neurology and psychiatry," *J. nerv. ment. Dis.*, **125**, 73–86.

YOUNG, P. C. (1941). "Experimental hypnotism: A review," *Psychol. Bull.*, **38**, 92–104.

17

Comparative Aspects of Hypnosis

STANLEY C. RATNER[1]
Michigan State University

THE topic of comparative aspects of hypnosis is both familiar and unfamiliar in general treatments of the topic of hypnosis. It is familiar in that a number of texts on hypnosis include material generally regarded as comparative; it is unfamiliar in that the principles of comparative analysis are rarely followed in these texts. In other words, comparative analysis and citation of data from infrahumans are different. This chapter will take the comparative approach insofar as it is appropriate in this analysis of a literature that spans more than three hundred years and forty different species.

PRELIMINARY CONSIDERATIONS

Before discussing the current status of research and theory regarding animal hypnosis, several topics will be considered to give perspective to this research and theory.

[1] Portions of the research reported in this chapter and portions of the review of the literature were done during the author's tenure as a National Science Foundation Faculty Fellow at Cambridge University.

Basic Observation of Animal Hypnosis

One type of response ties together the literature that is subsumed under the name of animal hypnosis. This response is *immobility.* The response of immobility has durations from several seconds to several hours and extends across a variety of species of vertebrates and invertebrates. Some examples of familiar creatures that show the response are the octopus, lizard, rabbit, guinea pig, rat, chicken, monkey, and species of beetles that curl up when they are touched. In short, not only the opposum plays "possum." However, a number of conditions associated with the response differ between and within species. Among these differences are the physiological responses and the necessary eliciting stimuli. Thus, one of the major questions regarding animal hypnosis is the question of whether immobility is characteristic of one behavior process or of a number of them.

In the past, immobility has been treated as a single process and characterized by such names as animal hypnosis, tonic immobility, catalepsy, and death feigning. However, another possibility is that the immobility reaction is a component of a variety of different behavior processes. That is, immobility may be like change in latency of responding, namely, a dependent variable that is systematically related to a variety of different independent variables and processes. The comparative approach is particularly concerned with establishing bases for drawing conclusions about similarities and differences beyond superficial appearances. That is, comparative analysis involves *functional analysis* and not *capricious comparison* between the formal properties of grossly similar and dissimilar objects, such as rats and chickens (Ratner and Denny, 1964). Comparative analysis will be applied to the data of animal hypnosis after these data are presented in categories that are close to the traditional categories that arose in the history of observation and experimentation relating to animal hypnosis.

History

Several historical reviews of animal hypnosis are available. Volgyesi (1938) has the most complete account of animal hypnosis, but his book is somewhat difficult to obtain. Gilman and Marcuse (1949) and Lerner (1962) have brief reviews based on Volgyesi. Armstrong (1942, pp. 65–75) provides a detailed discussion of observations of so-called trance states of birds. Most of these observations were made under field conditions.

A formidable list of names has been applied to the reaction presently called animal hypnosis. It is reported (Volgyesi, 1938) that Kircher in 1646 labeled the reaction he observed in hens as "*fascination*" and attributed the reaction to their imaginations while they attended to the chalk line that was drawn away from their beaks. The reaction was subsequently called mesmerism, monoideism, death feigning, catalepsy, immobilization reflex, akinesis, tonic immobility, myotonia congenita, inhibitory state, animal hypnosis, catatonic trance, and in my laboratory, it is simply called *rho*. These various labels indicate something of the conceptual frameworks in which animal hypnosis has been viewed and the conflict about its relationship to human hypnotic phenomena.

Scientific interest in animal hypnosis flagged between the time of Kircher's description of fascination of chickens and the middle of the nineteenth century (Volgyesi, 1938). However, as might be expected, Mesmer's work on animal magnetism was extended to the animal world when it was found that creatures such as cats, dogs, chickens, and horses could be immobilized by "passes." In 1834 Wilson, as quoted by Gilman and Marcuse (1949), discussed the effects of "passes" of a magnetic nature and suggested hypotheses that involved the combination of the thinking of Mesmer and Kircher. At about the same time Braid was attempting to relate his theory of human hypnosis to the observation of animal hypnosis. Braid's psychological theory propounded in 1847, called monoideism, provided a reasonable description of the immobility reactions of animals as exemplified by the response of a bird to the slow movements and stare of a snake. Although Preyer in 1881 agreed that fixation was an important aspect of animal hypnosis, he concluded that only special fear-producing objects could elicit this fixation and the resulting immobility (Gilman and Marcuse, 1949). Thus, Preyer is responsible for introducing the idea that fear may be an important aspect of animal hypnosis. This idea has persisted in current theories.

Some of the facts of immobility reactions had not escaped Darwin who came upon them in the context of naturalistic observations of animals and their predators. Darwin took a rather novel approach in his analysis of immobility reactions. His view was conditioned by his zoological theory that emphasized the adaptive significance of structures and behaviors in the development of animals. He interpreted immobility reactions in terms of the concept of death feigning and felt that they occurred when an animal was attacked by a predator. This interpretation triggered a great deal of opposition because of its apparent teleological and anthropomorphic ring. Specifically, it has been argued (Gilman and Marcuse, 1949; Weitzenhoffer, 1953, p. 112) that an animal could not know that an immobile animal is less attractive to a predator than a moving one, nor could it know that predators of living animals do not generally eat dead ones. However, it is my view that Darwin did not suggest that an animal has knowledge of the functions of its structures or behaviors as suggested by these criticisms. The criticisms are no more valid than they would be if they were applied to the currently acceptable idea that salivation functions in the digestion of food.

It will be seen in later sections that a version of the death-feigning interpretation of animal hypnosis is favored by some of the biologically oriented investigators. Other biologically oriented investigators have followed the research and theory of Pavlov who noted immobility and trance in the course of his work on conditioning. Pavlov's general theory and some data related to it are reported in a paper entitled "Concerning the So-called Hypnotism of Animals" (1955). At a behavioral level Pavlov interpreted animal hypnosis in terms of "a self-protecting reflex of an inhibitory character" (p. 352). He used the Darwinian notion of the adaptive functions of such responses but took a broader view of the classes of stimuli that could elicit them and suggested the physiological process that he thought led to the responses. At the physiological level Pavlov (p. 354) postulated that hypnotism arose from inhibition of the cortical cells. He further postulated that such inhibition could be of different degrees of intensity and extent over the cortex and other areas of the brain. One of the sources of this inhibition according to Pavlov was monotonous stimulation (p. 354), such as occurs in some conditioning situations. Another source was sudden and intense stimulation, such as occurs from attack by a predator.

In summary, four types of interpretations of animal hypnosis have been postulated from Kircher's original observations to the time of Pavlov. These interpretations are: fascination from fixation and reduction of attention, innate responses to predators, general fear, and cortical depression. Each of these interpretations has persisted into contemporary work and will be considered in later sections.

Informal Uses of Animal Hypnosis

Farmers, fishermen, and probably children were aware of the immobility reaction in connection with their work and amusement long before Kircher was investigating the properties of animal hypnosis with hens. It is reported that the Japanese immobilized giant land crabs and lobsters by placing the animals in a position so that they rested on their heads (Volgyesi, 1938). The familiar effect of turning a frog on its back and stroking its stomach is another example of folk knowledge of animal hypnosis. Similar procedures seem to be used in alligator wrestling and in the rodeo trick of immobilizing a wild calf by covering it and making some passes over it. In the case of the hypnotized calf, the spell is broken by a loud shout from the audience.

Animal hypnosis has also found its way informally into laboratory procedures and animal husbandry. Injections and blood samples are often taken from animals such as rabbits by inverting them into a V-shaped trough, holding them briefly and then working on them while they are immobile. Handbooks on banding of wild birds typically warn the novice that the bird may appear to have died while being held for banding, but the novice is not to become alarmed because the bird will fly if thrown into the air. Large farm animals also show a syndrome that is considered to be immobility associated with animal hypnosis. Fraser (1960) discusses these cases in detail and concludes that conditions such as confinement during shipping or forceful manipulation of tired animals may lead to immobility that persists for hours or even days. This immobility may occur when the animal is lying down or upright. John Steinbeck was also aware of immobility reactions among octopi and speculated through Doc in *Sweet Thursday* (1954, p. 27) that: "... they appear to feel terror and rage. They change color when they're disturbed and angry. ... sometimes they get so mad they collapse and die of something that parallels apoplexy."

Summary

Comparative analysis of animal hypnosis is differentiated from the specification of animals that can be hypnotized. Preliminary to the task of comparative analysis of animal hypnosis the following background facts are noted: (1) *Immobility* is the behavioral characteristic that cuts across animal hypnosis of all species. (2) Theoretical analyses of the causes of hypnosis and its relationship to other behavioral processes are very diverse, although each has its historical counterpart. (3) Practical and folk uses of animal hypnosis antedate its scientific study and continue in current animal work.

CURRENT STATUS OF ANIMAL HYPNOSIS

Animal hypnosis has a number of compelling features that are probably responsible for a large portion of the interest and work that has been undertaken in its name. In general these features are associated with the breadth of the phenomena—breadth in terms of the number of species that show it, the ways of producing it, and its widespread behavioral and physiological consequences. This section will consider each of these aspects of animal hypnosis.

Species

The species that have been studied in terms of hypnotic reactions are concentrated in the highest invertebrate phylum, arthropoda, and in all of the classes of the vertebrate phylum, cordata. Within these two phyla animal hypnosis has been observed in scores of different species. For example, Armstrong (1942, Chap. 6) reports immobility reactions among more than 20 species of birds and details the conditions under which the reactions occurred; Crane (1952) reports immobility reactions among 15 species of mantids.

It is important to note that for purposes of gross description the behavioral characteristic of prolonged immobility for an otherwise very active animal is taken as the defining characteristic of animal hypnosis.

Such immobility typically follows simple restraint or restraint with rhythmic stimulation. However, stimulus conditions are not used as the defining characteristic at this time because in many cases specification of the effective stimulus is only guesswork and has not been subjected to systematic, controlled experimentation.

Lerner (1962) presents a typical list of animal forms that are known to respond to animal hypnosis. He indicates that results have been obtained with "cockroaches, horses, fish, serpents, mice, pigs, lions, monkeys, swans, rabbits, frogs, birds, guinea pigs and other creatures" (p. 57). Rather than simply lengthen the list of susceptible species, I will report species for which there are references that deal with inducing or measuring hypnotic responses.

Invertebrates. Animal hypnosis is described for several groups of higher invertebrates. Darwin (1900, p. 363) remarked that "insects are most notorious in this respect" and he reviewed some field conditions under which hypnotic reactions have been noted with insects. Darwin also regarded these reactions of insects as death feigning. Trance or hypnotic reactions are found among spiders during courtship. Savory (1928, p. 208) describes the cataleptic reactions of the female spider *Agelina labyrinthica* when the male courts her. During the courtship the male strokes the female and she lapses into immobility. Then the male carries the female grasped by her leg held in his jaws. The female does not awaken until reproductive behaviors are completed. Berland, quoted by Savory (1928, p. 207), reports hypnotic reactions of female spiders of the species *Dysdera erythrina* in which the male's caresses of the female lead eventually to a catatonic reaction on the part of the female. Immobility reactions of the cockroach are reported by Minami and Dallenbach (1946) in their often-cited study of retroactive inhibition and memory. Crane (1952) found immobility reactions among a number of species of mantids. These reactions occurred when an aggressor cornered one of the individuals.

Gunter and McCaughan (1959) describe in detail the immobility reaction produced in a common crustacean, the shrimp *Sicyonia brevirostris.* Immobility reactions are also reported for another species of marine invertebrate, the octopus. TenCate (1928b) found that the octopus became immobile after it had been held and prevented from moving.

Vertebrates. Although sufficient work has been done with invertebrates to be convincing, the majority of the experimental studies of animal hypnosis have been done with vertebrates. Gilman and Marcuse (1949) review a number of the studies of vertebrate species up to the time of the publication of their review. Thus, this section will mention a few of the older, representative studies but it will concentrate on more recent reports and those that Gilman and Marcuse have omitted.

Reliable reports of animal hypnosis with fish are given by TenCate (1928a) and Gunter and McCaughan (1959). These studies describe immobility reactions of the angel fish (TenCate, 1928a) and the toad fish. The toad fish (*Opsanus beta*), a commonly studied marine fish, gave a wide range of responses during the course of the immobility reaction. These included a change in color, vocalization (one of the more interesting things about these species), and rigidity. Lloyd Morgan (1891, p. 388) describes hypnotizing fish by shining a light at them. They reacted by slowly sinking to the bottom of the tank.

Amphibians and reptiles, particularly frogs and chameleons, have been subjects for experimental investigations of animal hypnosis. Some zoology texts deal specifically with the immobility reactions of frogs (Newman, 1924, p. 260; Noble, 1931, p. 424). A study of some of the physiological characteristics of immobility reactions was done with frogs by Schwarz and Bickford (1956). Their report includes an excellent photograph of the frog during immobility. In a long series of experiments also designed to study physiological characteristics of immobility, Hoagland (1928a) investigated the reaction with the chameleon, a reptile. Hypnotic reactions of the alligator are commonly known in southeastern United States in "alligator wrestling," but scientific reports on this were not found. Armstrong (1942, p. 75) hypothesizes that the earliest report of immobility reactions of reptiles may be found in the biblical passage (Exodus vii : 12) in which the pharoah's wizards turned snakes into sticks.

Birds have been the most intensively studied class of vertebrates in terms of animal hypnosis. The original scientific reports of these reactions by Kircher were based on the chicken, also called domestic fowl, and this bird continues to be investigated. Since Gilman and Marcuse's review (1949) three large studies of immobility reactions of domestic fowl have been reported. Gilman *et al.* (1950) studied adult birds and have very clear photographs of domestic fowl during hypnotic reactions. Ratner and Thompson (1960) studied the development of the reactions in young chicks and Salzen (1963) used their methods in a study of variables affecting immobility of young chicks.

Hypnotic reactions of many other species of birds have been described in detail in other reports. Armstrong (1942, Chap. 6) describes the reaction for more than 20 species of birds including the plover, oyster catcher, heron, and black-billed cuckoo. A strong hypnotic reaction was found by Vogel (1950) for the adult turkey vulture but not for the young of the species. Jackson (1952) reports immobility reaction of an American robin in response to the warning call of another robin. Patrick's study (1927) involved more than ten different species of birds ranging from owls to pigeons. The response of some of the species are described in detail in Patrick's paper and in an

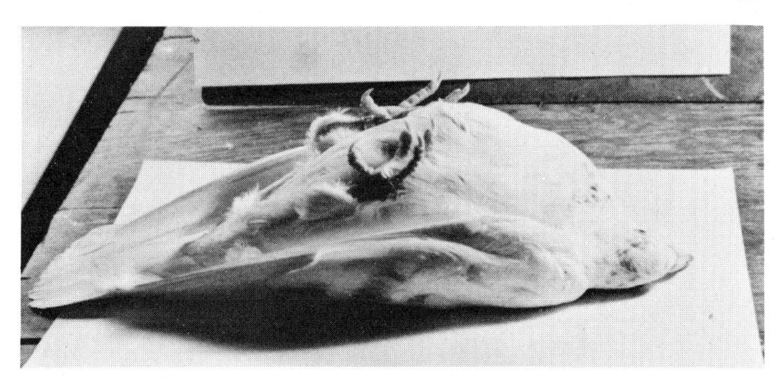

Figure 1. Photographs of a domestic canary, chaffinch and pigeon during animal hypnosis. Note the turning of the heads of the canary and pigeon and the general tonus of all of the birds. The responses were induced by holding the birds on their backs for 15 seconds.

earlier paper (Carlier, 1924) on which the Patrick paper is based.

In recent research Ratner studied hypnotic reactions of finch, pigeon, and Japanese quail (*coturnix*). Each of the species showed immobility typical of other birds. In all cases immobility was induced by holding the bird for 15 to 30 seconds. Photographs of some of the birds during immobility are shown in Figure 1. Other details of these studies will be discussed in later sections.

Hypnotic reactions of mammals are also thoroughly documented. Among the species with which there has been recent research are guinea pigs, rabbits, rats, goats, and coyotes. Gilman and Marcuse (1949) also indicate a large number of mammals have been tested and found to be susceptible. Research with guinea pigs has been reported in three recent papers. Bayard (1957) and Liberson (1948) tested changes in duration of response; Schwarz and Bickford (1956) worked with hypnotic reactions and the EEG. The papers of Schwarz and Bickford (1956) and Liberson (1948) have clear photographs of guinea pigs and frogs during immobility.

Marcuse notes that "So far as the writer knows, the rat has never been mentioned as being susceptible to animal hypnosis" (1955, p. 266). It seemed to me that the rat should be susceptible and that research with hypnotic reactions would be moved forward if the reaction could be readily elicited in the most typical inhabitant of psychology laboratories. Thus, the problem of investigating hypnotic reactions with rats was undertaken. Figure 2 shows the immobility reaction of two laboratory

Figure 2. Photograph of an albino and hooded rat during animal hypnosis. The albino is in a trough to keep it from rolling onto its side. The responses were induced by holding the rats on their backs for 15 seconds.

rats. The usual method of inducing the response by holding the animal was used and was found to be successful. However, it was found that one condition must obtain to induce immobility reactions in laboratory rats. It is necessary that the animals not be tamed to handling. The relevance of this condition will be described in the section on variables affecting hypnotic reactions.

Among other laboratory animals that show hypnotic reactions are the rabbit (Ratner, 1958; Svorad, 1957), the dog (Pavlov, 1955, p. 352) and the monkey (Foley, 1938). Hypnotic reactions of domestic animals such as goats and cattle have been observed (Fraser, 1960) and studied (Moore and Amstey, 1962a, 1962b). A field experiment by Ratner and Ozoga found hypnotic reactions for coyotes when the animals were confined by a rope.

Conflicting reports exist about the occurrence of hypnotic reactions for the fox. Both coyotes (*Canis latrans*) and red foxes (*Vulpes fulval*) were tested in the field experiment of Ratner and Ozoga. The coyotes showed a strong hypnotic reaction but the red foxes did not, although they were both treated in the same ways. Specifically, the animals were trapped and then grasped by a choker collar that was attached to a stick. The red foxes continued fighting during the entire procedure that included binding their legs. However, Armstrong (1942, p. 66) notes that foxes (unreported species and conditions) do show immobility.

The European wren (*Troglodytes troglodytes*) provides a negative instance of hypnotic response. In a book entirely devoted to the wren, Armstrong states (1955, p. 249): "As is well known, many birds are apt to assume an inert state when handled but I have never known a wren to collapse in this way." Armstrong relates this fact to the general behavior of the species.

The question of hypnotic reactions of humans that are similar to those of animals has been considered by Lloyd Morgan, Armstrong, and Hoagland. Lloyd Morgan (1891, p. 388) and Armstrong (1942, p. 70) describe cases of humans who were immobilized and analgesic during terrifying experiences. Hoagland (1928b, p. 716) describes the induction of immobility with humans by suddenly inverting them.

RESEARCH ON ANIMAL HYPNOSIS

The extensive data and research methods regarding animal hypnosis will be dealt with in terms of four major topics: (1) measurement of animal hypnosis; (2) producing and terminating the reaction; (3) behavioral and physiological characteristics of the reaction; and (4) variables affecting it. The data that are reviewed will provide background material for the theoretical section on animal hypnosis. However, one theoretical position will be described briefly at this point to serve as an orienting idea around which the data of animal hypnosis can be viewed.

There is general agreement that the event is not a simple animal example of human hypnosis. Thus, for present purposes an idea that serves to integrate the data is the idea that animal hypnosis is an innate or unlearned fear reaction. This reaction is assumed to represent the extreme along a continuum from startle and watchfulness to prolonged immobility. The validity of this idea will be examined in the theoretical portions of the chapter, but for the present purposes it can serve as an orienting idea for the reader.

Measurement of Animal Hypnosis

The general and obvious characteristics of animal hypnosis are immobility and reduced responsiveness to external stimulation during this immobility. Thus, the specific measures of animal hypnosis that are used in experimental studies are related to characteristics of immobility and reduced responsiveness. Typical measures are duration of immobility, time to induce immobility, percentage of animals becoming immobile, and intensity or duration of stimulation required to terminate immobility. Each of the measures has been used in one or more experiments, although the first measure, duration of immobility, is the one most frequently used to quantify hypnotic reactions of animals.

Duration of Immobility. This measure of hypnotic reaction refers to the time during which the animal remains in a single position after immobility has occurred. Ratner and Thompson (1960, p. 187) define duration operationally as follows: "Duration of immobility was measured from the time the experimenter's hand was lifted (from the bird) until the bird got to its feet. Small movements of the bird's head and feet frequently occurred but were not counted as the termination of the reaction." Implicit in this method are requirements for establishing a standard way for inducing the reaction and a criterion for judging the termination of immobility. As noted by Gilman *et al.* (1950), one method of inducing immobility often used in working with birds and mammals involves turning the animal on its side or back, holding it for a fixed time, and then releasing it. Because the animal is not on its feet when this procedure is used, the termination of hypnosis is readily indicated by the animal returning to its feet. However, immobility is evident even with a standing animal and most field observations of immobility (Armstrong, 1942, Chap. 6) are made when the animals are upright.

Duration of immobility, especially with animals that have had little handling prior to testing, may last from several minutes to several hours. The measure has been used with a variety of species such as birds (Ratner and Thompson, 1960), rabbits (Ratner, 1958), goats and sheep (Moore and Amstey, 1962a and 1962b) and lizards (Hoagland, 1928a and 1928b).

Time to Induce Immobility. This measure of hypnotic reaction refers to the time during which the animal has to be restrained or otherwise stimulated until it becomes obviously immobile. For example, Mowrer (1932) measured time to induce immobility as follows: the bird was grasped and laid on its side, the experimenter then began to stroke gently the comb and eyes of the bird and continued until the eyes remained closed for 30 seconds. Time to induce immobility was counted from the onset of stroking until the eyes remained closed for 30 seconds.

Table 1
Means of Time to Induce Hypnotic Response and Duration of Response for Rats*

TEST TRIAL	*N*	MEAN TIME TO INDUCE	MEAN DURATION
1	9	30 sec	85 sec
4	9	50 sec	55 sec
8	8	90 sec	25 sec
11	3	110 sec	13 sec

* Note: The same animals were tested, one trial per day, but data are included only for those that showed the hypnotic response.

In general, there is an inverse relationship between time to induce immobility and duration of the response. Although specific psychometric studies comparing these measures have not been undertaken, the data in Table 1 show the trend. Specifically, Table 1 shows the mean number of seconds for induction of immobility and duration of hypnotic responses for a group of rats. These data were collected in the laboratory of the writer under controlled experimental conditions. The durations of immobility for these rats are less than the durations that are ordinarily obtained with birds, especially on the early test trials with birds.

Percentage of Animals Becoming Immobile. This measure refers to the proportion of animals in a particular group that become immobile for some minimal period of time. The measure was used by Gilman *et al.* (1950) in their study of domestic fowl. The measure involves use of a standard induction procedure with all birds and establishment of some minimal criteria of hypnotic response. Gilman *et al.* used the criterion of 15 seconds of immobility after the bird was released by the experimenter. This measure has the advantage of being very economical of experimental time, because durations of more than 15 seconds are terminated by the experimenter. It has the disadvantage of not being amenable to complex statistical analyses, because individual scores are lost in obtaining the percentages. However, the measure can be used in conjunction with duration of response by allowing animals to remain immobile until they spontaneously terminate the response. This method, as used by Ratner and Thompson (1960), indicates that percentage of animals responding and duration of response are positively correlated, but duration of response is a more sensitive measure at the extremes of responsiveness. Gilman *et al.* (1950) use percentage of animals becoming immobile as an operational definition of susceptibility to hypnosis.

Stimulation Required to Terminate Immobility. The fourth measure that has been used as a quantitative index of immobility involves stimulating the immobile animal and measuring the amount of stimulation required to terminate immobility. In general, it is assumed that the greater the amount of stimulation required to terminate immobility, the greater the intensity of the hypnotic reaction. Only a limited amount of work using this measure has been undertaken. Mangold and Eckstein (1919) found that hypnotized frogs took many more electric shocks (21 to 24 shocks per minute) than normal frogs before the animal sprang away. They also found that dogs hypnotized on their backs took more shocks than those hypnotized belly down. Pavlov (1955, p. 358) used the fact that frogs did not take food in a conditioning situation as an index of hypnotic responses and quantified this measure in terms of the number of refusals of food. Other observations reported by Gilman and Marcuse (1949, p. 156) indicate that a number of classes of stimulation could be used with hypnotized animals to test the intensity of the reaction. For example, light, sound, touch, and temperature are possible test stimuli. In each case the amount of stimulation might serve as an index of degree of hypnotic response.

Response to stimulation during immobility has some methodological problems. Under some conditions stimulation may increase the hypnotic response, especially if this response is related to innate fear reactions. In addition, different loci, frequency, or intensity of stimulation may have special effects and confound interpretations of amounts of stimulation as indices of intensity of reaction. However, the basic fact that electric shock, cutting, pin pricks, and movement may not terminate the reaction is itself of importance and will be considered in detail in later sections.

Methods for Producing and Terminating Hypnotic Reactions

A variety of methods have been used to produce hypnotic reactions with animals. Some of the methods are reviewed and classified by Foley (1938), Gilman and Marcuse (1949), and Weitzenhoffer (1953, p. 109). In Foley's classification, on which the others are based, four principal methods for producing hypnotic reactions are identified.

These methods are: *repetitive stimuli*, *pressure on body parts*, *inversion*, and *restraint from movement*. In actual practice these methods are always used in some combination of two or more. For example, Gilman and Marcuse note (1949, p. 154) that: "... some degree of restraint seems to have been present in all the investigations." It is also important to note that restraint is an integral part of production of hypnotic reactions that have been reported to have occurred in natural conditions (Armstrong, 1942, Chap. 6).

Conditions Necessary for Producing Hypnosis. In the context of the present discussion, *restraint as the necessary condition to produce hypnosis* is used as a concept and not in a simple operational way. That is, review of the many methods and species that have been used in studies of hypnotic reactions suggests that restraint is present in some form. However, different stimulus conditions may function to restrain particular individuals and different conditions may be necessary for different species. The condition of restraint that functions across the widest number of species and is used in the largest number of studies is manual restraint. This is reported to be effective with animals such as the octopus (TenCate, 1928b; Steinbeck, 1954, p. 32), marine shrimp (Gunter and McCaughan, 1959), lizards (Hoagland, 1928a), domestic fowl (Ratner and Thompson, 1960), guinea pigs (Bayard, 1957), and monkeys (Foley, 1938). In all of these cases hypnotic reactions were associated with the animals being restrained by the experimenter's hands so that their movements were restricted.

Restraint can, of course, occur without the actual application of hands to the animal. As has been noted by Gilman and Marcuse (1949), Pavlov confined his dogs in a conditioning harness (1955, p. 358), Marcuse and Moore (1944) also confined pigs in a conditioning harness, and other investigators have tied their animals on boards and then inverted them suddenly (Boas and Landauer, 1933). Prolonged hypnotic responses have also been obtained with birds by putting a cloth over their heads, that is, *hooding them*. The hypnotic reaction to hooding occurred whether the cloth covered the bird's eyes or not (Carlier, 1924). These observations with hooded birds were verified by Ratner with more than five species of finch. However, it is important to note that before the bird is immobilized by placing a cloth or some hood over it, it must be restrained at least briefly. In the field observations of hypnotic reactions restraint can also be inferred from the details provided by the observers. Vogel (1950) trapped turkey vultures against their nests and prodded them with a stick. J. Ozoga and Ratner at Michigan State University restrained coyotes with a stick and an attached collar—these animals also showed hypnotic response. Under somewhat different conditions of restraint, James (1937) confined opossums in a box and gave them electric shock from a grid floor. The animals made the classic "possum response"—they rolled over and curled up. In general, then, restraint is taken to include entrapment with or without actual tactile pressure on the organism.

A second feature of the conditions associated with the production of hypnotic reactions is that of the *novelty* (unfamiliarity) of the restraining stimulus. In general, the less novel the stimulus the weaker the hypnotic reaction. Data regarding the function of novelty in the production of hypnotic reactions have been obtained by Mowrer (1932), Gilman *et al.* (1950), Ratner and Thompson (1960), and Salzen (1963). In each of these studies, decreasing novelty of the restraining condition (that is, increasing experience with the experimenter), was associated with decreasing hypnotic response.

The effect of novelty will be considered in greater detail as a variable associated with hypnotic responses of animals, but lack of novelty is probably the reason that restraint of the family pet, even by sudden inversion, does not produce immobility when the restraint is removed.

The case of animal hypnosis reported by Pavlov (1955, p. 352) that occurred in the usual conditioning situation seems at first glance to be a contrary instance to the foregoing analysis. However, careful examination of Pavlov's discussion (1955, p. 352) and Pavlov and Petrova's procedure (1955, p. 358) indicated that the occurrence of hypnotic reactions was not typical with the dogs that were used, and such occurrences required specific stimulus conditions. Pavlov notes that it was necessary to have "extraordinary external stimuli highly intense or very unusual in form" It is further noted (Pavlov, 1955, p. 358) that: "the alert (unhypnotized) dogs struggle against the apparatus only when it is first attached to them" and later Pavlov notes: "I repeat that if the dog is subject to hypnotization under experimental conditions, the hypnotic state usually develops immediately after the dog is placed in the stand and sometimes the very moment it crosses the threshold of the experimental chamber."

In summary, the production of hypnotic reactions with animals requires restraint and novelty or unfamiliarity of the restraining stimulus. Restraint is conceived broadly. It is also suggested that effects of conditions such as pressure on body parts and rhythmic stimulation are also associated with conditions of restraint and novelty when they are effective as hypnotizing procedures. It is suggested that conditions such as pressure on body parts and rhythmic stimulation are similar to Kircher's chalk line that was slowly drawn from the hen's beak while the hen was restrained on the ground. Gilman and Marcuse indicate (1949, p. 155): "For a long time the chalk line was held to be the essential part of the experiment. . . . However, it was shown that the experiment could be successfully performed by merely holding the hen down on the ground."

Conditions for Terminating Hypnosis

Little research has dealt rigorously with the problem of termination of hypnosis. However, many observers who have been concerned primarily with demonstrations of hypnosis with animals have commented on the conditions of termination. Two general conditions for termination of hypnosis can be identified: *self-paced termination* and *externally produced termination.*

Self-paced Termination. When duration of immobility is used as the index of hypnosis, the experimenter observes self-paced termination. A review of studies using this measure provides very few clues about the specific conditions or behaviors that precede self-paced termination. However, some descriptions of self-paced termination are provided by Hoagland (1928a), Mowrer (1932), Liberson (1948), Schwarz and Bickford (1956), Gunter and McCaughan (1959), Ratner (1958), and Ratner and Thompson (1960). As Ratner and Thompson commented (1960, p. 188): "Close observation for behaviors or conditions associated with termination of immobility yielded no clues. Birds just suddenly jumped up and moved away." This is not to say that animals are completely rigid until spontaneous termination. It is commonly reported that during immobility small movements including the head or legs may occur (Gilman and Marcuse, 1949, p. 157; Salzen, 1963) but none of these movements is reliably associated with termination of immobility. One contrary report is provided by Gunter and McCaughan (1959, p. 1195) in observation of the toad fish, a marine species. They report that: "Finally (after immobility) the fish gives a convulsive gasp and revives. The fish recovers its color slowly. . ." Unfortunately, the writers report the total number of fish tested as more than a dozen, but they do not report the proportion that showed these responses in association with self-paced termination. The systematic change in color during and at the termination of hypnosis is one of the physiological responses that will be discussed in detail in the next section that deals with characteristics of hypnotic reactions.

Thus, with the exception of the report by Gunter and McCaughan (1959), the best predictor of self-paced termination of hypnotic responses that is available is the duration of immobility. In general, the longer the immobility has gone on, the greater the probability the response will be terminated. But it should be noted that this parameter requires many more parameters such as species and number of previous experiences, in order to make a specific prediction of the occurrence of self-paced termination.

Externally Produced Termination. Externally produced termination of hypnotic reactions has received some experimental attention and comments are available about a variety of species. Gilman and Marcuse (1949, pp. 156–157) summarize information on such species as beetles, scorpions, crawfish, frogs, lizards, and owls in terms of general reactivity to stimulation during immobility. Their review combined with the later literature suggests little generality of effects of specific external stimuli on termination of immobility. That is, no single class of stimuli regularly leads to termination of immobility for a number of species. The general consensus of reports is that any of a variety of stimuli such as loud noises, sudden visual presentations, or electric shock may lead to termination, particularly if the stimulation is intense and the onset is abrupt. For example, immobility responses of rabbits were reliably terminated by a sudden loud sound (Ratner, 1958), but a number of species of birds that were hypnotized by hooding did not respond to sudden loud sounds (Carlier, 1924; Patrick, 1927).

Data and conclusions regarding externally produced termination are subject to two confounding circumstances. One of these is the problem that self-paced termination may coincide with the presentation of the external stimulus. An insufficient number of controlled studies have been done to separate these events. The other confounding circumstance is the fact that one of the typical characteristics of hypnotic reactions is that the animals are unresponsive or analgesic during immobility. Thus, termination in response to stimulation may be an index to the fact that the reaction has ceased. It will be remembered that the lack of response to external stimulation such as electric shock and food may be used as a measure of intensity of the hypnotic response.

Characteristics of the Hypnotized Animal

Some of the dramatic behavior changes that characterize animal hypnosis are undoubtedly responsible for the continued investigation and reporting of the event. In addition, recent investigations have revealed systematic physiological changes that are associated with animal hypnosis. The behavioral and physiological characteristics of animal hypnosis will be treated in this section under three headings: characteristics at onset, characteristics during immobility, and characteristics at termination.

Characteristics at Onset. Remarkable agreement exists among the reports of the behaviors of animals just prior to the onset of immobility. In general, the animals struggle and fight against the restraining agent. For example, chasing shrimp or toad fish around the aquarium and grasping them led to almost immediate immobility. The behavior of a shrimp is described by Gunter and McCaughan (1959, p. 1194) as follows: ". . . it will go into a rigid state with the body arched concavely from the head to tail and with the legs and swimmerets drawn up tightly against the body." The shrimp will then sink to the bottom. The very brief struggle of the shrimp and toad fish was only found on the first several trials. On later trials the struggle continued for a longer time and the period of immobility was abbreviated.

Behaviors of birds just prior to the onset of immobility have characteristics in common with those of the shrimp, namely, the *struggle* against the restraining agent, and the *tonic posture*. In tests with chaffinch (such as are illustrated in Figure 1) the birds, even when held on their sides, pushed against the experimenter's hand with their feet and wings and turned their heads vigorously and bit the experimenter's fingers. The struggle ceased after five to 30 seconds and the birds lapsed into the characteristic posture shown in Figure 1. In this posture the head is thrown back and the legs are extended, frequently with a gross tremor. Salzen (1963, p. 67) also noted the gross tremor of birds at the onset and during immobility. The legs of some birds remained extended and others slowly retracted at the onset of immobility. The eyes of some birds were sometimes open and sometimes closed. Extended legs are also characteristic of the reacting frog and guinea pig (Schwarz and Bickford, 1956). The onset of immobility associated with hooding or covering birds is also characteristic and unique. Wild chaffinch were cornered in a small cage and then a cloth was dropped over their heads and bodies. The birds became immobile immediately after the cloth hit their bodies, and they gradually sank into a posture in which the head was lowered, the tail erect, and the legs bent. This posture was assumed and maintained whether the head was covered by the cloth or not.

Several physiological indices have also been obtained at the onset of immobility. Electroencephalographic recordings from frogs are described by Schwartz and Bickford (1956, p. 434) as follows: "always within ten seconds and usually simultaneously with the onset of the cataleptic state, the electroencephalogram showed changes. These appeared as 50-to-100 microvolt, 5-to-7 cycle per second waves . . . and disappearance of the 7-to-9 cycle per second normal background rhythm." Almost identical changes involving replacement of normal alpha rhythms with slower frequencies have been observed with the guinea pig (Schwarz and Bickford, 1956). The changes noted at the onset of immobility were not found for control animals that had not been immobilized.

Large differences in heart rate were found by Ratner in comparisons between pigeons under control conditions and pigeons at the onset of immobility. The mean heart rate of control birds ($N = 8$) within one minute after being handled on the first day of testing was 220 beats per minute; the rates of a comparable group that was restrained on its back for 30 seconds was 255 beats per minute. The difference was statistically significant and the magnitude of the difference between the experimental (immobilized) group and control group increased across four days of testing. The heart rates of the experimental group at onset of immobility remained at the high level originally found, whereas the rates for the control group gradually declined.

The onset of immobility of the toad fish is characterized by a change in body color. The fish is usually mottled brown but at the onset of immobility, according to Gunter and McCaughan (1959, p. 1195): "the fish begins to pale all over and rapidly begins to lose its color to such an extent that it becomes yellow." Color changes are also noted for the octopus at the onset of immobility (TenCate, 1928b).

Characteristics During Immobility. Suppression of responses to external stimulation is one of the most typical aspects of the behavior of an animal during immobility. Unresponsiveness is so characteristic that it is used as a measure of the hypnotic state. In the discussion of this as a measure (stimulation to terminate immobility), it was noted that animals have been tested with electric shock, pin pricks, cutting, and a variety of other stimuli. Gilman and Marcuse (1949) cited 15 experiments that report suppressed response to external stimulation. The suppression was noted for both vertebrates and invertebrates, including suppressed responding to painful auditory, visual, and tactile stimuli. The suppression of responding to painful stimuli leads to the special characterization of *analgesia* as an index of immobility.

Because the validity of the observation of suppressed responding seems to be established, establishing the limits of this suppression and establishing precisely what the animals do when an insufficient stimulus is presented become pertinent. Little data exist regarding the effects of a controlled series of stimuli. However, upper limits have been investigated with monkeys (Foley, 1938), dogs (Pavlov, 1955, p. 358), and frogs (Mangold and Eckstein, 1919). Ratner has obtained evidence about some of the specific characteristics of an animal's reaction to stimuli in the absence of an overt reaction. In the study of immobility reactions and heart rate of pigeons relatively intense auditory stimuli were presented. These stimuli were presented to both experimental (immobilized) and control groups. The stimulus, the sound of the blow of a hammer dropping several inches onto a piece of wood, led control birds to look toward the sound source but did not lead to an increase in heart rate. The birds in the experimental group did not startle, orient, or look toward the sound source. That is, they appeared unresponsive but large and reliable increases in heart rate were recorded. These increases in heart rate were noted for every bird and occurred on each of six presentations of the auditory stimulus. These data provide indirect evidence that immobile animals detect stimuli but do not react overtly to them. In other words, the suppression is motor, not sensory.

The posture of animals during immobility is distinctive and closely related to that of the animals at the onset of immobility. As noted in my field notes from work with chaffinch, if the bird is upright during immobility, it stands with its "head lowered almost touching the ground, tail erect, and legs flexed." Small and very slow movements, such as turning of the head, occur. The eyes open and close, and respiration is slow and shallow as compared with control birds. In short, the birds show none of the rapid twittering movements that characterize small song birds under normal conditions.

The posture of an animal immobilized on its side or back is also unique. The head is typically arched back and the muscle tonus is one of waxy flexibility. This posture led Hoagland (1928a, p. 427) to call the hypnotic state one of "plastic tonus." Such a state of tonus has also been noted by Dearborn (1900), Foley (1938), and Ratner (1958). Although the posture during immobility is unique and characteristic, the position of the limbs is not fixed. The animal's limbs may be extended or one limb may be extended while the contralateral one is flexed. Small movements may also occur during immobility when the animal is on its back or side. Chicks of domestic fowl even make occasional distress calls during immobility (Ratner and Thompson, 1960; Salzen, 1963). Both birds and guinea pigs have been observed to eliminate during immobility (Bayard, 1957), and Liberson (1948) reports that guinea pigs exhibit exophthalmos during immobility. He uses this as one of the signs of the hypnotic response.

The data regarding rate of respiration during immobility appear highly controversial. There are reports that respiration is increased, decreased, and unaffected. Unfortunately, none of the observations on which these reports are based are quantitative. I found all three observations can be made at some time during the course of an immobility reaction. If the animal struggles during restraint and this struggle is prolonged, then respiration is increased and only gradually approaches that of the normal animal. If, on the other hand, the animal is immobilized quickly, respiration seems to be slow and shallow and then gradually approaches that of the normal animal. However, these data, like those that were noted above, are relatively unquantitative, and were obtained only from birds.

The data regarding heart rate during immobility are as controversial as the data regarding respiration (Gilman and Marcuse, 1949, p. 155). The present writer studied heart rate during immobility of pigeons and found large and significant differences between control and experimental groups both at the onset of immobility and during the course of immobility. That is, heart rate at the onset of immobility and during the first portion of the response was greatly accelerated for the experimental subjects as compared with the control subjects. As the response approached termination (self-paced), the heart rate of the experimental animals approached that of the control animals. This fact makes it possible to interpret the finding of no differences in heart rate of immobile and control birds that is reported by Gilman *et al.* (1950). These workers averaged the heart rates during the first and last 15 seconds of immobility as their measure of heart rate. This measure tends to wash out differences between groups, because heart rate at the termination of immobility is very close to that of control animals. Thus, it is concluded that heart rate is elevated during immobility as compared with control animals, but the rate approaches the normal rate as the immobility reaction approaches termination.

Two studies of EEG and animal hypnosis report comparable findings. Schwarz and Bickford (1956) tested frogs and guinea pigs and found an EEG pattern during immobility much like that at the onset of the reaction. Specifically, they found that the frequencies were slow and background rhythms disappeared as compared with control animals. Svorad (1957) made an almost identical finding and in addition reported that the reticular activation system is capable of functioning during immobility. Schwarz and Bickford (1956) and Svorad (1957) comment on the similarity of EEG patterns during immobility and sleep.

Although the usual withdrawal reflexes to pin pricks and deeper assaults are not present during immobility, Ratner has tested the pupillary reflex with domestic fowl and found it is intact. That is, shining a bright light into the eyes of birds led to pupillary contraction; removing the light led to dilation. This was tested with six birds.

Characteristics at Termination. As indicated in the section on conditions for terminating immobility, little systematic work has been done on the topic of termination of these responses. However, all reports of behaviors associated with self-paced termination are in agreement about the abruptness and completeness of the termination. The animals that are immobile while upright, such as hooded birds, abruptly throw off the hood and move away. Those that are immobilized on their sides or backs suddenly right themselves and then move away. Descriptions of activities associated with self-paced termination are given by Gunter and McCaughan (1959) in relation to the toad fish, Armstrong (1942, pp. 67–70) in relation to several species of wild birds, and Ratner and Thompson (1960) in relation to domestic fowl. Hypnotic reactions of rats studied in the laboratory of the writer were also observed to terminate with characteristic abruptness. Gilman *et al.* (1950, p. 103) and Armstrong (1942, p. 67) report that after self-paced termination, birds may show other complex defensive responses. These may involve injury feigning, in which the animal moves away but drags one wing or "limps." Such postimmobility responses are noted especially for ground-nesting species of birds.

The heart rate of pigeons was found by the writer to approach the heart rate of normal birds just prior to the termination of immobility.

However, the EEG does not show this gradual return to normality. Schwarz and Bickford (1959, p. 436) state that: "The end of catalepsy was always marked by an immediate change in the electroencephalogram which resembled the control record."

Externally produced termination of immobility is sometimes associated with sudden and complete recovery and sometimes associated with incomplete recovery. In the case of incomplete recovery the animal rights itself or is lifted to its feet and then slumps into immobility while upright. These events are still incompletely investigated and described.

Variables Affecting Animal Hypnosis

Three classes of variables that affect hypnosis can be identified: (1) early experience and other past history; (2) the stimulus or test situation; and (3) biological and evolutionary variables. Each of the variables subsumed under these classes has been shown to have some quantitative relationship to animal hypnosis. That is, each affects degree of hypnosis in terms of duration, time to induce the reaction, percentage of animals responding, or amount of stimulation required to terminate the reaction.

Early Experience and Other Past History. Several recent experiments have shown the effects of specific early experiences on animal hypnosis. Moore and Amstey (1962b) raised control animals (five kids, five lambs) under normal conditions with their natural mothers. Experimental animals (four kids, five lambs) were raised by foster-mothers that subjected the young to varying periods of butting and other hardships. Tests of both groups for immobility reactions at one year of age showed that control animals had immobility reactions of seven times longer duration than experimental animals. Moore and Amstey (1962b) relate this difference to the early nursing experiences of the experimental group that led them to adapt to fear and threatening stimuli that included humans.

Salzen (1963) reports two experiments that showed the effect of early socialization on hypnotic reactions of chicks of domestic fowl. Specifically, birds in one group were raised in social isolation and those in other groups raised under normal conditions. Tests for immobility reactions at the ages of 14 to 16 days indicated that socially isolated birds showed much briefer immobility reactions than normal birds. These results and the results of a second experiment in the series led the researcher to conclude that early experience with isolation led the isolated chicks to be less fearful than normal chicks when taken to the test situation (a situation that did not include other animals). The normal chicks had always been near another bird. The results of the studies by Moore and Amstey (1962b) and Salzen (1963) indicate that hypnotic reactions are reduced by early experiences that lead to general adaptation of fear responses or that lead the test situation to be a more familiar situation.

Variables associated with past practice other than early experience have also been shown to affect hypnotic reactions. The effects of two kinds of past experiences can be identified. Some research has dealt with the effect of general experience with some aspect of the test situation; other research has dealt with the effect of prior testing for hypnotic reactions. Gilman *et al.* (1950) studied the effect of taming (handling) adult chickens on their subsequent reactions to hypnotic tests. They found that tamed birds showed significantly less response to immobilization procedures than either untamed or normal birds. Ratner and Thompson (1960) noted that the greater the number of days of feeding and other associations with the experimenters, the less the duration of immobility when the domestic fowl were eventually tested. Gilman *et al.* (1950) demonstrated the effects of familiarity with aspects of the test situation in another way. They tested a group of birds regularly for 25 days at which time hypnotic reactions had greatly diminished. Then on the twenty-sixth day they changed specific items in the test situation such as the table and experimenter. Each item of change led to an increase in the hypnotic response, but the change in the appearance of the experimenter led to the largest change in response.

One of the most common findings regarding the variable of prior experience and animal hypnosis is that hypnotic response decreases as amount of prior testing increases. Such results have been found by Gunter and McCaughan (1959) with shrimp and toad fish; TenCate (1928a) with octopus; Ratner with laboratory rats, chaffinch, and pigeons; and by a number of researchers such as Mowrer (1932), Gilman *et al.* (1950), and Ratner and Thompson (1960), who used domestic fowl.

The decrease in hypnotic response as a function of repeated test trials does not occur under certain special conditions. Bayard (1957) and Liberson (1948) found with guinea pigs that massing test trials for two hours in the most extreme way by returning the animal to its back the moment that it arose led to a progressive *increase in duration* of immobility. Liberson (1948) reports that the mean durations of immobility rose from about 30 seconds on the first session to two hours by the tenth session. The effects of a procedure intermediate between daily tests and massed tests involving repeated testings was used by Gilman *et al.* (1950) with birds. They conducted a total of 40 test trials with approximately 15 seconds between trials. Under these conditions duration of immobility remained at the same level for the entire set of 40 trials. That is, immobility reactions do not decrease as they do with widely spaced experiences, nor do they increase as they do with greatly massed trials. Although none of these effects is inconsistent with an interpretation of hypnotic reactions in terms of fear, they point out the complexity of the relationships between the restraining stimulus and adaptation to it.

Stimulus and Testing Situation Variables. The fact that an animal's experience prior to testing for an hypnotic reaction can affect the reaction means that stimulus conditions associated with the test and the situation exert some control over the reaction. *In general, the more familiar the restraining stimulus and the test situation the weaker the hypnotic response; and the less profound the restraining stimulus in terms of strength, duration, and physical proximity the weaker the hypnotic response.*

The evidence from the preceding section bears on this principle of familiarity and profundity as do other less direct lines of evidence. For example, hooding (covering the heads of rabbits) after the response had nearly disappeared from a number of days of testing led to an abrupt recovery of the hypnotic response (Ratner, 1958). Immobility reactions of frogs are more prolonged if the animals are held belly up, the unfamiliar position, than if they are held belly down (Mangold and Eckstein, 1919). Liberson (1948), testing guinea pigs, and Salzen (1963), testing chickens, noted that hypnotic reactions are reduced in duration if another animal of the same species (a familiar object) is in a test situation. Finally, it can be easily demonstrated that hypnotic reactions are not found with family pets when they are tested by members of the family in a familiar situation, although members of the same or related species do show these reactions under more suitable stimulus conditions.

Biological and Evolutionary Variables. Biological development and associated behavior development are closely related to the occurrence of immobility reactions. Several lines of evidence support this relationship. One line comes from recent studies specifically designed to test the relation between age and hypnotic response. Ratner and Thompson (1960) and Salzen (1963) showed that hypnotic reactions do not occur with chicks of domestic fowl before the chicks are approximately eight days of age. Sturkie (1954, p. 122) has pointed out that between seven and 14 days of age chicks of domestic fowl are undergoing important physiological changes, such as establishing temperature control, and these changes are associated with growing biological and behavioral independence. In other words, the chick at about eight days of age is quite different physiologically and behaviorally from the chick at four days of age.

The second line of evidence bearing on the relationship between biological development and onset of immobility reactions comes from studies of the development of species of wild birds. Dewar (1920, p. 208) notes in a description of the development of the oyster catcher that: "On the fifth day, the response of immobility is almost perfect, limpness is marked and any position is maintained except the upside-down position." By the tenth day even the upside-down position is maintained. Similar observations are reported for the young of the turkey vulture (Vogel, 1950), black-headed gull (Kirkman, 1937, p. 180), sparrow (Nice, 1943, p. 153), curve-billed thrasher (Rand, 1941, p. 218), and a variety of other species (Palmer, 1909). Thus, it seems clear that biological development and the age of the animal are factors in hypnotic reaction.

Adrenalin, neural ablation, and drug injection have also been investigated in relation to their effects on hypnotic reactions on animals. Hoagland (1928a) found with lizards that injections of adrenalin increased the durations of hypnotic reactions as compared with control groups that received saline. The adrenalin injections did not induce immobility reactions but they prolonged them. Amstey and Moore (1962) report in an abstract that hypnotic reactions of goats were decreased in duration by injections of adrenalin, caffeine, and perphenozine (a tranquilizer). These results are difficult to interpret in terms of the findings of Hoagland (1928a). The effects of ablations of various neural centers on hypnotic reactions are reviewed by Gilman and Marcuse (1949, p. 158). No systematic effect of ablation was found with vertebrates or invertebrates. For example, Holmes (1906) performed profound neural ablations with water scorpions (an invertebrate) and found that immobility reactions continued in spite of these ablations. The failure of neural ablation to affect hypnotic reaction led Hoagland (1928a) to consider endocrine processes in relation to animal hypnosis.

The relevance of evolutionary variables for hypnotic reactions of animals has been pointed out by a number of biologists (Armstrong, 1955, p. 249; Nice, 1943, p. 53; Hoagland, 1928a, p. 430; Palmer, 1909, p. 23). In general, the point is made that some species of animals have evolved immobility and associated reactions to a higher degree than others. So, for example, in the discussions of hypnotic reactions across species, it was pointed out that the European wren, characterized by great activity and nimbleness, has never been observed to show hypnotic reactions (Armstrong, 1955, p. 249), as do most other species of birds. The stimuli that elicit hypnotic reactions also may have an evolutionary basis. That is, different specific stimuli may be most appropriate to elicit hypnotic reactions for different species and these special sensitivities to specific stimuli may have evolutionary origins. So, for example, the immobility reactions of mantids seem to be elicited most readily by the attack of another mantid (Crane, 1952), and the immobility reactions of some spiders seem to be elicited by movements of the male of the species (Savory, 1928). A detailed analysis of evolutionary variables in relation to the stimulus has been made by Tinbergen (1951) especially with regard to fighting and reproduction.

Summary

Four major topics were considered in this section on research on animal hypnosis. The first two topics dealt primarily with methodological problems of measuring animal hypnosis, and producing and terminating the reaction. Four measures were presented and discussed: duration of immobility, time to induce immobility, percentage of animals becoming immobile, and amount of stimulation required to terminate immobility. Conditions for producing animal hypnosis were examined and were reduced to a set of conditions that involved *restraint and novelty*. Two conditions of termination of animal hypnosis were identified, namely self-paced termination in which the animal terminates the reaction with no cues apparent to the experimenter, and externally produced termination in which occurrence of some sudden and intense external stimulus is associated with termination of the reaction.

The third and fourth topics in this section dealt with the characteristics of the hypnotized animal and variables that affect the degree of hypnosis. Behavioral and physiological characteristics, including postures, responsiveness to external stimuli, heart rate, and EEG were discussed in relation to the onset, course, and termination of hypnosis. Three classes of variables that have been shown to affect animal hypnosis were discussed in relation to supporting experimental data. The classes of variables were: early experience and other past history, stimulus and test conditions, and biological and evolutionary variables.

THEORIES OF ANIMAL HYPNOSIS

From the time of the first report of animal hypnosis in 1646 until the beginning of the twentieth century, four types of theories of animal hypnosis have been propounded. As noted in the section on history, aspects of each of these early explanations are present in current theoretical positions.

Current Theoretical Positions

The most complete review and classification of current theories of animal hypnosis are given by Volgyesi (1938) and Gilman and Marcuse (1949). The classification of theories by Gilman and Marcuse is followed by Weitzenhoffer (1953, pp. 110–113) and by Marcuse (1955) in a later review of the topic. In this chapter several theoretical positions that are identified by Gilman and Marcuse (1949) will be described briefly and examined critically.

Hypnosis. The explanation of animal hypnosis in terms of human hypnosis probably arose from gross similarities in names that were applied to the two events and from gross similarities in behaviors associated with the events. That is, such words as "animal magnetism," "passes," and "trance" can be and have been associated with both human and with animal hypnosis. Aspects of the induction of the reaction (some of which are found to be irrelevant for animals) and the passiveness of the hypnotized subject are associated with both animal and human hypnosis. However, with the exception of Volgyesi (1938), who had training in hypnosis, and Armstrong (1942), a biologist, the consensus of opinion is that human hypnosis and animal hypnosis are probably not related.

Some views regarding this question are noted in the following quotations. Marcuse (1955, p. 270) states: "This latter theory (explaining animal in terms of human hypnosis) not only assumes that we possess more knowledge about hypnosis at the human level than we have, but it also ignores the question of the different phylogenetic levels involved." Weitzenhoffer (1953, p. 110) mentions in a discussion entitled "Hypnosis in Animals and Humans" that: "It appears rather certain that *there is no evidence that this sort of phenomena is at all identifiable with hypnosis as observed in humans.*" Wolberg (1948, p. 71) also addresses himself to the problem of the interpretation of animal hypnosis and concludes: "The question arises whether such manifestations are really hypnotic in nature. There is serious doubt that catalepsy in animals is similar to a trance in human beings. Even though humans do show signs of catalepsy during hypnosis, these are among the more minor phenomena of the trance state."

In summary, the consensus of opinion among people who have had experience with human hypnosis and have reviewed or contributed to the literature of animal hypnosis, is that these two phenomena are not related. The opinions of people experienced with human hypnosis are used because this event is judged by the writer to be more complex and difficult to comprehend from reading than is animal hypnosis. When one of the processes is well analyzed and described, it might be profitable to use it as a tentative model for the analysis and description of the other process. But until that time, it seems that the understanding of animal hypnosis is not moved ahead by linking it verbally with human hypnosis.

Reflex Response and Cerebral Inhibition. Several biologically oriented investigators have suggested that animal hypnosis arises from cerebral inhibition. Among these are Pavlov (1955), Holmes (1906), and Hoagland (1927). The general idea of these theories is that something about the induction procedure, such as repetitive stimulation, prolonged restraint, or visual fixation, releases a product that inhibits cerebral activity or itself fatigues or satiates cerebral centers. The inhibitory or satiating product is assumed to produce immobility and unresponsiveness.

Although this is a familiar theoretical form, having been applied to a number of different processes including learning, extinction, and perceptual changes, the explicit experimental support for the theory as applied to animal hypnosis is absent. Even the results of Pavlov's carefully conceived experiments on animal hypnosis in the conditioning situation can be interpreted without using the hypothetical constructs referring to cerebral processes. However, Pavlov's theory may still have validity in accounting for human hypnosis as presented in Chapter 12 of this Handbook.

Sleep. The explanation of animal hypnosis in terms of sleep is closely related to the explanation in terms of cerebral inhibition. Pavlov (1955), for example, adopted these related ideas and used them in his interpretations of a number of findings, including some from the conditioning situation. When the interpretation of animal hypnosis in terms of sleep was in favor, it was also used as an interpretation of human hypnosis (Gilman and Marcuse, 1949, p. 162). However, little explanatory power is achieved by likening one process that is not understood to another process that is not understood. The chief support for the view that animal hypnosis can be explained as sleep comes from the findings that EEG's from immobile frogs and guinea pigs resembled a sleep record. Although the similarities of the EEG records between sleep and hypnosis are of interest, the lack of similarity between many of the other characteristics of the two states weakens the interpretation.

Spatial Disorientation. The hypothesis that animal hypnosis occurs as a function of spatial disorientation has been suggested by Rabaud and Hoagland (Gilman and Marcuse, 1949, p. 162). The theory seems to be based on the fact that inverting the animal is a common procedure in inducing the reaction. However, animal hypnosis has been observed and studied in a number of cases in which the animals are not inverted. Armstrong (1942) reports many field observations of the immobility reaction in upright animals, especially birds. Patrick (1927) studied immobility with upright birds that had been hooded, and Ratner (1958) found that hypnotic reactions of rabbits were not terminated by turning the rabbits upright after immobility had occurred. Thus, it seems clear that spatial disorientation is not an explanation of animal hypnosis, although it may be one feature that contributes to the unfamiliarity of the stimulus situation and therefore facilitates the hypnotic reaction.

Paralysis of Fear. McGonigal (1920), Armstrong (1942, p. 70), Gilman *et al.* (1950), Ratner and Thompson (1960) and Salzen (1963) have all used an interpretation of animal hypnosis that relates the reaction in some way to fear. Although the interpretation has never been developed in detail, it is based on several kinds of data regarding animal hypnosis. One is the common observation that animals freeze, become temporarily immobile, when a novel or threatening stimulus is presented. Another fact is the repeated finding that the reaction decreases in strength with repeated testing when the same stimulus is used; a third finding is that heart rate and respiration change during immobility. Thus, this interpretation of animal hypnosis has persisted since Preyer discussed the relationship in 1881 (Gilman and Marcuse, 1949, p. 163).

However, several problems exist in this interpretation. The most obvious is that the meaning of paralysis of fear becomes very clouded when extended to lower vertebrates and invertebrates. Although the concept has some meaning as applied to mammals and possibly even birds, it is difficult to conceive an adequate definition of fear that applies equally well to lower forms. In short, the interpretation is suggestive but does not seem to tie together the diverse characteristics and great generality of the reaction.

Closely allied to the explanation of hypnosis in terms of fear is the explanation in terms of *death feigning*. This interpretation does not seem to have any contemporary proponents, but it is important for several reasons. One reason is that it leads to an explanation that fits all species, given the assumption that the presence of a predator or an enemy (which exist for all species) can elicit unlearned and complex responses. The second reason that death feigning as suggested by Darwin is an important interpretation is that it has been subjected to so much misunderstanding and "bad press." For example, Gilman and Marcuse (1949, p. 161), Marcuse (1955, p. 258), and Weitzenhoffer (1953, p. 12) deal with the interpretation in terms of the cognitions of the immobile animal and the predator. That is, these writers seem to assume that for this interpretation to be valid the animals must have knowledge of the effects of their behaviors and the writers then point out that this is rather unlikely. This assumption is no more necessary to describe death feigning than it is to assume that in reproductive behaviors the male's mounting of the female is a situation in which both or either party is aware of the consequences of its behavior. In short, the male is responding to a stimulus with a complex, innate reaction.

Summary. Each of five interpretations of animal hypnosis is examined. The interpretations, labeled in terms of the basic processes that are assumed to explain the reaction are called: hypnosis, reflex response and cerebral inhibition, sleep, spatial disorientation, and paralysis of fear. Each of the theories has one or more defects, such as being inconsistent with some data from animal hypnosis or being inappropriate in terms of the data. In addition, the explanations are largely alternate names for the process and with one exception have failed to lead to more than a single research. The exception is the explanation in terms of paralysis of fear. The research of the past 15 years for the most part has involved experimental study of variables affecting immobility reactions and descriptive studies of immobility and the species that show it. The event is well verified in terms of its general properties and the species that show it. Thus, it seems ripe for a comparative analysis, and in the next section such an analysis will be applied to animal hypnosis.

Comparative Analysis of Animal Hypnosis

Comparative study refers to a method of analysis rather than a particular content. It is a method that can be applied to any diverse set of events or processes that seem to be related to each other. Comparative study, as it is applied to the behavior of organisms, is called comparative psychology. Comparative psychology can be likened to mathematical psychology. That is, mathematical psychology refers to a method of analysis and implies a particular form to the analysis. Although the method has been applied most conspicuously to learning and such psychological processes, mathematical psychology is not limited to them, nor is it equal to them. Similarly, comparative psychology frequently deals with infrahuman learning, perception, and innate processes, but it is not limited to these topics nor is it equal to them. In addition, comparative analysis is not necessarily tied to a theory of evolution any more than mathematical analysis is necessarily tied to a probability theory, but the comparative approach has a number of characteristics and aims that set it apart from other methods.

General Model. Some of the properties of comparative analysis will be briefly outlined before the model is applied to the data of animal hypnosis. Comparative analysis involves at least five related steps that can be characterized in the following way.

1. Describing and classifying behavior from a wide range of forms with an emphasis on functional rather than formal characteristics.
2. Identifying the situations, including the species, in which particular classes of behavior can be studied to best advantage—that is, identification of good examples for intensive study.
3. Establishing conceptual relationships among the behaviors that are under study.
4. Relating the behaviors under study to other behavioral events with the particular aim of postulating the mechanisms or processes that are operating.
5. Generating a theory of behavior that relates a great many behaviors and identifies the mechanisms associated with the relationships.

Toward a Theory of Animal Hypnosis. This brief statement of the comparative model, adapted from an analysis by Ratner and Denny (1964), can readily be applied to the data of animal hypnosis. This analysis, like any other theoretical analysis, requires that a considerable backlog of data, especially experimental data, be available. Gaps in information about animal hypnosis are known to exist; but four of the five steps of comparative analysis will be undertaken.

Description and Classification. The descriptive material regarding animal hypnosis was provided in the earlier portions of this chapter. The material can be summarized in the following way. For a variety of species of animals *restraint* by some threatening or predatory stimulus condition, especially an *unfamiliar stimulus in an unfamiliar situation*, leads to struggling, which is followed by *immobility and unresponsiveness.* The eliciting value of the stimulus condition is reduced on repeated presentation unless the stimulus is applied without interuption for very long periods of time (for example, two hours). In this case, the eliciting value of the restraining stimulus is enhanced and leads to immobility of progressively longer durations. The effect on responsiveness is not known. Physiological measures from vertebrates during hypnosis show *heightened autonomic activity* and a *flattened EEG.*

Identification of Good Examples for Study. The study of learning by psychologists can be used to illustrate the problem of the importance of identifying good examples of a process for experimental study. It is probably true that all species that have been tested show learning; but if the shrew had been selected as an experimental subject, the analysis of learning would have focused on somewhat different processes than if another animal were selected. That is, some aspects of the behavior of the shrew would have masked many of the subtle learning processes; and in addition, the behavior of the shrew is not typical of mammalian species. Thus, it is one of the jobs of the comparative psychologist to assist in the identification of good examples of a process for experimental study.

Based on the general description and classification of animal hypnosis, experimental study is required with regard to stimulus conditions, overt responses, and physiological responses. The fact that so many species of different animal groups show the response makes it particularly likely to find species and test conditions that represent the event of animal hypnosis most clearly. Birds, including domestic fowl, seem to be particularly appropriate for the study of the effects of stimulus conditions. Because birds have excellent vision and good hearing, a great range of stimuli can be used and the salient aspects of the eliciting stimulus readily identified. The hypnotic response of birds is of sufficient duration to allow measurement of changes in the response and the concurrent physiological processes. Study of adrenal processes is difficult with birds because their adrenals are not readily accessible. The lizard has been used for these purposes, as could almost any mammal. However, the problem of studying hypnotic reactions with mammals is that these reactions seem to adapt as a function of the normal handling and other associations with humans. Thus, the study of animal hypnosis with mammals is somewhat difficult. Most birds can be raised with little handling by humans yet they are not dangerous to work with even if this handling is omitted. The neurological study of animal hypnosis has been undertaken with higher invertebrates and could surely be extended to many vertebrate species, including birds.

Conceptual Analysis of Animal Hypnosis. In the first step of comparative analysis, description and classification, some concepts that apply to the event were identified. Among these concepts were threatening stimulus, restraint, unfamiliar stimulus, adaptation, struggle, immobility, and unresponsiveness. In this section these descriptive concepts will be amplified and some relationships among them examined.

It is proposed that any stimulus, such as a natural predator, that functions as a threatening stimulus, elicits a sequence of responses as a function of the *distance between this stimulus and the animal.* This distance, a psychological scale rather than a simple metric scale, is called the *defensive distance* and is adapted from a concept suggested by Moore (Moore and Amstey, 1962b). It is postulated by the writer that each species reacts to defensive distance as a function of organismic variables such as age, speed of escape, and size, and as a function of psychological variables, such as degree of prior adaptation to the stimulus and familiarity with the general situation.

As the defensive distance between the threatening stimulus and the animal is reduced by the movement of this stimulus a sequence of responses occur. This sequence is shown in Table 2. First the animal is alert (freezes), then it moves away; as the distance reaches zero, it struggles or fights; and finally, as the defensive distance remains at zero, it becomes immobile and unresponsive (animal hypnosis). It is further noted that the analysis of termination requires more data than are presently available. In summary, a remote predator functions in one way, an approaching predator in another way, and so forth.

Each characteristic reaction that is associated with a particular defensive distance, such as freezing or moving away, requires detailed

Table 2
Analysis of the Sequence of Stimuli and Responses Associated with Decreasing Defensive Distance Between the Threatening Object and the Test Animal

DEFENSIVE DISTANCE	TYPICAL STIMULUS	ELICITED RESPONSE
Great	Visual, auditory	Freeze
Reduced distance	Moving visual	Escape
Zero	Moving visual, tactile	Fight
Prolonged zero	Prolonged tactile	Immobility (animal hypnosis)

experimental study. It seems possible that early reactions in the sequence are predictive of later ones. Some study of these early responses has been undertaken (Armstrong, 1942, Chap. 6; Andrews, 1956).

Conceptual Relationships Between Animal Hypnosis and Other Behavior Processes. This review of current theories of animal hypnosis indicated that attempts have been made to tie the explanation of animal hypnosis to a variety of different processes including sleep, human hypnosis, and fear. Although each of these theories has merit, none is considered to be adequate. Thus, the question is open as to the behavior process to which animal hypnosis is related. Table 3 shows a number of features of innate or instinctive behavior that are drawn from statements by Tinbergen (1951), following the theory of Konrad Lorenz. Table 3 also shows the extent to which features of animal hypnosis are congruent with features of innate behavior.

Table 3
Characteristics of an Innate Behavior, Such as Reproduction, and Characteristics of Animal Hypnosis*

INNATE BEHAVIOR	ANIMAL HYPNOSIS	SPECIFIC EXAMPLES
1. Observed among wide range of species	Yes	Invertebrates and vertebrates
2. Relevant for survival of species	Yes	Relationship between predator and animal
3. Occurs in natural life of animal	Yes	Natural observation with birds
4. Specific stimulus and fixed response pattern	Yes	Restraint leads to fixed responses
5. Response adapts	Yes	Waning of response with repeated trials
6. Complex response	Yes	Change in responses with defensive distance
7. Participation of physiological factors	Yes	Heart rate and EEG
8. Learning not important for early occurrences	Yes	Ontogenetic data

* Note: General characteristics are listed.

The degree of correspondence between features of innate behavior and animal hypnosis is marked. Eight characteristics of innate behavior seem applicable to animal hypnosis. Thus, it is suggested that the conceptual framework applicable to innate behavior is also applicable to animal hypnosis.

Other innate behaviors are reproduction and fighting and the discussions of these by Beach (1951) and Tinbergen (1951) are particularly clear and relevant examples of analyses of such behaviors. As suggested in Table 3, the general idea of innate behavior is that species specific stimuli, analogous to unconditioned stimuli, elicit complex responses or sequences of responses with little or no prior learning. The stimuli, called releasers or sign stimuli, and the associated responses, are assumed to be relevant to the survival of the species. The point about survival is made as a general guide to permit preliminary identification of behavior patterns that might be described in terms of innate behavior. It is not meant as a working theoretical statement.

It is consistent with other research on innate behavior to bring the animal into the laboratory to determine the specific characteristics of a stimulus that elicit a response. That is, features of the natural stimulus can be imitated in the laboratory to identify those features that are salient. Animal hypnosis lends itself to such a style of investigation. For example, specifying metric distances that are associated with defensive distances for various species would be of interest.

Physiological changes associated with innate behaviors are assumed to precede these behaviors (Tinbergen, 1951). However, evidence is accumulating that suggests that the physiological changes associated with an innate pattern are actually precipitated by other behaviors earlier in the sequence. Because animal hypnosis can be induced so readily and its course is relatively brief, especially in comparison with some of the reproductive behaviors, animal hypnosis suggests itself as a fruitful behavior process for the study of the relationship of physiological changes and innate behavior.

Summary

Five theoretical positions regarding animal hypnosis are discussed. Although each position provides some characterization of the process, none has adequately handled the data of animal hypnosis nor has any of these, with the exception of the fear hypothesis, led to research beyond a single study.

Thus, it was concluded that a comparative analysis of animal hypnosis be made. The method of comparative analysis was discussed and characterized in terms of five interrelated steps: (1) description and classification of animal hypnosis; (2) identification of good examples for study; (3) conceptual analysis of animal hypnosis; (4) conceptual relations between animal hypnosis and other behavior processes, and (5) general theory of behavior.

The first four steps of comparative analysis led to the following conclusions: (1) For description and classification the data of earlier sections are summarized as follows: restraint by some threatening or predatory stimulus condition, especially in an unfamiliar situation, leads to struggling and then immobility and unresponsiveness. This behavior occurs for a great variety of animals. The eliciting value of the restraining stimulus is reduced following repeated presentations of this stimulus. Physiological measures during immobility of vertebrates suggest heightened autonomic activity and flattened EEG. (2) Good examples for study of animal hypnosis are identified in terms of the study of behavior (birds), the study of physiological processes (reptiles and rodents), and the study of neurological processes (higher invertebrates and rodents). (3) Animal hypnosis was then conceptualized as a terminal reaction in a sequence that occurs as a function of changes in the *defensive distance* between the threatening stimulus and the test animal. The intensity of the terminal reaction (*animal hypnosis*) is also affected by organismic variables such as species and age of the animal, and by psychological variables such as degree of adaptation to the threatening stimulus and the animals' familiarity with the general situation. (4) Animal hypnosis is then related conceptually to behavior processes currently viewed as innate behavior. The large number of points of congruence between this conceptual framework and animal hypnosis is noted. Some of the concepts associated with a Tinbergen-Lorenz theory of innate behavior are identified and the implications of the theory with regard to animal hypnosis are sketched briefly.

REFERENCES

AMSTEY, M. and MOORE, A. U. (1962). "Tonic immobility: decreased inhibitory activity as an effect of three different drugs in the induced catatonic state in goats," *Amer. Zool.*, **2**, 113 (abstract).

ANDREWS, R. J. (1956). "Fear responses in *Emberiza* Spp.," *Brit. J. anim. Behav.*, **4**, 125–132.

ARMSTRONG, E. A. (1942). *Bird Display*. Cambridge, England: Cambridge Univ. Press.

——— (1955). *The Wren*. London: Collins.

BAYARD, J. (1957). "The duration of tonic immobility in guinea pigs," *J. comp. physiol. Psychol.*, **50**, 130–134.

BEACH, F. A. (1951). "Instinctive behavior: reproductive activities," in Stevens, S. S. (Ed.). *Handbook of Experimental Psychology*. New York: Wiley.

BOAS, E. P., and LANDAUER, W. (1933). "The effects of elevated metabolism on the hearts of the frizzle fowl," *Amer. J. med. Sci.*, **185**, 654–664.

BRAID, J. (1899). *Neurypnology: Or the Rationale of Nervous Sleep Considered in Relation to Animal Magnetism or Mesmerism*. 2nd Ed. London: G. Redway.

CARLIER, W. (1924). "Hooding of birds," *J. physiol.*, **59**, 1–11.

CARRINGTON, H. (1931). "Hypnotizing animals," *Psychic. Res.*, **25**, 41–44.

CRANE, J. (1952). "A comparative study of innate defensive behavior in Trinidad mantids (*Orthoptera mantoidea*)," *Zoologica*, **37**, 254–293.

CROZIER, W. J. (1923). "Reflex immobility and the central nervous system," *Proc. soc. exp. Biol.*, **21**, 55–56.

DARWIN, C. (1900). "A posthumous essay on instinct," in Romanes, G. J. (Ed.) *Mental Evolution in Animals*, 360–364. New York: Appleton.

DEARBORN, G. V. N. (1900). "Psychophysiology of the crayfish," *Amer. J. Physiol.*, **3**, 404–443.

DEWAR, J. M. (1920). "The oyster catcher's progress toward maturity," *Brit. Birds*, **13**, 207–213.

FOLEY, J. P., Jr. (1938). "Tonic immobility in the rhesus monkey (*Macaca mulatta*) induced by manipulation, immobilization and experimental inversion of the visual field," *J. comp. Psychol.*, **26**, 515–526.

FRASER, A. F. (1960). "Spontaneously occurring forms of tonic immobility in farm animals," *Canad. J. comp. Med.*, **24**, 330–333.

GILMAN, T. T. and MARCUSE, F. L. (1949). "Animal hypnosis," *Psychol. Bull.*, **46**, 141–165.

GILMAN, T. T., MARCUSE, F. L. and MOORE, A. U. (1950). "Animal hypnosis: A study in the induction of tonic immobility in animals," *J. comp. physiol. Psychol.*, **43**, 99–111.

GUNTER, G., and MCCAUGHAN, D. (1959). "Catalepsy in two common marine animals," *Science*, **130**, 1194–1195.

HOAGLAND, H. (1927). "Quantitative aspects of tonic immobility in vertebrates," *Proc. Nat. Acad. Sci.*, **13**, 838–843.

——— (1928a). "The mechanism of tonic immobility," *J. gen. Psychol.*, **1**, 426–447.

——— (1928b). "On the mechanism of tonic immobility in vertebrates," *J. gen. Physiol.*, **11**, 715–741.

HOLMES, S. J. (1906). "Death-feigning in Renatra," *J. comp. neur. Psychol.*, **16**, 200–216.

JACKSON, M. (1952). "A warning call of the American Robin (*Turdus migratorius*)," *Auk*, **64**, 466.

JAMES, W. T. (1937). "An experimental study of the defense mechanisms in the opossum with emphasis on natural behavior and its mode of life," *J. genet. Psychol.*, **51**, 95–100.

KIRKMAN, F. B. (1937). *Bird Behaviour*. London: T. Nelson.

LERNER, M. (1962). "Comparative aspects of human and animal hypnosis," *Amer. J. clin. Hyp.*, **5**, 57–60.

LIBERSON, W. T. (1948). "Prolonged hypnotic states with local signs induced in guinea pigs," *Science*, **108**, 40–41.

MANGOLD, E., and ECKSTEIN, A. (1919). "*Die Reflexieregbarkeit in der tierischen Hypnose*," *Arch. ges. Physiol.*, **177**, 1–37.

MARCUSE, F. L. (1955). "Animal hypnosis and psychology," in Kline, M. V. (Ed.) *Hypnodynamic Psychology*, New York: Julian.

MARCUSE, F. L., and MOORE, A. U. (1944). "Tantrum behavior in the pig," *J. comp. Psychol.*, **37**, 235–541.

MCGONIGAL, J. P. (1920). "Immobility: an inquiry into the mechanism of fear reaction," *J. abnorm. Psychol.*, **27**, 73–80.

MINAMI, H. and DALLENBACH, K. M. (1946). "The effect of activity upon learning and retention in the cockroach," *Amer. J. Psychol.*, **59**, 1–58.

MOORE, A. U., and AMSTEY, M. (1962a). "Tonic immobility: Decreased inhibitory activity as an effect of three different drugs in the induced catatonic state in goats," *Amer. Zool.*, **2**, 113 (abstract).

——— (1962b). "Tonic immobility: Differences in susceptibility of experimental and normal sheep and goats," *Science*, **135**, 129–730.

MORGAN, L. (1891). *Animal Life and Intelligence*. 2nd Ed. London: Edward Arnold.

MOWRER, O. H. (1932). "A note on the effect of repeated hypnotic stimulation," *J. abnorm. soc. Psychol.*, **27**, 60–62.

NEWMAN, H. H. (1924). *Outlines of General Zoology*. New York: Macmillan.

NICE, M. M. (1943). "Studies of the life history of the song sparrow. II. The behavior of the song sparrow and other passerines," *Trans. Linn. Soc. N.Y.*, **6**, 1–328.

NOBLE, G. K. (1931). *The Biology of the Amphibia*, New York: McGraw-Hill.

PALMER, W. (1909). "Instinctive stillness of birds," *Auk*, **26**, 23–36.

PATRICK, D. M. (1927). "Some effects produced by hooding of birds," *Brit. J. exp. Biol.*, **4**, 322–326.

PAVLOV, I. P. (1955). *Selected Works*. Moscow: Foreign Language Publishing House.

RAND, A. L. (1941). "Development and enemy recognition of the curve billed thrasher (*Toxostoma curvirostre*)," *Bull. Amer. Mus. Nat. Hist.*, **78**, 213–242.

RATNER, S. C. (1958). "Hypnotic reactions of rabbits," *Psychol. Rep.*, **4**, 209–210.

RATNER, S. C., and DENNY, M. R. (1964). *Comparative Psychology: Research in Animal Behavior*. Homewood, Illinois: Dorsey.

RATNER, S. C., and THOMPSON, R. W. (1960). "Immobility reactions (fear) of domestic fowl as a function of age and prior experiences," *Anim. Behav.*, **8**, 186–191.

SALZEN, E. A. (1963). "Imprinting and the immobility reactions of domestic fowl," *Anim. Behav.*, **11**, 66–71.

SAVORY, T. H. (1928). *The Biology of Spiders*. New York: Macmillan.

SCHWARZ, B. E., and BICKFORD, R. G. (1956). "Encephalographic changes in animals under the influence of hypnosis," *J. nerv. ment. Dis.*, **124**, 433–439.

STEINBECK, J. (1954). *Sweet Thursday*. New York: Viking.

STURKIE, P. D. (1954). *Avian Physiology*. Ithaca, N.Y.: Comstock.

SVORAD, D. (1957). "Reticular activating system of brain stems and animal hypnosis," *Science*, **125**, 156.

TENCATE, J. (1928a). "*Sur la production de ce qu'on appelle l'état d'hypnose animale chez la raie*," *Arch. néerl. Physiol.*, **12**, 188–190.

——— (1928b). "*Nouvelles observations sur l'hypnose dite animale. État d'hypnose chez octopus vulgaris*," *Arch. néerl. Physiol.*, **13**, 402–406.

TINBERGEN, N. (1951). *The Study of Instinct*, Oxford: Oxford Univ. Press.

VOGEL, H. H. (1950). "Observations on social behavior in turkey vultures," *Auk*, **67**, 210–216.

Volgyesi, F. (1938). *Menschen—und Tierhypnose.* Leipzig: Fussli.
Weitzenhoffer, A. M. (1953). *Hypnotism: An Objective Study in Suggestibility.* New York: Wiley.
Wolberg, C. R. (1948). *Medical Hypnosis*, Vol. 1: *The Principles of Hypnotherapy.* New York: Grune & Stratton.
Yerkes, R. M. (1903). "The instincts, habits and reactions of the frog," *Psychol. Rev.*, **1**, 579–597.

VI

AN OVERALL LOOK AT HYPNOSIS

18

Ethics in Hypnosis

PERRY LONDON[1]
University of Southern California

THERE is almost certainly no other psychological technique as obviously subject to ethical concerns as is hypnosis, for no other seems to hold such morbid fascination for so many people as a possible source of evildoing. There are reasons enough why hypnosis has achieved this dubious distinction and why it maintains it even in the face of constantly increasing knowledge and generally favorable publicity. Not all the reasons are bad ones either, though most of them involve some misinformation. The first part of this chapter concerns the reasons, historical and current, for the peculiar reputation that attends hypnosis and hypnotists.

The ethical issues surrounding a subject do not depend only on its reputation, however, but also upon the character of the enterprise and the way it is potentially related to the norms of the social order in which it operates. Hypnosis is used both in scientific and in professional settings for study and for therapeutic purposes. Its implications for ethical

[1] The preparation of this article was supported in part by the United States Public Health Service, National Institute of Mental Health, Research Grant MH-08598.

conduct or misconduct are subtopics of the ethical obligations of scientific and professional personnel in general toward their subjects, clients, and patients.

Such a treatment assumes a reasonable consensus within society about professional roles, which is reflected in professional codes of ethics, in civil and criminal laws governing the practice of professions, and in writings on the subject of ethics. These will be discussed next.

Finally, the ethical issues surrounding hypnosis have some special reference to the properties of hypnotic phenomena themselves, so a discussion is in order of the current state of knowledge of those hypnotic phenomena about which ethical problems are most commonly encountered. Most of these problems come under the heading "Antisocial Uses of Hypnosis."

THE NEGATIVE AURA OF HYPNOSIS

Since early times, hypnosis and hypnotists have been regarded by many people with hostility, suspicion, and distrust. This is often the case in modern times as well. The explanations of hypnotic phenomena and the attendant reasons that were once popular bases for such sentiments are generally regarded as superstitions today. But many of the uses to which hypnosis was put in the past, and many of the social roles that hypnotists portrayed, have probably remained the same from the magicians of Egypt to the nightclub healers and spiritual counselors of Sunset Strip. The divorce of medical from religious and other mysterious and supernatural-appearing events is a recent one in the history of human experience, and is not altogether complete even now (Moss, Logan, and Lynch, 1962). Many of the events that characterize hypnosis are manifestly the same as those that traditionally represent ecstatic religious experience, the effects of the mumblings of shamans and witch doctors, or the consequences of the formulae of medicine men (the latter term used in both its common meanings). Profound hypnotic trances sometimes appear to be identical with the cataleptic states of oracles and fakirs and, for all anyone knows to the contrary, they may involve the same kinds of subjective experience as well.

Mystery and supernaturalism are not enough by themselves to explain the negative aura of hypnosis, though they do remove it from the category of everyday events. In very recent times, among very sophisticated people in the West, it is true, all irrational-seeming experiences are suspected symptoms either of neurosis or naïveté, but this is not a very general public concern. Historically, the negative aura of hypnosis may have more to do with the fact that some common hypnotic phenomena have been associated with particularly *malevolent* supernatural forces. Gormley (1961) points out, for example, in a discussion of "prescientific hypnosis," that skin anesthesia was considered by some

Christians one of the *stigmata diaboli* (devil's marks) that identified people possessed by the devil. Hypnotic phenomena in general, he alleges, were considered signs of "possession," especially since Luther's time.

The general public recovery from witch-hunting and from concern with Satanism did not do as much for the reputation of hypnotists as it might have, however, for people remained as concerned as ever with other nefarious possibilities, which seemed inherent in the subject. The most important and most appropriate of these was probably charlatanism. Mesmer was in effect accused of this, though neither precisely nor justly, and hypnosis has, to this day, been as much the object of the flirtations of sordid entertainers and elegant confidence men as it has ever been of medical or scientific inquirers. Spiritualists, secular faith healers, and the inventors of religions are not always either clowns or con men, but are sometimes closely enough associated with both to help confirm hypnosis' ill repute. John Graham, O. W. L. (O Wonderful Love!), for example, may actually have succeeded in restoring the fervor of British roués who lay in his Celestial Magnetico-Electrico Bed at the end of the eighteenth century. Phineas Quimby undoubtedly aided Mary Baker Eddy with hypnosis in the nineteenth, and she in turn aided America's contribution to the history of religion. And Pat Collins may be a real boon to those current visitors to Los Angeles nightclubs who want to stop smoking—but the total impact of these figures on the reputation and on the medical and scientific development of hypnotic knowledge is at best a mixed blessing.

People and subject matters can both live down questionable reputations if the source of doubt is not replenished. There is enough reinforcement of popular concern over hypnosis, however, to sustain it indefinitely. Some of it is related to the reputations of the purveyors, as indicated, which has led protagonists of hypnosis who seek social respectability to propose legal controls over the use of hypnotic techniques by nonmedical or nonscientific persons. But part of the problem may be a function of the anxieties that are often aroused in people by the very nature of hypnotic phenomena, and insofar as this is the case, it is unlikely that hypnosis will ever be the object of altogether casual regard, whether it is practiced by license or not. The properties of hypnosis itself thus finally give rise to most of the ethical issues connected with it.

The most obvious conclusion that a casual observer of a hypnotic session would probably reach concerning the interpersonal transaction is that, in some fashion that is not altogether intelligible, the hypnotist has gained *control* of the mind of the subject. If the observer is psychologically sophisticated and knows that people do not have minds, he can still observe that the hypnotist apparently controls the behavior of the subject. Because the hypnotist and subject probably think the same thing, and will likely tell the observer so later, he has no evidence to contradict either his sensory data or the conclusions he drew from them.

It is not strange, therefore, that the main question that has always concerned people about hypnosis is one of interpersonal control. In functional terms, *control* is the main concern people have always had about supernatural and mysterious forces. The functional origins of religion have been attributed to man's desire to exert control over the forces of nature that could benefit or harm him, and the power of religious agencies, including sacrifices, priests, and the populace of the underworld, has always been associated with their ability either to exert directly or to mediate control over events (Mencken, 1963). It is precisely this aura, now thoroughly secularized, which is transmitted to hypnosis and hypnotists by the more or less mutual agreement of subjects, hypnotists, and observers. In this case, control means the ability, actual or potential, of one person to manipulate the behavior of another; and the ethical problems of hypnosis, viewed this way, are simply special cases of the general ethics of behavior manipulation.

THE ETHICS OF BEHAVIOR CONTROL

The Meaning of Manipulation

Although manipulation and control of behavior have always been the main goal of applied psychologists, they have often been embarrassed about openly recognizing this object of their professional behavior. The reason for their diffidence is that the term "manipulation" has acquired a pejorative connotation that implies unethical conduct on the part of behavior manipulators. This issue is particularly familiar in the psychological literature on psychotherapy, where the most extreme positions respectively argue that it is the business of psychotherapists to help people understand themselves without influencing their conduct or values one way or the other and, conversely, that it is the therapist's business to manipulate people's behavior in some generally desirable direction whether or not they are able to understand themselves and point their own directions in the process. The best-known proponents of these respective positions are Carl Rogers and B. F. Skinner, who have formally debated them (Rogers and Skinner, 1956).

If the concept of manipulation is taken broadly to include any and all processes by which a therapist or anybody, for that matter, *deliberately* and planfully interacts with another person, then it is simultaneously relieved of particularly humanistic and particularly pejorative connotations and becomes simply a label for describing any planful, purposive interpersonal behavior. Used this way, the concept of manipulation includes the processes of helping people to understand themselves, and the important moral issue of what constitutes proper conduct or values is separable from the technical one of what constitute effective means of manipulation. The technical uses of social reinforcement in psychotherapy are presented in an excellent discussion by Krasner (1961); and the moral implications of therapeutic interaction, in terms both of ideology and social responsibility, have received attention from a number of sources (Buhler, 1962; Krasner, 1962; London, 1964; Masserman, 1960; Watson, 1958).

Unethical Behavior Manipulations

Ethical problems seem to arise in connection with behavior manipulations on the basis of only two assumptions; namely (1) that manipulators are capable of eliciting involuntary responses; and (2) that they are able to exert undue influence on voluntary decision and response processes. Although similar statements could be made about many professions, from policeman to surgeon, these assumptions are paramount in connection with psychological personnel because of the global and potentially insidious character of psychological manipulations. In the case of hypnosis, they are particularly important because of the possibility that hypnotic techniques can be used seductively and efficiently to elicit antisocial responses or behaviors, which are otherwise somehow not in the best interests of the subject, however voluntary they may be. This problem has been of sufficient historical interest to require a separate discussion below of antisocial behavior manipulations.

Involuntary Responses. Any discussion of involuntary responses presupposes some definition of volition, but there does not seem to be a single satisfactory one. This is a very serious practical problem just as it is an academic one, as witness the furor whenever issues of *legal* responsibility such as the M'naghten rule, fit motherhood, or the exercise of undue influence on the contents of last wills and testaments come to public attention.

In law, volition is sometimes defined presumptively; it is presumed, for example, that young children are less able to control their behavior than are adults and that the mentally ill are less able to do so than others. Such definitions have an implied statistical character; they are normative in the sense that they are rationalized or justified on the basis of a presumed consensus of observations, in this case about the average or typical behavior of children, of the mentally ill, and of most other adults (London, 1962). This consensus would be that minors and that the mentally ill, as groups, characteristically behave in less self-controlled ways than do others.

Presumptive definitions of volition have only limited utility because group traits are often untrue of single members of the group, and another basis for definition is therefore individual. It concerns subjective impressions or experiences of self-control or compulsion that are not assumed to be uniform for everyone. This definition is less reliable than a presumptive one, but it is also more relevant. For one thing, it incorporates a very much wider range of variable individual experiences, such as the influence of special stimulus conditions and situations, like drugs, impulses, and emergencies. Perhaps more important, however, is the notion that volition may be usefully and validly defined as identical with the subjective experience of having it (Sherrington, 1940). This is an old philosophical problem, and cannot be dealt with here. For practical purposes, volitional processes may be understood best as experiences along a continuum of subjective impressions of volition, expressed in terms of ability to verbalize subjective degrees of self-control over past, present, or future events. Consciousness of one's own experience is implicitly a part of this definition, for consciousness is expressed primarily as verbal descriptions of past events, that is, memory.

At the involuntary end of the continuum, experiences are commonly divided—by source or motive of the response rather than by content—between the intrapersonal and the interpersonal. The former has an internal source, either physiological or psychological, and includes the consequences of compulsions, irresistible impulses, habits, or reflexes where control seems to be beyond the normal executive capacities of the person responding. Interpersonal sources, on the other hand, are coercions or threats imposed by a force external to the recipient. The difference between coercion and threat rests in the symbolic character of the latter as opposed to the direct stimulus value of the former. Again there is a continuum implied; twisting a person's arm is a clear instance of coercion, proposing contingent violence in words alone is a clear case of threat, and pointing a gun while making a demand partakes of both. In any case, the reference point for the subject's (victim's) decision is the behavior of another person, not of himself.

Undue Influence. There are a large number of behaviors that are performed voluntarily, in the view of the performer, but that seem in retrospect to have had some of the characteristics of a compulsion. When the inspiration for such behavior can be attributed to someone other than its performer, the latter is said to have acted under undue influence. There seem to be two situations to which the concept of undue influence most often applies: (1) where the behavior was suggested in circumstances where the subject was unusually susceptible to suggestions, and therefore unlikely to assert executive capacities for decision, which might otherwise have been available to him; and (2) where the behavior is an indirect consequence of the relationship between subject and manipulator rather than a result of the manipulator's direct suggestions. Such a relationship is assumed to achieve peculiarly suggestive characteristics because of circumstances that normally reduce the choice behavior of the subject, as when he becomes very dependent for care, attention, or approval from the manipulator.

Antisocial Responses. Behaviors in this category, like voluntary behaviors that are not in the best interests of the subject, do not necessarily require retrospective remorse on the subject's part or even awareness of their performance in order to be ethical problems. It is always assumed that such behavior is the outcome of manipulations of involuntary responses or the exertion of undue influence on the subject, regardless of his subsequent attitude.

Actually, manipulation of involuntary responses is not ordinarily a problem in the ethical conduct of psychiatric or psychological research or practice. Neither doctors nor scientists in these professions are likely to use coercion or threat in office or laboratory, except perhaps the threat of discontinuing service if the patient does not accept the conditions that the doctor lays down. Coercion occasionally becomes the subject of concern in hospital psychiatric treatment, especially in connection with the use of physical assault therapies, like electric shock, or physical restraint, and sometimes in connection with drug treatments. But although there are serious questions of civil rights and personal rights connected with these matters, they are also subjects to which both professional and legal authorities are sensitive enough to pay some attention and are outside the usual scope of ethical problems to be discussed here.

The most common ethical problems of behavior manipulators concern the exercise of undue influence on significant aspects of the behavior of patients or subjects both within and outside the professional relationship. The most dramatic instances of such problems undoubtedly involve antisocial behaviors, improper professional conduct, or events that are construed as damaging the general interests of the patient. These are the problems of which hypnotic practitioners are most likely to be aware and in connection with which they are most likely to be objects of suspicion, insult, and occasionally legal attack. Already endowed with magical properties in the eyes of many people, hypnosis is also an apparently seductive means of influencing behavior. The combination of myth and appearance is often irresistible.

There are a number of more subtle problems that deserve more attention than they ordinarily get, however, and though they are not unique to the ethics of hypnotic manipulations, they are as relevant to them as to any other psychological technique. These problems include the communication of values from doctor to patient or scientist to subject, the transmission of false or misleading information for the elicitation of specified response patterns, and the limitations of responsibility for aftermath effects or follow-up study.

Communication of Values. As indicated, problems of the communication of values in psychotherapy have received some attention, and it is only in treatment rather than research that such problems are very likely to appear. The difference between the situations, except in research deliberately designed to manipulate values, is that contacts between research investigator and subject are usually shorter, fewer, and less emotionally significant than contacts between therapist and patient. The value problem is something of a dilemma that does not permit many hard and fast rules (Jahoda, 1958; London, 1964); sometimes questions of ethics arise from therapists' failure to communicate value concepts, as when patients confess or threaten to commit grossly antisocial, illegal, or destructive behavior. More common still are cases where ethical issues arise from the therapist's communication of his values. This is especially true when the communication is insidious, as is sometimes the case if the value is rationalized in terms of "mental health." A very powerful illustration of this phenomenon in recent literature is presented by Lillian Ross (1963) in *Vertical and Horizontal* in connection with a psychoanalyst named Dr. Blauberman. The communications to which Miss Ross alludes involve values concerning family relationships and career aspirations, both rationalized by the therapist in terms of neurotic dependency. But sexual mores, educational values, religious beliefs, and other areas are also subject to value problems, and responsible practitioners must be sufficiently sensitive to them to separate carefully their personal values, the facts of human behavior and mental hygiene, and the aspirations they may have for the development of their particular patients. The naïve belief that these matters can be easily separated and resolved in some manner that inevitably serves the best interests of all concerned is unjustifiable.

The Deception or Stress Design. Deliberate transmission of false information is more likely to occur in research than in psychotherapy, though in therapy it is occasionally used when a therapist feels that he cannot evoke a necessary change in behavior without the communication of some "white lie." (The ethics of white lies extend far beyond the domain of psychology, of course, and cannot receive any detailed treatment here.) The use of a "deception design" in research does not involve white lies told for the subject's benefit, however, but planned falsehoods used by the experimenter for the explicit purpose of eliciting a certain kind of response, often stressful and unpleasant, from the subject. Such procedures may be necessary to produce laboratory conditions that approximate real-life situations to which people are rarely exposed or that could not be properly observed in the field without contamination from other situational variables. Methodological questions can be raised about whether such approximations are really legitimate bases for generalization about the dynamics of personality in real life, but such questions are irrelevant to an ethical consideration of their use. Consequently, the ethical problems of stress and deception designs have been discussed extensively by behavior scientists. One such discussion of these problems is presented in *Ethical Standards of Psychologists* (American Psychological Association, 1953):

> It is generally accepted that the psychologist, like other scientists, assumes obligations for the welfare of his research subjects, both animal and human. However, decisions as to what constitutes a potential threat to a human subject's welfare, and when, if ever, the possible significance of the research warrants exposing the subject to potential harm or difficulty are often hard to make. . . the need for such decisions arises in a number of areas. (p. 120)

A number of incidents connected with this problem are then discussed, and the section concludes with statements of two principles intended to guide researchers in this matter:

> Principle 4.31–1. Only when a problem is significant and can be investigated in no other way is the psychologist justified in exposing research subjects to emotional stress. He must seriously consider the possibility of possible harmful after-effects and should be prepared to remove them as soon as permitted by the design of the experiment. Where the danger of serious after-effects exists, research should be conducted only when the subjects or their responsible agents are fully informed of this possibility and volunteer nevertheless.
>
> Principle 4.31–2. The psychologist is justified in withholding information from or giving misinformation to research subjects only when in his judgment this is clearly required by his research problem and when the provisions of the above principle regarding the protection of the subjects are adhered to. (p. 129)

It is impossible, of course, for a problem of this kind to be resolved in a professional ethical code without either stifling psychological research or implying a kind of carte blanche for the researcher to assault people in the ostensible interests of science. In a totalitarian social organization, professional guilds are not likely to be left to their own devices in this connection—but the Nazis demonstrated that extreme social control over scientists harms their subjects only if the source of control is itself brutal. In a society such as ours, the subjective tolerance of subjects for exploitation and the fundamental decency of experimenters seem to be the most effective means of preventing excesses while permitting exploration.

The Ethics of Aftermath. Research personnel probably do pay close attention to the possible harmful aftermath to subjects of stress and deception experiments and also, as the Ethics Code demands, probably do "remove them as soon as permitted by the design of the experiment." Oddly enough, the ethical problems related to the dangers of after-effects are probably much more serious in psychotherapy than in research, even though therapists are generally better equipped than researchers to anticipate and to ameliorate baneful sequelae. The very feeling of lack of therapeutic expertize may sensitize conscientious researchers to aftereffects, the more so when they plan their experiments to be stressful; whereas therapists, whose bread-and-butter business is human distress to begin with, may be more casual about following up the effects of their manipulations over long periods of time. Also, the history of scientific success in experimentally creating neuroses is so much longer and richer than that of any parallel success in treating them, that scientific personnel are likely to be more sanguine about their ability to create stress in experiments than to remove it (Liddell, 1944; Wolpe, 1962). Certainly, all behavior manipulators have an ethical obligation not only to remove the aftereffects of potentially hurtful experimental or therapeutic techniques, but also to maintain sufficient contact with their subjects or patients over time to be sure that their ameliorative efforts have been effective. Therapists often fail to do this, which is both scientifically and ethically irresponsible (Eysenck, 1961).

Unconcern with aftereffects creates one kind of ethical problem, but too much concern with them creates another. The disease model of psychological disorder, with its nice distinctions between superficial symptoms and underlying sources of malady, has contributed a mythology to psychotherapy, which alleges that direct therapeutic attacks on symptomatic behaviors leave patients vulnerable to further eruptions and disorders stemming from the unchecked internal agents that caused the symptoms in the first place (Bandura, 1961; Szasz, 1961). Because the psychoanalytic theory is so much in vogue that symptoms reflect functional, if only partial, resolutions of their motivating sources, many therapists conclude that the danger of aftereffects from direct treatment of symptoms is greater if the treatment works than if it doesn't—for the assuaging properties of the symptom disappear when it does.

These dangers cause many therapists to avoid making use of symptomatic Action Therapies (London, 1964). Because hypnotic suggestions are sometimes used as direct symptom-removal techniques, this danger is also one of the reasons for the unpopularity of hypnosis among many therapists.

It is reasonable to say that errors of omission are more tolerable in psychotherapeutic practice than errors of commission, provided that they are less likely to be harmful than the latter. That is probably true in psychotherapy, and for that reason, therapists may be justified in using symptomatic and direct treatments only with caution and circumspection. The evidence, on the other hand, does not speak very well for the hypothesis that generated its collection. Wolpe's survey of follow-up studies of recoveries from neurosis among people who did not have psychoanalysis or other therapies oriented toward uncovering the dynamics of motivation revealed only four relapses among 249 patients (Wolpe, 1961). A similarly small proportion of sequelae to hypnosis were found among experimental subjects in a study by Hilgard, Hilgard, and Newman (1961). If these results prove reliable in future studies, it may suggest that the proper tolerance for error favors the commission rather than omission of direct treatment methods.

The ethical problem here is one that arises from the failure to manipulate in the first place rather than from not correcting harmful manipulations. An intelligent general solution to this problem cannot be found, however, until careful studies of therapeutic aftermath are conducted. Because experiments are, by nature, manipulative, the problem does not arise in connection with research.

THE ETHICS OF HYPNOSIS

Because hypnosis is generally regarded as a specialized technique of psychiatric and psychological research and practice, the ethical problems of those professions apply to the use of hypnotic techniques in much the same way as to any others. The difference, if any, is that some kinds of general ethical problems occur more frequently in connection with hypnosis than with other research or treatment instruments, and some special kinds of ethical problems come from what seem to be peculiar or unique properties of hypnotic behavior.

Challenge Suggestions

Coercion or threat are as uncommon in the use of hypnosis as of any other psychological techniques, and hypnotists are therefore no more likely than others to be subject to accusations in this connection. Hypnotic challenges and commands, on the other hand, often appear to be coercive, which is undoubtedly one of the reasons why some people feel that hypnotists "have them in their power." The retrospective reports of many subjects in connection with such suggestions, moreover, indicate a subjective experience of compulsion, which prevents them from breaking a challenge (Hilgard, 1963). Although they are aware that such compulsions do not involve any physical coercion by the hypnotist, they may still feel that he is responsible for their disability and has coerced them by placing them in his power. Inasmuch as the hypnotist instructs them more or less clearly that they will be unable to do something, then challenges them to do it, this subjective experience seems to justify the suggested definition of coercion, in which involuntary behavior is attributed to an interpersonal source.

Posthypnotic Suggestions

Even more dramatic events than those contained in challenge items are the peculiar things that people do as a result of posthypnotic suggestions. These behaviors are sometimes embarrassing and humiliating to the subject; therefore, it is easy to argue that, because they were suggested by the hypnotist in the first place, the subject cannot be solely responsible for having performed them. Posthypnotic suggestions commonly include suggestions of amnesia to the subject; it therefore seems even more reasonable to claim that, however difficult it may be for current behavior theory to find the proper concepts or jargon for explaining it, the hypnotist has indeed "got the subject in his power." Posthypnotic suggestions are less likely than challenges to be seen as coercive in that sense, but the only real difference between posthypnotic suggestions is the time lag between suggestion and response and an intervening episode of being awakened from the hypnotic trance. It is perfectly reasonable to regard a posthypnotic episode as an instance of a person reentering a hypnotic trance according to a prearranged signal and then carrying out a prearranged hypnotic suggestion (Erickson, 1958). In that event, the internal compulsive aspect of the posthypnotic behavior is itself a result of the hypnotist's suggestion of time lag and of amnesia for his very words. Posthypnotic suggestion, therefore, seems to be a clear-cut illustration of undue influence both by having an external source and by having originated under circumstances in which the subject was unusually susceptible to suggestions.

Ethical problems do not ordinarily arise in connection with the kinds of challenge suggestions typically used for the induction of hypnosis and for deepening hypnotic trances; these, however potent they may seem, are usually transitory events of very brief duration and obvious insignificance for any purpose other than to demonstrate to the subject his increasing involvement in the hypnotic state. Undue influence through posthypnotic suggestions is a more common allegation, and one more difficult to defend against. It is possible to argue that responses to hypnotic suggestions are transference phenomena and that hypnotists are no more liable to allegations of undue influence than are psychotherapists who deliberately elicit transference neuroses (Bookbinder, 1961; Gill and Brenman, 1961). But this argument fails to recognize that, even if the dynamics of these situations are the same, the time periods involved are not; the malignant potency of the posthypnotic suggestion would, if anything, be a result of the relative speed and ease with which it could be effected. Besides, the deliberate elicitation of transference phenomena might also be unethical, depending upon the behaviors and intentions involved.

Antisocial Uses of Hypnosis

The general utility of hypnosis as a persuasive rather than coercive technique applies to its antisocial as to other more banal potentialities. Among the former are generally included (a) the use of hypnosis in entertainment to elicit unconventional and undignified behavior, which will later be recalled by the subject with feelings of humiliation; (b) the use of hypnosis to elicit acts of violence and aggression; and (c) the use of hypnosis to increase susceptibility to immoral, illegal, or otherwise improper conduct.

There is no doubt at all that hypnosis is sometimes used for one or another of these purposes; as an entertainment device in particular, hypnosis seems to excite public interest more strongly in connection with its capabilities for inducing bizarre behavior than anything else. There are some known cases of the use of hypnosis for purposes (b) and (c) as well, and it goes without saying that there must be many more such cases that have never been exposed (Barber, 1961; Orne, 1961; Reiter and Thoman, 1958).

There are two problems connected with such phenomena, and it is quite important to separate them to assess the ethical issues involved. One of these problems concerns the effectiveness of hypnosis as such for eliciting antisocial behavior, and the other involves the ethics of intent on the part of the hypnotist, regardless of the efficacy of the technique.

The rather extensive literature on the nefarious use of hypnosis has been recently reviewed in considerable detail by Martin T. Orne (1961), whose sober conclusions on the subject are that, by and large, there is almost no evidence that hypnosis can be used effectively for eliciting antisocial behavior *against the wishes of the subject* and that, in the few cases in which it is unmistakably clear that hypnosis was used as an agent for persuading people to commit crimes,

> . . . close scrutiny of these instances reveals that in each case an intense emotional relationship existed between hypnotist and subject. The bearing of these cases on the question at hand is consequently in doubt. One need not invoke hypnosis to explain behavior on the part of one individual to please another, be it criminal or not, when an intense emotional relationship exists between the individuals involved. (p. 211)

If the question of the utility of hypnosis is thus limited by the narrow issue of its technical efficacy in the face of intended resistance, then it is possible to answer rather unequivocally that it has none, and that there is therefore no ethical issue at stake.

The argument used here is precisely that which hypnotists often invoke in their own defense, namely, that hypnotic suggestions simply will not take when they run counter to the moral scruples of the subject. In effect, this says that the subject bears his own built-in protection against malicious or witless moral undoing on the part of the hypnotist. In that case, there is no need for hypnotists to worry about the moral dispositions of their subjects or colleagues and vice versa, as responsibility for any behavior rests with the behaver, not with the instigator.

There is some merit to this position, but it cannot be accepted as an altogether valid one. For one thing, it oversimplifies the events involved, failing to distinguish, in Orne's terms, "between the use of hypnosis per se and the hypnotic situation." For another, it takes no account of the ethics of intent or the complexities of mixed motives that might be aroused and acted upon by hypnotist or by subject, resulting in the violation of personal or social codes of conduct, which would have remained intact had hypnosis not been involved.

Orne's position, stated briefly, is that although hypnosis may be inherently useless in overcoming resistance to some unacceptable hypnotist demand, the context in which it is used does not have these limitations. On the contrary, the popular view of the hypnotic situation as one in which the subject is helpless to resist the hypnotist, and is consequently not culpable for acquiescing to him, may effectively weaken any resistance even before hypnosis is attempted. A skillful manipulator, under such circumstances, may very well exploit the situation to elicit the behavior he desires even if he never hypnotizes the subject at all! The fact that hypnosis per se did not produce the behavior in question then has little ethical import—for ethical problems, as opposed to scientific ones, attempt *to relate* the persons involved to the behaviors they perform, not *to separate* these elements of the total situation and treat them independently of each other.

Orne's argument is addressed to the specific problem of whether hypnosis can be used to compel unwilling captives to release secret information, but the generality of his conclusions is quite apparent:

> If it were to be used on interrogation subjects, hypnosis itself may be quite innocuous, but it is entirely possible that the utilization of the hypnotic *situation* for this purpose could be a serious threat. The common belief that an individual in hypnosis is not responsible for his actions, although probably incorrect, could be exploited. The hypnotic situation would alleviate the informant's guilt by relieving him of the responsibility of his behavior, and would supply him with an alternative to a dreaded and potentially stressful situation. (Collage from pp. 210, 211–212.)

Just as the ethical issues of manipulation do not require any separation of hypnosis from the hypnotic situation, they do not necessitate reliance on the subject's volition as a sufficient or even necessary criterion of the ethical status of his own or the hypnotist's behavior. It seems contradictory for the hypnotist to propose before the fact, that is, in the course of induction, that the subject will accept the hypnotic suggestions and do what he is told, and then to shrug off responsibility after the fact by hypothesizing a moral thermostat in the subject that makes him altogether self-responsible. It seems much more reasonable to say that, if a subject does unacceptable things suggested to him by the hypnotist, the hypnotist is, at the least, an accessory before the fact.

Even if the hypnotist does not use a blanket explication during induction of his expectation that the subject will do what he wants, the conclusion that he is responsible in some measure for acceptance of his suggestions remains unchanged. Whatever explanations or definitions of hypnosis one ventures, there is no doubt that hypnotic behavior may be accurately described in terms of some functional acceptance of unreality by the subject. Whatever his internal state may be, a hypnotic subject responds to hypnotic suggestions of unreality as though they were reality. Otherwise there would be nothing whatsoever to distinguish hypnotized from unhypnotized behavior. If I tell someone to hold his arm out straight and then gradually lower it to his lap, for example, I am not involved in hypnotic behavior. It is only when I couch the same direction in terms that divorce it from an everyday sequence of directions and deliberately pose it in terms of unrealities such as a hypothetical weight pressing it down that I then perceive or discuss it as hypnotic behavior rather than as mere social acquiescence. And the acceptance of such unreality by the subject does not imply hypnotic behavior unless the suggestion of it comes from the hypnotist. If the hypnotist wishes to call the behavior hypnotic, therefore, it is hard to see how he can consider himself utterly innocent of its occurrence.

Suppose that the hypnotist does not directly suggest that the subject perform some objectionable act, on the other hand, and does nothing more than hold his peace when it occurs. Responsibility in this case is certainly less than when the hypnotist has been explicit in suggesting the behavior, but it probably cannot be limited to the sole criterion of explication. At least two other factors are important: (1) the demand characteristics of the hypnotic situation (Orne, 1959); and (2) the predictability of untoward behavior resulting from a general relaxation of inhibitory mechanisms. For most purposes, these are the factors that finally make ethically irrelevant the inability of a hypnotist to coerce immoral behavior from his subject, and that place some ethical responsibility on him as an accessory in the events which give rise to *S*'s behavior.

The essence of the concept of demand characteristics is that subjects are not passive recipients of hypnotic suggestions but active respondents to them. As such, the performances that willing subjects render are not necessarily limited to the explicit suggestions that the hypnotist makes, but are defined by the interaction between the subject's interpretation of what is *generally* expected from him, what is in fact explicitly demanded, and what he is willing to do. The first and last of these, however, are themselves almost always indeterminate, variable, and mutually reinforcing. The very lack of general explication by the hypnotist creates an atmosphere in which the subject is free to respond to his own fantasies about the proprieties of the situation, and the definition of limits shifts with both the immediate awareness of his own impulses and the extent to which the proprieties of this situation seem alike or different from other ones. If the general situation implied by the hypnotist is one in which the subject is not expected to be responsible for his behavior, and if the subject experiences impulses to respond in uninhibitedly irresponsible ways, then the consequences of this interaction will be predictably unconventional behavior. The fact that the hypnotist may not have suggested it outright and may even be surprised at its occurrence may testify to his naïveté, but does not necessarily reduce the predictability of the events nor his responsibility for precipitating them.

The simplistic fallacy in the doctrine of the subject's self-responsibility comes from the assumption that a subject's brakes on his own behavior are engaged simply by his moral scruples rather than by a variety of inhibitors, many of which, such as embarrassment, fear of scorn or reprisal, or distaste, may be quite independent of internalized values. Moral scruples are themselves likely to have complicated bases, moreover, and people's dispositions even with respect to thoroughly internalized moral principles will nevertheless vary with the situations in which these principles are tested by impulse and opportunity. That hypnosis is likely to constitute such a situation is most evident on consideration of its many routine aspects that violate the conventions of interpersonal relationships: It tends to be carried on under circumstances in which the subject is denied normal visual cues for assessing another's response, it involves the repeated performance of uncommon behaviors on the basis of uncommon demands, and it tends to specify that the subject is not responsible for his conduct. As Orne (1962) puts it:

> The situation which is probably most relevant to the central issue. . . is that in which a subject is ambivalent toward an item of behavior. In such a situation, he might well refuse to carry out the behavior in his normal waking state, but he could be induced to carry it out under certain special circumstances. One condition sufficient to resolve the ambivalence might be hypnosis. . . Quite possibly, in some instances hypnosis, like alcohol, might provide the necessary rationalization for the execution of normally unacceptable actions. (p. 187)

THE ETHICS OF HYPNOTISTS

It is apparent at this point that the ethical problems of hypnosis do not depend upon any *unique* efficacy that hypnosis may or may not have for the manipulation of behavior. Hypnosis *is* a very deliberate technique for manipulating behavior, and once the point is granted that it can be used for this purpose, whether directly or through the charisma of the hypnotic situation, the ethical problems of greatest importance concern hypnotists' activities rather than hypnosis per se.

Deliberately disregarding the difficult problem of the effects of hypnosis per se upon the subject, it is reasonable to believe that the disinhibiting behaviors and emotional upheavals that sometimes take place in hypnosis result in part from the oddities of the situation, which influence the subject's view of it. If that is the case, then those same situational peculiarities might exert similar or correlated influences upon the hypnotist's view of the situation, the subject, and his own relationship to them. To whatever extent some personal needs of the hypnotist thereby achieve more prominence than would otherwise be given them, his behavior is likely to increase the demand characteristics of the situation for subject behaviors that would satisfy those needs. Unless those behaviors also serve the interests of the subject, the hypnotist is seriously at fault.

If the ethical sensibilities of the hypnotist are considered as things apart from his technical skill and self-knowledge, then perhaps this problem could be classified under a technical rather than an ethical heading. In that case, it might appear to be of a piece with the essentially technical problem of psychotherapy, namely, that the selective responses of the therapist inevitably influence the kinds of material that patients produce. The difference between hypnotherapy and other psychotherapy in this connection would then be a quantitative one; the interpersonal interactions of hypnotherapy seem to occur with greater speed and emotional intensity than in other psychotherapy (see Shaw, 1961, on hypnodontics). But this difference between hypnotic and other situations only increases the need for hypnotists to be hypersensitive to their own needs and the ethics of professional conduct. Other aspects of the hypnotic situation, moreover, differ enough from most psychotherapies to suggest that a hypnotist's ethical sensibilities may be essential parts of his technical qualifications. For one thing, he has deliberately structured the interpersonal situation in a way that makes him more responsible and the subject less responsible for what transpires than is usually the case in psychotherapy. For another, he has invested himself with the authority to make suggestions, has divested the subject of responsibility for his own conduct, and has invited an intensity of experience that would not be displayed ordinarily under any other circumstances. Finally, he has created an atmosphere of relaxation and unreality that may affect him just as it affects his subject. Having done all these things, he is certainly under some ethical obligation to guard against the untoward effects of it all on himself.

It is perhaps in relation to the fulfillment of his own sexual, sadistic, and dependency needs that the hypnotist must be most alert to avoid placing subtle and improper demands upon his subject. The fact that sexual material, sadistic impulses, and dependent feelings are likely to be somewhat restrained during ordinary interpersonal traffic makes these areas especially prone to the disinhibiting effects of the hypnotic trance. Because the production of such material may be easily rationalized as critical to the therapeutic enterprise, moreover, it is fairly easy for hypnotherapists to satisfy personal voyeuristic or dependency needs by exploiting the relative readiness of patients to cooperate.

The personal needs of hypnotists may affect their conduct beyond the areas of sex, sadism, and dependency, of course. Lindner (1960) believes that a need for personal power characterizes the general use of hypnosis:

> The hypnotic phantasy. . . can be characterized as a megalomanic and omnipotent sort of daydream which is evoked by the hypnotist on infantile levels below consciousness and which serves to flatter his ego through the successful utilization of a "power tool" such as hypnosis represents. (p. 64)

Insofar as the "hypnotic phantasy" operates in the professional behavior of hypnotherapists, and he seems to think that it is nearly universal, Lindner contends that "the hypnotic relationship is. . . a shared neurotic experience. . ." in which each of the parties satisfies somewhat different emotional needs. Similar themes are mentioned by Wolberg, Moss, and Brownfain in this Handbook. It is not clear just how hypnotists may defray the burden of their own needs in the conduct of their professional affairs, but it may be reasonable to suggest that greater sensitivity to this problem is required of hypnotic therapists than of others.

Hypnosis as Placebo

A final question concerning the ethics of hypnotists involves simply the decision to make use of hypnosis in situations in which the practitioner would not ordinarily choose it, as for example, when a patient comes for treatment of some psychological disorder with an *ideé fixe* that hypnosis should be used upon him.

For some workers, the question is irrelevant because they are inclined to use hypnosis for everything anyway. For most practitioners and situations, the problem is minimal by virtue of established routines of use. The ethical question occurs for situations in which hypnosis would not be undertaken by the therapist except as a placebo for the patient, and was then used only in the hope that it would give the therapist access to some other means of treatment.

The use of hypnosis as placebo involves the same problems as does the indirect induction of hypnosis or, for that matter, the use of any treatment device that is actually irrelevant to the symptom or entity in question. Physicians faced with similar problems in connection with physical ailments, are likely *de facto* to use placebos rather uncritically. The job of psychotherapists, however, may be more of an educational than an ameliorative one, by virtue of both the kinds of problems that confront them and the armamentarium of techniques they have available for attacking them. Hypnotherapy, because of its implications of mumbo-jumbo and charismatic healing, has some of the educational vices of its ameliorative virtues, and its practitioners must therefore be even more concerned than other therapists about the possibility of net loss to their social function from overelaborate use or too eager advocacy of the seeming powers they control. The same ethical problem is involved in the use of any procedure designed to manipulate patients into making themselves available for treatment, and has been mentioned briefly above under "white lies." Like most ethical problems of professional practice, its proper resolution "all depends"—on the urgency of providing treatment, the reason the patient resists a frank presentation in the first place, and the practical difference that the hypnotist's decision will make in the patient's life, and finally, in his own.

SUMMARY AND CONCLUSION

The ethical problems that attend research and practice with hypnosis are not very different from those of any service or scientific profession that deals directly with human beings. To that extent, the codes of conduct of medical, psychiatric, and psychological associations are about as adequate to the conduct of hypnotists as to the professionals for whom they were originally written—the more so as most hypnotists are members of one or another of those associations.

Bypassing the problem of whether professional codes of conduct are themselves very useful, they do not entirely suffice as discussions of ethical problems in connection with hypnosis, for the combinations of hostile mythology and true peculiarity that surround hypnosis and hypnotists set it somewhat apart from other psychological techniques.

There is a negative aura surrounding hypnosis, partly because of associations between hypnotic and nefarious supernatural events and partly because of the connection between hypnosis and one or another variety of professional entertaining or downright bunkum. These unfortunate associations are partly historical and partly current, but more important, they are partly true and justified as well as false and superstitious. There is no obvious prospect of laying all such public concerns to rest, moreover, though hypnosis currently has a good popular press.

The major ethical problems of hypnosis are a result of its potential use as a means of manipulating behavior. Hypnotists are liable to charges both of controlling involuntary behavior and of unduly influencing voluntary behavior, and they are mainly accused of using their apparent powers either for the purpose of inducing antisocial behavior in their subjects and clients or for otherwise harmfully exploiting clients for the satisfaction of their own desires. The use of challenge suggestions and posthypnotic suggestions seems to illustrate these hypnotic powers to the casual observer. Though the powers are undoubtedly exaggerated in the minds of many people, there is no doubt that hypnosis can be very useful for the unethical purposes indicated, especially when the subject is himself ambivalent about their performance. There are a few instances of hypnosis having been used quite successfully to induce antisocial behavior, though there is no evidence that this could be done against the blatant opposition of the subject. Apologists for hypnosis have avoided the issue in much of their research, chiefly by concentrating on the efficacy of *hypnosis*, which is about nil, and disregarding that of the *hypnotic situation*, which is often very great, for eliciting undesirable behavior.

Problems of the communication of values, the possible indecency of deceptive or stressful research designs, and the ethics of aftermath and follow-up in research and therapy are essentially the same for hypnotists as for others, and generally receive less attention than they deserve.

If there are any important differences in the ethical problems of hypnotists and other behavior manipulators, they come from the apparent fact that hypnosis is more effective than some other techniques for accomplishing the same thing that other methods do. In the long run, it may not make much difference ethically whether this is true or not as long as anybody in the hypnotic situation thinks it is true. Nor does it really make any difference whether their reasons for thinking it are superstitious and naïve, as might sometimes be the case with patients, or multisyllabically scientistic, as is more likely with hypnotists. In either event, the hypnotic situation becomes invested with more psychological potency than it otherwise would have, sometimes perhaps with more than it ought to have. As long as this can happen, it is the responsibility of the hypnotist, not of the patient or subject, to be sensitized both to his own and the other person's needs and frailties, and to plan his activities in whatever manner will be most beneficial and least painful or dangerous to the individual he exploits, and finally, the society he serves.

REFERENCES

American Psychological Association (1953). *Ethical Standards of Psychologists.* Washington D.C.: The American Psychological Association.

Bandura, A. (1961). "Psychotherapy as a learning process," *Psychol. Bull.*, **58**, 143–159.

Barber, T. X. (1961). "Antisocial and criminal acts induced by 'hypnosis'," *Arch. gen. Psychiat.*, **5**, 301–312.

BOOKBINDER, L. J. (1961). "The application of psychodynamic thinking to hypnotic behavior," *Psychiat. Quart.*, July, 1–9.

BUHLER, CHARLOTTE (1962). *Values in Psychotherapy*. New York: Glencoe Free Press.

ERICKSON, M. H. (1958). "Deep hypnosis and its induction," in LeCron, L. M. (Ed.) *Experimental Hypnosis*. New York: Macmillan.

EYSENCK, H. (1961). "The effects of psychotherapy," in Eysenck, H. (Ed.) *Handbook of Abnormal Psychology*. New York: Basic Books.

GILL, M., and BRENMAN, MARGARET (1961). *Hypnosis and Related States*. New York: International Universities Press.

GORMLEY, W. J. (1961). *Medical Hypnosis: Historical Introduction to Its Morality in the Light of Papal, Theological and Medical Teaching*. Washington D.C.: Catholic University Press.

HILGARD, E. R. (1963). "Ability to resist suggestions within the hypnotic state: Responsiveness to conflicting communications," *Psychol. Rep.*, **12**, 3–13.

HILGARD, JOSEPHINE R., HILGARD, E. R., and NEWMAN, MARTHA. (1961). "Sequelae to hypnotic induction with special reference to earlier chemical anesthesia," *J. nerv. ment. Dis.*, **133**, 461–478.

JAHODA, MARIE (1958). *Current Concepts of Positive Mental Health*. New York: Basic Books.

KRASNER, L. (1961). "The therapist as a social reinforcement machine," in *Research in Psychotherapy*, Vol. II, Proceedings of the 2nd Conference on Research in Psychotherapy, University of North Carolina, Chapel Hill.

——— (1962). "Behavior control and social responsibility," *Amer. Psychol.*, **17**, 199–204.

LIDDELL, H. S. (1944). "Conditioned reflex method and experimental neuroses," in Hunt, J. McV. (Ed.) *Personality and the Behavior Disorders*. New York: Ronald.

LINDNER, H. (1960). "The shared neurosis: Hypnotist and subject," *Int. J. clin. Hyp.*, **8**, 61–70.

LONDON, P. (1962). "The meanjoing normal," *Columbia Univ. Forum*, **5**, 45–46.

——— (1964). *The Modes and Morals of Psychotherapy*. New York: Holt, Rinehart and Winston.

MASSERMAN, J. (Ed.) (1960). *Psychoanalysis and Human Values*. New York: Grune & Stratton.

MENCKEN, H. L. (1963). *Treatise on the Gods*. New York: Vintage.

MOSS, C. S., LOGAN, J. C., and LYNCH, DOROTHY (1962). "Present status of psychological research and training in hypnosis: A developing professional problem," *Amer. Psychol.*, **16**, 542–549.

ORNE, M. T. (1959). "The nature of hypnosis: Artifact and essence," *J. abnorm. soc. Psychol.*, **58**, 277–299.

——— (1961). "The potential uses of hypnosis in interrogation," in Biderman, A. D., and Zimmer, H. (Eds.) *The Manipulation of Human Behavior*. New York: Wiley.

——— (1962) "Antisocial behavior and hypnosis," in Estabrooks, G. H. (Ed.) *Hypnosis: Current Problems*. New York: Harper & Row.

REITER, P. J., and THOMAN, C. C. (1958). *Antisocial or Criminal Acts and Hypnosis: A Case Study*. Springfield, Ill.

ROGERS, C. R., and SKINNER, B. F. (1956). "Some issues concerning the control of human behavior: A symposium," *Science*, **124**, 1057–1066.

ROSS, LILLIAN (1963). *Vertical and Horizontal*. New York: Simon and Shuster.

SHAW, S. I. (1961). "The dangers of hypnosis (the mental hypodermic) as applied to dentistry," *Int. J. clin. exp. Hyp.*, **9**, 53–57.

SHERRINGTON, C. S. (1940). *Man on his Nature*. Baltimore: Penguin.

SZASZ, T. S. (1961). *The Myth of Mental Illness*. New York: Hoeber-Harper.

WATSON, G. (1958). "Moral issues in psychotherapy," *Amer. Psychol.*, **13**, 574–575.

WOLPE, J. (1961). "The prognosis in unpsychoanalyzed recovery from neurosis," *Amer. J. Psychiat.*, 35–39.

——— (1962). "The experimental foundations of some new psychotherapeutic methods," in Bachrach, A. J. (Ed.) *Experimental Foundations of Clinical Psychology*. New York: Basic Books.

19

Conclusions

JESSE E. GORDON
University of Michigan

Hypnosis is just emerging from the captivity of its history. The preceding pages have described new beginnings, promising leads, here and there a thorough exploration, but by and large, only the first steps toward the establishment of a data base broad and deep enough to support some fairly firm conclusions. The gaps, the hiatuses, are ever present; and if this Handbook has made them more apparent, and thus more accessible to the curiosity and industry of psychologists, then its purposes have been well served. Given this state of the field, no possibility exists for ending the presentation with a neatly integrated and definitive statement. Neither are we left speechless in a welter of confused data; some themes recur among the several chapters, and a consideration of them must serve in lieu of a final statement.

FACTORS IN HYPNOTISTS AND THEIR PERFORMANCE

Personalism

Having so little advanced beyond its prescientific status, the field of hypnosis still suffers from residuals of the charisma with which the pioneers surrounded themselves. It is perhaps a reflection of its origin in the myth of animal magnetism that there remains an undercurrent of personalism, of the mystique of the hypnotist's power, of rivalries with other hypnotists over which has the greater control. There is still evident an element of pride in assertions about the numbers of subjects one is able to hypnotize, or about the speed with which one can achieve deep trance in his subjects. Such competition is first on the hidden agenda in many discussions of hypnosis, expressed through arguments of priority in the discovery of phenomena, or in the debunking of phenomena that participate in the identities of the rivals. This remaining personalism also reveals itself in the strengths with which various investigators invest their commitments to already formed views of the nature and reality of hypnotic phenomena, a strength that cannot be accounted for solely on the basis of a dispassionate search for truth. We are still close to Mesmer, to the embattled Elliotson, to Charcot's demonstrations of his awesome authority, to the rival claimants of the Nancy school, and to the ambivalences about human power and human mystery cited in Chapter 1.

Perhaps this legacy of personalism was maintained by the self-selection, which determined who would and who would not become associated with hypnotism and which was given its character by the vague disapproval of hypnosis and hypnotists by many scientists and academicians. Many of those now working in hypnosis can recall incidents in which their interests were discouraged by colleagues who, with varying degrees of subtlety, indicated that hypnosis was so close to the realm of the carnival (and the carnal) and so titillated public fancy, that it behooved a serious investigator to stay clear of it, lest his reputation acquire overtones of pandering to mass taste and curiosity. An interest in hypnosis became, in some staid departments, synonymous with being a crackpot. The student of hypnosis then had to go out of the university for his knowledge; this alone was sufficient to discourage his curiosity, and to make those who persisted feel as if they were in some sense sneaking into forbidden territories, asking the questions about which the members of his family had constructed a conspiracy of discreet silence. Such a state of affairs is attractive to the rebellious, to those who must seek their identity outside the gallery of approved psychologist-types. Thus the field tended to continue in its appeal to the offbeat and to those with needs to maintain themselves through the kind of personalism described. Happily this process seems to be dissolving, and the participants defining the field today are much freer of personal charismas than their forbears. Nevertheless, this process has had its effect on the state of knowledge in the field and on the character of that knowledge, an effect that is only now beginning to be altered.

The effect of this history may lie in a recurrent theme in the papers in this volume: the role of the hypnotist's attitudes in influencing his decision to use hypnosis, the way in which he uses it, his ability to elicit various performances from his subjects, and his perceptions of subjects' performances. In the clinical papers, this theme is treated as countertransference; in the experimental papers it is treated in the context of implicit demand characteristics, the hypnotist's structuring of the relationship and the dependence of subjects' performances on this structuring, and in the discussions of the effects of the hypnotist's attitudes and expectancies on his perception of the hypnotic events and on the behavior and reports of the subjects. Thus modern research and theorizing is concerning itself with an extraordinary blind spot of the past, in which hypnosis was ascribed to the subject, whereas the character of the hypnotist was left unexamined.

Countertransference

In different ways, all of the clinical writers have referred to countertransference. Wolberg points out that the willingness of a therapist to use hypnotic techniques, though rationalized by appeal to various theoretical and historical arguments, may in many cases be related to the presence or absence of anxieties in the therapist. For example, he suggests that the apparent passivity of hypnotized patients may threaten the therapist's control over sadistic impulses sufficiently to make the therapist fearful of his use of hypnosis. Brownfain suggests a similar thing when he notes that psychologists have resisted learning about and using hypnosis because of a resistance to "touching" patients. Moss ascribes resistance to the use of hypnosis as a kind of conservatism and cites a study suggesting that those who do use hypnosis in therapeutic practice may be characterized by independence and adventurousness and an openness to trying new things. All three thus suggest that the attitudes of clinicians toward the use of hypnosis are more understandable from the vantage points of the psychodynamics of therapists than from a consideration of the theoretical and empirical bases that supposedly determine choice of technique. They further suggest that these psychodynamics are involved with factors that determine the practitioner's willingness to come into closer contact with patients, to take more active control over events in therapy, than the usual therapeutic relationship permits. Brownfain and Wolberg seem to agree in suggesting that the hypnotic relationship is one that, for the therapist, has overtones of sexuality, which can give rise to anxieties in the therapist. Thus we have a very interesting about-face from the early psychoanalytic theorists who ascribed their patients' participation in the hypnotic state to the acting-out of sexual and transference needs! Upon reflection it should have been apparent that if the patient was entering into the kind of sexual relationship described by the early psychoanalysts, then obviously so was the hypnotist, thus converting a theoretical interpretation into what borders on a projection.

By implication this theme also suggests that where hypnotic techniques have been used successfully in diagnosis and therapy, the success may be as properly ascribed to other manifestations of the same factors in the therapist, which inclined them to use hypnosis, as to the hypnosis itself. As in other kinds of therapeutic techniques, it is not possible clearly to separate technique from the character of those who have preferred the technique, worked comfortably with it, and achieved a degree of expertness with it, as psychotherapy researchers attempting to compare alternative schools of therapy have learned. In other words, we cannot yet be certain that where hypnosis is efficacious, it is because of the hypnosis or because of events associated with its use, such as the implicit demonstration by the hypnotist of his commitment to the patient and his desire to use all means and to enter into the most intimate contact with him to help him, or the implied communication to the patient that allows the therapist to be perceived as one who can serve some defensive functions for the patient in case of need, thus providing the patient with greater freedom to weaken repressive controls.

As Moss points out, this question may be of more theoretical than practical interest: it is sufficient for the therapist to know that he can use hypnotic techniques in certain situations, without the present confusion over whether the effects are native to trance states or are responses to events that are confounded with the trance induction, such as the kind of relationship established, the increased therapist dominance, and so on. If the same phenomena may be produced by other means, it nevertheless remains true that they can still be produced efficiently by the use of hypnotic induction techniques.

Transference

All three clinical chapters discuss the argument that the use of hypnosis disturbs or alters the transference aspect of the relationship. I think that the writers of the chapters would agree to the truth of the argument; were it not so, there would perhaps be little point in using hypnotic techniques, whose effectiveness may lie directly in the alteration in the character of the therapist-patient relationship. An affirmative answer here does not, however, imply an affirmation that hypnosis therefore interferes with therapy. The history of ameliorative efforts—medical, psychological, economic, political, ecological—demonstrates over and over again that almost any treatment techniques have consequences beyond those specifically intended. Heart surgery may correct a structural defect at the same time that it produces an assault on the homeostatic processes of the body almost as dangerous as the structural defect itself. The existence of side effects is by itself not a counterindicant.

Rather, these side effects must be evaluated relative to the gains anticipated through the use of the treatment; they ought not to be overemphasized beyond their true proportions because of anxiety and the countertransference elements already discussed. In a certain sense, transference itself, perceived by many as the very vehicle of therapy, began as an unlooked-for and discomforting side effect of the therapeutic relationships built up between Freud and Breuer and their patients. And where this was sufficient to force Breuer to withdraw from the therapy, it was the genius of Freud that enabled him to convert what seemed like a dangerous side effect into an asset. It seems just as possible for therapists of today to use the altered relationship induced by the use of hypnosis as a therapeutic asset, once the fact is admitted and accepted that the relationship is altered, so that it may be dealt with by reason. A patient's response to the hypnosis is as interpretable as his response to any other aspects of the therapy. The way in which the hypnotist introduces and handles the hypnosis will have a profound effect on the character of the transference, just as his handling of the intake and introduction to therapy does. But an alteration does not necessarily imply inferiority if the therapist is prepared to deal with the state of affairs that exists, rather than attempt to maintain a belief that there is only one kind of therapeutically useful transference, or that the introduction of hypnosis does not affect it. As in any other kind of ameliorative activity, efforts can be made to minimize side effects, and the clinical chapters agree in suggesting that the hypnotist-patient relationship need not be as authoritarianly structured as once was thought, nor must it involve a perception of the complete surrender of the patient's ego to the therapist.

Control

This raises another issue in the clinical use of hypnosis. Some reluctance to consider hypnotic techniques, where they are appropriate and potentially fruitful, arises from an unwillingness of the therapist to take too direct a hand in the therapeutic process. Therapists prefer to think of assisting therapeutic processes within the patient, rather than of self-consciously controlling therapeutic events. Thus, some "save" hypnosis for use as a very last resort, when all else has failed (hardly providing a fair test of therapeutic techniques, compared to other alternatives). This notion is predicated on the assumption that, in using hypnosis, therapists are playing a more active role, compared to the passivity of reflection, communication of understanding, and the pointing out to the patient of ideas and affects implicit in what the patient has already done or said. Thus it is said that the hypnotherapist muddies the transference by converting himself from an ambiguous object of the patient's projections into a reality source of stimuli for the patient's perceptions, which cannot therefore be interpreted as manifestations of the neurotic process.

However, it must be pointed out that the typical passivity of the therapist is itself a reality for the patient, that therapists do quite clearly take the side of the healthy functioning of the ego, and that even in such matters as communicating understanding, asking the patient to think about his dreams, or suggesting that the patient think about some connections the therapist has made for him, the therapist is taking active steps, which must and do alter the course of the therapy. It is thus not a question of whether a therapist does or does not participate actively in the therapy, so that the use of hypnosis cannot be seen as an alteration from passivity to involvement, from neutrality to commitment. Activity and commitment are present even in the use of ambiguity by the therapist that produces specifiable and predictable effects on the patient (Bordin, 1955). He is active in encouraging the development of transference, and therefore responsible for it, whether or not he uses hypnosis.

The anxiety over the issue of therapist control and activity, the frequent necessity to remind ourselves that even passivity is a manipulative procedure, the discomfort produced by the findings of reinforcement effects in even modest responses to clients, all support the importance of countertransference aspects in decisions regarding therapeutic tactics, including the use of hypnosis.

Hypnotist Expectancies

This discussion of countertransference in hypnosis, and the theoretical arguments motivated by it, assume special significance when one notes the coincidence that it has just become an important theoretical issue in clinical hypnosis, when the direction of experimental research on hypnosis has turned to a consideration of the dependence of hypnotic effects on characteristics of the hypnotist's performance. In earlier days, the clinical emphasis was on trance behavior as a function of characteristics inherent in the subject, while experimental work was concerned with characteristics of the trance state; the parallelism between clinical and experimental approaches continues today, but with inverted emphasis. Where studies in the recent past "located" hypnosis in subjects, perhaps in reaction to the overemphasis on personal power in Mesmer, today hypnosis is once again being "located" in the hypnotist to a great extent. Today, while clinicians consider countertransference, the experimentalists stress the hypnotist's implicit communications to his subjects, his implied structuring, and the effects of his expectancies on subjects' performance and on his perception of subjects' performance. This theme is repeated in several chapters, in which it is suggested that much of the phenomena that has in the past been ascribed to characteristics inherent in the hypnotic trance state may instead represent compliance by the subject with the instructions issued to him by the hypnotist. Such hypnotic compliance may not be different in quality from that observed among experimental subjects who scan their environments carefully to discover clues concerning kinds of performances expected of them. Thus the hypnotist's expectancies, in any but the most rigidly controlled induction procedures, are communicated to the subject, who confirms them, either as a function of his performance of the role assigned to him by the hypnotist, as Sarbin and Andersen theorize, or out of a desire to "do the right thing" as it is interpreted to him by the demand characteristics of the experiment. Thus the nature of the hypnotist's expectancies participates, not only by determining his interest in hypnosis research, but further by determining the kinds of hypnotic phenomena he elicits.

It may even be that these expectancies influence the experimenter's ability to perceive accurately the nature of the subject's response. Certainly this is implied in the admonition by Barber, Blum, Reyher, and others, that an experimenter ought to inquire very carefully into his subjects' reactions before he can allow himself to be satisfied with the validity of his conclusions. Even here, of course, it is possible for the experimenter, by the nature, inflection, and intensity of his questions, to communicate to his subject his hope or expectation that the subject should or should not report particular events. It is not difficult to imagine that an investigator might fail to follow up on a question when he notes a flicker of doubt in the eyes of a subject that contradicts the verbal answer he has just given, or he may follow up with pertinacious tenacity on a line of questioning until he has been able to sow the doubt in the subject that he is anxious to obtain: "Are you *sure*. . . ?" One does not expect a serious investigator knowingly to do such things, but the line between a "careful interrogation" and a "third degree" is not easy to set. And when one notes how unquestioning of hypnotic phenomena even highly sophisticated psychologists have been in the past—so unquestioning that the most elementary principles of experimental control were felt to be unnecessary—it is easy to see how the hypnotist's implicit beliefs can be so overriding that they obscure for him his own rigorous attitude. The experiments using faking controls demonstrate how clearly a hypnotist's perceptions of a subject as hypnotized are dependent on his prior knowledge or impression that hypnotic induction procedures were used.

Controls on the Experimenter

It should be noted that the emphasis in several of the chapters on the institution of adequate controls for research on hypnosis may constitute the most significant development in the field for a long time. A demonstrated necessity for controls implies that there has been a growth in knowledge about what factors affect performance. Thus the emphasis on the use of adequate control groups may be thought of as one evidence of the growth of knowledge in hypnosis. Nevertheless, the precise character of these controls remains problematic. Although several investigators stress the standardization of hypnotic induction techniques, such as those involved in the Stanford Scales, Blum's work suggests that induction methods may be varied to obtain performance at a criterial level. As in verbal learning experiments, there are occasions on which a fixed number of trials is the appropriate standardization and other times when number of trials may be allowed to vary to bring all subjects up to a common standard of performance.

Barber and Reyher stress the use of nonhypnotized control groups, but Reyher points out that this is not always definitive. If it is not easy to determine, on the basis of performance alone, whether or not a subject is hypnotized when he is told to be hypnotized, then it may be equally true that instructing a subject *not* to be hypnotized is no guarantor that he will not in fact be hypnotized.

Reyher also proposes another kind of control, which appears to have much value: to be sure that he is not treating his hypnotized subjects differently from nonhypnotized controls, in obtaining his dependent measures, he records sessions with both groups and submits these recordings, unlabeled, to a panel of experts who are asked to assign the recordings to either experimental or control group. Their inability to assign them correctly constitutes evidence that, at least in his verbal behavior, Reyher has managed to avoid the intrusion of his own biases and expectations into his treatments of his subjects.

The use of an independent control group, compared to own-controls, has also been advocated in several of the chapters in the Handbook. Here again, it appears that each method is suitable to particular problems. When the question is of the effects of differences between hypnotized and nonhypnotized *people*, the former control is relevant. If the research question is concerned with differences between hypnotic and nonhypnotic performances *within* people, then the own-control method is relevant. In either case, it would be appropriate for the experimenter who records or measures performance to be ignorant of whether he is running an experimental or a control treatment. If an independent control group is used, the experimenter ought to be sure that this group is not different from the experimental group in hypnotizability (with whatever personality characteristics may be subsumed under this heading) or in hypnotic experience. However, when this is done, the experiment is exposed to the danger of control subjects actually being hypnotized. On the other hand, the use of own-controls must deal with the problem of counterbalancing the order of conditions, to control for sequence effects in altering subjects' expectancies about the treatment conditions and in altering their levels of performance as a function of practice and/or expectancy.

This discussion of the effects of hypnotists' attitudes on the behavior measured, as reflected in the institution of appropriate controls in research and in the insight with which a clinician must evaluate the contribution of his own dynamic processes to his clinical work, should not be limited to the field of hypnosis. It was indicated in the introductory chapter that advances in the understanding of hypnosis are likely to involve some reorganization of other branches of psychology; nowhere is this more true than in the area of experimenter controls. As Rosenhan points out, the effects of experimenter biases and expectations are not necessarily limited to hypnosis research, or even to research using human subjects. What has been discovered about subjects' abilities to respond to demand characteristics inherent in the design of hypnosis experiments and implied in the behavior of hypnotists is equally true for other experiments. Typically subjects are brought into ambiguously structured experimental situations, and, as Bordin (1955) points out with respect to psychotherapy, ambiguity itself serves to heighten anxiety. Many experimental subjects attempt to find out "what you are trying to prove," and most experienced experimenters have developed artful dodges for this question or ways of temporizing with the subject until the information will do no harm to the data. Some of the methods being used to counteract these effects, such as misleading subjects, have become so elaborate and common as to require recognition and control through the APA's code of ethics. These techniques, formalized by the use of code-names to denote experiments in progress so that even this source of biasing will be eliminated, constitute implicit recognition of the fact that the experimenter's behavior may be such as to elicit the kind of behavior that will have direct bearing on his hypotheses. Thus the strictures concerning controls for hypnosis experiments apply with equal force to nonhypnosis experiments: experiments on attitude change, involving test-retest methods, for example, implicitly communicate to subjects an expectation on the part of the experimenter that responses will be different on the two testings; as Rosenhan points out, even relatively standardized experimental procedures such as those involved in verbal conditioning allow room for experimenter effects, raising the frightening possibility that what we think we have learned in psychology may be more analogous to iatrogenic illness than to true facts. There is no reason why faking controls, for example, should not be used in nonhypnosis research where interpersonal influence is involved, and the indications are that their use would be justified. Another possibility would be the use of experimenters ignorant of the hypotheses to be tested, though this may be difficult to manage. Still other possibilities include the use of samples of experimenters, so that experimenter bias is at least to some extent diffused. A further possibility is the use of the kind of check on the experimenter's behavior described by Reyher. In any event, there is need for a consideration of the contributions of the experimenter to his data, as there is in hypnosis for examination of hypnotist-effects.

Hypnosis as Social Transaction

This discussion of controls is predicated on the emphasis in current work, both experimental and clinical, on the hypnotist as subject in his own experiment, in the sense that his behavior and performance may be as decisive, or more decisive than the hypnotic trance, in determining the natures of the observations made. This new emphasis does much to move the phenomena of hypnosis into a familiar psychological realm—that of social psychology—and thus weakens the boundaries that set it off as a special and unique set of phenomena not closely related to the mainstreams of psychology. This new status of hypnosis is reflected in two other themes represented in different contexts in this Handbook. These themes are concerned with subjects' responsiveness to the hypnotist's intentions, and with the sociology of knowledge as it influences performances of subjects.

THE SUBJECT'S ROLE

The current emphasis on implicit structuring and the demand characteristics of hypnosis research would be less striking were it not for the almost equal emphasis on the subject's tendencies to respond to these elements in particular ways. Sarbin has long been interested in hypnosis from this point of view, and his chapter with Andersen represents their current formulation of the subject as one who uses the cues in the hypnotic situation as guides for his role performance. History has again played a strange and ironic trick; it was just a little over a century ago that charges were made against Esdaile's use of mesmerism for producing surgical anesthesia, with the suggestion "that his success was due to the fact that the natives like to be operated upon and were trying to please Esdaile" (Boring, 1950). For many years this bit of scientific criticism has been used as a prime example of ludicrousness and fatuous prejudice in the face of overwhelming evidence. Little serious consideration was given to the criticism by modern authors: "It was quite unreasonable to suppose that these natives were merely indulging a fancy for pleasing Esdaile" (Boring, 1950). Now we are discovering that there may have been more wisdom in this criticism than has been thought, so that in the exploration of hypnosis as role-playing we have come full circle! If we have made progress, it is in the finer specification and operationalizing of the concepts associated with role performance, rather than in the insights from which the hypothesis grew. Thus it may be expected that the immediate future should see an increase in the applications of studies of role perceptions and the like to hypnotic performance. If we are convinced that subjects are responding to implicit structuring of roles, then the obvious next steps would include an anatomization of the elements of the roles, variables affecting subjects' perceptions of role-assigning cues, their ability to give the performances that compose the role, and the motivational factors in their willingness to do so.

If these variables influence performance in experiments defined as hypnotic, how may they also influence performance in nonhypnotic experiments, such as those on perception? The research reported by Barber, Shor, Rosenhan, and others in these pages strongly indicates that subjects who are not hypnotized may give performances as good as those given in trance when the situation contains sufficient role-structuring cues and motivational arousers. It is possible to turn some of the conclusions of these experiments around: although the ability to elicit performance comparable to that given under hypnosis may be manifested in experiments in which the appropriate motivational and cognitive variables are kept constant between the hypnotic and control conditions, does this mean that hypnosis does not contribute to performance over its "natural" or operant level, or does it mean that performance may be increased or at least drastically altered by the demand characteristics of the measurement situation even when hypnotic induction is absent?

Effects of Public Knowledge on Psychological Data

This view of hypnotic phenomena touches psychological concerns beyond the immediate field under consideration. Subjects' willingness and ability to play the role of hypnotized people, although greatly influenced by the expectations and structuring communicated to them by the hypnotist, are probably most powerfully evoked simply by the label "hypnosis." The ability of this identification to make salient a fairly complete repertoire of appropriate behavior testifies to the pervasiveness of their prior exposure to sources of information about hypnosis; several of the writers in the foregoing chapters have pointed to the popular familiarity with stereotypes of hypnotic behavior communicated through various kinds of entertainments and the like. In other words, the spread of knowledge about the phenomena has played a powerful role in modifying the behavior of people who may become subjects and who therefore are used as sources of further knowledge about the phenomena. To put it another way, the sociology of knowledge and its transmission puts us in danger of creating a huge solipsistic system that may be endlessly self-confirming, in which what is known or expected is communicated and thus tends to produce its own confirmation. To some extent this problem is a legacy of the ethic of helpfulness, which makes subjects willing to serve the cause of science and the experimenter, which guarantees their cooperativeness, and which, carried too far and combined with their anxious attention to the implicit demand characteristics described earlier, puts us in danger of their overwillingness to confirm the theories they think we are trying to test. For years psychoanalysts have been dealing with a similar problem in their therapy as knowledge about psychoanalytic theory has spread widely throughout our culture. Patients come ready to report sexual misadventures and fantasies, or to offer highly sophisticated explications of their dynamics, making it increasingly difficult for the practicing analyst to distinguish what is real from what is a defensive strategy and to use interpretations effectively when those he offers are in danger of becoming assimilated into the patient's intellectualizing theory about himself. Increasingly, in practice, defenses masquerade as insights, and the therapist's knottiest problem is to rob a patient's verbalizations of their defensive functions, while he must also agree to the truth of the same intellectualized verbalization. Similarly has the spread of knowledge affected diagnostic procedures; recent years have seen the publication of books that prepare people for intelligence testing, of imitation Rorschach cards to elicit free associations as a party game, and so forth. The effects of these events may so far be minimal, but the handwriting is on the wall. Manful attempts to protect the security of some of our knowledge are made (to the detriment of our public relations and to the development of a new kind of ethical consideration for psychology, posed by Hathaway recently [1964], in which we must accept some obligation concerning the sharing of knowledge when we ask subjects to surrender to us some of their rights to privacy). But the experience of the most elaborate secrecy organizations in the world, such as those connected with national defense organizations, should convince us that leaks do occur, and that the battle to maintain secrecy is always a losing one.

Thus the practice of experimental hypnosis joins psychotherapy and diagnosis in suggesting an interesting problem both for the practice of science and for a theory of knowledge. Erikson points out (1958) that psychotherapy is similar to the study of history in that the effort to reconstruct the past alters the course of the present and the future. If we learn at all from past experience, then the reconstruction of that past participates in the effort to guide the future. This notion may be extended by also noting that when the creation of knowledge about the past alters the future, it also alters the needs and perspectives developed in the future, which then guide *its* re-creations of the same past. Thus what the past appears to be depends on when it is being examined, which in turn depends on the effects of earlier studies of the past. This, then, is another expression of the idea that the creation of knowledge, not only about hypnosis, modifies in complex ways the nature of the new knowledge that may be created. If this is so, as it seems to be at least with reference to public knowledge about the role of hypnotic subjects, then there is need for further thinking about our conceptions of the immutability and the validity of facts. Here again, then, the study of hypnosis emphasizes a need for a readjustment of the larger field of science beyond itself.

Hypnotic Skills

The recent advances in the social psychology of hypnosis represent important breakthroughs. But these new views ought not to obscure the fact that although subjects may be performing roles in their hypnotic behavior, these roles are made up of particular performances whose nature is as yet ill-defined. That there are reliable individual differences in the ability to engage in such performances is revealed by Hilgard's work in the measurement of susceptibility, which clearly indicates that hypnotic trance is not a unitary event in which, once produced, all hypnotic performances may be elicited with equal ease. Rather, partial performance, or performance of only some parts of the role, is more the rule. In this connection we note Hilgard's findings that the Stanford Scale scores are highly reliable, that retesting does not raise scores considerably or increase susceptibility, although latency of response is reduced by practice. This conforms closely to a view of hypnotic performance as involving certain learned skills, which are sufficiently independent from each other that practice in one does not increase ability to perform in the others. If learning occurs as a function of practice, it is a learning manifested by more rapid performance rather than by "deepening" of trance to include performances which the subject had heretofore not given. The existence of such independent performances creates difficulty for a unitary view of hypnosis as a role, unless one invokes the idea of partial role performance.

An account of such partial performances would make use of one or several alternative propositions: (1) that there are degrees of conformity to role structuring, rather than simple acceptance or rejection of the role; (2) that differences in degree of role performance are a function either of differences in sensitivities to the structuring cues, differences in strength of desire to accept the proferred role definitions, or differences in the levels of ability or skills which the several parts of the overall performance require, or some combination of these. It is in the consideration of these issues that one can perceive an element of unity running through the various theories and approaches to hypnosis.

Motivation for Hypnosis

London points out that hypnotists can exert a negative influence on their subjects by their behavior, such that the necessary rapport is not established. Although he points out that extended efforts to establish rapport do not seem to increase performance, this observation may be taken to mean that ordinary standards of decent conduct are sufficient to enlist the cooperation or conformity and acquiescence of most subjects, so that extra efforts on the part of the hypnotist in this direction are unproductive because of a ceiling effect. Thus there is little basis for a conclusion that motivational elements in subjects are not relevant; there is reason to believe that these motivational elements are so ubiquitous and easily aroused that it takes almost a determined effort on the part of a hypnotist to discourage them. If there are such motivational elements then we must seek them from among those drives that are most likely to be readily elicited by the mere presence of another person who is at least not behaving outrageously. Gill and Brenman (1961) point to these drives as inherent in the psychoanalytic concept of transference, including the wish to be liked and approved by the hypnotist, which is at least necessary if the hypnotist's reinforcements and reassuring approvals of the subject are to be effective as rewards. Sarbin and Andersen identify the drive similarly: to be rewarded or approved by the hypnotist. Such motives may be supplemented by or even imitated by other motives more extrinsic to the situation, such as the offer of financial reward for a high level of performance, as used by Orne (1959). Those experiments in which comparable performances between hypnotized and nonhypnotized control groups are obtained, when efforts are made to motivate both groups highly, further support the notion that hypnotized subjects are motivated in their performances and motivated by drives that require relatively little support by extrinsic agents, compared to nonhypnotized subjects.

Skills in Hypnosis

The second thread of unity running through the several accounts of hypnosis involves the notion of skill. Gill and Brenman treat this topic under the heading of regressed ego states, implying that good hypnotic performance requires the ability to perceive and think in terms other than those typically used in waking, rational behavior. The nature of these skills has received relatively little attention by the experimental investigators, except for Shor's (1960) and Ås' (1963) studies on the relationship between extent of practice of hypnotic-like experiences in real life and hypnotizability.

It is not yet clear whether the ego skills involved are those that determine a subject's ability to perceive the structuring cues presented to him, or those concerned with the performances of responses to those cues.

Sarbin and Andersen describe an experiment in which ability to play a role per se was correlated with hypnotizability; because the particular performances involved in the roles subjects were asked to take and those involved in hypnosis are different, the commonality between the two situations is more likely to be one of the ability to discriminate the behaviors appropriate to the role than it is an ability to give particular motoric, affective, or verbal responses. On the other hand, London and Fuhrer (1961) and Gordon and Freston (1964) found no support for an interpretation that hypnotizability depends on the ability to enact role performances per se. Thus there is reason to believe that at least part of hypnotic role performance depends on the availability to the subject of particular skills associated with the kinds of phenomena induced by hypnosis: the ability to forget or block out stimuli, the ability to respond selectively to particular stimuli, and so on. That the role of a hypnotized subject includes such skills does not make the subject's performance any less "real." If I were to act the part of a French scholar acceptably, I would have to speak real French to carry the thing off. The presence of such skills exists with or without hypnosis. It is to be noted that individual differences in the ability to respond to hypnotic suggestions following induction are matched by a comparable order to individual differences in the ability to perform similarly without hypnotic induction. The published research on the use of nonhypnotized controls indicates that the variances in the control and experimental groups are not so disparate from each other as to preclude statistical treatment of the data. In effect, what we have learned is that some nonhypnotized subjects may, under appropriate circumstances, give performances comparable to those given by some hypnotized subjects. The skills required for hypnotic performance exist in people independently of hypnotic induction.

In the experiment on analgesia reported by Shor, nonhypnotized subjects were brought to a level of anesthesia ordinarily found only in hypnotic subjects, by the expedient of lowering anxiety associated with the pain stimulus. This experiment provides powerful evidence for the notion that much of what we experience as pain is psychological anxiety, rather than a direct product of the stimulation of particular receptors. Even more, the experiment emphasizes the anxiety-reducing property of hypnosis, a property that could be ascribed to the motivational and attitude components of the hypnotist-subject relationship, or to the ability of subjects who are hypnotizable to withdraw cathexes, block out stimuli, regress in the service of the ego when to do so is defined as part of the hypnotic role, the performance of which may be instrumental to them in assuring the hypnotist's goodwill, as suggested earlier, and also in providing a relief from the unpleasantness of the pain-associated anxiety. The continued employment of these skills during the hypnosis, as the subject continually refines his role performances in accordance with the hypnotist's further definitions, is part of the meaning for the assertions in the clinical papers and in the psychoanalytic theory described by Gill and Brenman (1961) that the subject's ego is active during hypnosis, rather than bypassed in some manner, as had been previously thought.

This concept of the hypnotized (as well as nonhypnotized) subject as one who continuously modulates his role performances in response to the further definitions of the role offered by the hypnotist raises questions about the conscious-unconscious dichotomy. Although there may be doubt as to whether it is unique to hypnosis, there is no doubt that hypnotized patients' associations are loosened to the point where primary process thinking is more evident, and ego controls over repressed impulses, affects, and ideas are weakened. How can these phenomena be reconciled with a view of the patient as engaging in certain role performances, as he understands them and as he is able to do so? It is not at all clear whether such a reconciliation is possible, but it may be suggested that part of the difficulty may reside in a rather static view of consciousness-unconsciousness, which treats these constructs as if they were nonfunctional and somehow immune from environmental influence. Noting that a patient's hypnosis presupposes his understanding or perception of the role performances expected of him, it may be hypothesized that he is also familiar with the image of the hypnotist as one who controls him and as, therefore, the person responsible for the subject's behavior while hypnotized. Viewed in this way, it is apparent that a patient may permit weakening of his own ego controls on the assumption that (1) the hypnotist will do the controlling for him; (2) forbidden and guilt-arousing gratifications, which he might receive from the release of instinctual material, assume a greater strength, vis-à-vis the repressive forces of the ego, if these gratifications can be obtained under circumstances in which the patient no longer need hold himself responsible for their occurrence. They can be disowned as the responsibility of the hypnosis and the hypnotist, and the memory of their occurrence can be repressed with the repression ascribed by the patient to the amnesic influence of the trance, rather than to his own defensive processes. Certainly other factors may also play a role, such as the effects of physiological relaxation concomitant with hypnosis (though not necessarily dependent on it). But it is worth noting that the hypnosis may serve the function of a defense and a control device for the patient, even though that control resides in the patient's *image* of hypnosis and his role as a hypnotized subject, rather than in the reality of it, an image that carries the mutual agreement of patient and therapist that hypnosis may function that way for both of them. It may be in this way that the hypnotherapist allies himself with "unconscious" forces in the patient and uses the hypnosis to alter the balance of the forces present. Thus the hypnotized patient puts the hypnotherapist in the position of an externalized superego, allowing a relaxation of internal constraints, in much the same way as a child uses the parent's presence to free him from cautions that he would exercise himself were the parent absent, as Levin and Turgeon (1957) have shown with respect to aggressive behavior. With a hypnotized subject in such a position of being "protected" by his externalized superego while he reclines, relaxes, and obeys—that is, when so many cues derived from childhood are reproduced—is it any wonder that recall of childhood events is facilitated and that hypnotized subjects can so easily produce primary process thinking and behavior associated with emotional and intellectual immaturity?

One implication of this view is that the status of impulses and wishes is one that is responsive, through the resources of the patient's active ego, which includes his conception of the hypnotic role, to the transactions occurring between himself and the hypnotist. This then is merely an extension of the idea that dynamic factors are influenced by the patient's ongoing experiences, although it implies that unconsciousness is less a realm than it is a description of functional behavior in response to the present needs of the patient and the therapist. This interpretation of the patient's use of hypnosis as an ego resource serving defensive functions, which permit him greater latitude in impulse expression and gratification through the image of hypnosis agreed upon by him and his therapist, may contribute to an understanding of why hypnotherapeutic efforts "work" in some cases and do not in others. In effect, it is here suggested that when hypnosis does prove effective it does so not by any magical bypassing of the usual psychodynamics, as if it were the one thing left that is not itself deterministic, but rather by the creation of conditions that the dynamic forces in the personality use in ways consonant with their natures. Thus the patient may do, say, and feel things when hypnotized that he would not under other circumstances, in which the gratification of the impulses underlying the actions and verbalizations would be attended by greater anxiety. Put another way, the image of hypnosis may function for the patient in the same way as does an image of the therapist as accepting, permissive, responsible, and committed to his best interests; in either case, the image serves to weaken repressive forces. Here then is another link between hypnosis and transference: if the motivation to play the hypnotized role is associated with what are typically called transference motives, it may also be suggested that the performance of the role gratifies these motivations in much the same way as does real transference and serves much the same functions. This suggests that one of the major advantages of the use of hypnosis in therapy and diagnosis is that it can provide a kind of "instant transference," which can be put to therapeutic purposes; it also suggests that if a patient should begin to make demands on his therapist to be hypnotized, this ought to be interpreted as a reflection of the failure of the therapeutic transference relationship, leading the patient to seek for its replacement by the hypnosis. Thus, such demands ought to be thought of not as factors that interefere with therapy but, rather, as symptoms of latent problems already existing in the relationship.

Trance Behavior, Self-Report, and Dissonance Reduction

In this discussion of the skills involved in hypnosis, mention has been made of skills in role-playing per se, as well as of skills in the behavioral elements of the role to be played. It was also suggested that some of the skills involved in hypnotic performance include the ability to engage in kinds and contents of thinking, which are usually considered unconscious, but which become conscious as a result of the subject's and the hypnotist's implicit agreements on the nature and function of hypnosis. This agreement may serve in much the same way as the transference does, in its weakening of repressive forces, so that hypnosis may be seen as mimetic of transference and actuated by similar drives.

What, precisely, are these skills? Sarbin (1964) describes them as role expectations and role perceptions, as discussed in the context of subject's and experimenter's implicit understandings about hypnosis. Sarbin also includes a specificity component and briefly reviews some studies indicating that the ability to give specific hypnotic performances, such as hallucinations, is dependent on the existence of abilities to give similar performances without hypnosis. It has been suggested here that these abilities seem to be related to ease of, or willingness to engage in, or availability of access to, primary process kinds of thinking. They might include the ability to entertain unusual ideas, to regress in public, to entertain illogical ideas—in short, what Orne (1959) refers to as "trance logic."

Thus, when Orne finds "trance logic" as the single distinguishing feature of hypnosis, it may well be not as a product of "trance" per se, but a result of the excuse the social definition of the situation as hypnotic gives to the subject for engaging in primary process thinking.

This suggests a further possibility: a subject's definition of himself as being or having been hypnotized may serve as a dissonance-reducing maneuver. It makes his primary process thinking, his weakened impulse control (based on his presumption that the hypnotist will take care of him and protect him from the consequences of his behavior)—it makes such behavior explicable without damaging his self-concept. Thus, the belief that one has been hypnotized may be a dissonance-reducing reaction to one's own behavior. Certainly the situation has many of the characteristics that lead to dissonance-reduction (Festinger, 1957): the subject's belief in what hypnosis is and does is a strongly held conviction, as is his belief in his own rationality. He is strongly committed to both beliefs and finds social support for the "hypnosis" explanation in the hypnotist's agreement to his interpretation. We would expect, therefore, that the greater the "pressure" to seek forbidden regressive gratifications, the greater will be the willingness to "be hypnotized," and the more dissonant the resulting behavior is with the subject's usual beliefs about himself, the more strongly he will be convinced that he was hypnotized. Sarbin (1964) describes an essentially similar process as "face-saving."

Although the data reviewed by Sarbin (1964) and exemplified by Ås' (1963) and Shor's (1960) demonstrations that ability to engage in hypnotic performances is related to experience in similar performances outside of hypnosis suggest no special role for hypnosis, it is still true that hypnosis functions as a reliable means for eliciting such performances in those capable of them. It may be that it does so through a dissonance-reducing process; the patient who yields to impulse expression while hypnotized, and the subject who engages in illogical behavior are both doing so because the agreement between themselves and the hypnotist, and their own understandings of hypnosis, tell them that it is *not* dissonant to engage in such ego regressions under the circumstances. The hypnosis thus reduces the dissonance between the subject's awareness of his present status as a mature, socialized adult in an interpersonal environment, and the repressed and "unconscious" affects, ideas, and modes of thinking whose expression would be gratifying but otherwise barred. To behave in these ways, to allow the hypnotist and the hypnosis to "take the rap" for the results, thus resolves the need for control without disturbing the subject's perception of himself as a normal, well-controlled adult. This is another way of describing the effect of hypnosis in shifting the balance between impulses and their controls, as discussed in the context of hypnotherapy. The treatment of this topic within the framework of dissonance theory further anchors hypnosis in the field of social psychology.

In effect, then, the subject's willingness to respond to the hypnotic situation with "trance logic" and his own conviction that he was hypnotized can be accounted for by the theory of cognitive dissonance reduction, obviating a need for a "trance theory" and accounting for the subject's own experience of "trance" by the same general dissonance hypothesis.

This discussion of the utilization by hypnosis of particular ego skills (or perceptual and performance skills, for those who prefer these usages) touches upon the chapters by Edmonston and Ratner. Ratner concludes that animal hypnosis is unrelated to human behavior.

Although he points to important differences between them, notably his observation that animals enter catalepsy when they are frightened, whereas humans enter hypnosis under conditions of relaxation, the issue may still remain open. As already indicated, there is much reason to think that human subjects must be motivated to perform hypnotically; although the motives involved may be other than fright, it is possible that humans have achieved sufficient functional mobility of central processes for interpersonal motives to function like fear in eliciting or arousing the processes that mediate the cataleptic state. Another, and further, possibility is that Ratner's comparative studies may point to the presence of instinctual processes which, although not as automatic in humans as they are among lower organisms—as is the case with so many other instincts—may nevertheless constitute the physiological basis for the kinds of ego skills of selective attention, relaxation, and so on, which are utilized by humans in performing hypnotically. Edmonston's chapter may also be considered as concerned with the central processes that provide the possibilities for behaving hypnotically, given the appropriate motivations and eliciting (defining, structuring) cues. Edmonston concludes his chapter by describing a two-process theory: is there a relationship between the two processes he describes and the two discussed by Gill and Brenman, who propose differing but related processes for induction and for the trance state itself?

IS HYPNOSIS REAL?

One can readily read between the lines of several of the chapters that their authors are very deeply concerned with a common underlying theme, one which has not changed very much in its nature since the French Academy first investigated Mesmer's claims. This theme is: is hypnosis real? As Sarbin and Andersen point out, the question has been asked in several different ways since then. Is it suggestion? Is it hysteria? Is it repression? Is it role performance? Is it merely compliance to demand characteristics? The skeptics have tended to answer each one affirmatively, each in his own time, whereas the credulous deny each in turn. When problems like this persist over many years in the history of a science, semantic-logic is often a good place at which to begin an attack on them. Upon examination the problem seems to hinge on the use of genotypical and phenotypical modes of definition.

Phenotypes and Genotypes

All of the "explanations" given by the skeptics for hypnosis have been based on the same line of reasoning: if the behavior produced by hypnosis can also be produced by giving suggestions (by hysterics, by repressors, by actors, by compliant subjects), then hypnosis is no different from these other variables. In effect, phenotypical similarity is taken as a criterion of identity. Thus is raised a confusion in the logic of operationalism. Should an event be defined by reference to phenotypic identities in the measured or observed characteristics of the event (operationalism considered as the procedures used to measure or observe the event) or should the event be defined by reference to the genotypic operations used in creating the event? By the former strategy, hypnosis may be "nothing but" several different things, such as those cited; by the latter it is unique.

This logical problem has particular relevance to the strategies involved in the research described by Barber, Rosenhan, and Shor, and others. In much of the research described by these authors, performances typically associated with hypnosis are found to be producible with equal strength by nonhypnotic arrangements, involving the experimenter's manipulation of the subject's motivations, attitudes, and expectancies. So many different kinds of presumably hypnotic performance have been examined in this way that there appears to be only the subject's own verbal report that he was hypnotized remaining as a reliable difference between the performances of hypnotized and nonhypnotized subjects, and the dissonance-reduction hypothesis throws doubt on the verbal report. Shall one conclude from these studies that hypnosis as such does not exist, except as a collection of experimenter behaviors that influence motivations, attitudes, and expectancies, which may be manipulated as well without the trance induction and the concept of hypnosis? Does phenotypical similarity between performances produced by hypnotized subjects and those produced by nonhypnotized subjects mean that the processes involved in the production of the behaviors in the two groups are identical? Although the same event may be produced by the use of the same processes, it is obvious that phenotypically identical events may also be produced by different processes. For example, equal levels of skill in bar-pressing may be achieved by either few massed trials with immediate and large reinforcements, or by more distributed trials with moderate reinforcements. Given two rats with equal performance at bar-pressing, it is not possible then to infer that the histories of their performances are identical.

What can be concluded is that hypnosis mimicks the effects of task structuring, creating positive attitudes and providing sufficient incentive for performance. It is possible that this mimetic action is achieved by hypnosis through inclusion of the structuring, motivating, and other variables described. To the extent that this is so, hypnosis is not a unique state, *sui generis*. Nor have any but the romantics in the history of hypnosis ever maintained that it is so unique as to be unrelated to any other psychological processes. However, it is true that hypnosis differs from the procedures used with control groups in the Barber-type experiment, if in nothing else than that it combines within the trance-producing procedures all of the variables that have been found to be efficacious without trance. Thus, instead of making arrangements to reduce the anxiety component of painful stimulation, instead of attempts to enlist subjects' strongest interest in the task performances, instead of careful rehearsal of nonhypnotized subjects in the desired actions, all of these may be accomplished by the expedient of inducing hypnosis. When all of these psychological variables are combined into a coherent form, and when the entire *gestalt*, with its mutually supporting roles, is either explicitly or implicitly labeled hypnosis *as a part of the combination*, then the role-playing and dissonance-reducing processes described earlier are evoked. To the extent that these processes depend on a subject's preformed expectations about situations labeled as hypnotic, to that extent is hypnosis unique, or at least different from the manipulation of any of its constituent variables separately. Thus hypnosis may be phenotypically nonunique and genotypically unique.

There is a further consideration. Is it possible that the combination of elements itself gives rise to processes that do not occur when the elements are presented separately or in differing combinations? Earlier it was suggested that the cognitive dissonance produced in a subject who compares his own behavior in response to the role demands of the hypnotic situation with his behavior in other kinds of social interactions may be the factor that leads him to reduce the dissonance by ascribing his behavior to a trance state. This suggestion was parallel to the notion that patients may use the hypnosis as a defense against anxiety and guilt, thus permitting them to express impulses more freely when hypnotized. Implicit in that formulation was the notion that the patient can ascribe his behavior to the hypnosis as a means of reducing dissonance between his perceptions of himself as a good and controlled person and the behavior that he actually displays in the hypnotic situation. The "trance logic" of which he is then capable, and which includes primary process thinking, regressive experiences, and so on, is considered to be unique to hypnosis by Orne; the dissonance-reducing belief that one has been hypnotized has not been demonstrated in subjects who were not exposed to induction procedures. These two phenomena—trance logic and conviction—may thus be unique features produced only by the combination of constituent variables into a *gestalt* labeled as hypnosis, and not properties of the constituent variables presented separately.

It may be that subjects require the induction and the label to give performances clearly different from those that they usually give—perhaps they require it as the only convincing argument that they can be capable of such performances—but they do seem to need it. Blum reports that he has not been able to elicit the very complicated (and conventionally bizarre) behaviors he gets from his subjects by any other means. If this is so, then hypnosis is different from other procedures.

Such a difference may rest only on a convention of the subject's and experimenter's agreement to and acceptance of the meaning of situations they label as hypnotic. But such conventions are not to be ignored or considered too unimportant for serious consideration; at bottom, conventions such as these underlie the subject's responses to any instructions and to most of the reinforcers we use in our research and daily behavior.

"Trance logic" and "conviction" may seem to be fairly small remaining remnants of all the dramatic phenomena to which hypnosis used to lay claim as unique to itself. But these remnants are important. There are not many techniques that can produce such subjective certainty, such admissions of an "altered mode of experiencing the self," as Gill and Brenman (1961) describe it. And if these remnants make possible shiftings of impulsive and repressive forces for therapeutic purposes, then they are very important remnants.

A caveat is in order here: these effects rest on the infirm base of shared conviction about "hypnosis." As the new knowledge summarized in this Handbook becomes more widely distributed among future subjects, there may be an erosion of conventional meaning of "being hypnotized," and thus a change in the subject's role performances, which could eliminate both its trance logic and the subjective conviction aspects. Thus the skeptical view, which is so dominant today, may ultimately create its own justification, and hypnosis will then pass into the same limbo of prescientific phenomena as seances, mystical visions, orgiastic possessions, and other such supernatural mysticisms, which were so much more common in the past than they are today.

In brief, then, hypnosis may be both unique and commonplace: commonplace in that it may include within it psychological variables identical to those underlying all kinds of mundane and arcane performances, and unique in the means by which these variables are invoked, a means which currently has a special meaning to hypnotist and subject, unique in the patterning of these variables, and unique in the trance-logic and conviction consequences of this means-patterning arrangement.

This uniqueness ought not to be overstressed; it is certainly one of the most significant developments that hypnotic performance has been embedded more and more solidly into the net of variables controlling performance per se, a development that has done much to reduce the penumbra of occultism that used to surround hypnosis, if only at the level of private fantasy, and to bring hypnosis into closer relationship with other psychological phenomena of more familiar cast. However, there is a danger of error in supposing that by doing this, hypnosis is made to disappear as a dispensable artifact. A desire to get rid of the mysticism becomes just as unreasonable as the mysticism if it also insists on throwing the baby out with the bath. It would be as foolish to deny the reality of hypnosis, and its particular properties, as it would be to deny the reality and properties of a department store on the grounds that it is really just a collection of what goes on in a large number of individual shops.

Some Research Implications

This phenotype-genotype distinction has implications for the research use of hypnosis. The research applications chapters report the use of hypnosis as a means for arranging experimental conditions to make possible certain dependent measures. The hypnosis is used as a means for the production and control of independent variables, which are otherwise resistant to experimental manipulation. The discussion here and in some of the preceding chapters suggests that there are at least three alternative processes involved in such experimental applications: (1) processes originated by the induction of the hypnotic state itself, such as the subject's use of the hypnosis as an ego control device and as a defense, the presence of positive attitudes toward the experimenter-hypnotist, desires to please him, and close attention to cues regarding the behaviors expected of him; (2) specific performances suggested by the experimenter, dependent for their execution on the subject's perceptions of the experimenter's demands, his understanding of the nature of the role desired, and his ability to give the performances that he understands to be expected, this last being a function of the level of his skill in the activities and cognitions associated with the suggested role; and (3) processes arising in the subject as psychologically determined consequents of either or both of the processes described in (1) and (2). This last group would include, for example, an increase in anxiety experienced by a subject who had been instructed only to think about a particular traumatic experience, but who was not specifically instructed to experience anxiety. This group of processes permits an experimenter to study relationships among psychological variables, such as those described by Reyher and Blum. As Reyher points out, this strategy preserves the genotypic characteristics of psychological events, because the events occur naturally in the subject in response to more directly induced processes. Behaviors produced in subjects by the first and second processes, directed at phenotypes, are more difficult to work with, because it is not always possible for an experimenter to determine the extent to which the processes are representative of the subject's behavior in other situations, and to what extent they are efforts to conform to the role requirements. In the latter case, performance is more a function of the subject's cognitive structures than it is of characteristics inherent in the psychological processes being studied. Put another way, what appears to be anxiety in a subject is more acceptable as such if it is a response to hypnotically induced threat than if it is a response to a direct suggestion on which the performance depends, to some extent at least, on the subject's understanding of what the experimenter means by anxiety, and on the experimenter's recall of experiences in his own life that might approximate that definition, and so on. Phenotypically the two states may appear similar, but they are genotypically different, and they function differently, with the anxiety in the former subject serving psychodynamic functions associated with impulse-defense systems, and the anxiety in the latter subject functioning as an instrumental act, the reinforcement of which comes from obtaining the experimenter's approval for the performance.

This discussion of genotypic-phenotypic considerations has relevance not only to the study of hypnosis, but to any study using laboratory analogues, and by extension, to any experimental study in which laboratory control of variables is analogic to the operation of those variables outside the laboratory. That is, when a certain class of behavior is produced in a laboratory, as through verbal instructions, and then studied for its responsiveness to variations in the independent variables, the question must always arise as to whether the induced process is in fact representative of processes outside the laboratory that are phenotypically similar, but that may be genotypically different. Is there a difference in learning when a student gives himself instructions from what it is like when an experimenter gives a subject instructions? On the strictest level of interpretation, one would be on safest ground in not generalizing from experimental data to nonexperimental realms, on the principle that the operations used to produce and measure behavior in laboratories are almost always such as to influence the behavior being measured, so that the resulting behavior is genotypically different from similar behavior not being subjected to investigation. This matter seems to have been a greater concern with clinical psychologists than with many other groups, possibly because clinicians are in positions to observe the extent of the match between laboratory behavior and behavior as it occurs in naturalistic situations, whereas nonapplied branches of psychology do not provide themselves with the opportunities to make such comparative observations.

This does not put the genotypic kind of research of Reyher, Blum, and Gordon on clear high ground. It must still be admitted that the genotypic validity of the induced processes rests on the fact that they are elicited in reaction to induced processes of the type described in (1) and (2), and there may be a gap between what an experimenter is seeking to produce in a subject by direct suggestion, as in (2), and what the subject understands and does about it. For example, an experimenter may wish to produce anxiety in a subject by a genotypically correct method, by asking the subject to hallucinate or fantasize an experience he found upsetting. Whether the affect produced is anxiety of the type usually produced by traumatic events then depends on the assumption that the subject has in fact fantasized an upsetting experience. But this, as a directly suggested performance, is subject to the cognitive and social considerations that govern the subject's performance of the role assigned to him, so that his actual performance may deviate from the performance intended by the experimenter. If it does, then the processes set up in the subject by his own performance—the processes described in (3) above—will not be those that the experimenter thinks they are.

The chapter on psychotherapy research deals with one part of this issue in its discussion of the factors that determine a subject's ability to accept and act on a suggested paramnesia. It was argued there that his ability to play the role implied by the paramnesic instructions probably depends heavily on his actual experience in such roles. If so, then the validity of the role-induced processes is ensured by the validity of the performed role. However, it must be recognized that this may not always be so. A particularly imaginative subject who has had many vicarious experiences through reading, movies, and TV, may assay the role assigned to him, but without the personal involvement produced by actual recall of his own experiences, which would give rise to valid psychodynamic processes. For much of the research reported in the research applications chapters, these considerations are not relevant or realistic; there is no greater reason to doubt a hypnotized subject's response to an instruction to recall a particular experience in his life than there is to doubt the efficacy of similar verbal instructions to subjects in nonhypnotic experiments. Nevertheless, it would be wise for an experimenter who wishes to use hypnosis as a means for obtaining control over independent variables to consider whether his particular design is dependent on assumptions about the subject's ability to respond appropriately to direct suggestions, upon which the genotypic validity of the induced behavior rests.

In the preceding discussion it was suggested that it would be as unreasonable to doubt the effectiveness of certain hypnotic instruction, such as to recall a particular event, as to doubt the efficacy of similar instructions given in the waking state. If so, then would it not be preferable to dispense with the hypnosis altogether, and simply use waking instructions? As an example, Gordon and Farris (1965) asked waking subjects to recall and talk about an occasion on which they came into conflict with their fathers, the purpose of which was to reintegrate the affects of conflicted anger directed against the father, to test for displacement of anger in TAT stories. Their data indicate that the instructions to recall were effective in inducing aggression, which was not directly suggested, and that the aggression so aroused conformed to theoretical expectations so far as displacement was concerned. If this worked, what advantage is to be gained by using hypnosis to create the "implant" that will elicit the desired psychodynamic responses? It is not at all certain that there is such an advantage, although Blum indicates in his chapter that he has not yet been able to obtain the induced processes he studies by means of waking instructions.

One possibility is based on the same considerations described with reference to psychotherapy: if the subject requires hypnosis as a justification for role performances, which he would not otherwise give even though capable of them in response to an experimenter's instructions, then hypnosis does have a distinctive role in research, as it does in the clinic. For example, although non-hypnotized subjects might be capable of dreaming upon instruction, they are likely to respond to an instruction to do so with such incredulity that the instruction would be ineffective. The same instruction, given after hypnotic induction, may be effective because the subject accepts this as part of the hypnotic role. The instruction is no longer a bizarre or unrealistic one, as far as the subject's perceptions are concerned, as long as he can count on and use the fact of hypnosis as a reasonable account for his behavior. One might be able to get dreaming behavior without hypnosis, through the use of the careful preparation, motivation, instruction, and rapport-establishment used by Orne, Sutcliffe, Barber, and others, but this is laborious, inefficient, and might so alter the relationship between the experimenter and the subject that the goal of the research—to study the dreams themselves—would be interfered with. In short, hypnosis has a valid role in research, which may not be matched by other procedures, if the use made of the hypnosis is predicated on what is so far known about its operation.

SUMMARY

The purpose of this chapter has been fourfold: to expand the implications of current thinking about hypnosis beyond the boundaries of hypnosis per se; to bring this subject into closer relationship with the larger body of psychology; to attempt to place some reasonably integrated, albeit speculative, construction on the data and viewpoints presented in the several chapters of this Handbook; and, finally, to highlight the implications of some of these for future research and theory.

In doing this, hypnosis has been treated as motivated response to role-defining cues in a social situation in which these responses are instrumental in eliciting from the hypnotist gratifications of those drives that made the subject responsive to the expectancies and demands of the hypnotist. The availability to the subject of the necessary skills—cognitive, perceptual, motoric, and affective—required for his performance was stressed, and dissonance-reduction was suggested as the mechanism which permits subjects to use such skills in responding to the hypnotist. The chapter stressed the implications of this view for research and practice that uses hypnosis, for the evaluation of research on hypnosis, and for the conduct of research and theorizing in other areas in which interpersonal influence is involved.

In a clinical context, the hypnotist-patient interaction was described with reference to transference-countertransference transactions. In the nonclinical realm the interaction was described by reference to the mutual expectations that hypnotist and subject have for each other, and the role of these expectations in shaping the hypnotic behavior. Questions regarding the "validity" of hypnotic phenomena and the uniqueness of hypnosis were discussed within this theoretical framework. Finally, an attempt has been made to discover similarities between problems that afflict the study of hypnosis and those that exist or may soon exist in the larger field of psychology, such as those involved in the dissemination of scientific knowledge.

The theorizing presented in this chapter may be said to be premature; in relation to the small amount of data available, and to some ultimate or final truth, extensive theorizing is premature. Yet it is valuable in suggesting paths for the reduction of errors in the theory, which is a means for progress. Further, the loosely connected theory presented here is offered in the spirit of an effort to discern the lines of thinking that seem to be emerging from the more detailed consideration of issues in the individual chapters; it is more of a description of where we seem to be heading than it is a program for getting there.

The field of hypnosis has undergone tremendous revision and expansion in the past five to ten years. This period of new and exciting developments has done much to replace earlier feelings of futility at ever achieving an understanding (a futility that may have contributed much to an acceptance of its arcane and mystical nature); it has replaced them with feelings of ebullience and optimism. If our theories have outrun our data base, it is one expression of this optimism, and an expression that will be curtailed by the increasing sophistication of research and observation. If this Handbook has contributed something to the further expansion of the field, then its authors are well satisfied.

REFERENCES

Ås, A. (1963). "Hypnotizability as a function of nonhypnotic experiences," *J. abnorm. soc. Psychol.*, **66**, 142–150.

Bordin, E. S. (1955). "Ambiguity as a therapeutic variable," *J. consult. Psychol.*, **19**, 9–15.

Boring, E. G. (1950). *A History of Experimental Psychology*. New York: Appleton-Century-Crofts.

Erikson, E. H. (1958). "The nature of clinical evidence," *Daedalus*, **87**, 65–87.

Festinger, L. (1957). *A Theory of Cognitive Dissonance*. Evanston, Ill.: Row, Peterson.

Gill, M., and Brenman, M. (1961). *Hypnosis and Related States*. New York: International Univ. Press.

Gordon, J., and Farris, G. (1965). "The semantic differential in measuring displacement of aggression from the father" (mimeo), Univ. of Mich.

Gordon, J., and Freston, M. (1964). "Role-playing and age regression in hypnotized and nonhypnotized subjects," *J. Pers.*, **32**, 411-419.

Hathaway, S. R. (1964). "The President's column," *Division of Clinical Psychology Newsletter*, **17,** 1–4.

Levin, H., and Turgeon, V. (1957). "The influence of the mother's presence on children's doll play aggression," *J. abnorm. soc. Psychol.*, **55**, 304–308.

London, P., and Fuhrer, M. (1961). "Hypnosis, motivation, and performance," *J. Pers.*, **29**, 321–333.

Orne, M. (1959). "The nature of hypnosis: Artifact and essence," *J. abnorm. soc. Psychol.*, **58**, 277–299.

Sarbin, T. (1964). "Role theoretical interpretation of psychological change," in Worchel and Byrne, *Personality Change*, New York: Wiley, pp. 176–279.

Shor, R. E. (1960). "The frequency of naturally occurring 'hypnotic-like' experiences in the normal college population," *Int. J. clin. exp. Hyp.*, **8,** 151–163.

INDEX